the Lyle official ANTIQUES *review*

1973-74

the Lyle official ANTIQUES review

Compiled and Edited by

TONY CURTIS

Illustrated by

JOHN THOMPSON
BOB CORRALL
RICHARD MUNDAY
JOHN R. NABBS
MARY HAYMAN

Features by

STUART BARTON

Published by Lyle Publications Liverpool Terrace Worthing Sussex

Third year of issue

First edition November 1972

Printed by Hazell Watson and Viney Ltd. Tring Road, Aylesbury, Bucks.

Paper by P. F. Bingham, 185 London Road, Croydon, Surrey.

Preface

With Britain's entry into the Common Market and the consequent introduction of Value Added Tax, members of the Antique Trade have the feeling that something is about to happen to their cosy world and, as yet there seems to be no clear idea of what that something will be.

On the one hand there are the pessimists who envisage the smaller Dealers being swamped out of business by an overwhelming welter of paper work and bureaucratic interference while others, the supreme optimists, have convinced themselves that entry into Europe will open the floodgates of increased wealth without noticeably adding to their workload.

The one thing that is certain is that British Antique Dealers will have to break free from the air of somnolence which clouds their unique trade. We will have to shake off our blanket of cosy insularity and accept the fact that entry into the European Economic Community presents a challenging situation which will yield rich prizes, but only to those bold enough to grasp and fully exploit the opportunities it offers.

Most British Dealers would be extremely surprised at the high prices fetched by Antiques on the Continent and, in my opinion, this is likely to present an additional problem for home Dealers to overcome – it will not merely be local opposition which has to be contended with at the Auctions of the future; Dealers from all over Europe are likely to come to this country to buy from whatever sources are available to them, and they are likely to come in greater numbers than ever before.

Prices generally have increased by about 10 percent over the past year and there already seems to be a quickening of the pace. I expect values to increase with a rush throughout 1973 and would not be at all surprised to see the same escalation in prices of Antiques as we have already experienced in the property market. There are already indications that Antiques are an attractively profitable sphere for the investment of capital and the inevitable boom which will follow Britain's entry into the E.E.C. is likely to attract a growing number of big businessmen into the field.

From the surveys conducted by this Company it is clear that great opportunities exist and it is equally clear that, if they are to reap the fullest benefits arising out of this new situation, the vast majority of British Antique Dealers are going to have to adopt fresh attitudes and approach their work in a far more businesslike manner.

TONY CURTIS

While every care has been taken in the compiling of information contained in this volume the publishers cannot accept any liability for loss, financial or otherwise, incurred by reliance placed on the information herein.

Lyle Publications

7 LIVERPOOL TERRACE, WORTHING, SUSSEX.

phone Worthing 36373

The Contents

ACKNOWLEDGEMENTS

The publishers wish to acknowledge and thank the following for their kind help and assistance in the production of this volume.

Fiona Ford, Sotheby & Co
Susan Rose, Christies
S. R. Butler, Wallis and Wallis
Ian Whitfield, Bermondsey Antique Market
Tony Gill, Wedgfield Securities Limited
Ken Newman, Fox & Sons
Michael Gorton Design
Mike Deasy.
Annette Hogg.
Martin Miller.

All photographs and the text of the Arms were provided by Wallis & Wallis, 210 High Street Lewes, Sussex.

Monarchs

HENRY 1V	1399 - 1413
HENRY V	1413 - 1422
HENRY V1	1422 - 1461
EDWARD 1V	1461 - 1483
EDWARD V	1483 - 1483
RICHARD 111	1483 - 1485
HENRY V11	1485 - 1509
HENRY V111	1509 - 1547
EDWARD V1	1547 - 1553
MARY	1553 - 1558
ELIZABETH	1558 - 1603
JAMES 1	1603 - 1625
CHARLES 1	1625 - 1649
COMMONWEALTH	1649 - 1660
CHARLES 11	1660 - 1685
JAMES 11	1685 - 1689
WILLIAM & MARY	1689 - 1695
WILLIAM 111	1695 - 1702
ANNE	1702 - 1714
GEORGE 1	1714 - 1727
GEORGE 11	1727 - 1760
GEORGE 111	1760 - 1820
GEORGE 1V	1820 - 1830
WILLIAM 1V	1830 - 1837
VICTORIA	1837 - 1901
EDWARD V11	1901 - 1910

Periods

TUDOR PERIOD	1485 - 1603
ELIZABETHAN PERIOD	1558 - 1603
INIGO JONES "	1572 - 1652
JACOBEAN PERIOD	1603 - 1688
STUART PERIOD	1603 - 1714
A. C. BOULLE	1642 - 1732
LOUIS X1V PERIOD	1643 - 1715
GRINLING GIBBONS	1648 - 1726
CROMWELLIAN PERIOD	1649 - 1660
CAROLEAN PERIOD	1660 - 1685
WILLIAM KENT	1684 - 1748
WILLIAM & MARY PERIOD	1689 - 1702
QUEEN ANNE PERIOD	1702 - 1714
GEORGIAN PERIOD	1714 - 1820
T. CHIPPENDALE	1715 - 1762
LOUIS XV PERIOD	1723 - 1774
A. HEPPLEWHITE	1727 - 1788
ADAM PERIOD	1728 - 1792
ANGELICA KAUFMANN	1741 - 1807
T. SHERATON	1751 - 1806
LOUIS XV1	1774 - 1793
T. SHEARER	(circa) 1780
REGENCY PERIOD	1800 - 1830
EMPIRE PERIOD	1804 - 1815
VICTORIAN PERIOD	1830 - 1901
EDWARDIAN PERIOD	1901 - 1910

Registry of Designs

USED 1842 to 1883

BELOW ARE ILLUSTRATED THE TWO FORMS OF ' REGISTRY OF DESIGN' MARK USED BETWEEN THE YEARS OF 1842 TO 1883.

EXAMPLE: An article produced between 1842 and 1867 would bear the following marks. (example for the 12th of November 1852)

CLASS OF GOODS

YEAR

IV

D

MONTH

K

R^D

12

DAY

7

BUNDLE

EXAMPLE; An article produced between 1868 and 1883 would bear the following marks. (example for the 22nd October 1875).

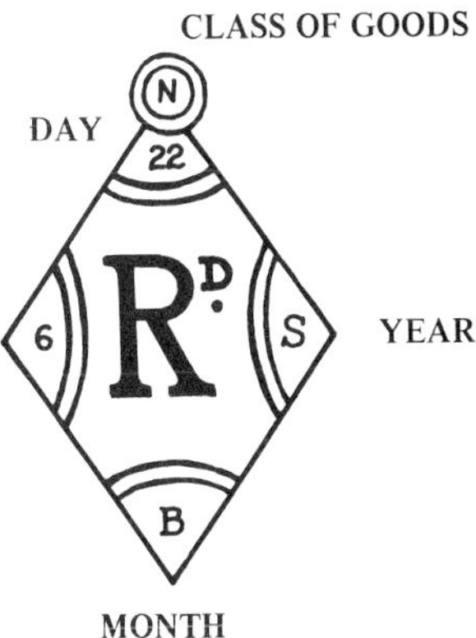

DATE AND LETTER CODE

Month	Letter	Year	Letter	Year	Letter	Year	Letter	Year	Letter
JANUARY	C	1842	X	54	J	66	Q	78	D
FEBRUARY	G	43	H	55	E	67	T	79	Y
MARCH	W	44	C	56	L	68	X	80	J
APRIL	H	45	A	57	K	69	H	81	E
MAY	E	46	I	58	B	70	O	82	L
JUNE	M	47	F	59	M	71	A	83	K
JULY	I	48	U	60	Z	72	I		
AUGUST	R	49	S	61	R	73	F		
SEPTEMBER	D	50	V	62	O	74	U		
OCTOBER	B	51	P	63	G	75	S		
NOVEMBER	K	52	D	64	N	76	V		
DECEMBER	A	53	Y	65	W	77	P		

Under the Hammer

Mention 'arms' almost anywhere in the world and one of the first names to spring to mind is that of Wallis and Wallis of Lewes, Sussex.

Begun over 40 years ago as Estate Agents in Guildford, the Company achieved only local recognition until the period following the Second World War, when sporting guns and equipment were in short supply. During this period, the Lewes Office was opened by one of the original partners, J. P. S. Wallis, and, in the course of his normal business as an auctioneer, he began to encourage the inclusion of sporting guns and fishing tackle in his regular sales. One such sale included a number of antique guns and the enthusiastic bidding which took place convinced Wallis that there was considerable potential in this field. He accordingly cultivated this aspect of his sales until it became evident that the firm would do well to specialise almost exclusively in the sale of arms and military paraphernalia.

Upon the retirement of J. P. S. Wallis, the business was continued by S. R. Butler and D. J. Fryer for some years until Mr. Butler bought out his partner in 1968, since which time the

Company of Wallis and Wallis has continued to progress under his personal guidance.

The cataloguing of weapons is a highly specialised art and one which demands considerable experience. Important weapons and militaria are catalogued by Mr. Butler personally and there can be little doubt that he is one of the leading authorities on these subjects. Modern weapons are entrusted to the experience of Mr. R. Homard who was for twenty years an Armourer in the British Services before he joined the staff of Wallis and Wallis.

Besides the immense knowledge of these two men, the Firm employs three other experts on the cataloguing side whose experience is as general as possible. In this way, the descriptions contained in the catalogues of Wallis and Wallis are ensured to be as accurate as it is possible to make them and this is made doubly important by virtue of the fact that much of the Firm's work is of a worldwide nature.

Much of the bidding for every Wallis and Wallis sale is done by post and it says much for the confidence which has been created in the accuracy of the sale certificates that between 25 and 30 percent of sales are made to overseas customers, a large proportion of whom bid exclusively by post.

Articles for sale, too, arrive by post from all parts of the world and these not infrequently arrive with no indication of of the sender's identity or wishes. 'When this happens' says Mr. Butler, 'We keep them safely and hope that a letter will arrive to identify the owners and give their instructions. Sometimes we are asked to overlook defects when compiling our catalogues, but, of course, we are obliged to enter descriptions impartially and fairly for the sakes of all concerned. On the very rare occasions when a purchaser is dissatisfied, every effort is made to put the matter right. Firstly the catalogue description is scrutinised to recheck its accuracy and, if no fault can be found with our description, we often offer to resell the article under the identical description in our next sale. If, however, we were found to be at fault, we would have no hesitation in setting the affair to rights – our reputation has been established upon

Above. Mr. Butler with part of his collection.
Below. Some of the varied items in the saleroom.

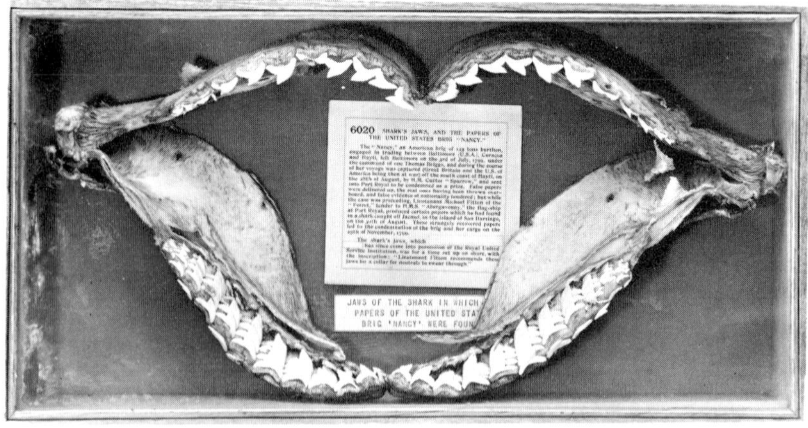

Above. Jaws of the Shark in which papers of the United States Brig 'Nancy' were found.

confidence of clients throughout the world and it is a matter of great pride to us that that reputation should remain always at its present high level.'

Not unnaturally, a number of very unusual articles have passed through the Wallis and Wallis saleroom over the years, but, of all these the strangest was probably the jawbone of a shark whose history might be a work of pure fiction but for the documentary evidence to establish its truth.

Mounted in the case with the jawbone is a brief version of this extraordinary story which runs as follows;

"The NANCY, an American brig of 125 tons burthen, engaged in trading between Baltimore USA, Curacoa and Hayti, left Baltimore on the Third of July 1799, under the command of one Thomas Briggs, and during the course of her voyage was captured (Great Britain and the U.S. of America being then at war) off the South coast of Hayti, on the 28th August, by H. M. Cutter, 'Sparrow' and sent into Port Royal to be condemned as a prize.

False papers were delivered up, the real ones having been thrown overboard, and false evidence of nationality tendered; but while the case was proceeding, Lt. Michael Fitton of the 'Ferret', tender to HMS ABERGAVENNY, the flagship at Port Royal, produced certain papers which he had found in a shark caught off Jacmel, in the Island of San Domingo, on the 30th August.

These strangely recovered papers led to the condemnation of the brig and her cargo on the 25th of November 1799."

The prize was thus returned to the British Navy and the jawbone of the shark who had been unwittingly instrumental in the service of justice was preserved, along with the account of the tale, to pass over one hundred and fifty years later through the saleroom of Wallis and Wallis.

Apart from their early schedule of sales, Wallis and Wallis are called upon to handle sales of important private collections. The most recent of these was that of the late Lional McCardle of Sheffield Park, Sussex, which took some three months to catalogue and was sold in two parts, realising a total of over £122,000. Besides postal bids, the sale attracted buyers from fourteen countries and provided some real headaches for the Wallis and Wallis team of experts who had to fit the cataloguing in on top of their normal fulltime schedule of work for regular sales.

Dispatch and transportation of arms and other valuable objects might appear to present something of a problem, particularly when undertaken on the scale demanded by the worldwide scope of the Wallis and Wallis operation. Apart from their own experienced packing department however, Wallis and Wallis make extensive use of one of the major Shipping Companies (who are in league with a Company specialising in air freight) and they find that the headaches are few and far between. Naturally, they are well insured against all eventualities and tie up with air freighting ensures rapid transportation of goods to all parts of the globe with a minimum of fuss and delay.

Despite the fact that meticulous organisation is required to ensure the satisfactory working of a company such as Wallis and Wallis, there is a deceptively chaotic air which pervades both office and saleroom during this period of preparation for a sale. Difficult and obscure items are shuttled from expert to expert for comments and opinions until, gradually, experience and that certain sixth sense (possessed and recognised by all experts in all walks of life) dictate an answer to the problem. Gradually, in the days before a sale, the mountains of miscellaneous arms, medals, uniforms, models, and bric a brac are listed, sorted and placed in their appointed positions around the saleroom so that any member of the staff (or regular visitor) can go straight to any category of items knowing that Scottish Weapons, for instance, will always be found on the wall directly opposite the entrance and to the right of Nazi dress weapons. Mr. Butler's own office is piled high with assorted articles from boxes of badges to items of weaponry and uniforms apart from the countless reference books and catalogues of previous sales.

In contrast to the apparent confusion, the staff move and talk with reassuring calm as they methodically identify each piece, occasionally conferring or checking references, quietly sure of the accuracy of their judgement and respectful of the worth of the objects they handle in their daily work.

A quart, however, cannot be fitted into a pint pot, and the steady growth of trade carried on by Wallis and Wallis has demanded that new, larger premises be found. These, close to the offices at present in use, are currently being made ready and will give substance to one of the great dreams indulged by S. R. Butler for many years now – the opening in Lewes of a Military and Arms Museum. The first floor of the newly acquired building will be used to house Mr. Butler's personal collection (which is acknowledged to be very fine indeed) and will be open to the public on payment of a small entrance fee.

Meanwhile the business of Wallis and Wallis continues to grow steadily with proceeds of each sale now to over £40,000 as the trade in antique arms, coins and military equipment enjoys increasing popularity around the world.

Below. Part of the interesting and varied selection of items auctioned monthly.

The New Antiques?

Exceptionally fine Louis XV style Boulle type three drawer commode. Exquisitely inlaid and adorned in the traditional style Ormolu mountings ending in Ormolu foliate hoof feet. The whole is surmounted by a grained and mottled marble top with moulded and shaped border.

French style grande fille clock. This clock is unique in the field of reproduction, blending with any decor in the French style. It is an eight day, quarter hourly chiming movement with period style white enamel dial and roman numerals, with very heavy Ormolu surround the longcase being quarter veneered on all panels and heavily adorned with Ormolu plaques festooning and edging.

Modern reproductions of period furniture are normally held in some contempt by Dealers and serious collectors of the real thing, and not, it must be agreed, totally without justification. The reasons are many and too well understood to warrant further discussion in general terms but, aesthetic consideration aside, there can be no doubt that good reproduction furniture fulfills a useful and economically valuable function, a fact which is receiving increasingly widespread recognition, even at the higher end of the market.

A man committed to the spread of Reproduction Gospel is Bernard Clarke, Managing Director of the Southwick, Sussex, Company of Meubles Francais (Reproductions) Ltd.

Specialists in Louis XV and XVI styles, Meubles Francais produce reproduction furniture of very high quality indeed. Manufactured in France, the pieces are made by means of a happy blend of mass – production and craftsman finishing methods, thereby ensuring that price is kept relatively low without making too many sacrifices in respect of fine workmanship and finish.

Many pieces in the Meubles Francais Trade Showrooms are based closely on some of the most important items of furniture to have survived from their periods and, in the words of Bernard Clarke, 'There are no short cuts with furniture of this quality – certain alterations are sometimes made on points of detail but every piece is made with the same care and craftmanship that was employed in the workshops of old France'.

Carcases, he says, are all of oak, as are drawer linings and these are the parts which are made by mass production methods. Each piece is then individually veneered and polished, many being embellished with finely executed marquetry.

The extensive use of oak, of course, makes the pieces extremely heavy and solid - feeling and, in Bernard Clarke's opinion, the use of modern adhesives and polishes will ensure that this furniture retains its strength and appearance, for many years to come.

In this respect, Mr. Clarke's boast that he is selling 'new antiques' could be said to be justified; there can be little doubt that the pieces being sold today from the showrooms of Meubles Francais have useful life potentials well in excess of the statutory hundred and thirty years that they will have to survive before they are themselves accepted as antiques but, of course, a great deal of water will have flowed beneath many bridges before that day comes.

Modern reproduction furniture of the same style and quality is gaining recognition in France and elsewhere on the continent, where it is enjoying wide sales largely through the Antiques Trade.

'The reason for this is plain', declares Bernard Clarke, 'all the time you have more and more people chasing fewer goods. Much of the original furniture is now so difficult to find at a reasonable price . Here we have furniture, beautifully reproducing the original furniture as it was and available at a fraction of the cost of the surviving pieces.

Although dealers were finding it difficult to obtain genuine antique pieces, there was some early reluctance on their part to handle our product but that is rapidly being overcome in the most practical way possible.

They would come in here and look around, marvelling at everything – the quality, the finish, the attention to detail – but would hesitate to buy anything. Gradually they were persuaded to try one or two of the smaller pieces and, before you could say Jack Robinson they had sold them and were back for more. We are now serving many of the largest dealers in the country, and are experiencing some difficulty in keeping abreast of the demand.

'This is as it should be – the furniture is not just churned off a production line – and there is a waiting period of from six to eight weeks for delivery of some pieces. Being the sole importers of this furniture, we feel it only right that we should deal exclusively with the Trade. Naturally we get the occasional private enquiry and these are always referred to dealers in the area from which the enquiry comes'.

Accepting that the products of Meubles Francais are beautifully made and finely styled in the best of French traditions, the only question which can remain in the mind of the average Antique Dealer is that of the proper outlet – and this is a question which is being clearly answered by the Antiques Traders and buying public alike in a manner which every businessman can understand.

Typical French style vitrine.

Profile on Mike Deasy

Mike Deasy is a man who knows the meaning of the word dedication.

For twenty years he and his blonde wife, Peggy, have worked together toward the realisation of their ambition to head the biggest Antiques shipping business in the United Kingdom and now, at the age of forty, Mike Deasy handles well over £1m worth of business annually from his Partridge Green, Sussex, warehouse complex.

Situated in the quiet downland countryside, Mike Deasy Antiques exude a deceptive atmosphere of somnolence. The large main showroom attracts few visitors, since retail business is minimal, and the storage warehouses, piled high with stock, seem strangely silent to anyone accustomed to the hustle of the saleroom and the turmoil of the Antique Markets. It is difficult for the visitor to equate this air of casual quiet with the massive turnover which Deasy and his wife achieve, particularly when it is learned that they employ a total labour force of only five people.

The clue is to be found in the group of vast, metal, shipping containers which stand beside the power boat in the surrounding yard.

One hundred of these are dispatched each year to America, and the goods they contain represent some £850,000 of Mike Deasy's annual turnover. Add to this exports to Italy and Malta to the tune of nearly £200,000 per year and domestic sales of around £100,000 and you have some idea of the extent of Deasy's business dealings.

Like all the best success stories, Mike Deasy's started from small beginnings. For three years after his marriage he worked for his father in law before branching out on his own: ' We took a small basement in Prince Albert Street, Brighton, and worked all the hours God sent ' he recalls. ' We sold to the trade and concentrated on turnover rather than big profit margins and this I think, is the factor which contributed most to our steady growth in the business. After a time we began to be known and gradually our horizons broadened. We moved to larger premises, still in Brighton, and carried on in the same way, concentrating all the time on turnover. '

In Mike Deasy's view, it is the ability to resist the lure of high percentage profits which gives him the edge over many of his fellow dealers: ' What happens is this: a dealer marks an article up at a fiver and sells it with no trouble. Then he gets to thinking that he could have asked a bit more for it so, next time, he marks it up at six pounds. If it still sells he puts the price up again, until, one day he finds that nobody is buying anymore. A typical example of this kind of thing is the way wash jugs and basins shot up in price. At one time you could buy them for about £1 and the Americans went mad over them - we have exported about half a million of them to America by the way, but after a bit, people began to bang the prices up and up until, suddenly, the Americans were no longer interested. Now this is the point: the Americans have got a great deal of money to spend and they are very happy to spend it but they are not stupid. They expect a fair deal for their money and this is what we give them'.

With exports to America of £850,000 there can be little doubt that Mike Deasy's marketing philosophy works, but where does he obtain the right goods at the right price?

Again Deasy explains; ' We have about thirty suppliers in different parts of the country who know what we want and how much we can pay. Our overseas customers give us advance warning of the various trends and fashions and this again gives us our slight edge. It all comes back to what I was saying earlier; the minute the trade gets wind of what the Americans want, prices start to climb. Most of the stuff here is sold before we buy it and that automatically means that it is sold at a fair price - beside saving us lot of headaches'.

Although Mike Deasy has suppliers in all parts of the country, he reluctantly admitts London to be the best (and cheapest) place to buy, despite the fact that he has strong feelings of loyalty toward Brighton, the town which gave him his start in business, not that he travels much himself these days, preferring to remain in Partridge Green and let the trade come to him.

Left. One of Mike Deasey's five employees arranging Antiques in the extensive showrooms.

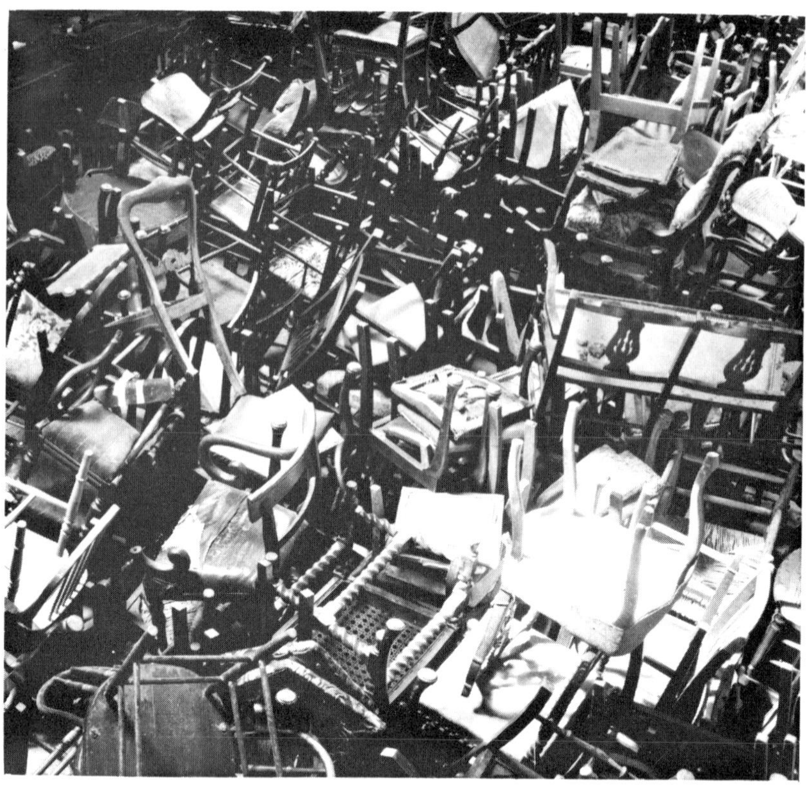

Above. A small selection of some of the hundreds of chairs in the Trade Warehouse.

Nevertheless, he still makes private calls in answer to local enquiries, even though these rarely prove fruitfull. ' The trouble ' he says, ' is that there has been too much attention paid through the mass media to high - priced and over - valued articles. The general public seem to forget that an item is only worth what you can get for it. Again I can give you an example. Some time ago, an elderly lady came to see us bringing a barometer with her. It was worth about thirty pounds and this is what we offered her. She was very upset about this and it seems that she had seen somewhere, in a magazine or on television, a barometer which they had valued at a couple of hundred pounds and which she said was exactly the same as hers. Having seen this, the poor old soul had relied on being able to sell her barometer for the same money in order to pay the rates bill.

' Something of this sort must have happened to every dealer in the country and it is this kind of thing which creates the idea in the public mind that dealers are not to be trusted.'

' The vast majority of Antiques Dealers in this country are honest businessmen who want nothing more than to buy and sell their goods at a fair profit, and none of these has any objection to the public being well informed on values. Books like the Lyle Official Antiques Review serve a useful purpose in this respect and I know of a great many dealers who use this book extensively in their dealings with the public. '

Owing to the size of his business operation, Mike Deasy's dealings are largely confined to bulk purchasing through the trade. One indication which stands out as an example of the size of his business is the fact that he regards dealing in pianos as just another aspect of his work.

' One grand piano would fill the average showroom, so not many dealers have anything to do with them. Because of the space we have here, we keep stocks of about two hundred and fifty pianos at the moment and I am hoping to increase to around the thousand mark'.

' Pianos are such good value for money - they are so cheap - and we send about six to Italy each month at the moment......'

In part, Mike Deasy's success results from the kind of thinking which he applies to pianos - he seems to be fascinated by size and bulk of numbers. The prospect of expanding his piano stocks by four hundred percent delights him. He is pleased that he always has more stock of anything than he can sell, despite the fact that this would give nightmares to most dealers. In short, where most dealers are trying to find ways of increasing profits as a means of making a better living from their stocks Mike Deasy is busy building up his stocks in order to keep prices and unit profits down to a level which will ensure that his sales continue to enjoy their steady rate of increase.

Below. The start of the second half million J & B's destined for the States.

The rise of containerisation in the middle sixties was the breakthrough point and Mike Deasy was the first Antiques Shipper to take advantage of metal containers as a means of expanding his business.

By learning the tastes and needs of the American market, Deasy was able to install the kind of confidence in his transatlantic customers which would enable them to order, sight unseen thousands of pounds worth of goods in the sure knowledge that they would be receiving the right sort of value for their money: ' You have to know what kind of furniture is unsuitable for the climatic conditions in the different parts of the continent: what the living conditions are like in different areas in terms of space and income: how tastes vary from East to West and North to South. There are dozens of factors to be taken into account each time we fill a container for the States and the big advantage in having large stocks is that we can always be sure of providing the right man with the right goods at the right time. '

' At the moment, the Americans are buying more period stuff than ever before but don't ask me what comes next: that is all the edge I have over my competitors......'

Looking Ahead to V.A.T.

With the rapid approach of Britain's entry into the EEC, it is not only the economists and lawmakers who find considerable material for debate. Members of the Antique Trade, perhaps more than most other sections of the community, are being given real cause for concern as the arrangements proceed, largely because, for the first time, their transactions are going to be made subject to the imposition of a tax.

Naturally, there has been a great deal of speculation concerning this and, as might be expected, the majority of Dealers regard the whole idea with some suspicion if not outright distaste. Nevertheless, There are a number of factors to be considered which make it necessary, if not actually desireable that a tax of some sort be levied and the proposed form of Value Added Tax (with the undoubted concessions which will be granted to Dealers in Antiques and Works of Art) should not prove too hard a pill to swallow once the initial rethinking has been done by members of the Antiques Trade.

At the present time, Antiques are subject to tax on the continent and there is considerable concern expressed by Dealers in the Common Market Countries that, if the British Dealers are not similarly treated, a grave imbalance could result once existing tariff barriers are altered to comply with the Common Market agreements. Although this might seem beneficial to British Dealers in the short term, the longer term effects are likely to prove far less attractive.

Ian Whitfield, of London Antique Dealers (London) Ltd., has spent a considerable time during the past year researching and talking to a large number of dealers throughout Europe. He has also engaged in consultation with senior Government and Departmental Heads and members of the CBI concerning the needs of the Antique Trade prior to Britain's entry into the Common Market. As a result of his activities in this direction, Mr. Whitfield feels that entry into the Common Market and the introduction of Value Added Tax could exert a beneficial influence on the British Antique Trade.

Firstly, he says, British Dealers will tend to concentrate on more goods that are over 100 years old (since these are liable to be subject to greater concessions).

Secondly, Export Antiques will become much more interesting to the average British Dealer and, thirdly, the necessity of keeping detailed records for tax purposes will have the inevitable result in increasing business efficiency.

Since Mr. Whitfield is convinced that entry into the Common Market must, inevitably cause a boom in the Antique Trade, he feels that much more money will become available as big business recognises the potential of Antiques as an area for major investment.

Although final details of the Value Added Tax are still to be confirmed at the time of going to press, there seems little doubt that the scheme will work broadly as follows:

Dealers will be required to record each purchase of goods within the scope of the scheme and to maintain a stockbook in which each item will be allocated a unique reference which will remain with the article all the time it is held in stock. The difference between a Dealer's buying and selling price will be regarded as tax inclusive and the dealer will account for tax on the basis of the difference between these two figures (i.e. his profit margin). Any work done on the article (cleaning, repair, or restoration) it seems, will not be taxable when determining that margin.

To avoid disclosure of the profit margin, it is proposed that no tax invoices will be required, even in respect of Dealer-to-Dealer sales.

If the final scheme follows this proposal it will be immediately clear that Dealers will not be able to claim any tax deduction in respect of the purchase of goods.

The imposition of Value Added Tax, particularly in the form proposed and described above, is going to be a small price to pay for the overall benefits which should emerge from Britain's entry into the EEC for, in the words of Mr. Ian Whitfield:

'There are some 30,000 people actively engaged in the Antique business in Britain alone and this number will grow as a result of the increased opportunities available through the Common Market. We are going to look more and more to overseas buyers as time goes by and the countries of interest to the British Dealer who sells in Europe are, in order of the numbers of personnel engaged in the Antiques Trade are; France, Italy, Spain, Belgium, Holland, Sweden, Germany, Portugal, Switzerland, Norway and Finland, of which in my opinion, Germany offers the biggest growth for exports for British Dealers.'

All in all, the year ahead should prove an exciting time for those British Dealers who are prepared to make the necessary effort and take advantage of the vast market which will be made more readily accessible by our entry into Europe. The various Government Departments concerned are making wide preparations for helping and advising Dealers who wish to extend their activities on the Continent and it is only to be hoped that British Dealers will avail themselves fully of these services.

The Customs and Excise authorities, too, will be found to be most helpful in explaining the details of Value Added Tax as they are finalised and, although Official Publications on the subjects are liable to be phrased in their usual incomprehensible manner, a direct approach to Local Officers will result in the same information being given in a far more readily assimilable form.

Antiques on the Wing

When the Antique buyer, be he private individual or Trade buyer, wishes to arrange the transport of his purchases to points overseas, he must take into consideration many factors besides that of pure cash outlay.

Among the other subjects to be taken into account are the safety of his valuable goods, the estimated delivery date, the convenience of the delivery point and the possibility of unscheduled delay, perhaps caused by bad weather or industrial disputes. For each of these factors can have a considerable effect on the total cost of the shipment quite disproportionate to the actual carrier's transportation fees.

Until quite recently it has been widely held that none but the most valuable of purchases could bear the apparent high cost of air transport but, as time goes by, more and more Dealers are recognising the advantages of air freight methods for the international movement of their stocks.

Probably the greatest single influence on the growth of acceptability of air transport of Antiques has been exerted by the development of the Unit Load Device (ULD) or Igloo. This is, in a sense, the air freight equivalent of the Container whose development in the mid sixties revolutionised the conventional surface transport methods.

Below. A standard 707 Air Container, capacity 410 cu.ft. awaiting loading

Above. Igloos awaiting loading into an all-cargo jet.

Built to internationally accepted standards, Igloos are readily available from all the major international airlines and are used on all major international routes. Providing, as they do, easily obtainable packing cases of known capacity, Igloos are not infrequently accepted by internal airlines thus facilitating delivery further by extending the lines of transport to a great number of relatively small local airports throughout the world.

The two sizes most commonly used provide cubic capacities of approximately 200 and 400 cubic feet. Besides providing a strong, secure and therefore safe outer package, Igloos can, in most instances, be transported between their loading and delivery points at a fixed rate for the container regardless of contents in much the same way that sea containership operates. There is another advantage in this too - airlines, preferring to have their cargoes loaded for them in convenient sized packages, charge less overall for an Igloo than they would for seperate, loose items of cargo. (An advantageous by - product of this method of shipment is a considerable reduction in the cost of insurance).

Although it would be impossible to give a blanket scale of charges owing to the size of the operational possibilities some indication of costs can be gleaned from the fact that, at the time of going to press, the shipping division of Wedgefield Securities Ltd. can load a container in London and in 48 hours have it landed in Washington D.C. at a cost (for a full Boeing 707 Igloo with a capacity of 410 cubic feet) of $ 5 per cubic foot.

This company introduced the first ever Air Consolidated Service only for Antiques shipped between London and the U.S.A., whereby small consignments (mainly individual purchases made by buyers) are loaded together into one container and landed within a few hours at a unit cost which is much less than it would have been had the items been individually dispatched.

The mechanics of air freight are very simple indeed.

All that is basically required is a copy of the supplier's invoice with the necessary information for Customs at both point of dispatch and destination - a competent freight contractor will do the rest. He will arrange the most economical method of air freight whether it be an individual consignment to some remote destination, part of a consolidated consignment to a major centre or a complete load by container. His routing should take advantage of any special rates, allowances, discounts or other agreements which may be in force on any particular route. He will arrange the Customs Invoices which are required by Governments for the importation of Antiques and he will also cut the Airway Bill (which is the main document covering transport by air freight).

A network of Customs Brokers and Freight Forwarders throughout the world ensure that, once your purchases have reached the country of destination, they are efficiently handled through Customs and forwarded to your address. This service too, should all be handled as a matter of routine by any reputable Freight Contractor, and it is, of course, a matter of considerable importance that handling at all stages of the journey be undertaken by people versed in the special procedures which are often required for movement of Antiques.

Besides the considerable time saved and wear and tear of nerves inevitably occasioned by the interminable form filling, your contractor will estimate all uncertainty about hidden costs and unnoticed extras by quoting a firm, inclusive price for the transportation of your air freight parcel from its point of departure to its final, agreed destination.

Apart from the benefit of speed, pure and simple, airfreighting is gaining considerably over sea transport in the field of reliability - recent years have seen protracted strikes and disputes on both sides of the Atlantic, occasioning delays (often of considerable duration) which, because of their unpredictable nature have caused great hardship and considerable losses to many who could ill afford them.

Already, many Antique Dealers are considering the higher cost of airfreight; money well spent in terms of the saving in time which appears in the transportation schedules. Once the possibility of protracted delays resulting from industrial disputes is added to this already considerable factor, most businessmen would happily spend the extra money purely for the sake of knowing that their goods are going to be where they want them at the time they want them there. Stocks tied up in transit are not only not earning money, they are actually losing money – and losing it fast. Small wonder, then, that air freight is the method of transportation favoured now by many of the world's major Antique export/import companies and is rapidly being accepted by the smaller businessman as an extremely viable method of extending his business beyond the boundaries of his own immediate locality.

The Flea Market ~ Paris

THE FLEA MARKET - PARIS

Of all the markets in the world, the best known is probably that situated in the St. Ouen district of Paris – the famous aux Puces – the Flea Market.

Spread along some four miles of streets, the Flea Market has an atmosphere curiously its own and one whose elements are very difficult to pin down or define; there are the inevitable tourist and sight-seer attractions – the souvenir stalls, the arty gift shops, the herb stalls and sweet stands whose aromas drift across the entire market when the wind is from the South and it is this blend of smells, perhaps, and the ubiquitous cafes, which contribute as much as any other factor to the Flea Market's individuality.

The South and East sides of the market are bordered by the seemingly interminable clothes, tool and domestic appliance stalls, crowded with people speaking all the tongues of Babel as they seek out the intermittent curio stalls and junk shops which, with the others, line the streets and sprawl across the pavements. Just behind these, however, lie three separate markets devoted almost exclusively to the sale of Antique furniture.

Strolling in the lanes.

Above. A well illuminated display.
Below. African carvings.

The pace here is more leisurely, with fewer crowds and considerably more room to move and breath. A few tourists wander around but there is little to hold their interest apart from the occasional Algerian selling African carvings from the pavements.

One of the first things to strike the attention of the British visitor is the orderliness and permanent-seeming nature of the hundreds of stalls – here is none of the early morning temporariness of such well known markets as the Caledonian – for the lanes and alleys of the Flea Market stretch between rows of shutter fronted buildings, each about the size of a very large domestic garage and each opening to reveal not so much a stall as an Antique Shop.

One of the many specialist stalls.

A very high proportion of the stall holders seem to specialise in furniture of a particular style or period, others dealing solely in chandeliers or ormolu mounts, handles and decorations. Here will be a shop devoted to bronzes and there another crammed with stone garden ornaments; here a dealer obviously specialises in second hand theatrical equipment, and there a man concentrates on brand new reproduction Regency style furniture.

British Dealers might do well to follow the example set by many of the Flea Market's traders in the matter of display – a great emphasis is placed on lighting as a means of adding depth and drama to the stalls, and concealed spotlights are widely used to emphasise the warmth of well polished mahogany or to throw a piece of decorative carving into high relief. This may seem like unnecessary window dressing to many British Dealers but it does save the potential buyer from having to peer through the gloom in an effort to see what is placed at the rear of the stall and it has the very positive advantage of making every piece seem individually displayed.

Above foreground. One of a set of six Victorian chairs.

For the past year or so, English furniture has enjoyed considerable popularity in the Paris market and, although it is at present strongly challenged by the fifteenth and sixteenth century French styles, its continuing high appeal is clearly demonstrated by the number of Paris Flea Market Dealers specialising in the products of the English Regency and Victorian periods.

Probably as a reaction to the bulk and elaborate ornamentation of much of the French furniture, the most sought after English pieces are the plain and simple things, particularly the smaller items; chairs, stripped pine chests and bow chests of drawers, desks, bureaux, loo tables and, everywhere, drop leaf and gateleg tables. Of the chairs the most commonly available are Windsors and Victorian dining chairs and by far the most remarkable feature of most of the English furniture displayed is the price at which it is marked for sale.

The asking price for a set of six late Victorian chairs is around 2,250 francs; a cricket table in poor condition fetches 750 francs and a good Windsor of the type illustrated may be marked at anything up to 1,000 francs. The two chests of drawers illustrated were quickly sold for 1,100 francs each and even a 19th century plain oak gateleg table might bear the decorative price of 500 francs. At the current rate of exchange at the time of going to press of one franc=8np, these prices are obviously far in excess of the current market values of such pieces in the United Kingdom and this is not solely because prices are generally high in France. The ornate French styled furniture such as the buhl table illustrated (which was in beautiful condition) fetches about the same money in France as it does in England (this particular piece was marked at 3,500 francs).

The reason for the current popularity of English Antique furniture in France lies primarily in its lack of ostentation – the French taste having swung strongly toward the simplicity of stripped pine and wax polish; indeed it is not uncommon to see stallholders in the Flea Market actually sanding and polishing recently stripped furniture on the pavement outside their stalls in between dealing with customer's enquiries.

Above. Windsor chairs.
Below. Cricket table.

Above. 19th century chest of drawers.
Left. Buhl card table.
Below. Victorian oak gateleg table.

The feeling among the French Dealers is that 'le boom Anglais' is likely to continue for some time to come, possibly broadening in scope as the French public becomes more discriminating and begins to seek furniture of better quality than most that is available to them at the present time. Most seem to welcome the idea of Britain joining the Common Market, though all express concern that, at the moment, the lack of a tax on Antiques in Britain gives the British Dealer an unfair advantage over his Continental counterpart. Value Added Tax, providing it is set at a rate comparable to the existing French Tax, will, they feel, create the right climate for vastly increasing opportunities for trade across the Channel once Britain has become a member of the EEC.

All that remains is for the British Dealers to grasp the opportunities which exist in France, taking full advantage of the market for their goods which is waiting, ready made and eager to do business.

Stuart Barton

Introduction

The LYLE OFFICIAL ANTIQUES REVIEW is published on the first of November of every year, enabling you to begin each new year with an up to date knowledge of the current trends, together with the verified values of antiques of all descriptions.

We have endeavoured to obtain a balance between the more expensive collector's items and those which, although not in their true sense antiques, are handled daily by the antique trade.

The illustrations and prices in the following sections have been arranged to make it easy for the reader to assess the period, and value of all items, with speed.

You will find illustrations for almost every category of antique and curio, together with a corresponding price collated during the last twelve months, from auction rooms and retail outlets throughout Britain.

When dealing with the more popular trade pieces, a calculation of an average price has been estimated from the varying accounts researched.

Lyle Publications

DINING CHAIRS

I. Set of six carved mahogany Edwardian chairs on turned legs. £15

2. Set of eight mahogany dining chairs with drop in seat,circa 1825. £225

3. Set of four Edwardian mahogany dining chairs inlaid with boxwood. £60

4. Set of four late 19th century walnut chairs in the French style . £24

5. Pair of mahogany dining chairs in the Chippendale style. £15

6. Set of eight Georgian mahogany chairs in the Chippendale style , circa 1780 £290

7. Set of eight Georgian mahogany dining chairs of good colour,circa 1795. £315

8. Set of four Georgian mahogany dining chairs. £65

9. Set of four Edwardian mahogany framed chairs with pierced back splats and cabriole legs. £12

10. Set of four late 18th century Hepplewhite dining chairs with Prince of Wales feathers. £185

11. Set of six good quality Hepplewhite shield back chairs. £510

12. Set of six Regency sabre leg dining chairs in mahogany with ebony string inlay. £285

1. Set of six Edwardian mahogany dining chairs with turned legs and padded backs. £18

2. Set of six Sheraton period mahogany chairs with reeded backs and legs,circa 1780. £345

3. Regency period black and gilt nursing chair. £13

4. Set of four early Victorian bar back chairs in mahogany with turned legs. £60

5. Set of six Regency mahogany chairs with reeded backs,turned front legs and overstuffed seats, circa 1830. £245

6. Set of four early 19th century dining chairs in mahogany. £75

7. Set of six Victorian oak dining chairs with padded backs and turned legs. £35

8. Set of four late Victorian mahogany dining chairs with pierced splat backs. £15

9. Set of six Regency mahogany chairs with bergere seats,the front inlaid with two bands of rosewood,circa 1830. £245

10. Set of four Regency mahogany dining chairs. £90

11. Set of four 19th century Hepplewhite style mahogany dining chairs. £80

12. Set of four Edwardian mahogany dining chairs. £10

DINING CHAIRS

1. Set of four Victorian balloon back chairs on turned legs. £50

2. Set of six Victorian cabriole leg chairs in walnut. £155

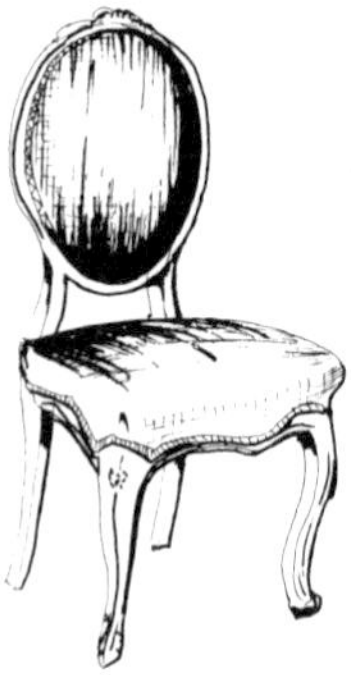

3. Set of four 19th century walnut dining chairs with padded backs. £75

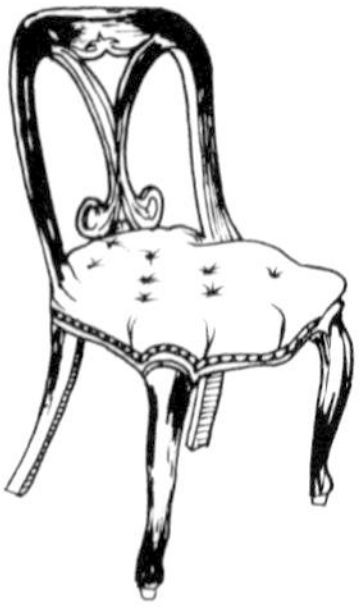

4. Set of six Victorian mahogany dining chairs. £145

5. Set of six Victorian cabriole leg chairs in mahogany. £140

6. Set of six Victorian turned leg chairs in mahogany. £51

7. A carved padouk wood chair with embossed leather seat and centre back splat, circa 1720. £85

8. Set of four early Victorian mahogany bar back chairs with fluted legs. £38

9. An unusual set of four Windsor chairs with star splats,circa 1790. £65

10. One of a set of six Georgian mahogany dining chairs. £265

11. Set of four 19th century Chippendale style mahogany dining chairs with ball and claw feet. £155

12. Set of four 19th century beechwood bar back chairs. £20

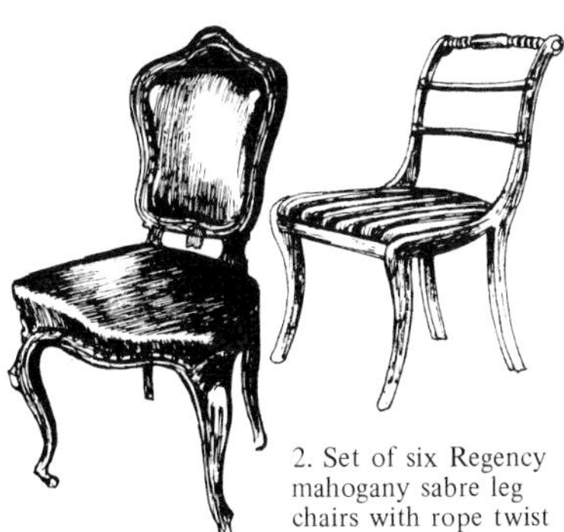

1. One of a set of seven mid 19th century beechwood chairs consisting of five diners and two easy chairs. £275

2. Set of six Regency mahogany sabre leg chairs with rope twist backs. £315

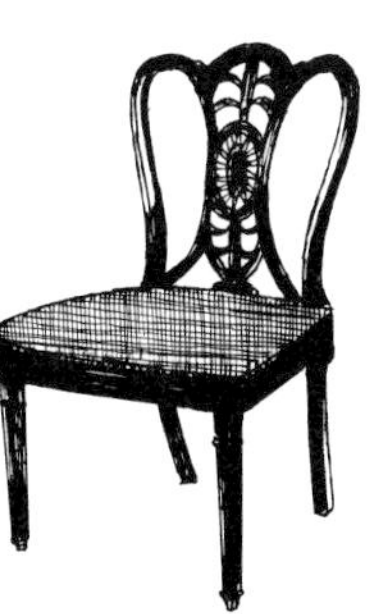

3. Set of fifteen George III mahogany dining chairs. 4,800gns

4. Pair of Victorian lacquered and inlaid mother of pearl cane seated bedroom chairs. £19

5. Beautifully carved William and Mary chair in walnut, of superb quality and proportions, 45 ins high, circa 1690. £165

6. 19th century Bentwood chair. £3

7. Queen Anne oak dining chair of good colour. £75

8. Set of six Edwardian mahogany dining chairs. £30

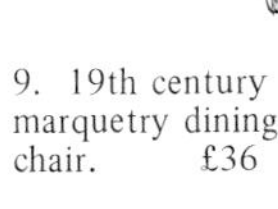

9. 19th century marquetry dining chair. £36

10. Set of four late Victorian, Queen Anne style beechwood chairs with drop in seats and cabriole legs. £17

11. Set of three mahogany balloon back chairs. £30

12. Set of six Regency mahogany sabre leg dining chairs. £310

DINING CHAIRS

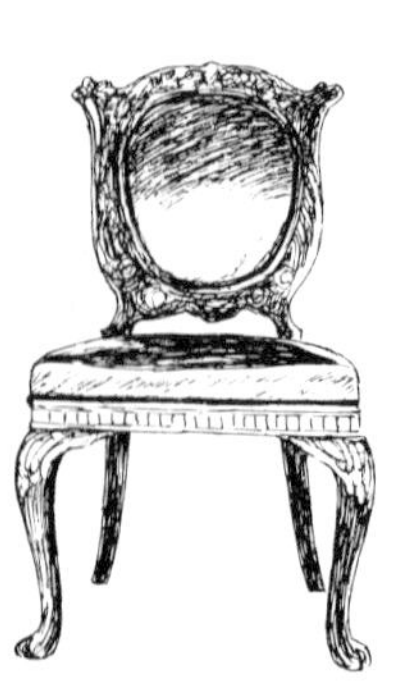

1. Set of six 19th century oak chairs by Gillow and Co. £60

2. Set of six 19th century reproduction Chippendale dining chairs in mahogany. £200

3. Set of six Hepplewhite chairs in mahogany, circa 1790. £375

4. Set of six 19th century Chippendale style chairs in mahogany. £170

5. A fine set of six Regency mahogany chairs with carved rope rails. £360

6. Set of four 19th century Elizabethan style chairs. £35

7. Set of six William IV dining chairs in mahogany with leather upholstery. £185

8. Set of six 19th century French walnut dining chairs upholstered in tapestry. £215

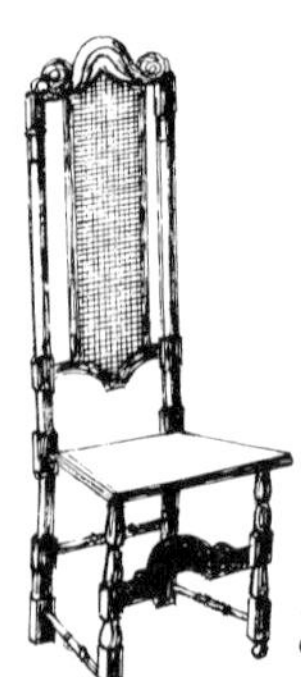

9. Pair of Charles II carved cane back chairs. £68

10. Simulated satinwood deportment chair with stylised decoration on the splats, 39ins high, circa 1810. £48

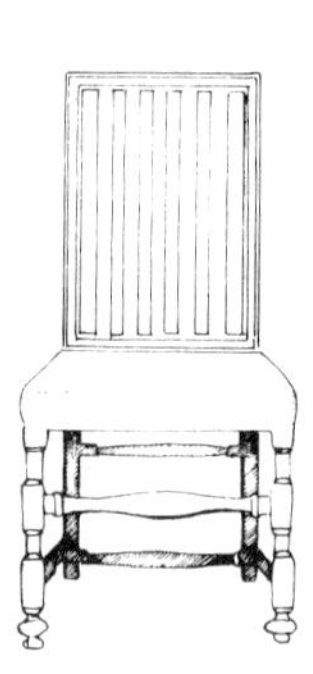

11. Set of four William III walnut dining chairs. £290

12. Set of twelve 18th century Spanish carved oak chairs with rush seats, 34ins high. £185.

1. Set of four 18th century Hepplewhite mahogany chairs, circa 1790. £248

2. Set of four 18th century elm ladderback chairs with rush seats. £75

3. Set of six early 18th century oak chairs of good colour. £230

4. Set of six early country Chippendale dining chairs, circa 1750. £175

5. Pair of Victorian cane seated bedroom chairs in simulated rosewood. £14

6. Set of six 19th century elm Windsor chairs. £27.50

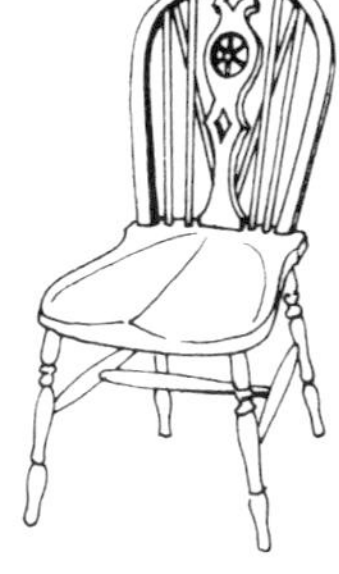

7. Set of ten Windsor wheelback chairs. £44

8. Set of four Victorian flat splat kitchen chairs. £16

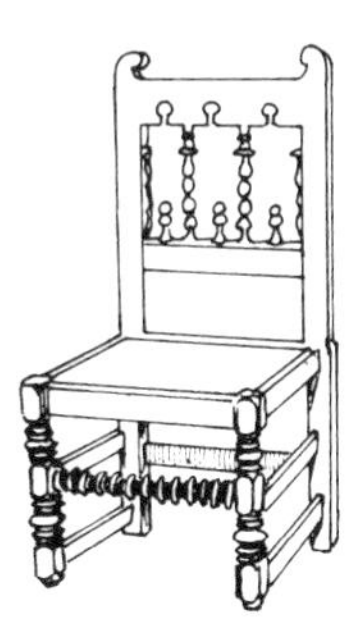

9. Pair of Derbyshire oak dining chairs. £55

10. Pair of 17th century Italian hall chairs, 3ft 7ins high. £175

11. Pair of 17th century Italian giltwood chairs. 580 gns

12. Victorian oak hall chair. £5.

DINING CHAIRS

1. Set of eight Regency mahogany dining chairs with reeded sabre legs. £330

2. Good quality set of six 19th century Hepplewhite style shield back chairs in mahogany. £160

3. A fine set of twelve Georgian mahogany dining chairs with satinwood inlay,comprising two carvers and ten singles. £900

4. Set of six late 19th century Georgian style dining chairs in mahogany with ball and claw feet. £175

5. Set of six Edwardian inlaid mahogany chairs on tapered legs with spade feet. £80

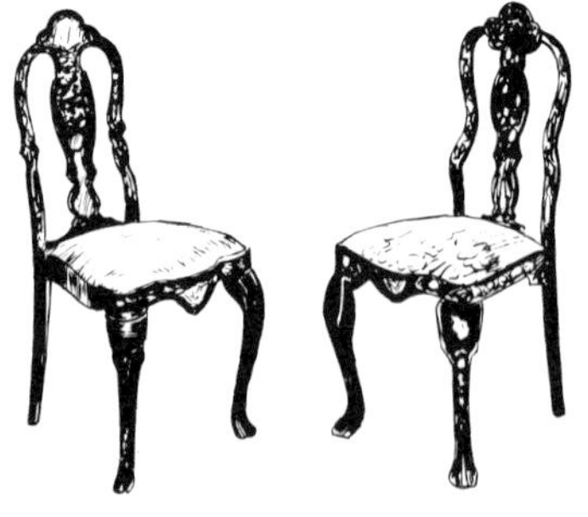

6. Set of six (three and three) William and Mary period marquetry chairs in walnut, circa 1690. £875

1. Set of eleven Chippendale mahogany leather seated dining chairs. £2,800

2. Set of eight Regency sabre leg dining chairs consisting of two carvers and six singles in simulated rosewood inlaid with brass. £375

3. Set of six near matching George III yew wood armchairs. £425

4. Set of seven William IV period mahogany chairs comprising one arm and six singles with Trafalgar seats and turned and fluted legs. £134

5. Set of six Hepplewhite period mahogany chairs consisting of two carvers and four singles. 1,500gns

6. Set of eight Carolean style dining chairs with carved oval cane panelled backs with a cresting of child and dolphin figures. £340

ELBOW CHAIRS

1. Set of six Georgian sabre leg mahogany chairs consisting of two arm and four standard,with drop in seats,circa 1820. £295

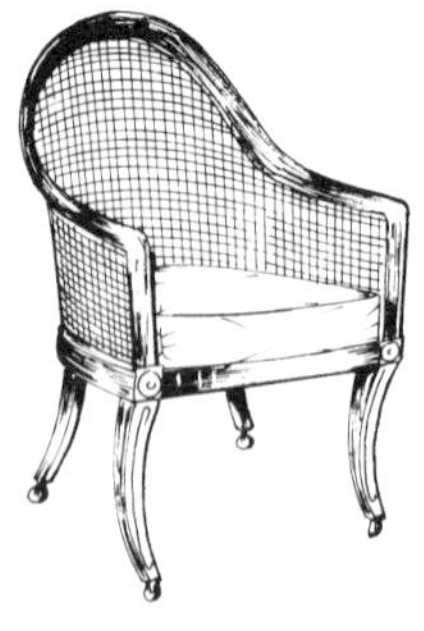

2. Pair of Regency Bergere chairs in rosewood with reeded sabre legs. £80

3. Fine Regency Trafalgar chair in light chesnut mahogany with reeded members and a rare carved rail,circa 1810. £75

4. Regency period mahogany carver. £30

5. A fine quality Charles II armchair in walnut. £100

6. Pair of Edwardian mahogany chairs with boxwood string inlay. £40

7. Late 18th century Chippendale mahogany ladder back carver. £75

8. Early 18th century Continental oak armchair with a cane back and seat. £85

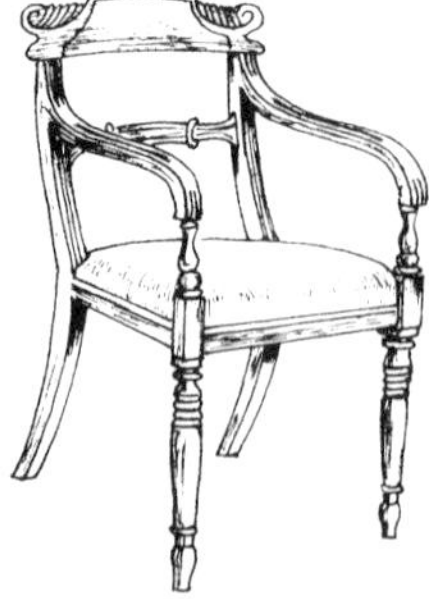

9. Set of six early 19th century mahogany chairs consisting of four singles and two carvers. £255

1. Unusual set of six English mahogany armchairs,circa 1800. £1,100

2. A good quality mid 18th century mahogany chair. £145

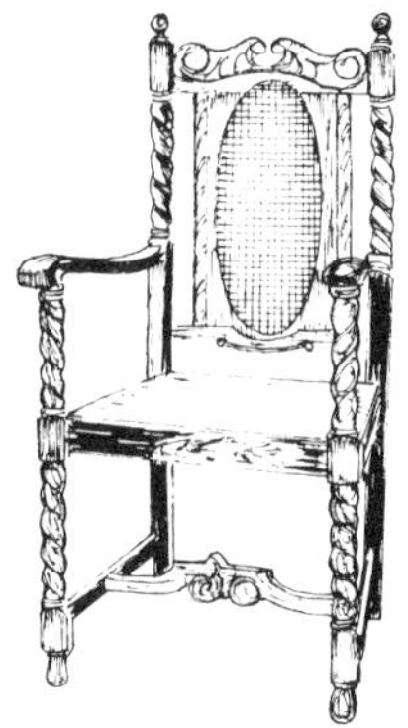

3. Set of six Victorian reproduction chairs in oak comprising two carvers and four singles. £38

4. A good quality Queen Anne japanned armchair. £500

5. Victorian elm smokers chair. £8.50

6. Set of six William IV dining chairs upholstered in leather. £210

7. Exceptionally fine quality George I walnut veneered armchair with cabriole legs and ball and claw feet. £370

8. 18th century German cane backed armchair in oak. £80

9. 18th century Dutch marquetry elbow chair. £60.

ELBOW CHAIRS

1. Pair of fine quality mahogany carvers, circa 1835. £120

2. 19th century Windsor wheel back childs high chair in figured elm. £14

3. Unusual Edwardian inlaid mahogany carver chair. £13.50

4. Mid 19th century Bentwood armchair. £3.50

5. Regency mahogany library chair-steps, the steps with inset tooled leather, height of chair 35 ins. £350

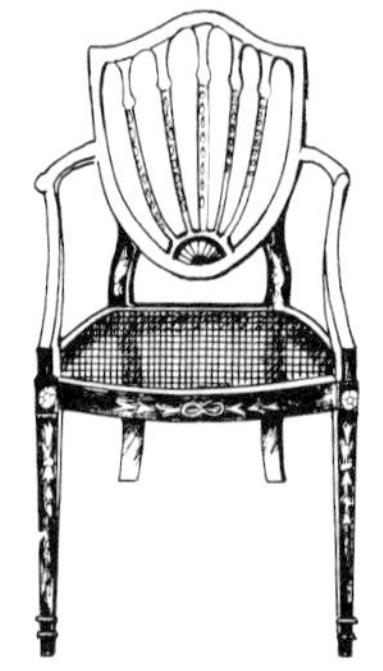

6. Good quality late 18th century Hepplewhite japanned armchair with a cane seat. £115

7. Set of four Regency open chairs with cane seats. £440

8. Chippendale period fruitwood childs chair of good colour and condition, 37 ins high. £75

9. Edwardian inlaid mahogany armchair. £20

1. Regency library chair-steps in mahogany, 35 ins high,21 ins wide, circa 1820. £185

2. George III collapsable mahogany Campaign chair circa 1750. £225

3. Set of eight Sheraton style dining chairs consisting of two carvers and six singles. £320

4. Edwardian inlaid mahogany armchair. £15

5. Edwardian inlaid mahogany carver chair. £20

6. Set of six late Georgian mahogany dining chairs. £235

7. Victorian mahogany chair-steps. £17.50

8. 17th century oak elbow chair. £150

9. One of a set of eight Regency black and gilt elbow chairs. £850

ELBOW CHAIRS

1. Carolean elbow chair of good colour. £95

2. Fine set of four George II Windsor chairs in yew wood. £360

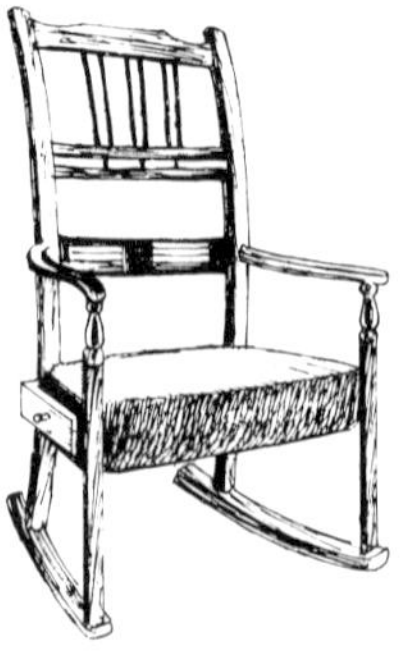

3. Early 19th century Farmhouse rocker in fruitwood with a pistol drawer. £37

4. A fine yew wood draught back armchair with a crinoline stretcher. £78

5. Queen Anne walnut elbow chair. £68

6. Set of six 19th century Windsor comb back chairs. £42

7. Yew wood Windsor armchair, circa 1790, 35 ins high. £45

8. A fine quality mid 18th century comb back Windsor chair with hoof feet. £55

9. American rocking chair with the original painted decoration,42 ins high,circa 1840. £55

1. Victorian lath back Windsor chair in elm. £12

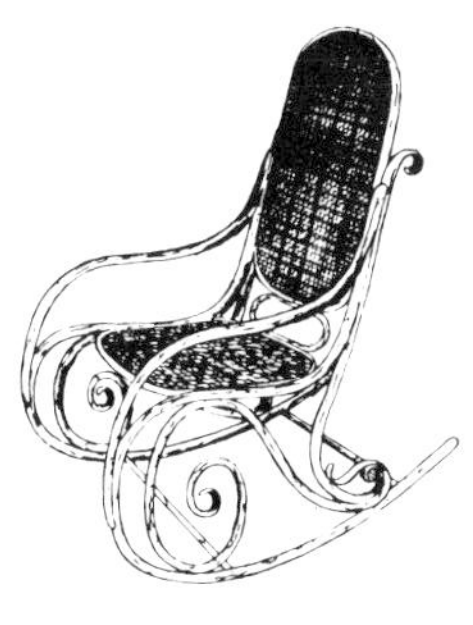

2. Mid-19th century Bentwood rocking chair with a cane seat and back. £35

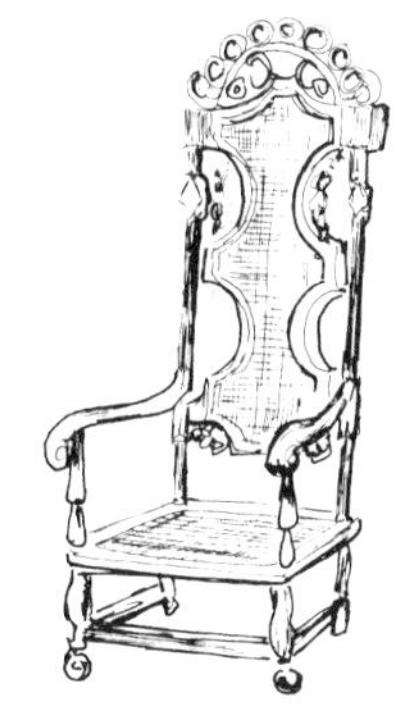

3. Carolean elbow chair of a good honey colour. £75

4. Set of six late 18th century cottage bow and spindle back elbow chairs. £190

5. Pair of late 18th century yew wood Windsor chairs with crinoline rails. £110

6. Yew wood Windsor chair circa 1790. £47

7. Good quality set of four George II Windsor chairs in yew wood. £360

8. 18th century yew wood Windsor chair of good colour and condition. £60

9. 19th century Windsor comb back armchair in elm. £12

EASY CHAIRS

1. Good quality walnut Victorian grandfather chair with cabriole legs. £70

2. Edwardian ebonised armchair on short cabriole legs. £13

3. A small Victorian iron frame button back chair. £25

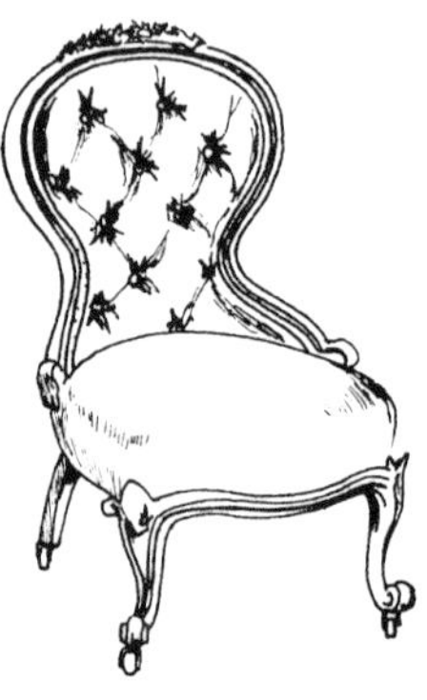

4. A good Victorian button back ladies chair. £45

5. Mahogany cock fighting chair with an adjustable table on a brass running track, circa 1825. £325

6. Victorian gents chair with padded arms and turned legs in mahogany. £37

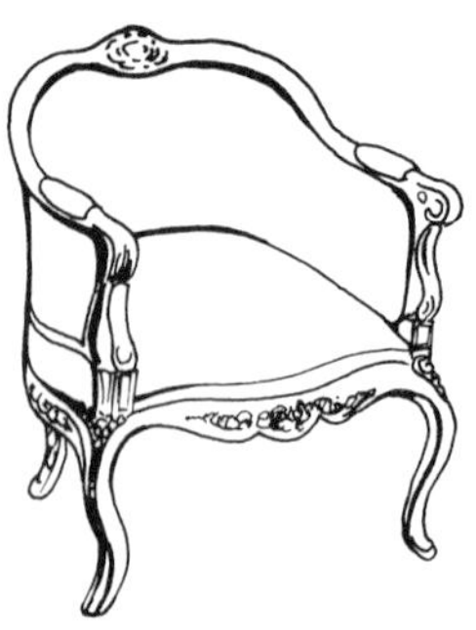

7. A good Louis XV period carved giltwood Bergere, circa 1760. £280

8. Victorian Prie Dieu chair with the original cover. £35

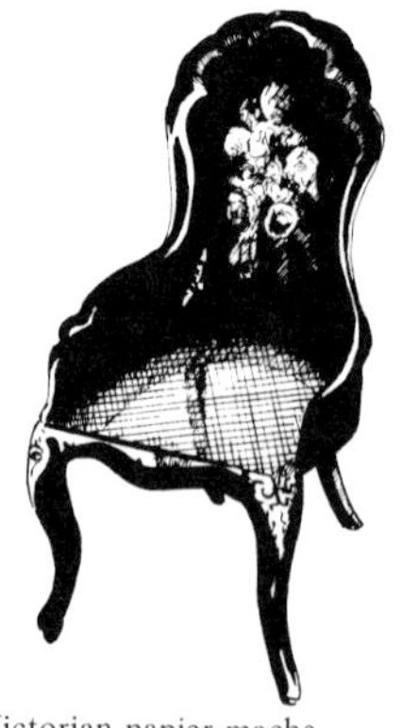

9. A Victorian papier mache occasional chair, the moulded back inlaid with mother of pearl. £105

1. Pair of Regency period library chairs covered in green hide. £375

2. Fine period wing chair, circa 1790. £195

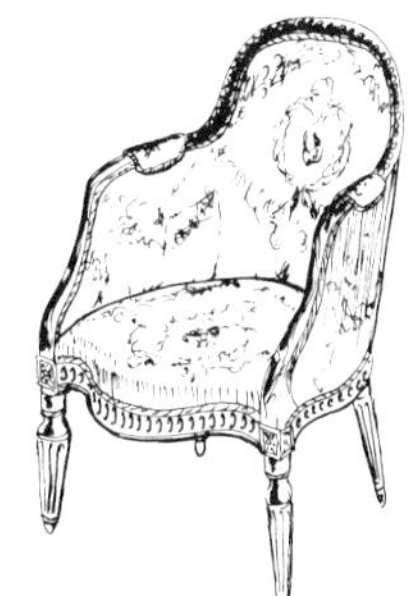

3. Good quality early 19th century French giltwood chair circa 1820. £65

4. Nicely shaped Victorian iron frame ladies chair on turned legs with brass cup castors. £50

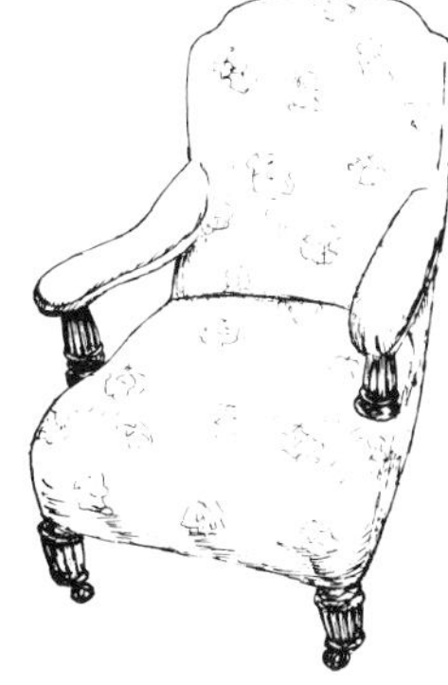

5. Victorian mahogany open sided armchair. £5

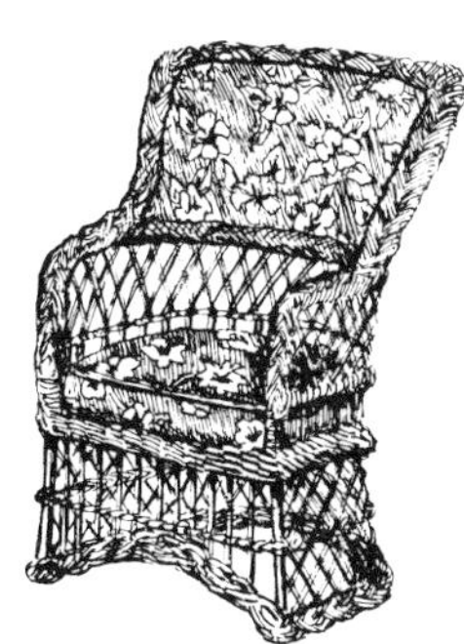

6. Late Victorian wicker chair. £7.50

7. Good quality Queen Anne wing chair. £355

8. Victorian cabriole leg occasional chair in mahogany covered in moss green velvet. £44

9. A fine quality George II library chair. £1,400

EASY CHAIRS

1. Victorian mahogany and iron framed chair on turned legs (needs recovering). £15

2. A rare collapsable military campaign chair, circa 1770. £430

3. Victorian mahogany open sided buttoned back armchair. £15

4. Victorian bobbin framed tub chair. £15

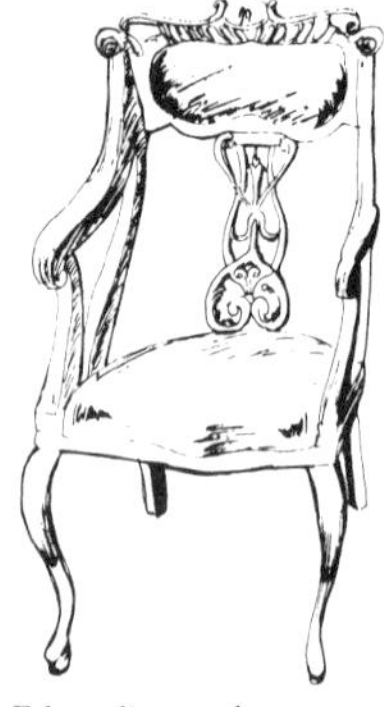

5. Edwardian mahogany open sided armchair with a pierced splat and cabriole legs. £8

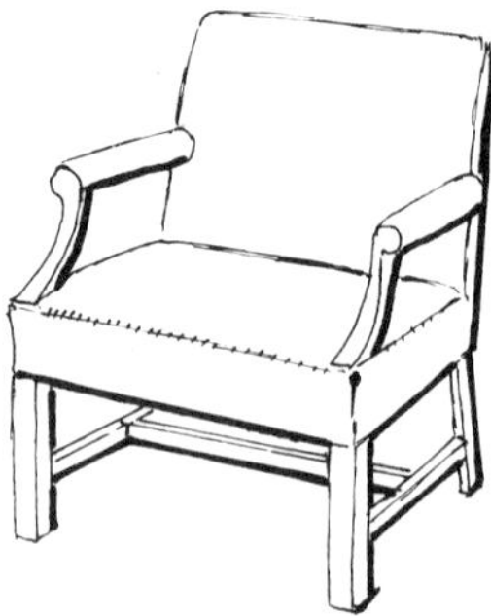

6. Mid 18th century open armchair upholstered in green hide. £180

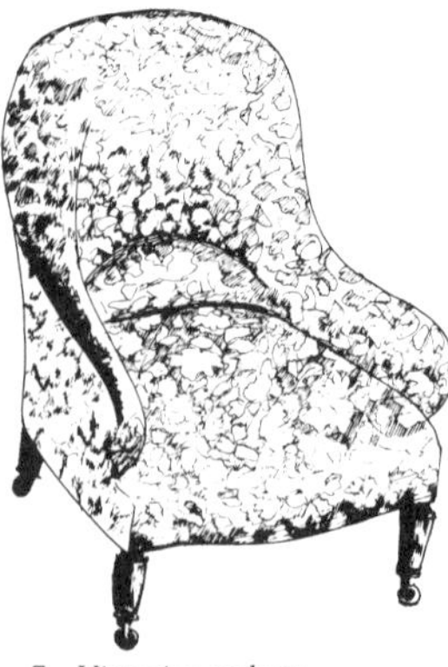

7. Victorian walnut framed armchair upholstered in embossed gold velvet. £27.50

8. Good quality finely carved rosewood Victorian grandfather chair with cabriole legs. £70

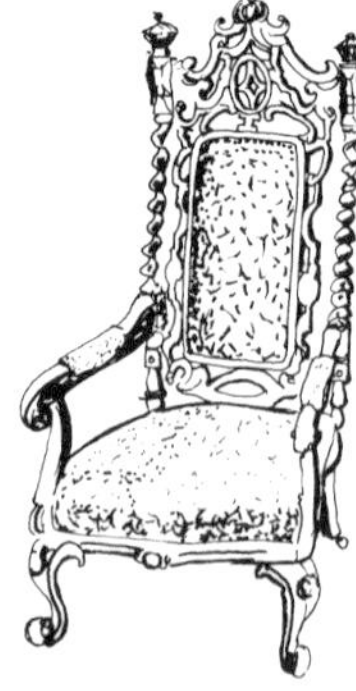

9. A fine Victorian open sided armchair in rosewood with cabriole legs and scroll feet. £45

1. Victorian ladies chair in walnut with a pierced splat back and turned legs. £13

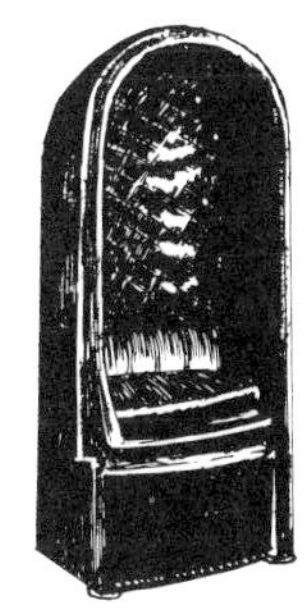

2. Fine reproduction hooded chair upholstered in leather. £235

3. Victorian walnut framed nursing chair upholstered in the original bead and needlework cover. £40

4. Late Victorian horseshoe backed ebonised occasional chair on fluted legs. £16

5. 18th century Chippendale mahogany armchair on carved cabriole legs with ball and claw feet. £305

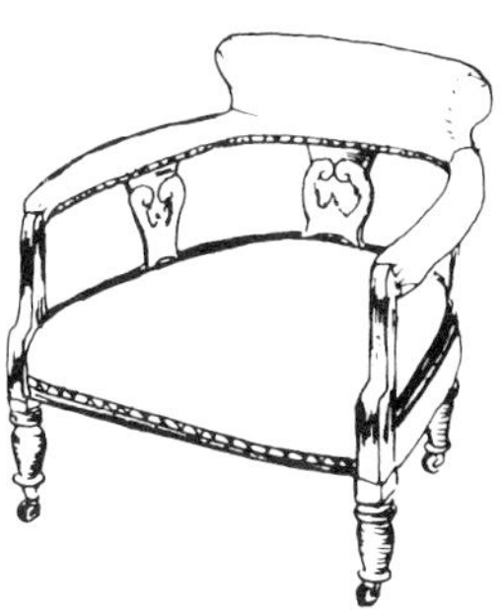

6. Edwardian mahogany open sided armchair on turned legs. £7.50

7. A highly carved Victorian oak hall chair. £26

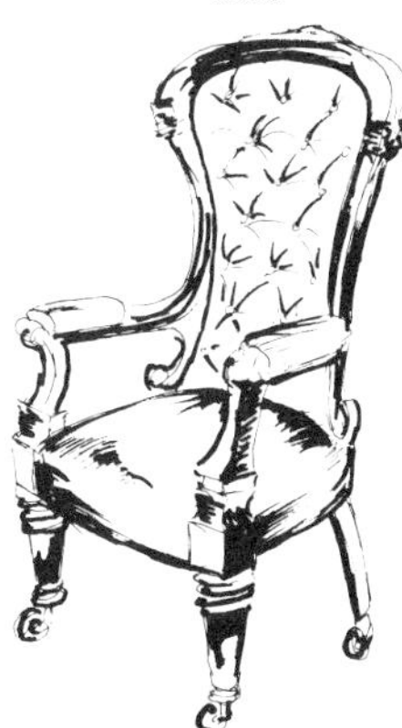

8. Victorian turned leg grandfather chair in walnut. £45

9. A Flemish walnut masters chair,supported on cabriole legs,circa 1700, 58 ins high. £275.

EASY CHAIRS

1. Early 19th century wing chair upholstered in leather. £145

2. Victorian cabriole leg chair with padded arms and cabriole legs. £50

3. Late Victorian Prie Dieu chair on turned legs. £15

4. Good quality 19th century mahogany sewing chair. £32

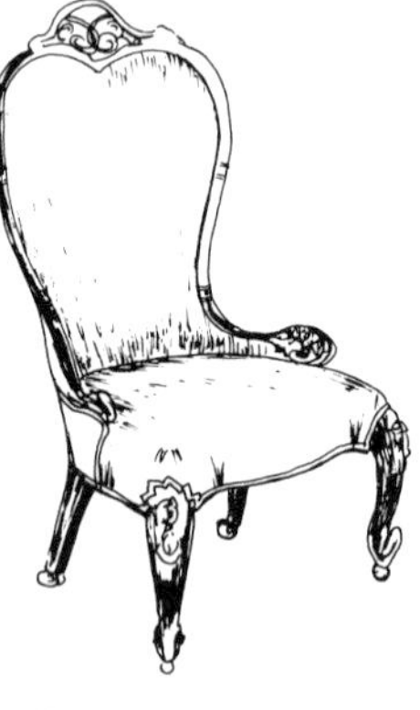

5. Victorian cabriole leg ladies chair in walnut. £40

6. 19th century inlaid walnut nursing chair. £18

7. 18th century French carved giltwood fauteuil with original tapestry cover. £155

8. A good quality George II giltwood armchair on cabriole legs. £285

9. 18th century French giltwood armchair with a tapestry cover. £270

1. Early 19th century buttoned armchair upholstered in leather with fluted legs and brass castors. £135

2. William IV mahogany armchair covered in tan leather. £65

3. Victorian walnut framed Prie Dieu chair with cabriole leg supports. £22

4. Late Victorian mahogany framed armchair with turned legs and brass cup castors. £7

5. 19th century French giltwood chair upholstered in embossed green velvet. £185

6. Late Victorian horseshoe back smokers chair in mahogany with turned legs. £20

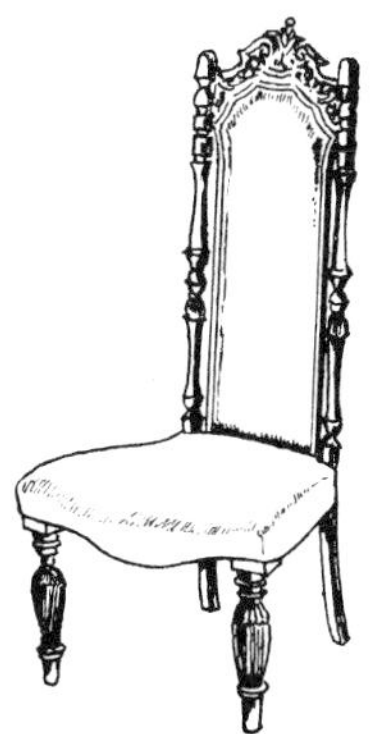

7. Mid 19th century walnut Abbotsford-chair. £18

8. Small Victorian ebonised childs chair. £37.50

9. Good quality early Victorian walnut ladies chair. £48

COUCHES

1. Edwardian inlaid mahogany settee on tapered legs with spade feet. £34

2. Edwardian pale mahogany open sided settee on cabriole leg supports. £30

3. Victorian mahogany chaise longue on turned legs. £38

4. A small qood quality Regency period rosewood settee on sabre legs with brass claw feet and brass inlay. £185

5. Victorian buttoned back sofa in walnut with cabriole legs. £135

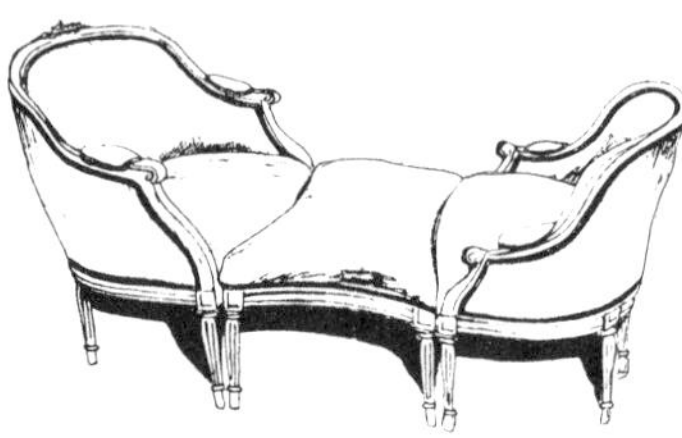

6. A good quality 19th century Louis XV style giltwood chaise longue in the form of a pair of chairs with shaped stool to match. £375

7. 19th century French giltwood settee on cabriole legs with scroll feet. £300

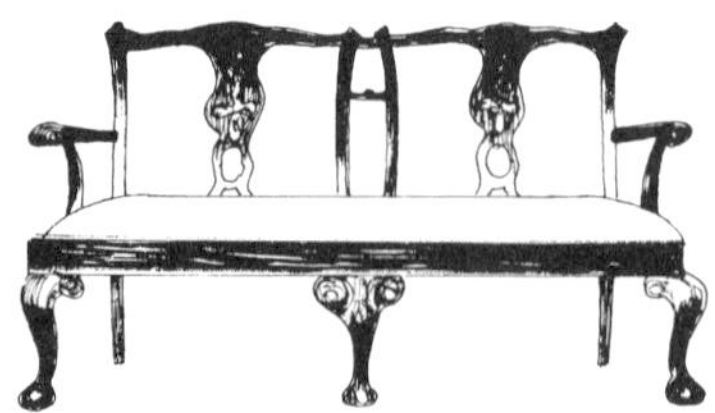

8. 18th century Chippendale two-chair back settee of excellent colour and condition. £700

1. Good quality Victorian walnut framed settee on turned legs with a finely carved centre back. £130

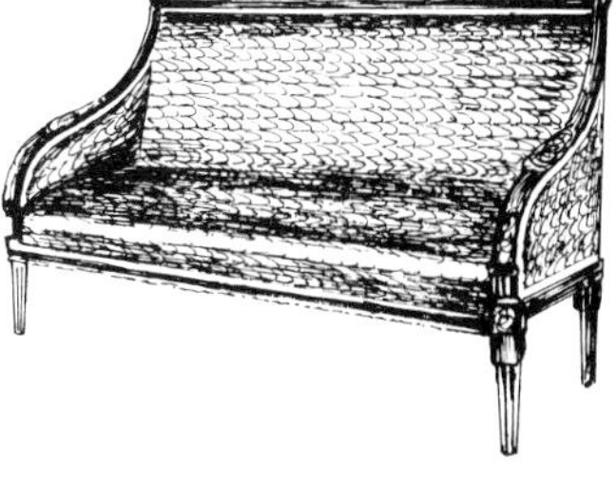

2. Mid 18th century French giltwood settee 5 ft 8 ins long. £85

3. Fine Victorian couch with cabriole legs. £95

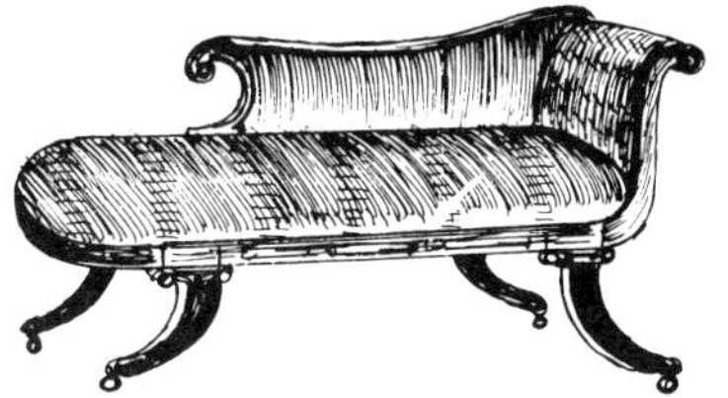

4. Georgian rosewood couch with brass inlay,sabre legs and brass castors. £86

5. Edwardian mahogany settee on square tapering legs with spade feet. £21

6. Good quality late 18th century mahogany sofa with satinwood inlay and fine turned legs. £380

7. Charles II oak settle with a finely carved panelled back. £300

8. Victorian shaped front settee on fine ebonised legs with brass castors. £90

COUCHES

1. A good quality Victorian rosewood double ended chaise longue upholstered in green velvet. £225

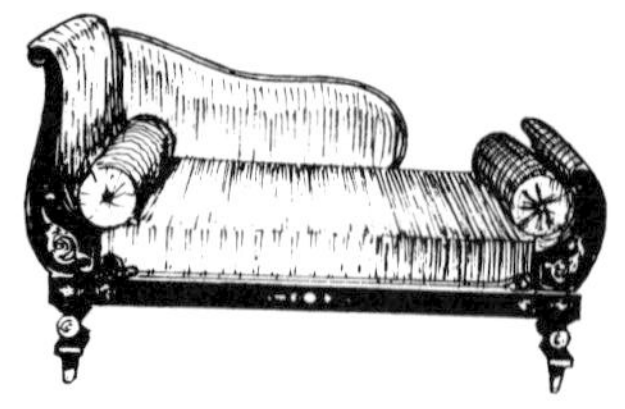

2. An attractive simulated rosewood couch of the Regency period with ormolu mounts. £135

3. A good quality scroll end sofa of the Regency period in rosewood, with sabre legs and brass claw castors. £145

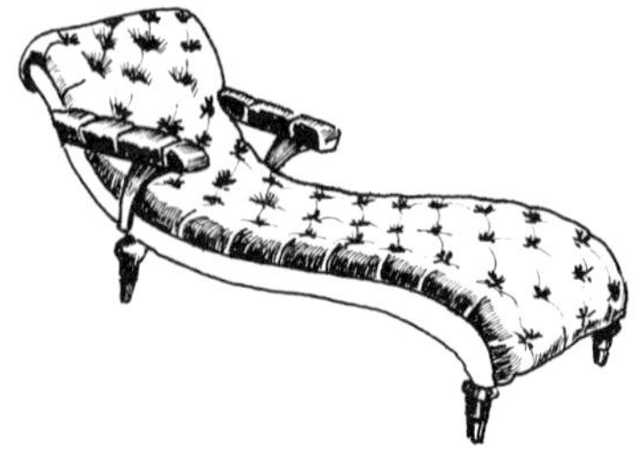

4. Good quality Victorian day bed upholstered in gold velvet. £160

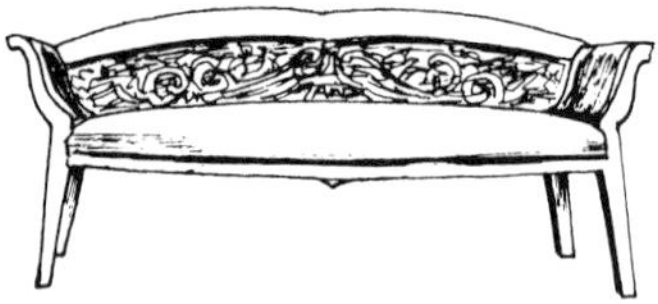

5. 19th century Continental fruitwood couch 6ft 2 ins long. £75

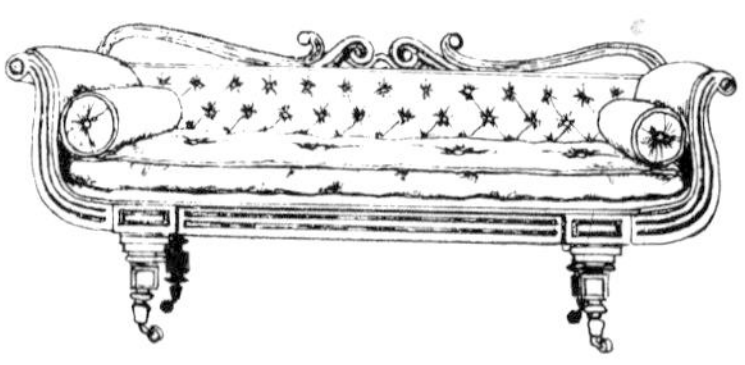

6. William IV scroll end sofa in mahogany with ebony banding. £90

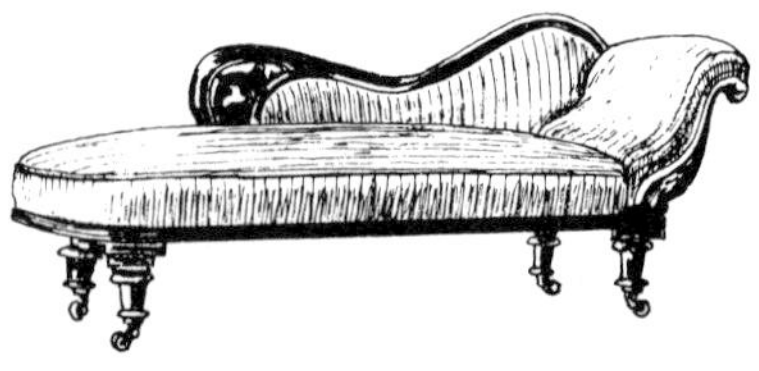

7. Victorian turned leg chaise longue in mahogany. £58

8. Victorian walnut scroll end sofa 6ft 2 ins long on turned legs. £50

1. Victorian Chesterfield with turned legs 6ft long (in need of recovering). £38

2. 19th century rosewood framed scroll end sofa on turned legs, 5ft 3 ins long. £85

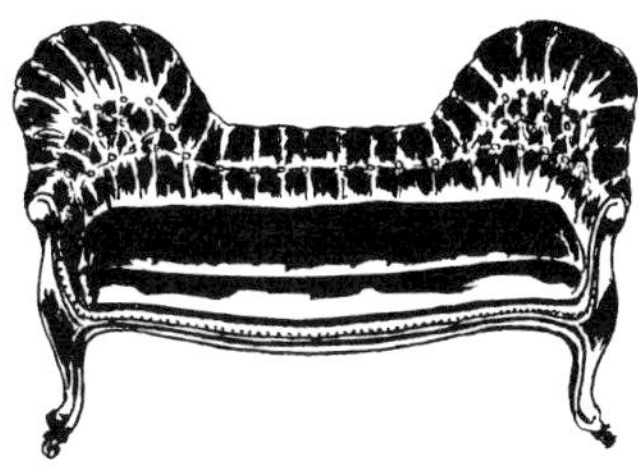

3. Good quality Victorian double ended chaise longue on cabriole legs with scroll feet. £150

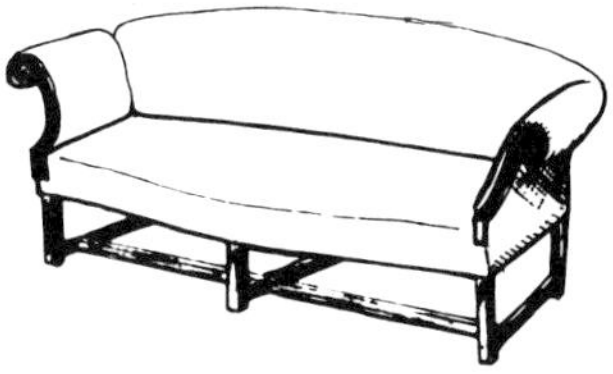

4. Late 18th century mahogany settee 7ft 5 ins long. £210

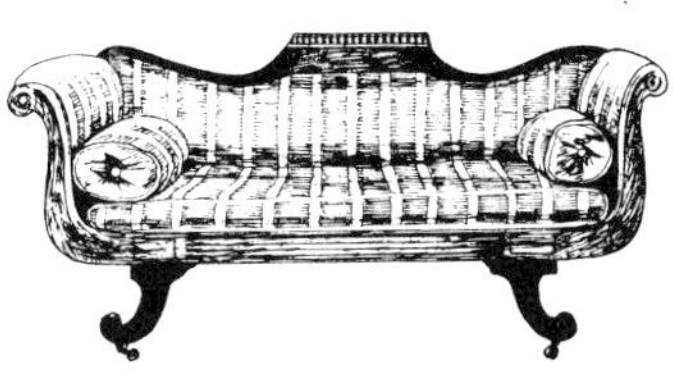

5. Regency period scroll end sofa in rosewood with sabre legs. £105

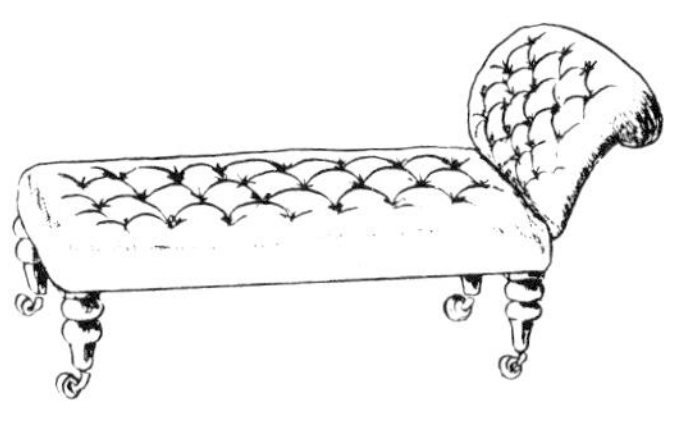

6. Late 19th century buttoned day bed on turned legs. £30

7. Rosewood framed Regency period chaise longue with brass mounts,circa 1815. £145

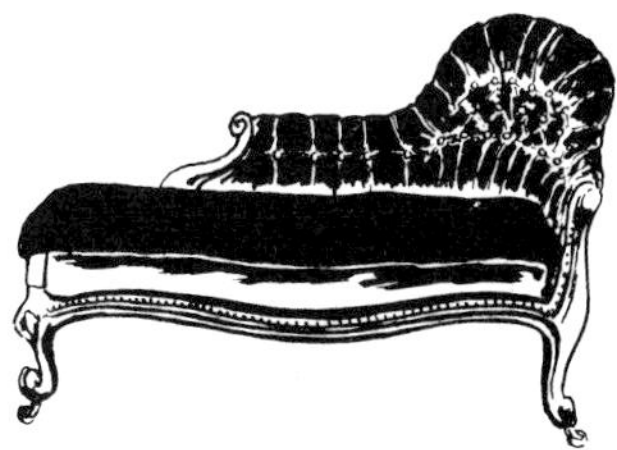

8. Victorian walnut framed chaise longue on cabriole legs with scroll feet. £78

SUITES

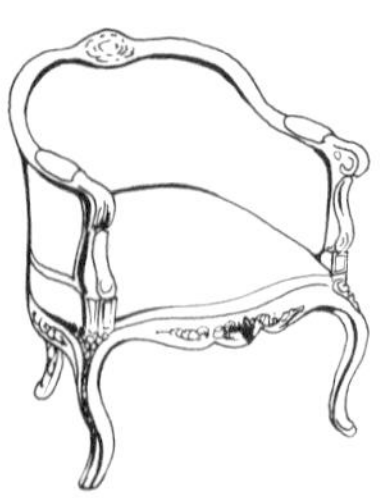

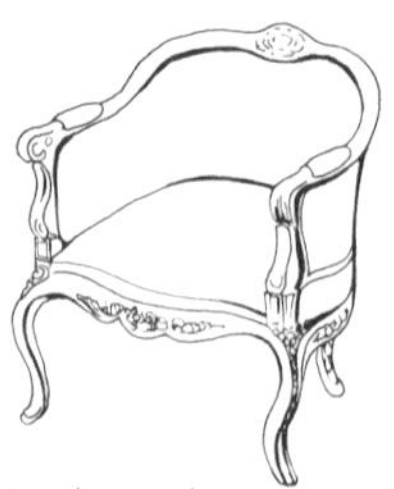

1. 19th century Louis XV style giltwood bergere suite comprising a two seater couch and two chairs. £455

2. Late 19th century nine piece inlaid mahogany suite comprising a couch, two armchairs, four dining chairs and two nursing chairs. £145

3. Early 19th century Empire style three piece suite. £500

4. Late 19th century inlaid mahogany three piece suite on square tapering legs. £100

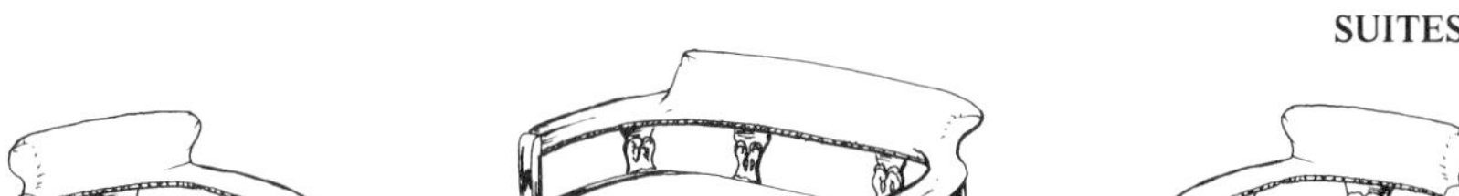

1. Late 19th century mahogany open sided three piece suite on fine turned legs terminating in brass castors. £40

2. A nine piece Edwardian mahogany drawing room suite comprising a settee, two armchairs, four dining chairs and two nursing chairs. £140

3. An 18th century Franco Flemish neo-classical giltwood suite de salon of a canape and eleven fauteuils. £6,530

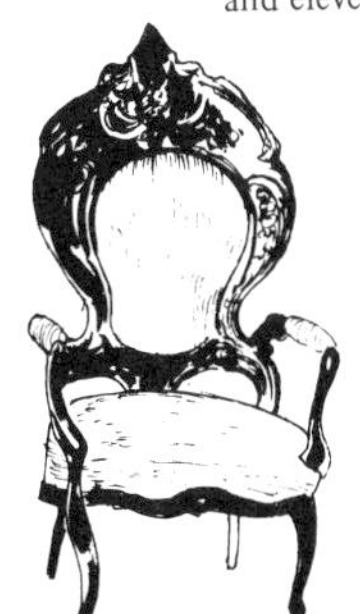

4. Mid 19th century mahogany three piece suite comprising a couch, ladies chair and gents chair. £210

SUITES

1. Small Victorian upholstered three piece suite on turned legs with brass castors (in need of recovering). £85

2. Late 19th century mahogany three piece suite with satinwood banding. £105

3. 19th century Oriental hardwood highly carved three piece suite comprising a settee and two armchairs. £175

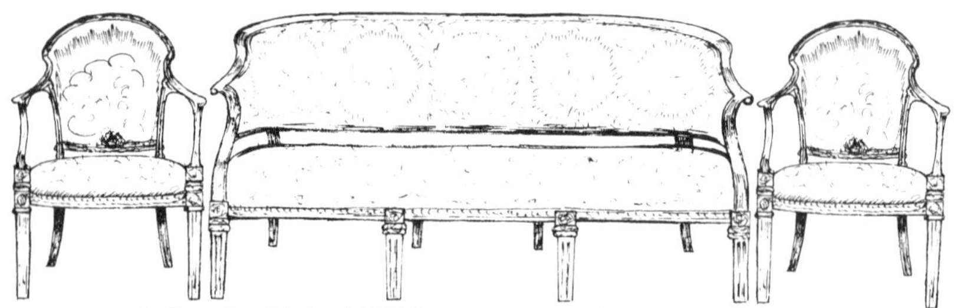

4. A good quality Louis XVI three seat settee and four armchairs. £845

1. A small mid Victorian walnut suite comprising a settee and two nursing chairs with fine fret cut centre splats and turned and fluted legs. £80

2. Good quality early Victorian walnut three piece suite with carved cabriole legs and scroll feet. £185

3. Late 19th century mahogany seven piece suite comprising a couch, two armchairs and four dining chairs. £120

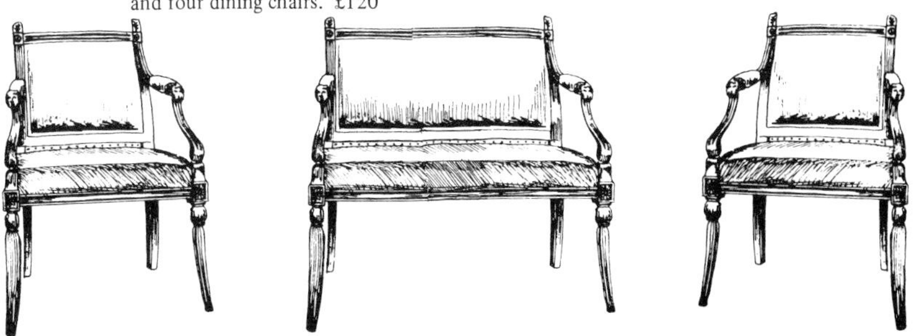

4. A good quality late 18th century giltwood three piece suite. £1,300

STOOLS

1. Good Victorian rosewood revolving piano stool. £15

2. Early Victorian mahogany dressing table stool on cabriole legs, 1ft 10 ins wide. £21

3. Victorian mahogany revolving piano stool. £8.50

4. Late 18th century mahogany window seat. £85

5. George III mahogany simulated bamboo stool. £35

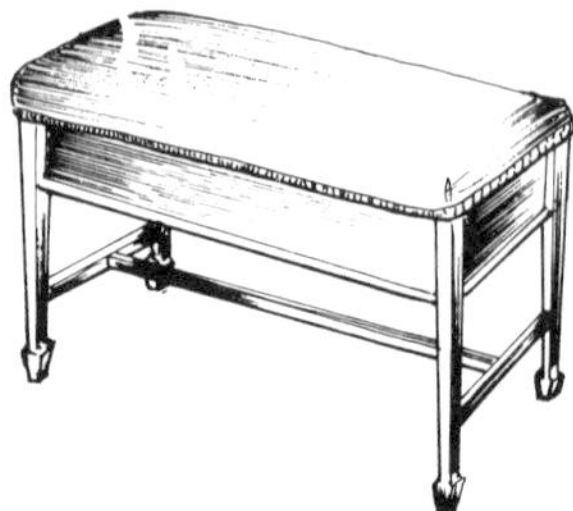

6. Edwardian inlaid mahogany duet stool with tapering legs and spade feet. £20

7. Small Victorian footstool with a beadwork cover. £8

8. A good quality William and Mary period footstool in walnut. £85

9. Late Victorian mahogany footstool on bun feet. £7

10. Late 19th century mahogany revolving piano stool. £8

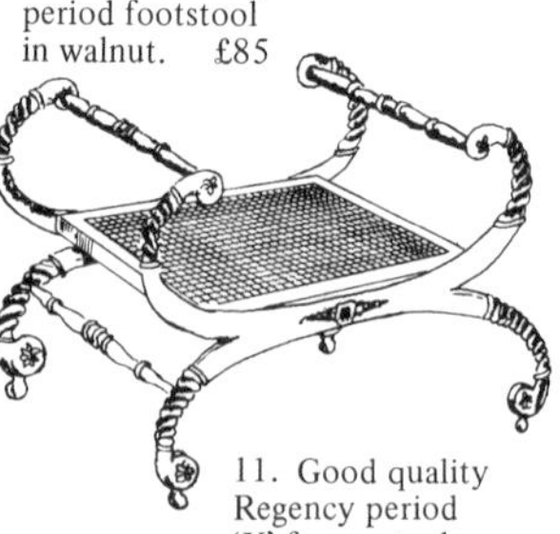

11. Good quality Regency period 'X' frame stool. £60

12. Victorian papier mache piano stool decorated with mother of pearl. £35

1. Early Victorian rosewood piano stool on a platform base with scroll feet. £14

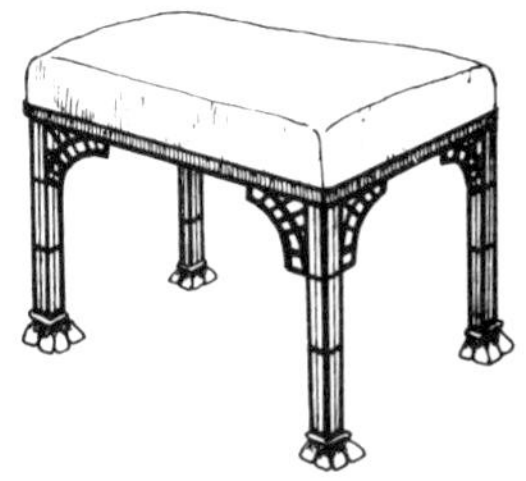

2. Late 18th century mahogany stool with cluster column legs. £70

3. Unusual Regency period revolving piano stool. £42

4. Edwardian inlaid mahogany piano stool, 1 ft 9 ins wide. £10

5. 19th century French style rosewood duet stool,circa 1840, 48 ins long. £40

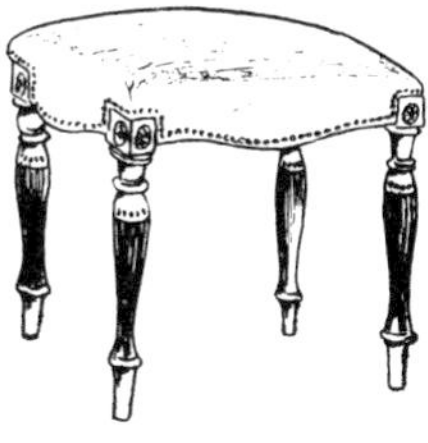

6. Late 18th century Hepplewhite stool in mahogany. £45

7. Early 19th century inlaid mahogany dressing table stool. £48

8. Early oak joint stool of good colour. £67

9. Edwardian mahogany piano stool with an upholstered seat and cabriole legs. £5

10. Small Regency rosewood footstool. £15

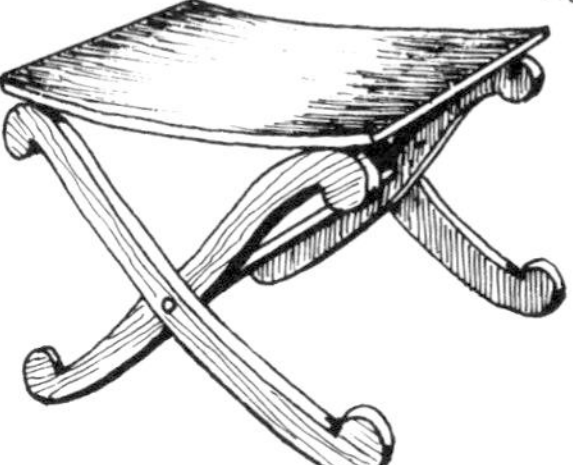

11. Early 19th century mahogany 'X' frame stool. £34

12. Good quality early Victorian rosewood piano stool with paw feet. £18

BUREAUX

1. Small late 18th century mahogany bureau on ogee feet with brass drop handles. £400

2. A good quality American Colonial bureau made in about 1765. £1,450

3. An attractive bureau in golden ash crossbanded in walnut with a fine patina, 36 ins wide, 41 ins high, 20 ins deep, circa 1740. £460

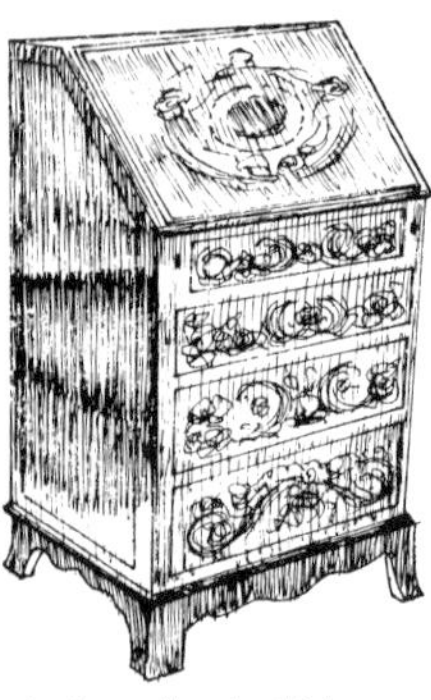

4. A small early 19th century mahogany bureau decorated with bows, ribbons and garlands of flowers, 2 ft 2 ins wide. £170

5. George I oak bureau of good colour, circa 1730, 36 ins wide, 20 ins deep, 40½ ins high. £185

6. Edwardian cylinder top bureau in satinwood. £250

7. A good quality 19th century Sheraton style cylinder bureau in sandalwood. £265

8. A good quality 18th century oak bureau with canted corners and bracket feet, 3 ft 3 ins wide. £140

9. A large Dutch walnut and marquetry bombe shaped bureau. £1,100

1. 19th century inlaid mahogany roll top desk, 3 ft 3 ins wide. £160

2. George I oak bureau of good colour and patination with a stepped interior and slide. £210

3. Small oak bureau with oak lined drawers and good patina, 34ins wide, circa 1735. £165

4. A good quality small Queen Anne walnut bureau. £1,900

5. Walnut crossbanded bureau with pierced brass handles,36 ins wide, 42 ins high, 18 ins deep, circa 1740. £275

6. Early 18th century solid walnut bureau, 34 ins wide. £335

7. Late 19th century mahogany and walnut veneered bureau on cabriole legs. £22

8. Small William and Mary period oak bureau on bun feet, with a shaped interior. £220

9. A fine William and Mary oak bureau. £260

BUREAUX

1. George III mahogany bureau on splayed feet, 3 ft 3 ins wide. £140

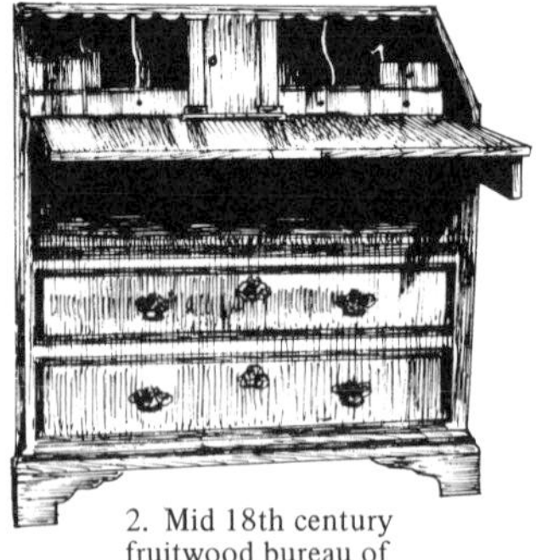

2. Mid 18th century fruitwood bureau of a good golden brown colour, 36 ins wide, 39 ins high, 19 ins deep. £415

3. Early 18th century mahogany ladies writing bureau 2 ft 2ins wide. £200

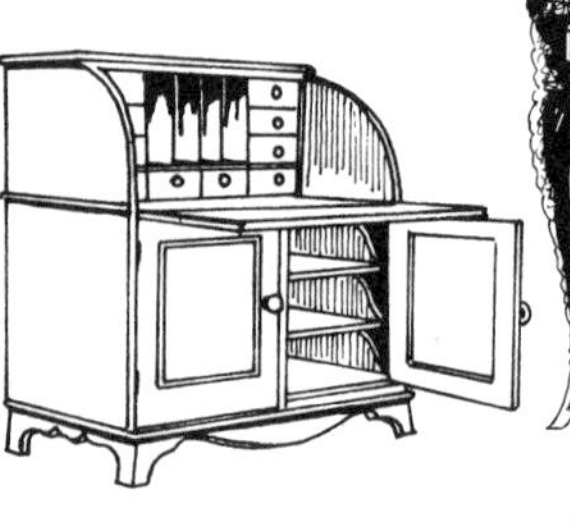

4. Large Edwardian mahogany cylinder top bureau with panelled cupboards below and boxwood string inlay, 3ft 7½ins wide. £55

5. A Continental ebonised bureau with fine cast ormolu enrichments and cabriole legs, circa 1780. £285

6. A good quality Georgian mahogany bureau with pierced brass handles, 3 ft wide. £205

7. Small early oak bureau with a secret compartment, only 34 ins wide. £130

8. Dutch bombe front cylinder desk in mahogany with a shaped interior, 3 ft 9 ins wide. £390

9. A small George III mahogany bureau with ogee feet and brass drop handles, 2ft 7½ ins wide. £215

1. Small late 19th century inlaid mahogany bureau with bracket feet, 27 ins wide, circa 1890. £85

2. A magnificent quality Dutch marquetry bureau 3 ft 5 ins wide. £920

3. Small 18th century oak bureau only 2ft 7ins wide. £180

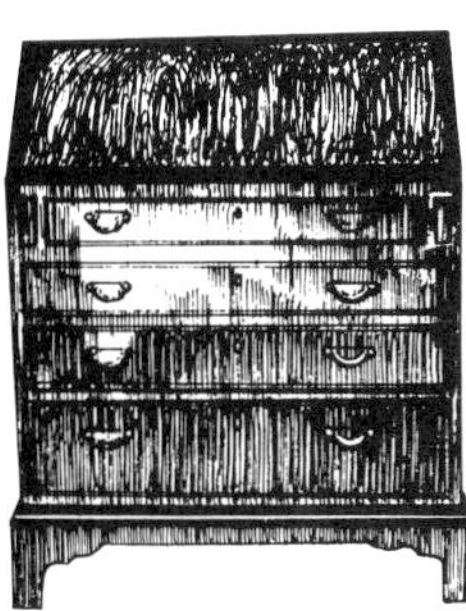

4. Small George I walnut bureau only 2ft 10 ins wide, circa 1720, of good colour and condition. £460

5. 19th century French rosewood and marquetry bureau with a pierced brass gallery and cabriole legs. £135

6. Early 20th century oak bureau on a stretcher base, 2 ft 9 ins wide. £10

7. Edwardian inlaid mahogany bureau with a conch shell on the flap and bracket feet, 2 ft 6 ins wide. £55

8. A good quality Dutch marquetry bureau. £1,200

9. Edwardian lacquered bureau decorated with Chinese domestic scenes, 2 ft 6 ins wide. £40

BUREAU BOOKCASES

1. 19th century fretted mahogany bureau bookcase on bracket feet, 3 ft 4 ins wide. £85

2. A fine Dutch marquetry bureau cabinet. 2,200 gns

3. An exceptionally fine quality inlaid mahogany bureau bookcase 3 ft 2 ins wide. £240

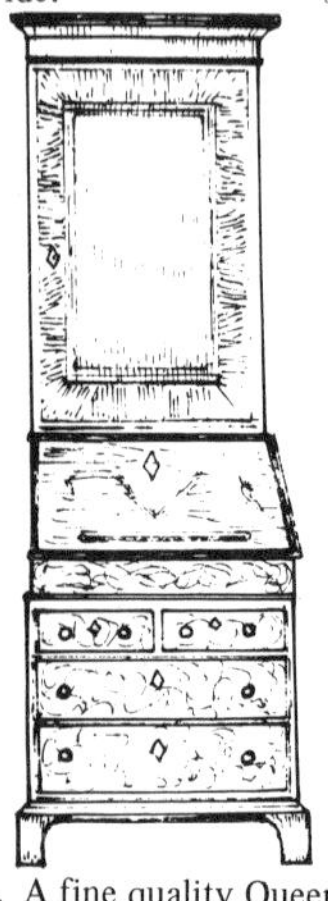

4. A fine quality Queen Anne walnut bureau bookcase only 26 ins wide, 79 ins high. £2,400

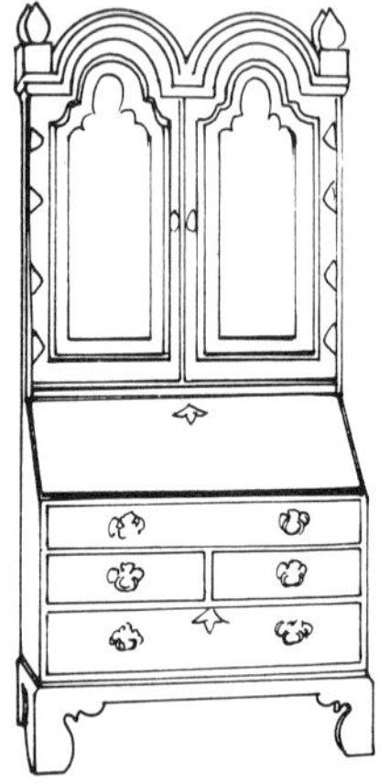

5. Queen Anne walnut bureau bookcase (in need of restoration). £890

6. A fine George III mahogany bookcase. £510

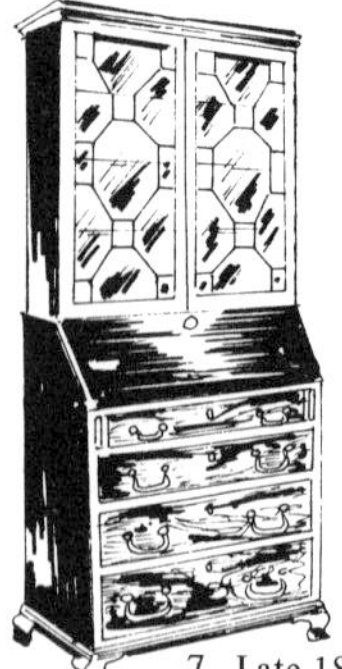

7. Late 18th century Chippendale mahogany bookcase. £720

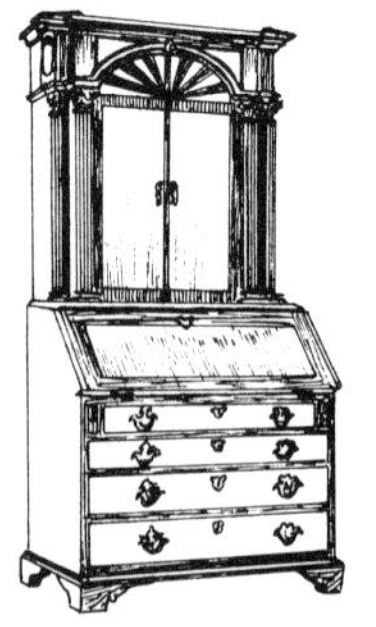

8. Good quality mahogany bureau bookcase, circa 1755. £700

9. A Queen Anne period walnut bureau cabinet with three long drawers below the flap. £1,050

1. Good quality George III mahogany bureau cabinet with a broken arch pediment and ogee feet. £800

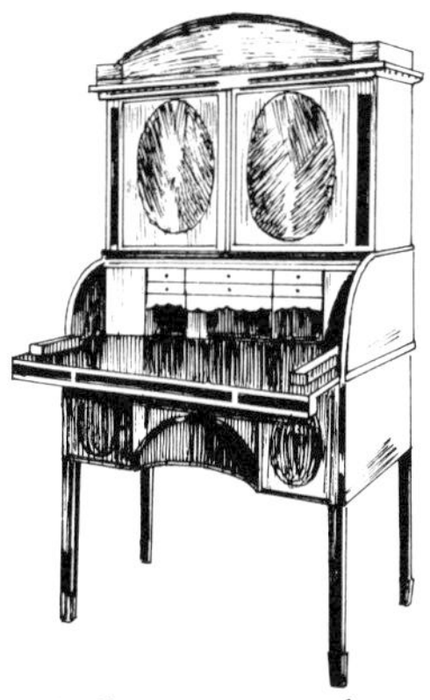

2. Sheraton harewood cylinder desk and bookcase with a tambour front, 6 ft high. £1,700

3. A good quality 18th century Venetian lacquered bureau cabinet. £1,995

4. Late 18th century mahogany bureau bookcase in the Sheraton manner, 36 ins wide. £405

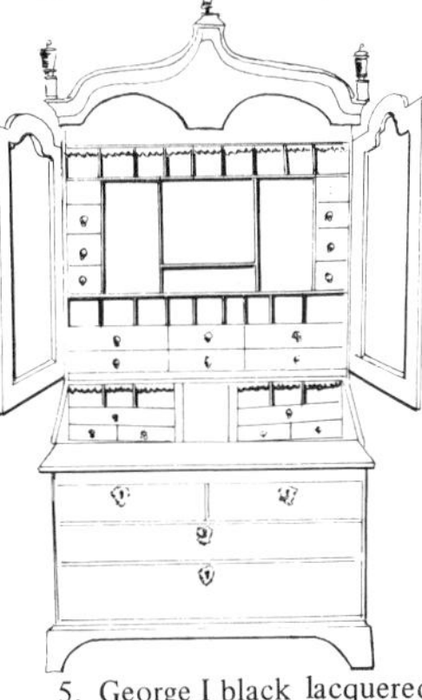

5. George I black lacquered bureau cabinet with a nicely fitted interior. £1,700

6. A fine quality Queen Anne walnut bureau bookcase. £1,550

7. Early 19th century mahogany bureau bookcase 3 ft 6 ins wide, 8ft 9 ins high. £450

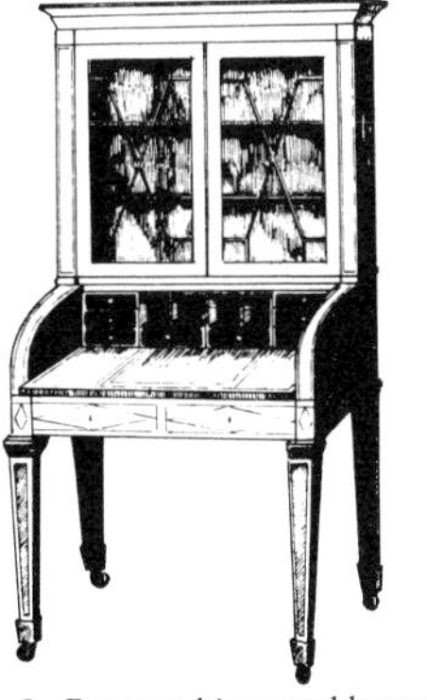

8. Regency kingwood bureau cabinet, inlaid to the front and sides. £740

9. Late 18th century Hepplewhite mahogany bureau bookcase. £2,100

BUREAU BOOKCASES

1. Queen Anne walnut bureau cabinet with a nicely stepped interior and fitted top section. £1,250

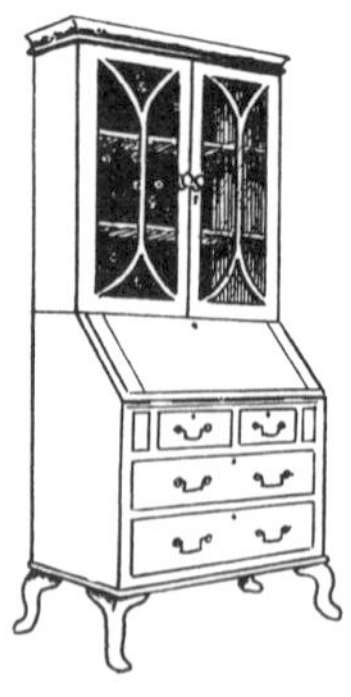

2. Edwardian walnut veneered bureau bookcase with astragal glazed doors and cabriole legs. £55

3. Flemish 18th century marquetry bureau cabinet. £1,200

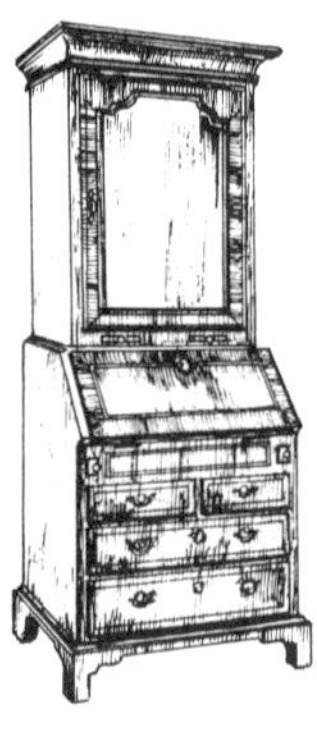

4. A small exceptionally fine Queen Anne walnut bureau bookcase with a bevelled mirror door. £5,250

5. Late 18th century mahogany bureau bookcase with astragal glazed doors. £320

6. 19th century double domed top bureau bookcase veneered in yew wood. £650

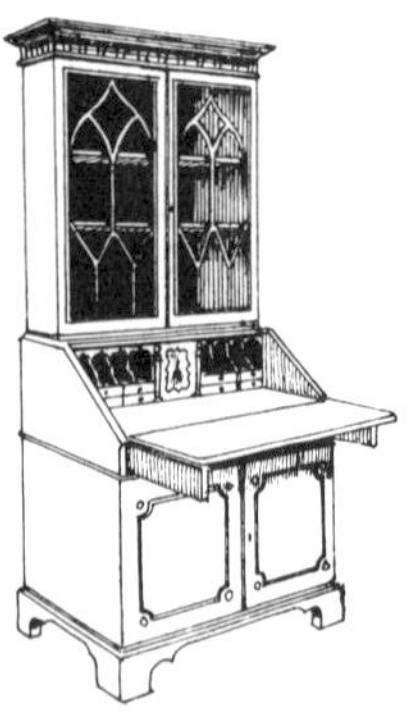

7. George III mahogany bureau bookcase with cupboards below. £630

8. An important Tuscan satinwood inlaid mahogany bureau cabinet, circa 1770. £1,100

9. Mid 18th century Dutch bureau bookcase decorated with floral marquetry. £1,600

1. A fine 18th century walnut bureau bookcase. £900

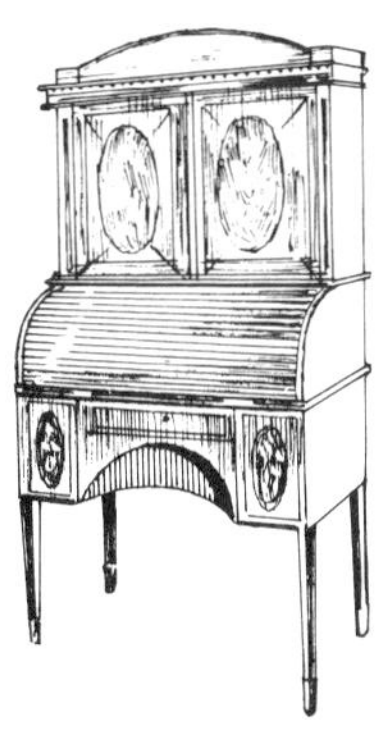

2. Sheraton period cylinder bureau cabinet. £1,700

3. An exceptionally fine quality 18th century Dutch marquetry bureau cabinet. £4,000

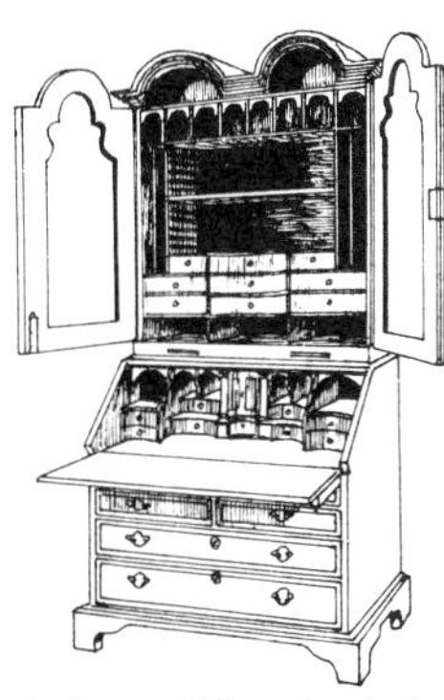

4. George II figured walnut bureau cabinet with a double domed top section. £1,000

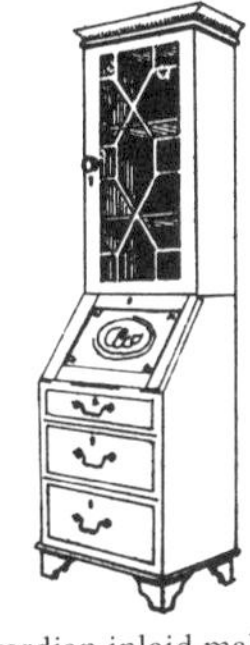

5. Edwardian inlaid mahogany single door bureau bookcase only 2 ft wide. £150

6. A fine quality Queen Anne bureau bookcase in walnut in good original condition, 3ft 3ins wide, 6 ft 11 ins high. £1,950

7. Edwardian mahogany domed top bureau bookcase on cabriole leg supports. £50

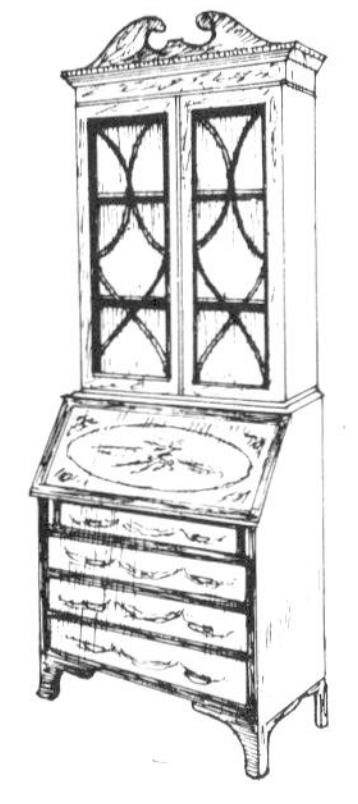

8. A fine quality mahogany bureau bookcase inlaid with floral garlands. £245

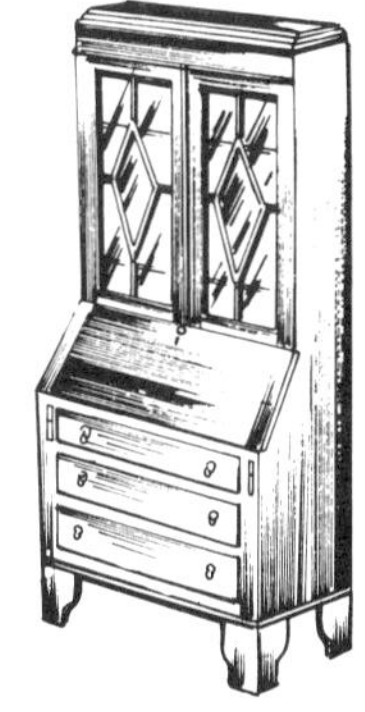

9. Edwardian oak bureau bookcase, 3 ft wide. £15

WRITING TABLES AND DESKS

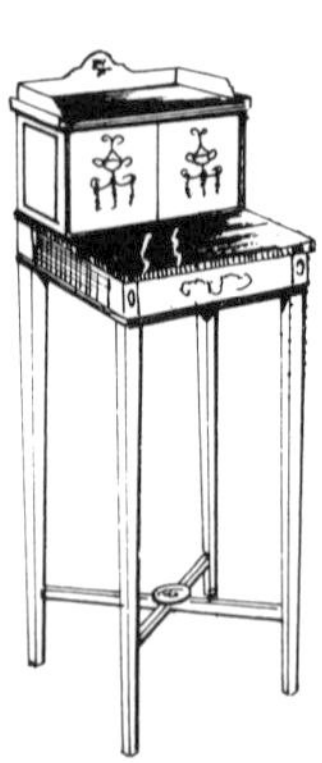

1. Late 18th century satinwood bonheur de jour with rosewood inlay, 18 ins wide. £205

2. Louis XVI bonheur de jour in the manner of Adam Weisweiler, 28 ins x 42 ins x 16½ ins deep decorated with a Sevres plaque. £3,671

3. Late 18th century decorative bonheur de jour 19 ins wide, 38ins high, circa 1790. £140

4. 19th century French writing table with a leather insert, Sevres panels on the four sides and fine ormolu mounts, circa 1840. £995

5. Victorian mahogany library table on turned and fluted legs. £12

6. 19th century brass inlaid bonheur de jour in mahogany with satinwood lining. £140

7. Regency mahogany reading and work table with an adjustable writing slide, a work cabinet below and standing on Egyptian style carved wood sphinx legs enriched with ormolu mounts. £700

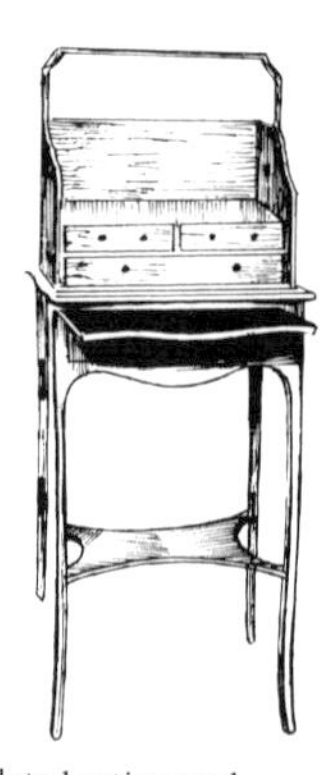

8. Simulated satinwood Cheveret portable bookstand on a matching writing table, circa 1790, 43 ins high. £495

1. A fine red boulle bonheur de jour with ormolu embellishments, circa 1850. £475

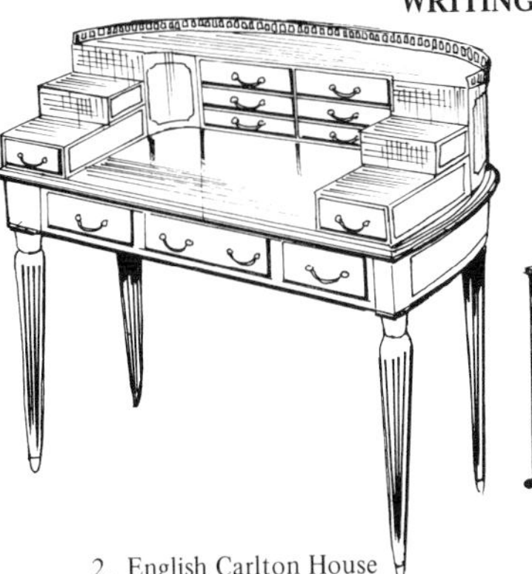

2. English Carlton House table in mahogany with ebony string inlay, circa 1800. £3,000

3. Late George III mahogany bonheur de jour. £560

4. Early 19th century mahogany writing table with fluted legs. £48

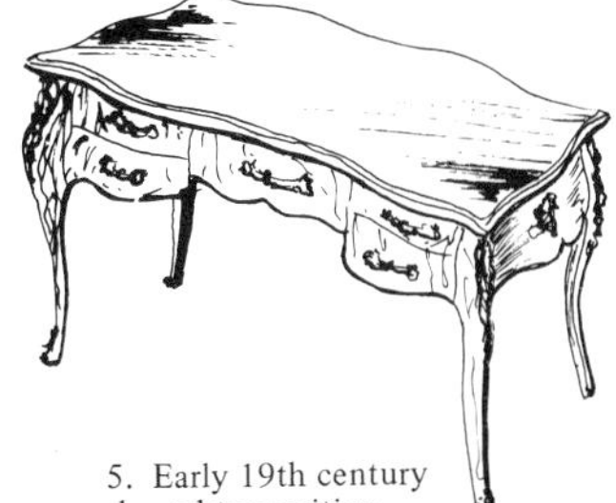

5. Early 19th century shaped top writing table on cabriole legs, with ormolu decoration, 54 ins wide. £380

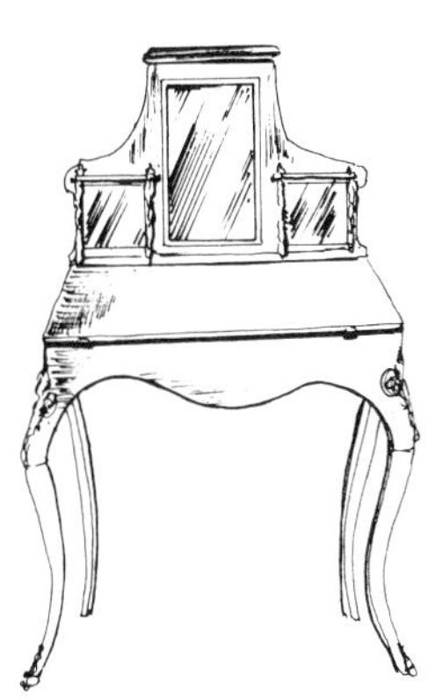

6. 19th century bonheur de jour in rosewood and marquetry supported on cabriole legs and mounted with ormolu, circa 1800. £175

7. A Georgian mahogany desk with a pull-out reading and writing drawer, circa 1760. £380

8. Early 19th century bonheur de jour in mahogany with satinwood inlay. £1,250

WRITING TABLES AND DESKS

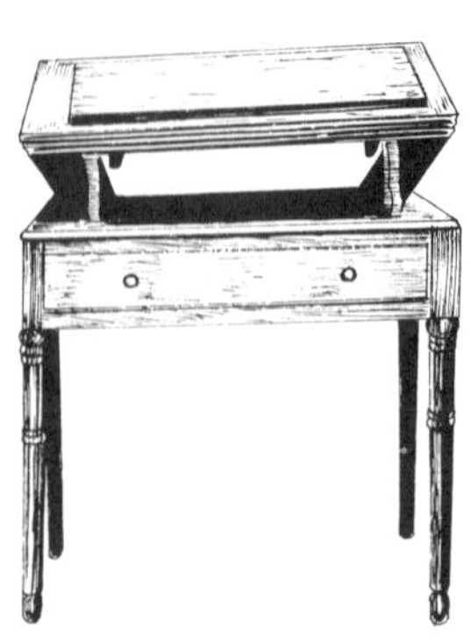

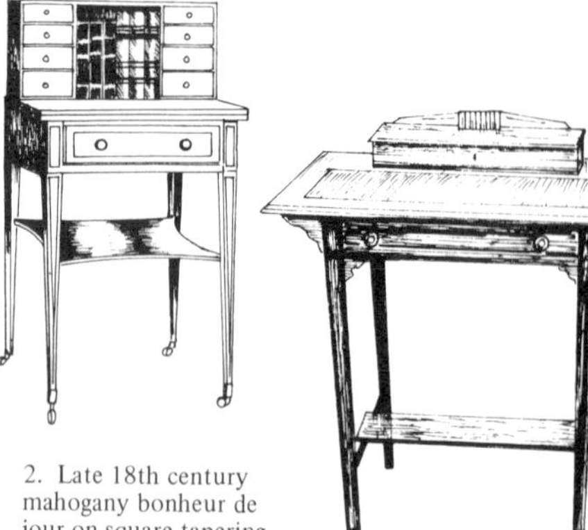

2. Late 18th century mahogany bonheur de jour on square tapering legs. £210

1. Early 18th century mahogany architect's table. £120

3. Edwardian inlaid rosewood writing table with inset leather top, 2 ft 6 ins wide. £22

4. A fine French bureau plat stamped B.V.R.B. for Bernard Van Risenburgh circa 1745 in kingwood veneered on oak with gilt metal mounts, 2·11 metres wide. £25,200

5. Hepplewhite double sided writing table in mahogany, circa 1785, 6 ft 3 ins wide, 2 ft 8 ins high. £385

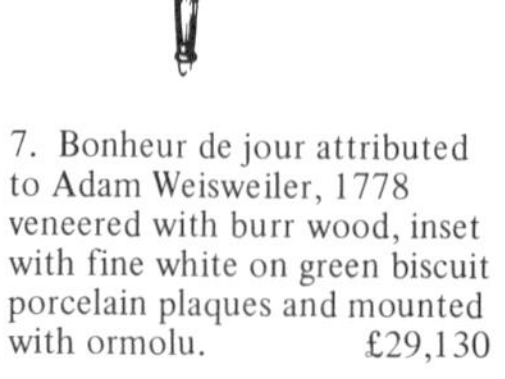

7. Bonheur de jour attributed to Adam Weisweiler, 1778 veneered with burr wood, inset with fine white on green biscuit porcelain plaques and mounted with ormolu. £29,130

6. 19th century brass inlaid mahogany and satinwood bonheur de jour. £140

8. Late 18th century mahogany cylinder desk crossbanded and inlaid with boxwood. £285

1. Early Louis XV kingwood and lacquer bureau by J.F. Dubut. £18, 900

2. George III finely grained mahogany bonheur de jour. £460

3. Victorian mahogany writing table on turned legs. £10

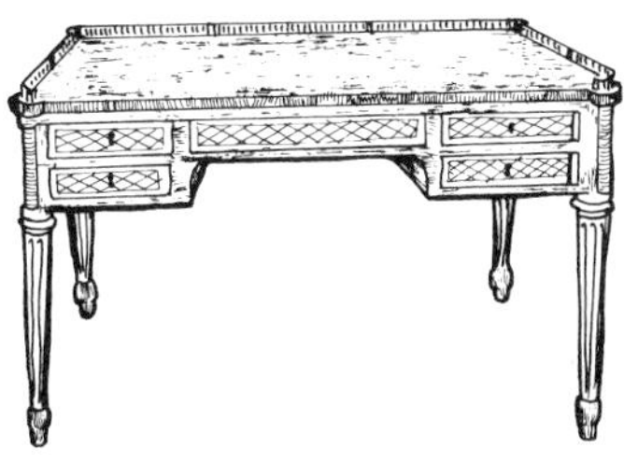

4. Louis XVI mahogany marquetry bureau plat by J.H. Reisener. £21, 000

5. A Louis XVI style marzarin profusely inlaid with brass and tortoiseshell, 5ft 11ins x 2ft 10 ins. £1, 800

6. A George III combined book trolley and reading stand in mahogany, 28½ ins wide, circa 1810. £225

7. 19th century French kingwood and marquetry bonheur de jour with an eight day striking clock fitted above the drawers, 28 ins wide. £400

8. William and Mary oak writing table. £94

DAVENPORTS

1. Regency rosewood sliding top davenport only 17½ ins wide. £200

2. Mid 19th century burr walnut davenport with cabriole leg front supports. £115

3. 19th century walnut davenport with boxwood string inlay, 22 ins wide. £85

4. A Victorian walnut davenport inlaid with boxwood. £55

5. Early Victorian burr walnut davenport with a serpentine front top and cabriole legs. £125

6. Late 19th century mahogany davenport with cupboards under. £40

7. George III mahogany davenport with a sliding top,pen drawer and slides each side. £285

8. An unusual Victorian cylindrical burr walnut davenport with a pierced brass gallery. £165

9. Regency rosewood davenport with sliding top,candle slides and stationery drawer,20 ins wide,33 ins high 21 ins deep,circa 1800. £185

1. Small Regency mahogany davenport with two slides. £170

2. George III mahogany davenport fitted with a sliding top,pen and ink drawer and two slides. £215

3. An unusual small rosewood davenport with a pierced brass gallery and panelled door concealing four drawers, 15½ins wide. £185

4. William IV mahogany davenport with side drawers and pierced brass gallery. £95

5. An exceptionally fine Regency satinwood davenport with a brass gallery,sliding top,side drawers and dummy drawers. £540

6. Victorian walnut davenport with pull-out pen and ink tray. £80

7. A small George III davenport in finely figured mahogany with rosewood crossbanding circa 1795,15 ins wide. £215

8. Fine quality early Victorian walnut piano top davenport with gilt decoration. £175

9. Early 19th century mahogany davenport. £160

KNEEHOLE & PEDESTAL DESKS

1. An 18th century Massachusetts kneehole writing desk in mahogany. £3,400

2. Small 18th century mahogany kneehole desk with original brass fittings. £425

3. Large Victorian mahogany cylinder top desk with a nicely fitted interior, turned wood handles and bun feet. £48

4. 19th century Sheraton style kneehole desk inlaid with satinwood shell and fan designs. £205

5. Fine quality Georgian mahogany dressing and writing table, 36 ins wide 23 ins deep, 31 ins high. £525

6. A nicely proportioned Georgian mahogany pedestal desk with a tambour shutter concealing drawers and pigeon holes. £425

7. William and Mary period walnut kneehole desk with ebony arabesque marquetry inlay. £650

8. Late 19th century oak pedestal desk, the tambour shutter concealing drawers and pigeon holes. £27.50

9. Unusual late 18th century mahogany kneehole desk with an adjustable top. £410

2. An attractive 19th century satinwood pedestal desk with a leather top. £360

1. 18th century Chippendale mahogany serpentine front kneehole desk. £1,000

3. 19th century pedestal desk with satinwood crossbanding. £85

5. A small 19th century marquetry kneehole desk decorated with flowers and floral sprays. £520

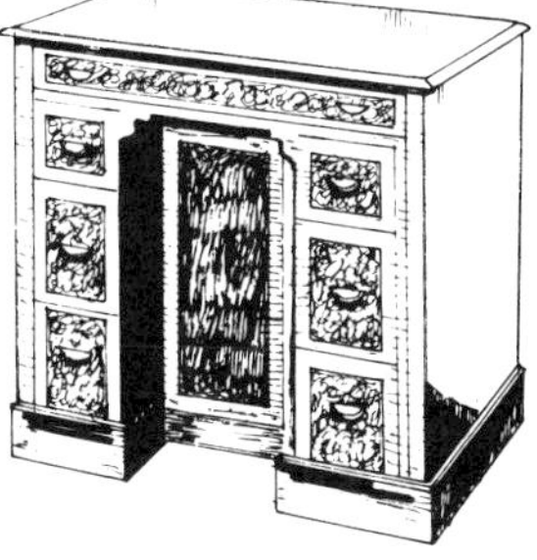

6. A fine George III walnut kneehole desk with crossbanded drawers. £248

4. Good quality George III satinwood kneehole desk. £610

8. A good George II kneehole desk with a flush top and bracket feet. £480

7. An 18th century Italian marquetry desk in good original condition. £425

9. Good quality George I walnut kneehole desk with canted corners, a recessed cupboard and crossbanding, only 2 ft 9 ins wide. £650

KNEEHOLE & PEDESTAL DESKS

1. Late 18th century mahogany kneehole desk with brass drop handles. £385

2. Late 19th century mahogany pedestal writing desk on a platform base, 4 ft 6 ins wide. £38

3. Small George III figured mahogany kneehole desk with writing slide and brass drop handles. £575

4. Good quality 19th century red boulle pedestal desk with fine ormolu mounts. £475

5. Late 18th century mahogany kneehole desk with a fall front secretaire drawer with a frieze drawer below, 36 ins x 21 ins x 32 ins high, circa 1790. £325

6. Early 19th century teak partner's desk with drawers on both sides with sunken brass handles. £210

7. Early 19th century ebonised pedestal desk decorated with brass moulding, circa 1820. £275

8. Late 18th century mahogany kneehole desk 3 ft 7 ins wide. £235

9. Late 18th century Sheraton inlaid and decorated satinwood kneehole desk. £650

2. 18th century walnut pedestal desk decorated with marquetry bone inlay depicting flower sprays, birds and a figure of a boy on a dolphin on the top. £400

3. An unusual 18th century walnut kneehole desk. £410

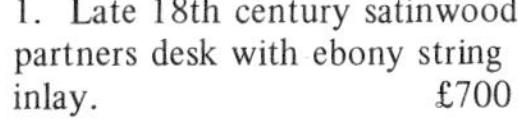

1. Late 18th century satinwood partners desk with ebony string inlay. £700

5. A good quality 18th century Florentine style kneehole writing desk. £520

4. Victorian mahogany pedestal desk with a centre writing flap, platform base and turned wood handles. £50

6. Good quality George III mahogany kneehole desk. £310

8. A George III mahogany architects kneehole desk with an adjustable top, 3 ft 2 ins wide. £405

7. Good quality 18th century walnut kneehole desk with raised moulding and bun feet. £425

9. George III kneehole desk in mahogany with a polished back, 46 ins wide. £450

SECRETAIRES AND ESCRITOIRES

1. A fine 19th century Dutch marquetry escritoire. £185

2. Early 19th century mahogany chiffonier with a fitted writing drawer. £200

3. Good quality Dutch marquetry secretaire, 3ft 2ins. wide. £220

4. George III mahogany chest on chest with fitted secretaire drawer, canted corners and ogee feet. £300

5. Secretaire a abattant attributed to Jean-Henri Reisener 1734-1806, of black lacquer mounted with gilt bronze 1.14 metres wide. £72,000

6. Mid 19th century secretaire in birds eye maple and mahogany with a satinwood interior and ormolu mounts, 54 ins high, 29 ins wide. £425

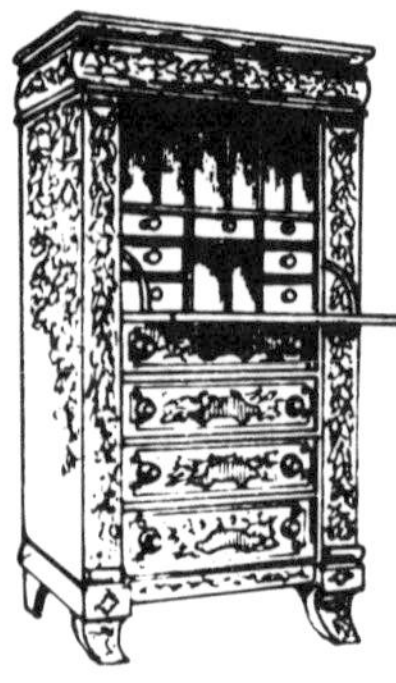

7. 19th century Dutch marquetry fall front escritoire. £225

8. Regency mahogany secretaire military chest with fold down bookshelves above, circa 1820, 39ins wide. £185

9. Late 17th century walnut veneered cabinet with a fall front concealing a multitude of drawers and pigeon holes. £450

1. Good quality Louis XVI kingwood fall front secretaire 36½ ins wide. 700gns

2. A Georgian serpentine front secretaire with a fitted top drawer. £425

3. A William and Mary period double domed escritoire in walnut. £1,150

4. Louis XVI black lacquer secretaire by Martin Carlin. £126, 000

5. Secretaire cabinet in walnut made by P. Waals. £960

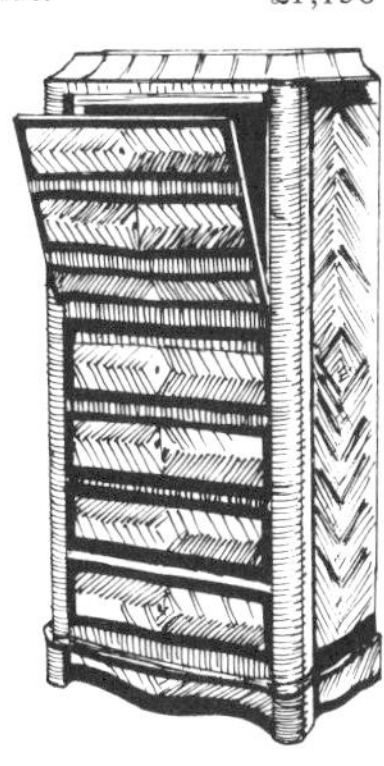

6. 19th century kingwood and rosewood escritoire with serpentine front and sides, 25½ ins wide, 49ins high. £385

7. William and Mary escritoire decorated with floral marquetry 3ft 4 ins wide. £685

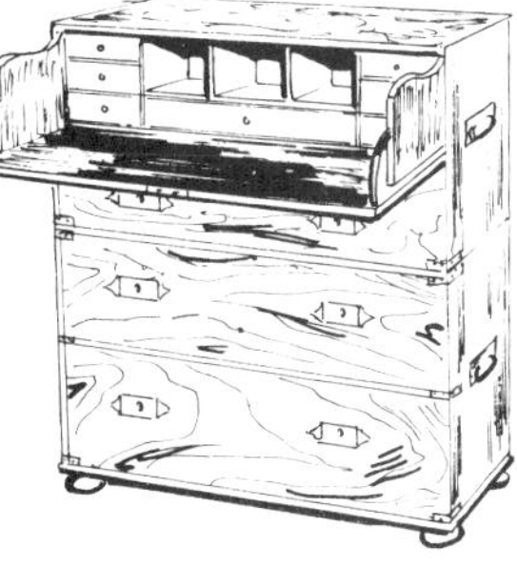

8. An exceptionally fine teak secretaire military chest ,only 30ins wide, circa 1820.£365

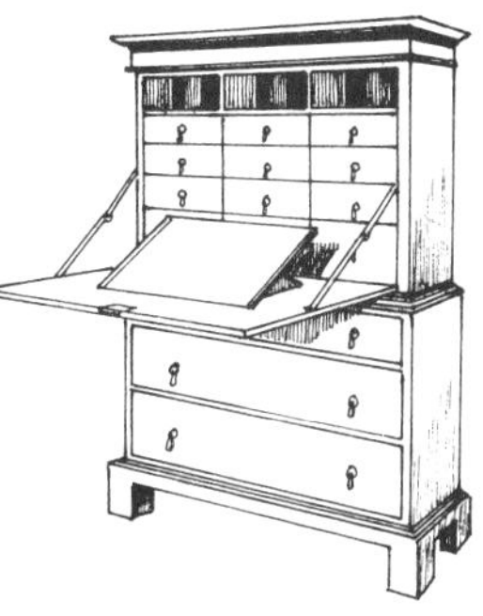

9. Queen Anne period burr walnut escritoire with a fall front and adjustable writing slide. £625

SECRETAIRES AND ESCRITOIRES

1. An attractive well figured mahogany secretaire, the writing drawer with satinwood drawers and cupboard, 42 ins wide, circa 1820. £165

2. 18th century Chippendale figured mahogany secretaire with a fitted top drawer and ogee feet. £300

3. Regency period secretaire bookcase in mahogany with ebony string inlay, 30ins wide. £285

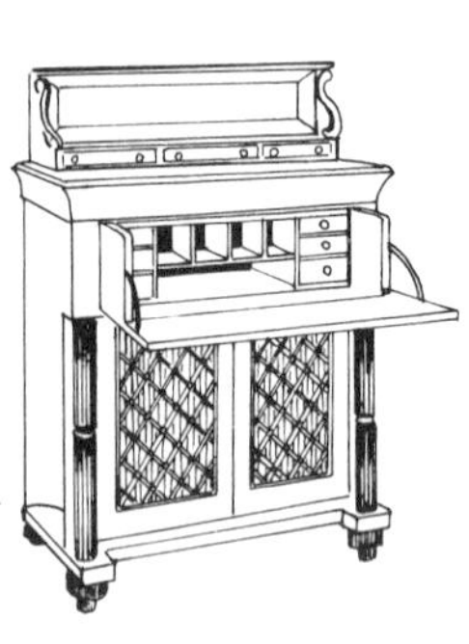

4. Early 19th century mahogany chiffonier with a fall front secretaire drawer. £180

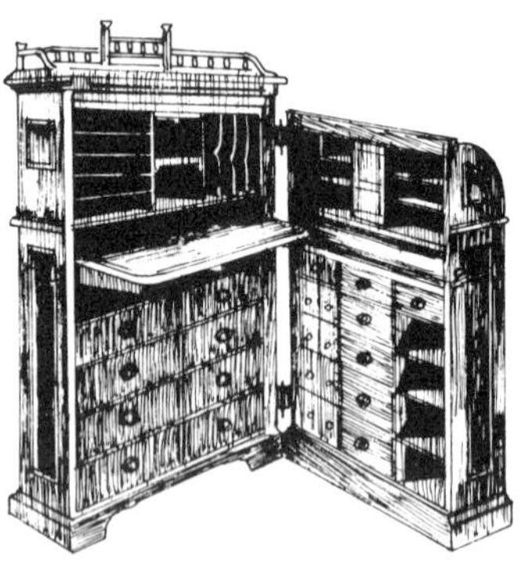

5. 19th century North American oak office desk, 4ft 9ins wide, circa 1880. £150

6. William and Mary walnut escritoire on stand. £410

7. Victorian mahogany secretaire chest with turned wood knobs and bun feet. £45

8. Late 18th century mahogany bow fronted secretaire. £235

9. Late 18th century straight front mahogany secretaire chest with stamped brass handles and splayed feet. £240

1. 19th century secretaire a abattant in kingwood. £525

2. Early 19th century, Sheraton style secretaire with a satinwood interior and hide liner. £198

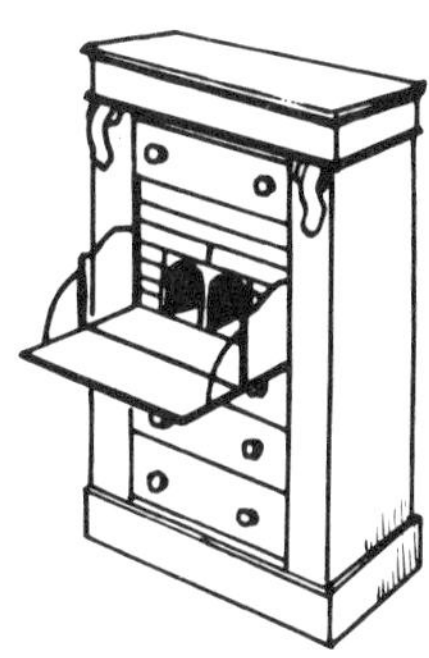

3. Early 19th century rosewood Wellington chest with a fitted secretaire drawer. £100

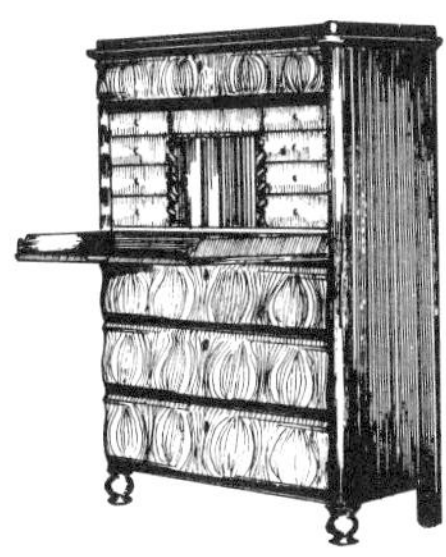

4. Victorian mahogany secretaire with a fall front revealing a cupboard and numerous drawers. £75

5. 19th century mahogany secretaire in good original condition, only 24ins. wide, circa 1825. £165

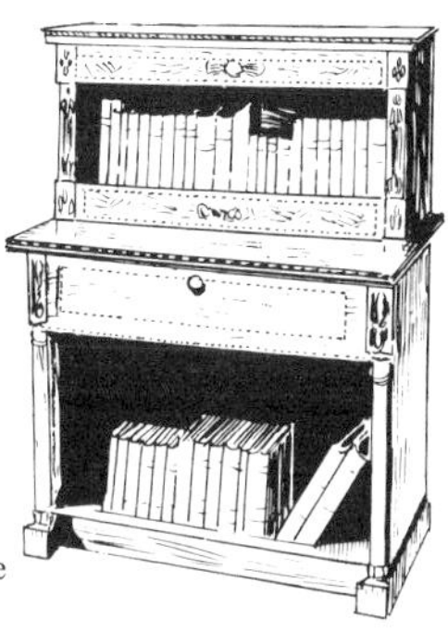

6. Regency period rosewood open bookcase with a fall front secretaire drawer with a satinwood interior. £240

7. Regency breakfast cabinet in mahogany with a secretaire drawer, 54ins wide, circa 1825. £245

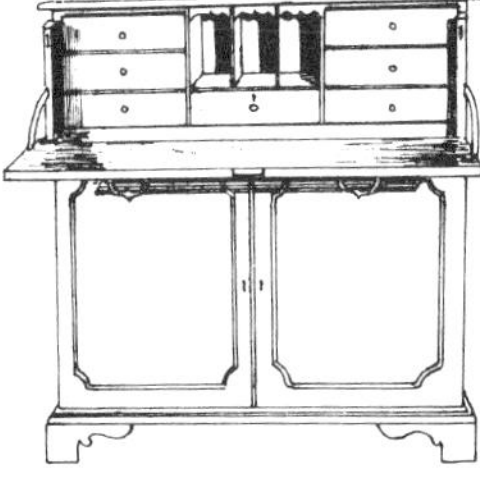

8. Early 19th century mahogany secretaire chest with panelled cupboard doors. £185

9. Georgian mahogany secretaire cabinet with panelled cupboard doors and bracket feet. £275

SECRETAIRE BOOKCASES

1. A fine George III mahogany secretaire bookcase, 42 ins wide. £1,480

2. Victorian mahogany secretaire bookcase of three adjustable shelves enclosed by two glazed doors, 3 ft 6 ins wide. £71

3. A South German secretaire cabinet veneered with walnut and fruitwood, 1·35 metres wide, circa 1760. £7,140

4. A good quality Regency mahogany secretaire bookcase 3 ft 7 ins wide. £265

5. Late Georgian mahogany secretaire bookcase of fine quality with a satinwood fitted drawer, 44 ins wide. £195

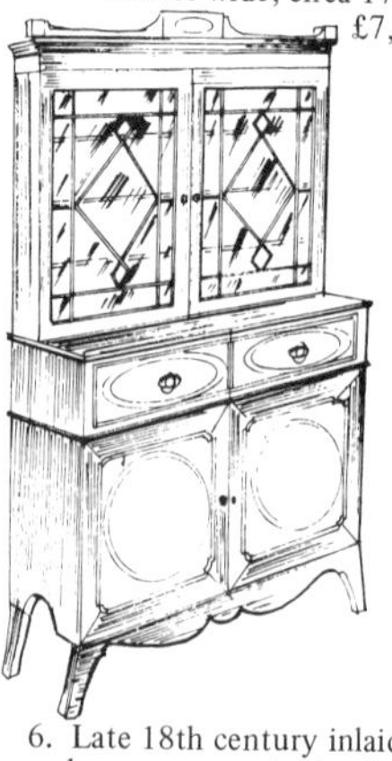

6. Late 18th century inlaid mahogany secretaire bookcase 4 ft wide, with a nicely fitted interior. £375

7. Regency rosewood secretaire bookcase inlaid with brass and ornamented with gilt metal marbled columns. £400

8. Late 18th century Chippendale style secretaire chest on chest with a swan neck pediment. £550

9. Regency period secretaire bookcase in mahogany 3 ft 3 ins wide, 7 ft 6 ins high, circa 1815. £465

SECRETAIRE BOOKCASES

1. William IV mahogany secretaire bookcase with ebony string inlay and astragal glazed doors. £275

2. Nicely proportioned George III mahogany secretaire bookcase with Gothic glazed doors. £360

3. One of a pair of English secretaire cabinets circa 1780, veneered with sycamore and decorated with rosewood and fruitwood, 1·2 metres wide. £5,800

4. Late 18th century mahogany secretaire tallboy with brass drop handles and bracket feet. £250

5. An attractive mahogany secretaire bookcase, circa 1825, 32 ins wide, 7 ft 3 ins high, 19 ins deep. £395

6. Good quality Hepplewhite secretaire bookcase with Gothic formations in the glazed door. £800

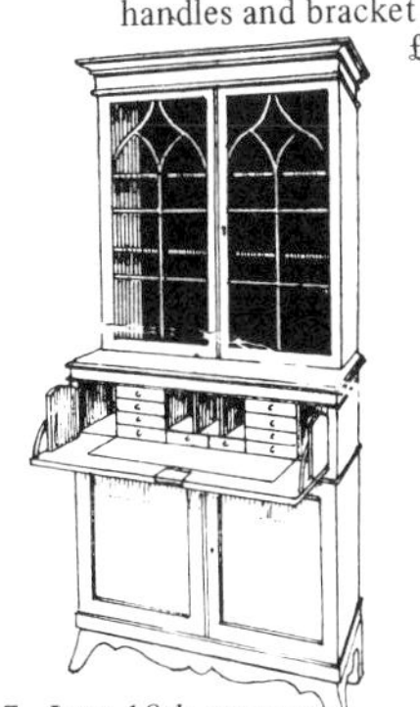

7. Late 18th century mahogany secretaire bookcase with panelled cupboard doors. £420

8. A fine quality secretaire bookcase in mahogany with a fitted satinwood interior and four drawers enclosed in each pedestal, 51 ins wide, 22 ins deep, 94 ins high, circa 1790. £275

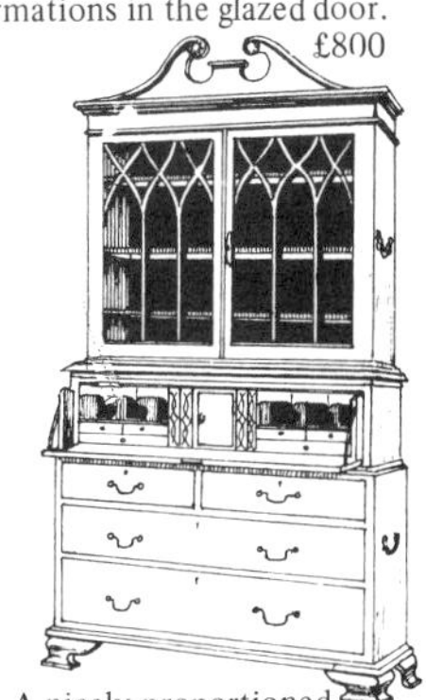

9. A nicely proportioned Chippendale period mahogany secretaire bookcase with ogee feet. £900

SMALL TABLES

1. Set of three Edwardian mahogany oval tables. £36

2. Small 19th century French style table in bleached walnut, 2 ft, 6 ins wide. £17

3. Small Edwardian mahogany kidney shaped occasional table. £5

4. Edwardian mahogany and satinwood banded occasional table. £7.50

5. 19th century French marble table with a pierced brass gallery and ormolu enrichments. £140

6. Edwardian mahogany two tier occasional table. £5

7. Small late 18th century tripod table. £40

8. Oval Edwardian mahogany and satinwood banded two tier occasional table on splayed legs, 2 ft 3 ins wide. £13

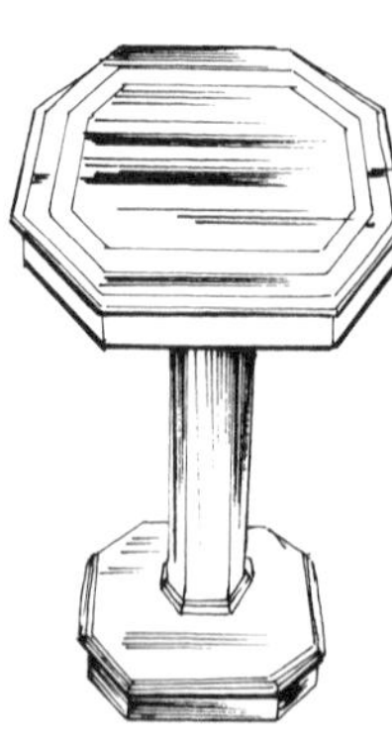

9. Victorian octagonal ebonised and birds eye maple pedestal table, 1 ft 10 ins wide. £5

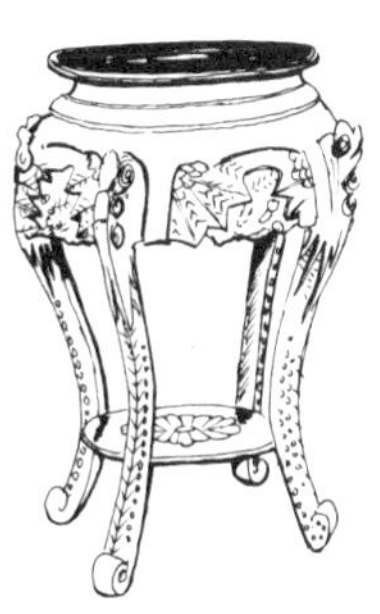

1. 19th century two tier Oriental hardwood stand, 15 ins diameter. £20

2. Edwardian octagonal table. £8

3. Small black and gilt centre table on a tripod base with figures inset in the columns. £78

4. A mahogany gueridon, the frieze with a drawer and four Japanese lacquered panels. £480

5. Small Edwardian table with a scratched carved top. £2.50

6. French ebony and kingwood jardiniere table with an inlaid top and metal liner, and unusual dog head mounts. £145

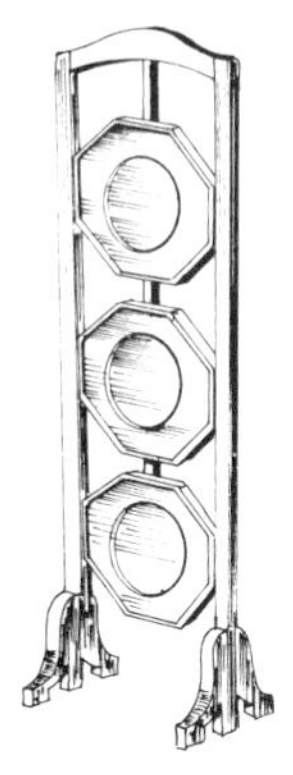

7. 19th century three tier mahogany folding cake stand. £5

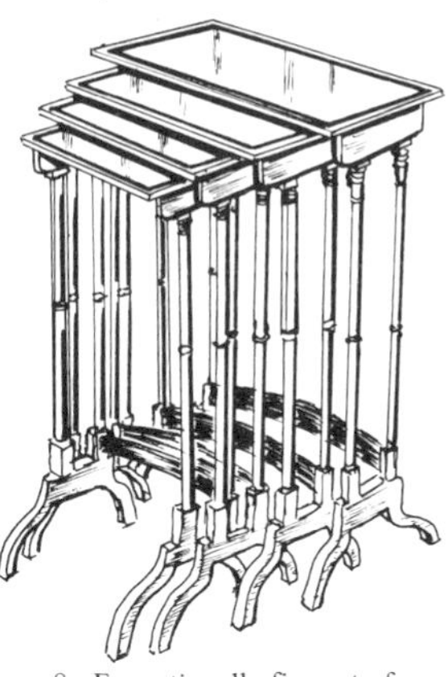

8. Exceptionally fine set of 18th century rosewood quartetto tables with cock beaded tops and crossbanded edges, in mint condition. £385

9. Victorian mahogany duet music stand on a tripod base. £40

SMALL TABLES

2. Early 19th century rosewood stretcher table. £44

3. 19th century Indian brass folding table. £9

1. Edwardian mahogany folding cake stand. £3.50

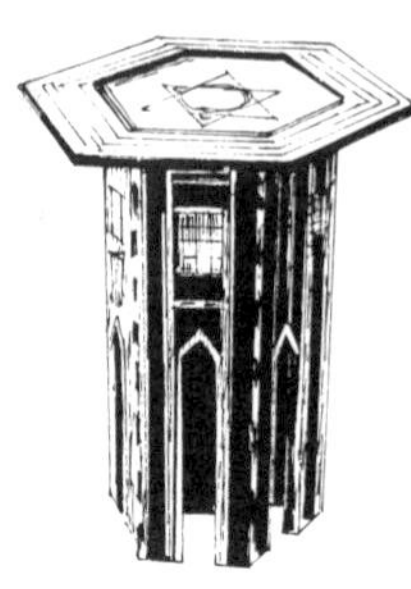

5. Rare George III set of quartetto tables in mahogany. £280

4. 19th century Japanese table with lacquered top. £23

6. 19th century inlaid Moorish table, 14 ins high. £5.50

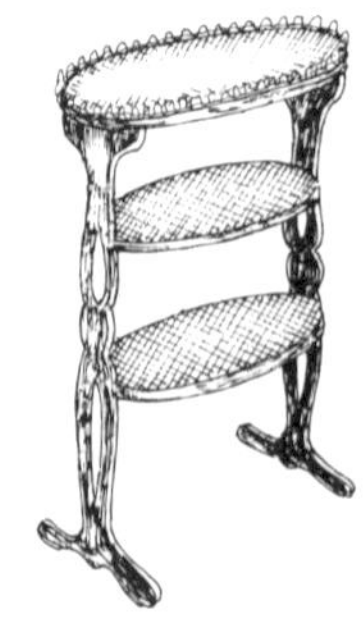

7. A small elegant bijouterie in the Sheraton manner, decorated on the stretchers and corners of the frieze, and having chevron and double fan satinwood patterea on the lid, circa 1830, 22 ins wide. £265

8. 19th century red boulle occasional table with cabriole legs and ormolu mounts, 2 ft wide. £160

9. Early 19th century marquetry etagere with a pierced brass gallery. £105

1. Louis Philippe period Gueridon table in kingwood with ormolu mounts and rose marble top. £135

2. Late 19th century satin birch table. £22

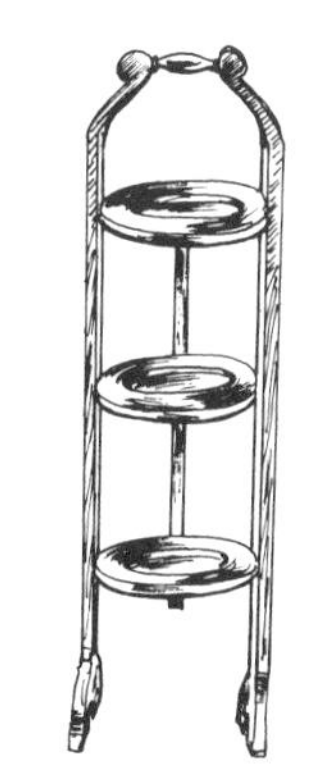

3. 19th century mahogany three tier folding cake stand. £5.50

4. Victorian bamboo plant stand. £2.50

5. Late 18th century Chinese Chippendale style serving table. £90

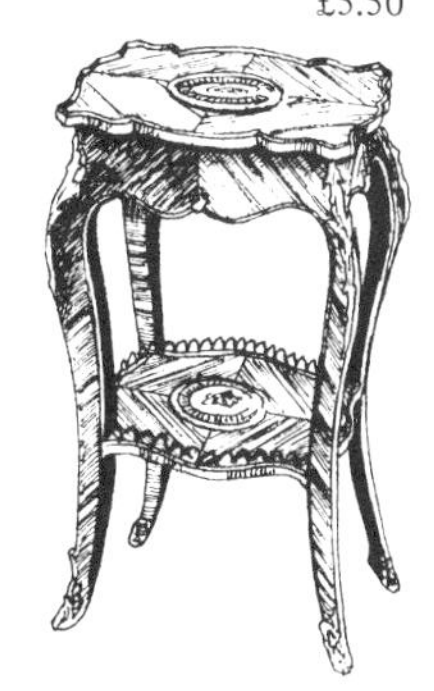

6. Louis Phillipe kingwood etagere decorated with Sevres plaques and ormolu mounts. £355

7. Victorian walnut games table with a tripod base. £40

8. Good quality Edwardian inlaid mahogany library table of two open and two dummy drawers on square tapering legs with spade feet. £80

9. Late 18th century mahogany pole fire-screen with writing flap. £50

SMALL TABLES

2. Victorian mahogany bedside table. £12

1. 19th century red boulle dressing table with a lift up mirror and fitted compartments. £175

3. Victorian rosewood table with barley twist supports and tripod base with cabriole legs. £18

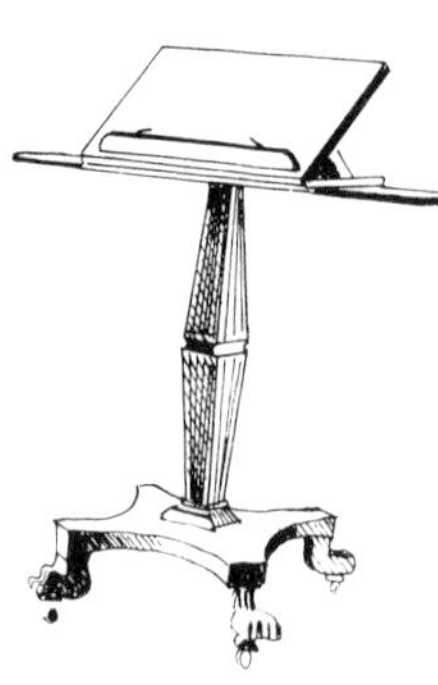

5. Small Regency breakfast table 45 ins wide with an unusual detachable leaf. £148

4. Good quality Regency period green marble table with ormolu decoration. £185

6. Early 19th century mahogany reading stand with a platform base and lions paw feet. £60

8. A Victorian burr walnut stretcher table with an inlaid games table top. £27.50

7. 18th century oak cricket table, 22 ins diameter, 20 ins high. £38

9. Regency mahogany work table. £40

1. Late 19th century Victorian beechwood stretcher table with ebony string inlay. £17.50

2. 19th century Victorian gypsy table with bobbin legs and a fringed velvet top. £7.50

3. 19th century walnut chess table on a platform base with bun feet. £25

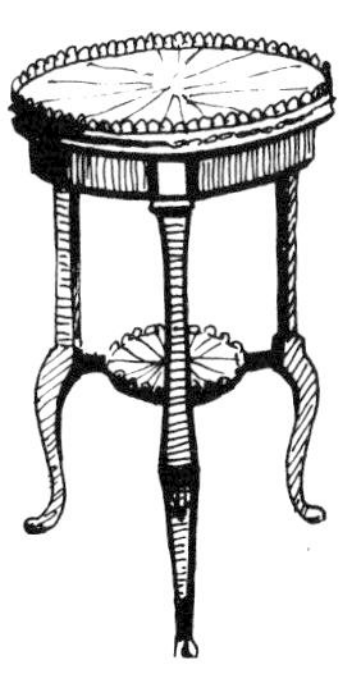

4. Louis XVI style satinwood occasional table crossbanded with mahogany with an ormolu gallery and shaped supports. £85

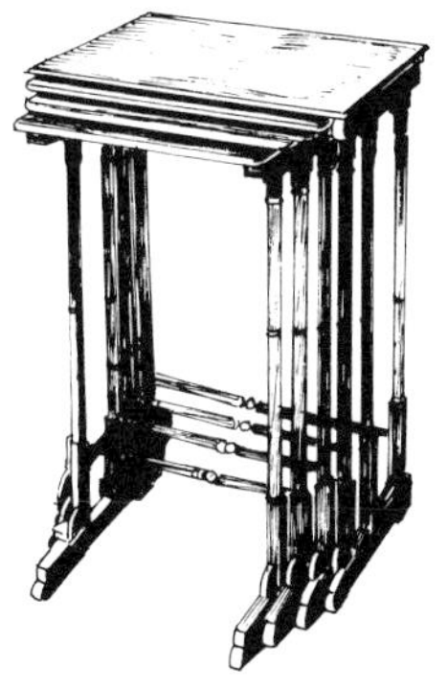

5. George III mahogany quarto tables, 27 ins high. £125

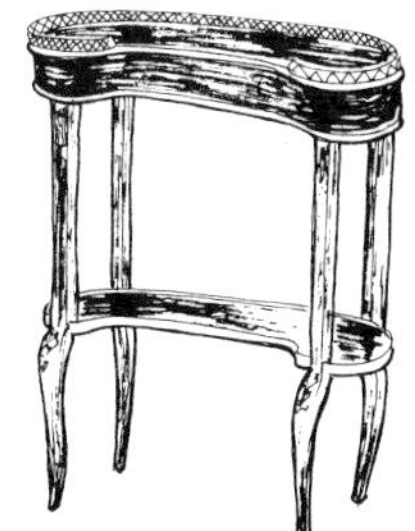

6. 19th century French tulipwood kidney shaped two tier table with a pierced brass gallery. £110

7. 18th century pinewood cricket table with a triangular shelf, 18 ins diameter top. £28

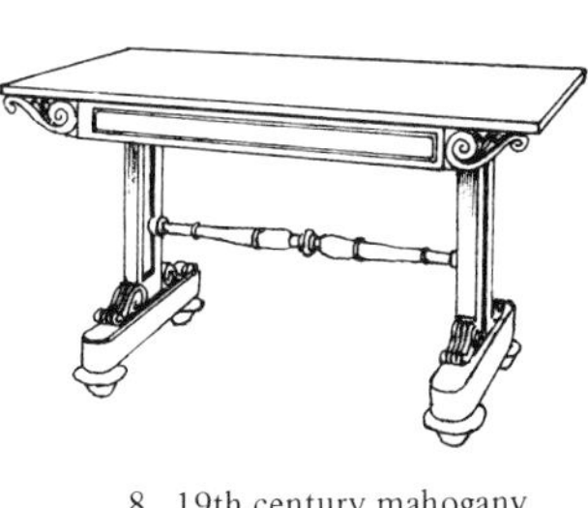

8. 19th century mahogany stretcher table 4 ft 6 ins long. £28

9. Good quality Regency period mahogany table with a parquetry top and platform base with paw feet. £135

SMALL TABLES

1. Small Victorian rosewood occasional table 20 ins diameter. £9

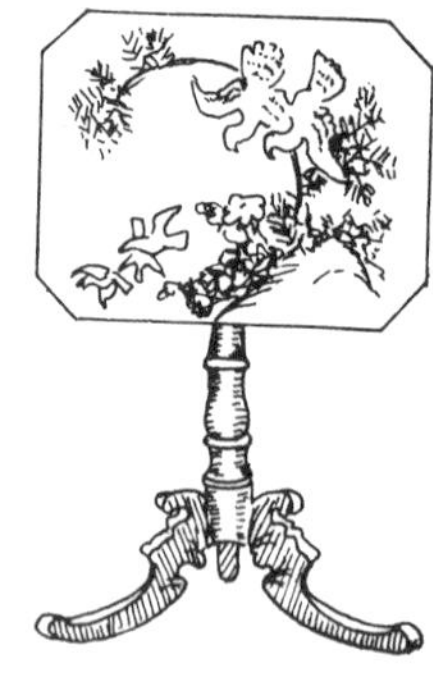

2. Good quality 19th century lacquered snap top table. £65

3. Small Victorian mahogany tripod table. £12

4. Victorian papier mache table inlaid with mother of pearl. £42

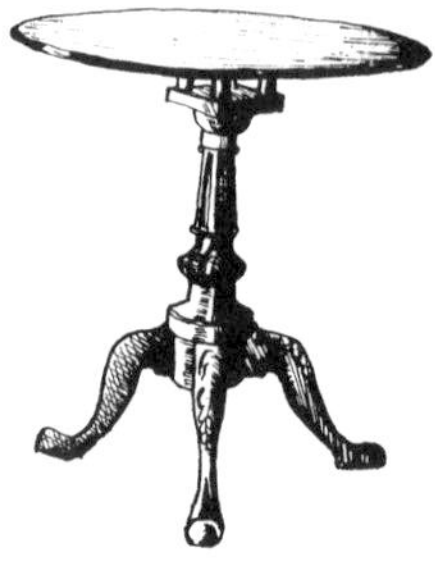

5. Late 18th century mahogany snap top table with a birdcage fitment and finely carved cabriole legs. £145

6. Victorian papier mache table on a tripod platform base with scroll feet. £48

7. Late 18th century yew wood tripod table. £65

8. 19th century mahogany snap top table. £35

9. 18th century mahogany supper table with a finely carved top. £105

1. Victorian burr walnut table on a spiral twist column and tripod base, 1 ft 8 ins diameter. £26

2. Late 18th century fruitwood tripod table. £32

3. Small Victorian inlaid mahogany occasional table. £8.50

4. Good quality 18th century Dutch marquetry snap top table. £135

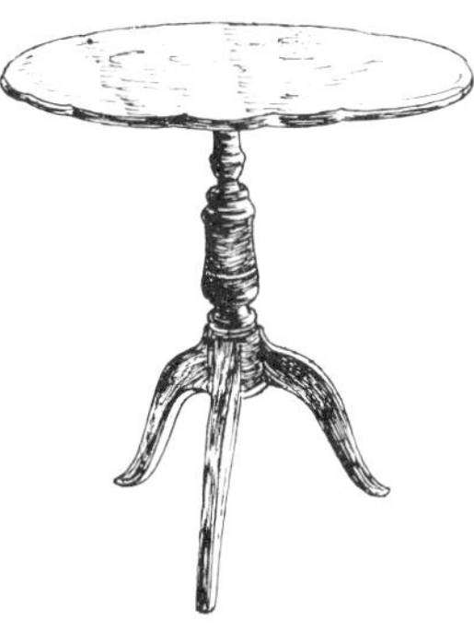

5. Victorian mahogany occasional table with a shaped top. £25

6. A good quality Welsh slate games table decorated with hunting scenes. £210

7. Victorian burr walnut table with boxwood string inlay and carved cabriole legs. £35

8. Late 18th century mahogany tripod table with pad feet. £45

9. 18th century Chippendale mahogany pedestal table with a carved piecrust top, carved pillar and splayed tripod. £550

CARD AND TEA TABLES

1. Edwardian folding top card table in walnut. £24

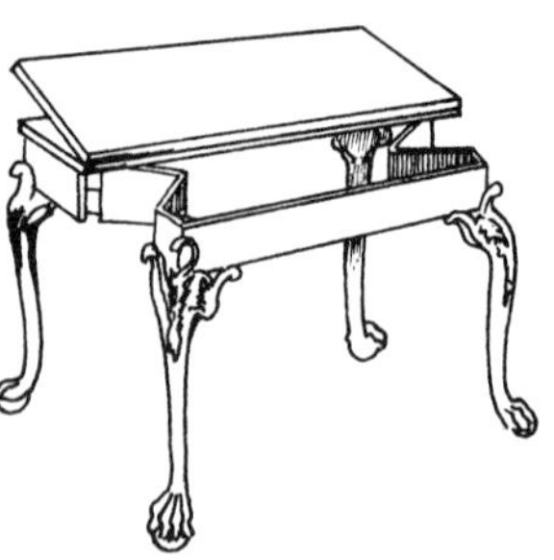

2. 18th century concertina action tea table in mahogany with finely carved cabriole legs with ball and claw feet. £325

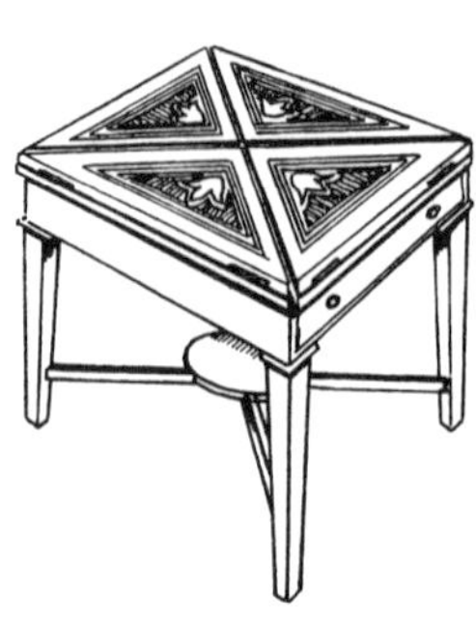

3. Edwardian inlaid mahogany envelope table on square tapering legs with cross stretchers. £75

4. George II period Cuban mahogany folding top card table, circa 1750. £180

5. A very fine quality late 18th century yew wood and marquetry folding top games table. £385

6. Finely figured mahogany concertina card table of medium colour and patina, 3 ft wide, circa 1795. £135

7. George III serpentine front tea table, 35 ins wide 17½ ins deep, 27¾ ins high. £195

8. Edwardian mahogany envelope card table with a drawer. £45

9. Regency period satinwood card table, circa 1815. £165

1. One of a pair of rare George I gaming tables in red walnut. £1,500

2. A finely figured mahogany card table inlaid with satinwood, 32½ ins wide, circa 1765. £210

3. Small Sheraton period card table of beautiful colour and figuring, 34 ins wide, circa 1790. £185

4. Edwardian mahogany envelope card table on cabriole legs. £35

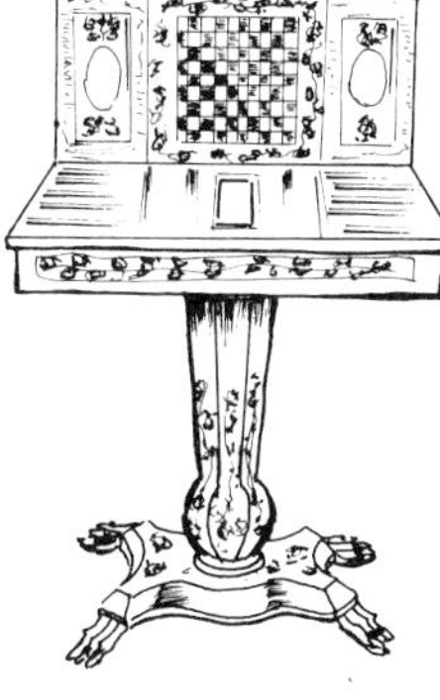

5. Fine quality 18th century yew wood games table. £265

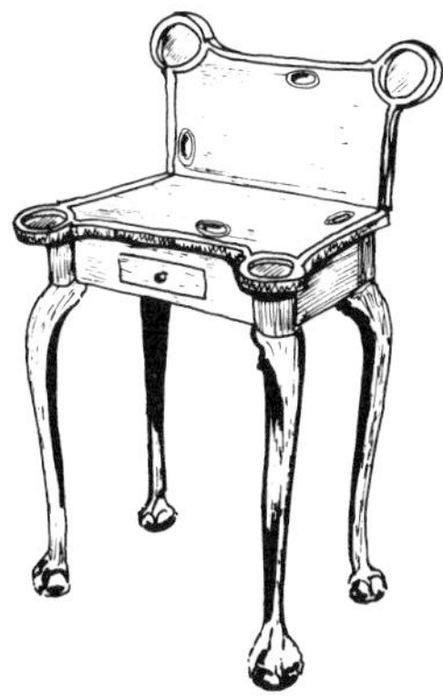

6. George II Cuban mahogany card table with drawer and fine ball and claw feet, 33 ins wide, circa 1745. £385

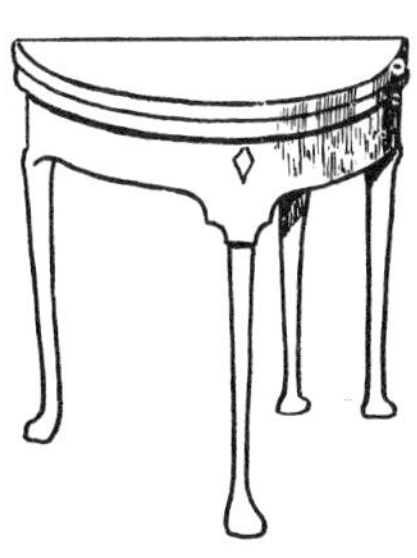

7. Georgian half round folding top mahogany tea table on shaped legs with pad feet. £265

8. George III concertina tea table in richly figured mahogany inlaid with a star motif of satinwood and ebony, 35 ins wide, circa 1775. £125

9. Chippendale period tea table in Cuban mahogany, circa 1780. £145

CARD AND TEA TABLES

1. Queen Anne marquetry folding top card table on fine cabriole legs. £550

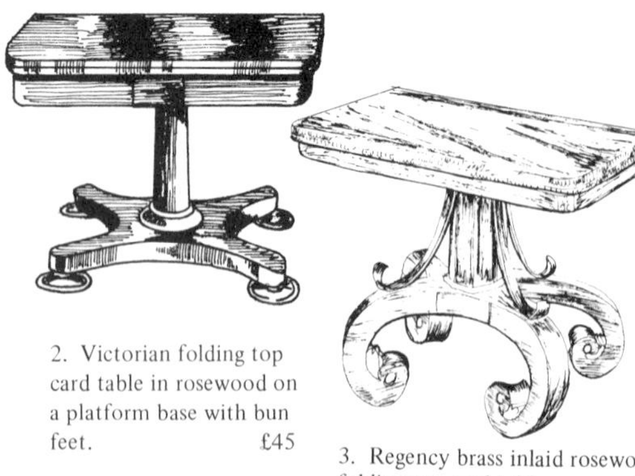

2. Victorian folding top card table in rosewood on a platform base with bun feet. £45

3. Regency brass inlaid rosewood folding top card table on a scroll base. £215

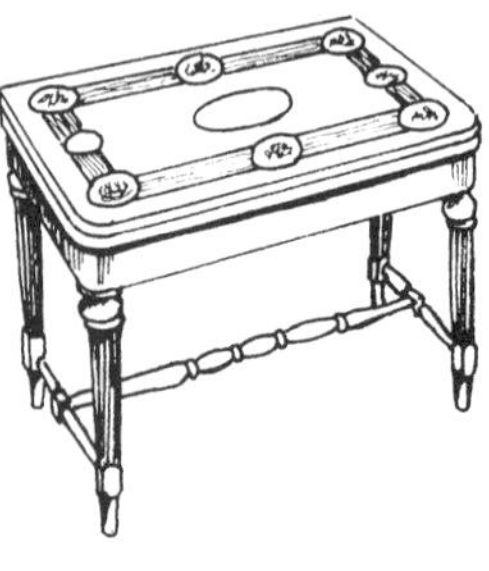

4. Victorian burr walnut folding top card table lined with green baize. £35

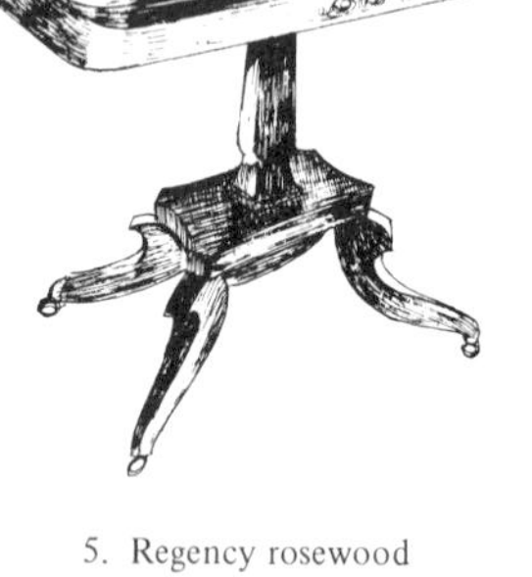

5. Regency rosewood folding top card table inlaid with brass. £125

6. Early 19th century mahogany card table inlaid with satinwood on fluted legs. £75

7. Regency mahogany folding top card table with ebony string inlay, on splayed feet with brass claw castors. £135

8. Good quality 19th century red boulle folding top card table with cabriole legs and ormolu mounts. £250

9. Good quality Regency period brass inlaid card table on a platform base with splay feet. £180

CARD AND TEA TABLES

1. Good quality early Victorian rosewood card table with a beaded frieze, shaped platform base and paw feet. £70

2. George II folding top mahogany card table with projecting corners, carved cabriole legs and scroll feet. £330

3. One of a pair of Regency rosewood card tables with gilt decoration. £235

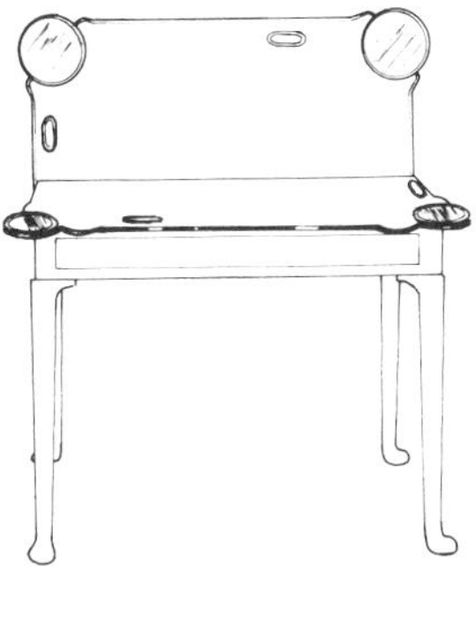

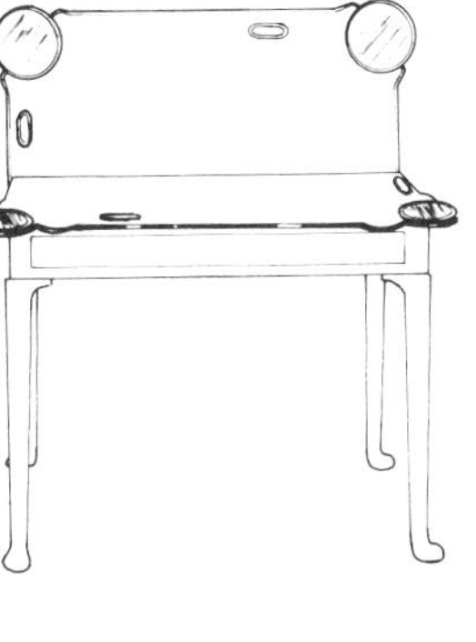

4. Victorian burr walnut shaped top fold-over card table on a turned centre column with carved cabriole legs. £75

5. Early 18th century walnut card table. £400

6. Late 18th century mahogany card table with satinwood crossbanding and ebony inlay. £180

7. Exceptionally small George III mahogany tea table with a folding serpentine top, 30ins wide, 15ins deep, 28¾ins high. £215

8. Edwardian mahogany folding top bridge table crossbanded with satinwood. £25

9. Chippendale mahogany card table with a carved frieze, 33 ins wide, 16 ins deep. £125

PEMBROKE TABLES

1. Early Regency Pembroke table in mahogany, crossbanded and inlaid with ebony. £168

2. Small late 18th century mahogany Pembroke table with drawer, on square tapering legs with brass cup castors. £115

3. An elegant George III mahogany Pembroke table in the French Hepplewhite style. 1,600 gns

4. Late Victorian stripped pine Pembroke table on turned legs. £10

5. 19th century mahogany Pembroke table on turned legs, 2 ft 9 ins wide when open. £20

6. Late 18th century Sheraton satinwood Pembroke table with butterfly leaves. £450

7. George III mahogany Pembroke table on square tapering legs. £70

8. Pembroke table of medium colour mahogany with an elegant stretcher, circa 1770, 41 ins wide when open, 23 ins deep, 27½ ins high. £225

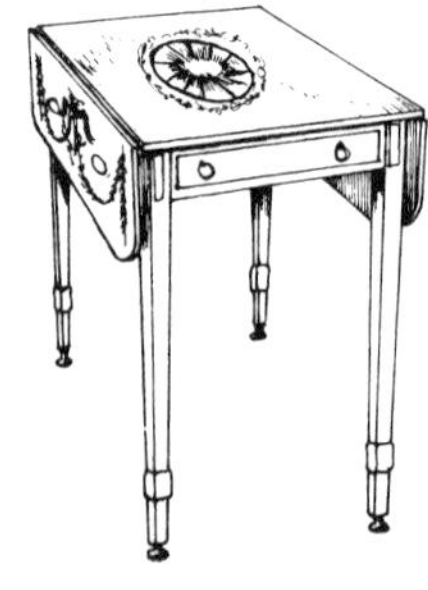

9. Good quality late 18th century satinwood Pembroke table inlaid with ribbons and swags. £245

1. Fine quality Sheraton satinwood Pembroke table. £280

2. Late 18th century satinwood inlaid Pembroke table on square tapering legs. £325

3. Regency period mahogany Pembroke table with satinwood crossbanding, 2 ft 3 ins wide when closed. £50

4. Late 18th century Hepplewhite mahogany Pembroke table with oval flaps, tapering legs and spade feet. £285

5. Early 19th century mahogany Pembroke table with boxwood string inlay and square tapering legs. £25

6. Sheraton satinwood Pembroke table crossbanded in kingwood and inlaid with ebony, 29 ins high. £125

7. Unusual mid 18th century breakfast table in dark mahogany. £250

8. Early 18th century mahogany Pembroke table crossbanded with birds eye maple, on square tapering legs, 2 ft 9 ins wide when open. £83

9. Small Sheraton period satinwood Pembroke table crossbanded in kingwood. £395

SOFA TABLES

1. A nice plain mahogany sofa table, circa 1800, 35ins wide, 26ins deep, 28ins high. £375

2. A finely figured Regency rosewood sofa table, circa 1830. £295

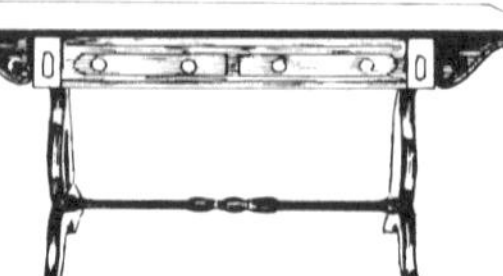

3. Exceptionally narrow Regency lyre ended mahogany sofa table, crossbanded on the top edges, frieze and drawer with kingwood, circa 1810. 5 ft 8 ins long, 2 ft wide. £750

4. Good quality Regency mahogany sofa table with tooled leather onthe top and flaps. £425

5. A superb Regency period faded rosewood sofa table with fine brass mounts. £385

6. Regency period rosewood sofa table with brass string inlay and crossbanded in satinwood with an unusual U shaped support. £450

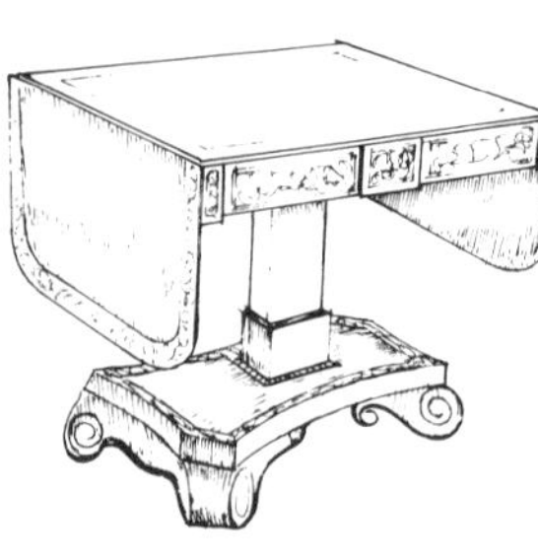

7. Early 18th century mahogany sofa table (in need of restoration). £120

8. George III mahogany sofa table with splayed legs, 59 ins long when open, 35 ins wide, 26 ins high. £365

1. An elegant Regency sofa table of faded mahogany, 63ins long, 26½ ins wide, 28½ ins high. £365

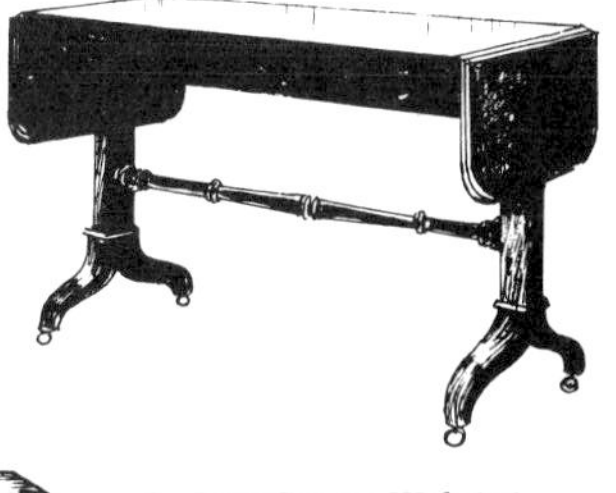

2. Late George III faded mahogany sofa table 25½ ins x 39½ ins when closed, 60 ins wide when open. £425

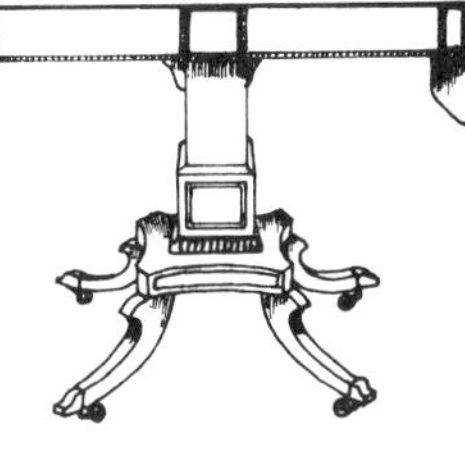

3. Good quality Regency sofa table in faded mahogany. £325

4. Early 19th century rosewood sofa table with turned supports and splayed feet with brass castors. £355

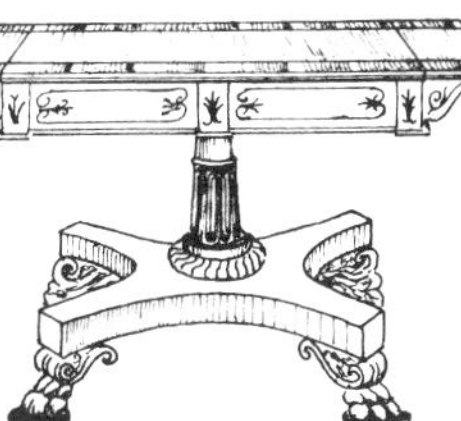

5. Regency rosewood sofa table with bobbin twist supports and ebony banding. £410

6. Good quality Regency rosewood sofa table inlaid with brass on a shaped platform base with claw feet. £565

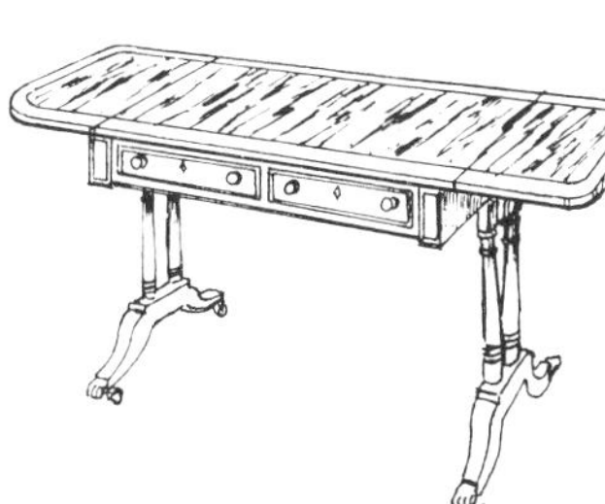

7. Late 18th century coromandel wood sofa table crossbanded with satinwood. £620

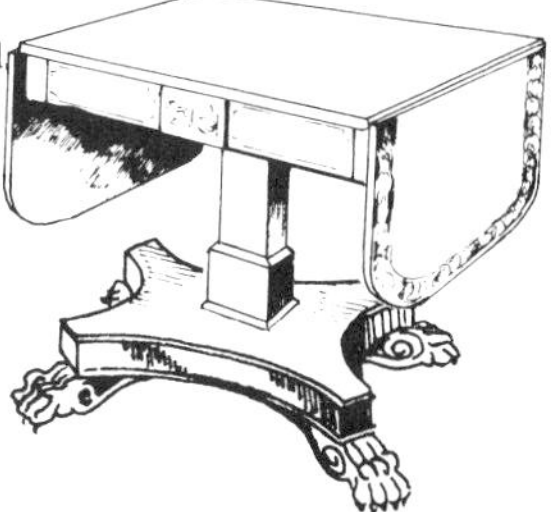

8. Early 19th century mahogany sofa table with a platform base and paw feet. £185

SIDE TABLES

1. Early 17th century oak side table of good colour. £78

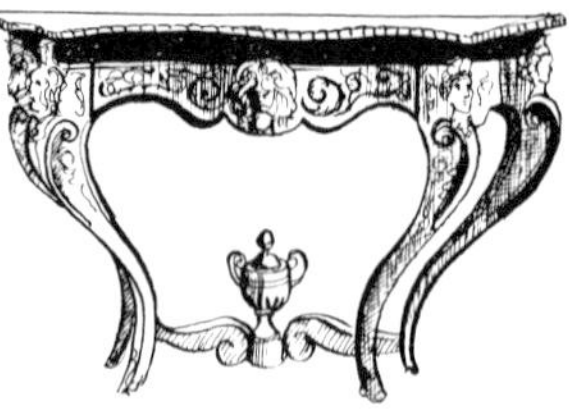

2. 19th century red boulle side table with shaped legs and fine ormolu mounts, 4 ft 8 ins wide. £280

3. 18th century French walnut side table with two drawers and ormolu mounts. £200

4. 18th century French walnut table 3 ft 8 ins long, 1 ft 10½ ins deep, 2 ft 5 ins high. £125

5. One of a pair of George II gilt tables with marble tops. £530

6. One of a pair of Georgian bowfront side tables in mahogany. £1.250

7. William and Mary period walnut side table decorated with seaweed marquetry panels. £415

8. One of a pair of Regency painted and parcel gilt side tables with marble tops, 1·55 metres wide. £2,400

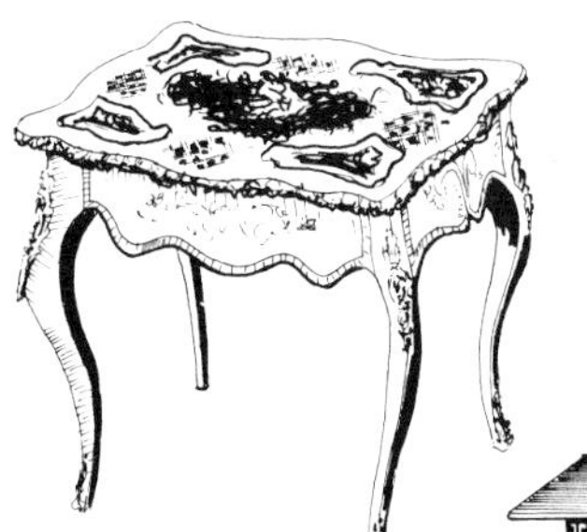

1. Good quality 18th century French marquetry side table mounted in ormolu, 27 ins wide. £225

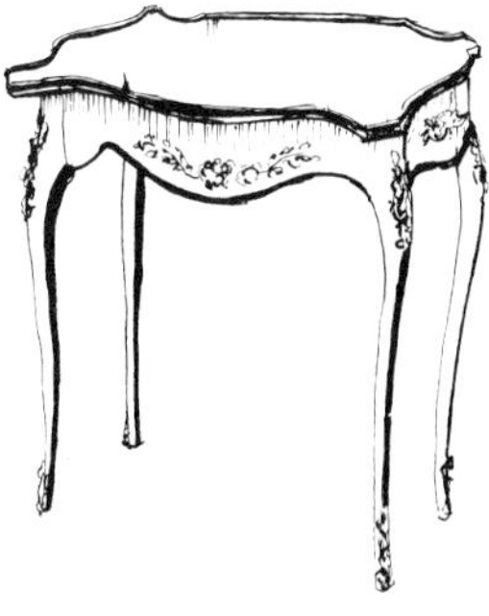

2. Louis Philippe mahogany side table with a rose marble top, 22 ins wide. £85

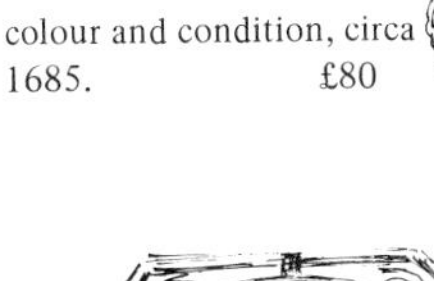

3. Oak side table of fine colour and condition, circa 1685. £80

4. A good quality Georgian mahogany serpentine front side table with a fitted drawer. £510

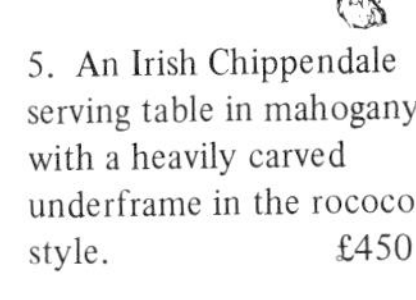

5. An Irish Chippendale serving table in mahogany with a heavily carved underframe in the rococo style. £450

6. Early 18th century walnut marquetry side table. £295

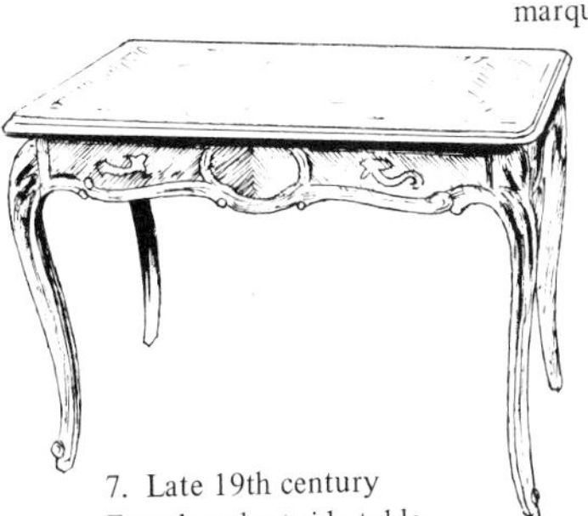

7. Late 19th century French walnut side table on cabriole legs with scroll feet. £45

8. Regency period brass inlaid rosewood side table. £125

DROP LEAF TABLES

1. Georgian mahogany two flap table with oval leaves and pad feet. £145

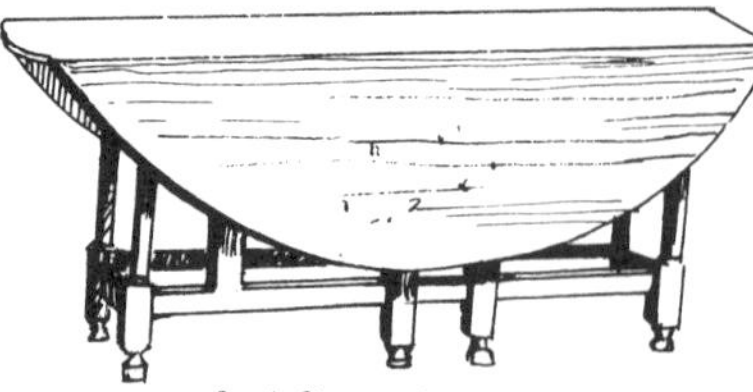

2. A fine quality late 18th century Irish wakes table in cherry wood. £240

3. An extremely fine large Irish wakes table in mahogany, from the mid 18th century. £680

4. Late 18th century oak drop leaf dining table opening to 5ft long. £115

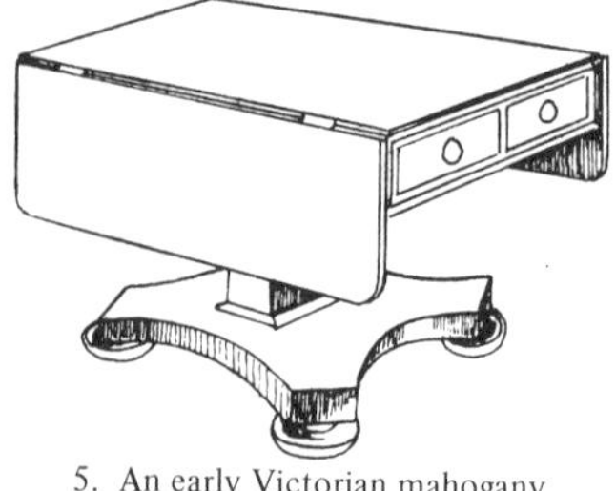

5. An early Victorian mahogany supper table on a centre column with a shaped platform base and bun feet. £45

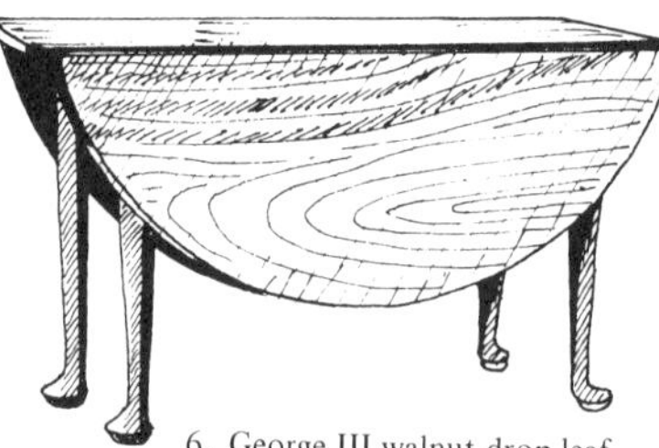

6. George III walnut drop leaf table on pad feet. £140

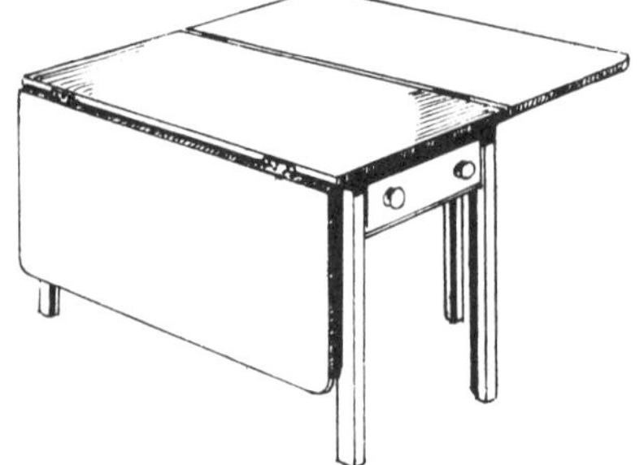

7. Late 18th century oak drop leaf cottage dining table. £32

8. Regency rosewood supper table with a fine crossbanded top, on a platform base with splayed feet. £125

1. A fine quality Charles I gateleg table. £650

2. 19th century oak gateleg table. £18

3. Large early 18th century oak gateleg table of good colour. £245

4. Late 19th century oak gateleg table with barley twist supports. £10

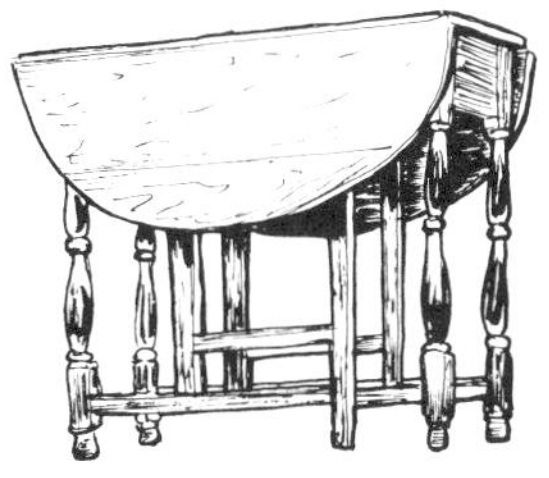

5. Victorian oak gateleg table. £8

6. 17th century oak gateleg table with square flaps and a double gate action. £300

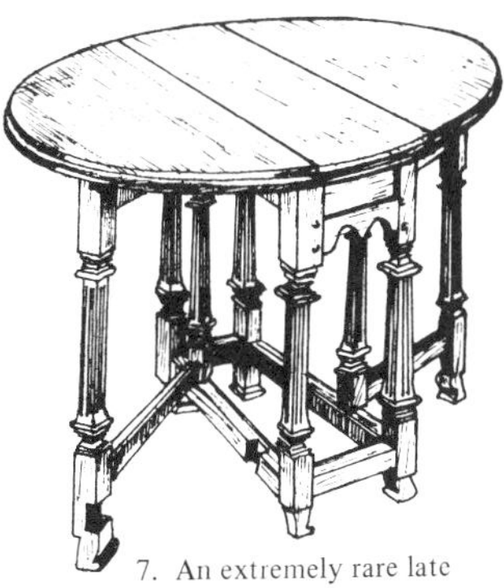

7. An extremely rare late 17th century oak gateleg table. £1,300

8. Small 17th century honey coloured oak gateleg table. 120gns

SUTHERLAND TABLES

1. An early Victorian rosewood Sutherland table on barley twist supports, 3ft 3ins x 6ins top when closed. £50

2. Early Victorian burr walnut Sutherland table with oval flaps. £55

3. Early Victorian burr walnut Sutherland table on cabriole leg supports. £65

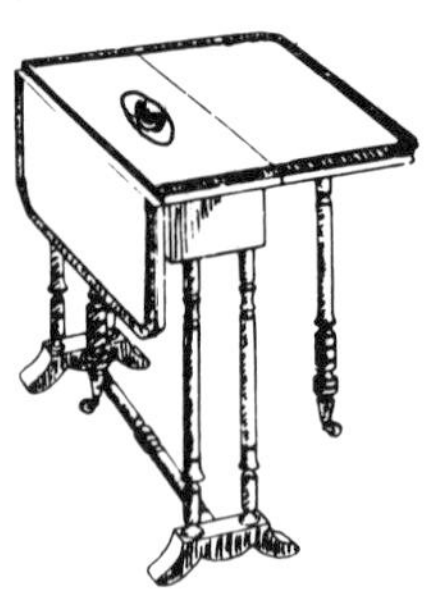

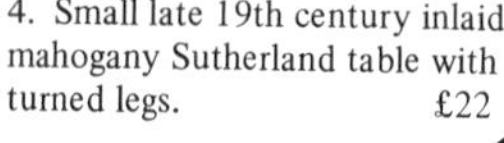

4. Small late 19th century inlaid mahogany Sutherland table with turned legs. £22

5. Edwardian ebonised Sutherland table with canted corners to the leaves. £20

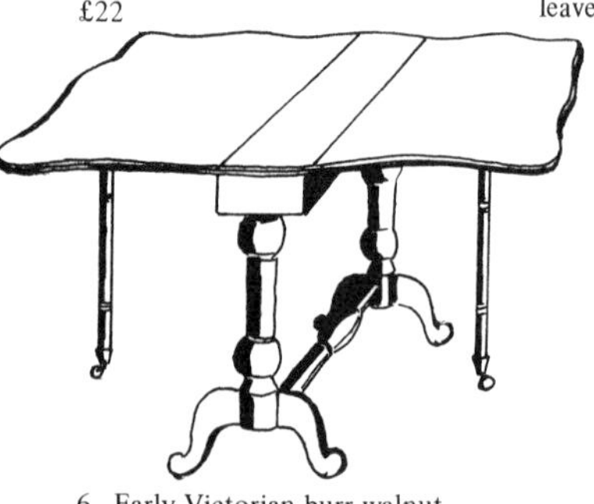

6. Early Victorian burr walnut Sutherland table on cabriole leg supports, with butterfly leaves. £80

1. A fine French Regency giltwood consol table 6ft 5ins wide. £1,900

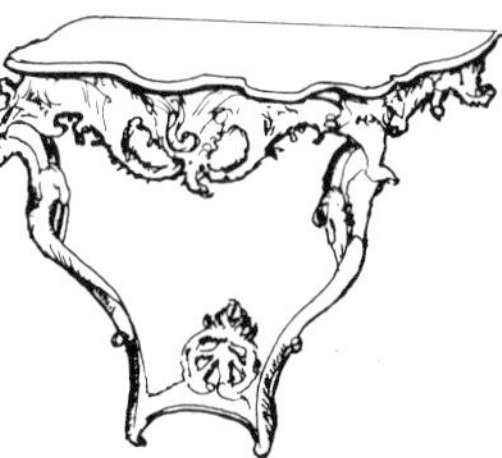

2. 19th century gilt consol table with a shaped green marble top. £140

3. A small mid 18th century giltwood consol table with a figured marble top, 25ins wide. £240

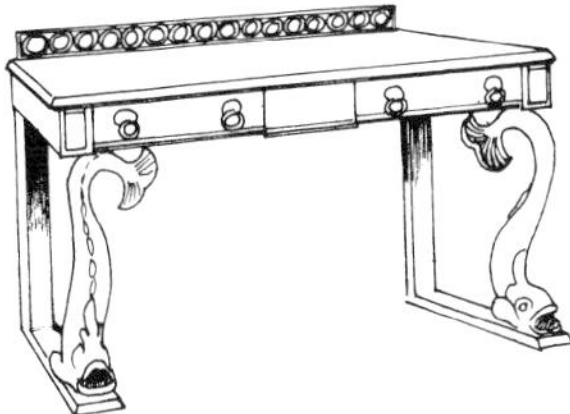

4. Regency period mahogany consol table with dolphin supports and a fine brass gallery. £465

5. Late 18th century giltwood consol table with a shaped white marble top. £250

6. A fine George II giltwood consol table with a carved eagle support. £550

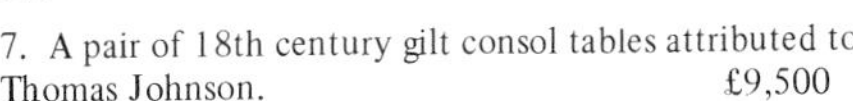

7. A pair of 18th century gilt consol tables attributed to Thomas Johnson. £9,500

DINING TABLES

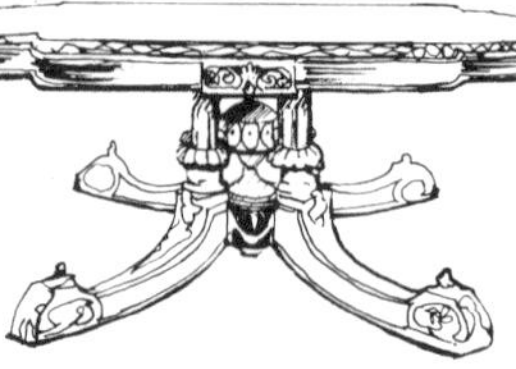

1. Victorian ebonised loo table with ormolu decoration. £50

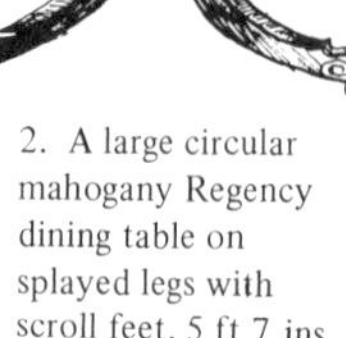

2. A large circular mahogany Regency dining table on splayed legs with scroll feet, 5 ft 7 ins diameter. £230

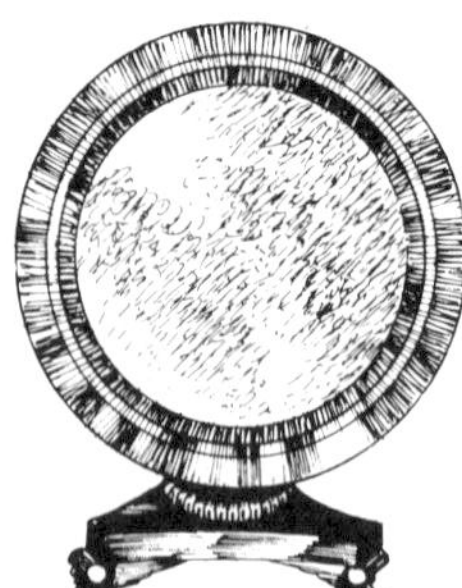

3. A good Regency table in burr walnut crossbanded with rosewood, 42 ins diameter. £165

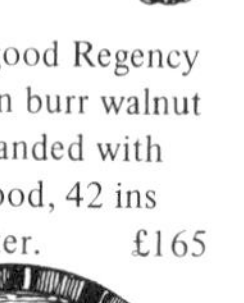

4. Regency rosewood circular table with brass string inlay and an unusual scroll base. £265

5. Early Victorian burr walnut loo table with an ornate centre column and carved cabriole leg base. £95

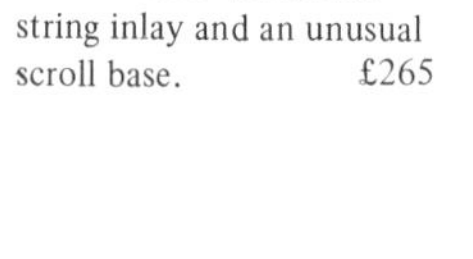

6. Good quality Regency rosewood centre table with wide crossbanding and splay feet terminating in brass claw castors, 4 ft 7 ins diameter. £175

7. An unusual single pedestal mahogany dining table with a draw-leaf action, 3 ft 11ins wide, 6ft 5 ins long when open, circa 1810. £395

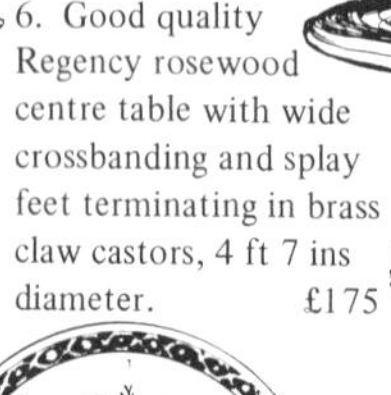

8. William IV mahogany centre table with a good quality shaped platform base and elaborate lions paw feet. £135

9. Fine quality Regency inlaid satinwood table, 49 ins diameter. £860

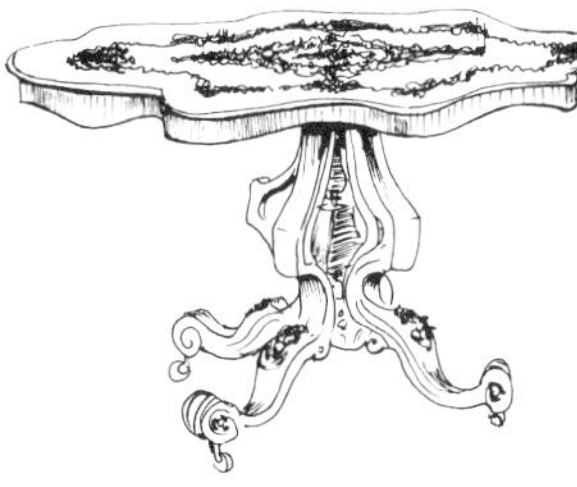

1. Fine quality Victorian burr walnut and marquetry shaped top loo table. £395

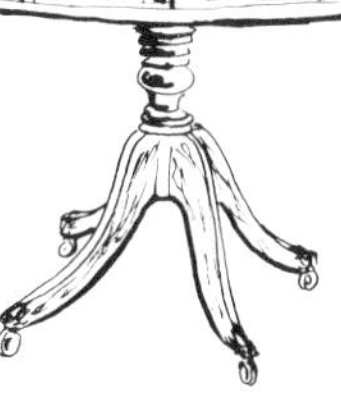

2. Early 19th century mahogany breakfast table on a quadruple base. £285

3. Fine Regency rosewood centre table crossbanded with brass scrollwork. £245

4. Fine Regency rosewood breakfast table with wide crossbanding. £310

5. Regency breakfast table in well figured mellow rosewood with brass inlay, 60ins long, 38ins wide. £480

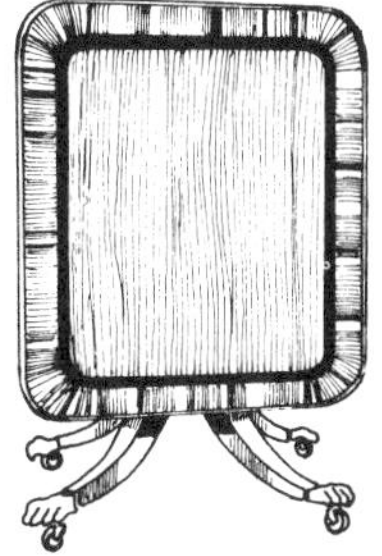

6. Regency rosewood breakfast table with wide crossbanding and ebony inlay. £210

7. Late 18th century library table in mahogany with ebony stringing on the legs and round the frieze. £650

8. Victorian burr walnut breakfast table with boxwood string inlay and an unusual base. £117

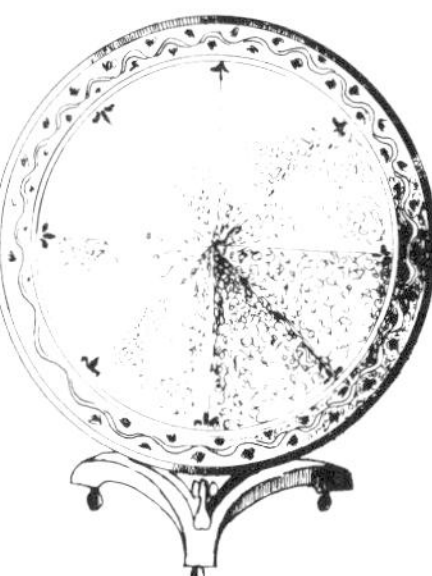

9. A fine Regency circular breakfast table in burr maple inlaid with rosewood, 4 ft 1½ ins diameter. £475

DINING TABLES

1. Good quality George III faded mahogany breakfast table crossbanded with satinwood. £400

3. Good quality brass inlaid rosewood centre table on a platform base with scroll feet. £350

2. Late Victorian ebonised table with boxwood inlay. £30

4. Victorian oval burr walnut loo table. £75

6. Victorian snap top centre table quarter veneered in mahogany. £90

5. 19th century red boulle centre table with cabriole legs and ormolu mounts. £285

7. Victorian mahogany centre table on a platform base with bun feet. £27.50

9. Early Victorian mahogany centre table on a shaped platform base with paw feet. £40

8. Late 18th century oval breakfast table in burr walnut with satinwood inlay. £350

1. Victorian carved oak table with a gadrooned edge and ornately carved base. £60

2. Victorian mahogany centre table on a round platform base with claw feet. £45

3. Fine quality late 18th century mahogany drum table. £420

4. Victorian burr walnut and ebonised loo table. £40

5. A good quality Regency period mahogany drum table with ormolu enrichments. £475

6. Rare late George III mahogany revolving library table 5 ft 3 ins diameter. £2,600

7. A good brass inlaid rosewood centre table on a platform base with ormolu decoration. £255

8. A large Regency period circular library table in pollard oak with a reeded edge, 6ft diameter. £175

9. A fine quality Regency period rosewood library table. £560

LARGE TABLES

1. Louis XVI style marquetry centre table inset with fine china plaques and decorated with ormolu. £1,000

2. Fine George II oak refectory table of good colour, 7 ft 3 ins long, 2 ft 9 ins wide, circa 1760. £450

3. Early 19th century twin pedestal mahogany dining table with a loose centre leaf. £275

4. Good quality late 18th century mahogany sectional table comprising two ' D ' shaped end tables with a drop flap centre section. £390

5. George III mahogany wakes table. £260

6. Early 17th century oak refectory serving table 4 ft 2 ins long, 2 ft 2 ins wide. £275

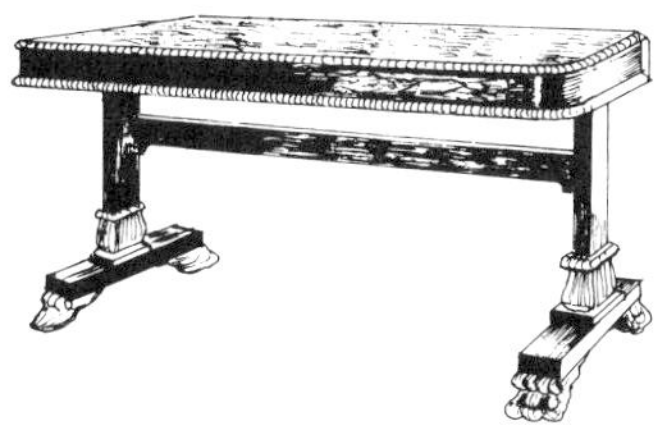

1. A fine quality French rosewood writing table with gilt decoration. £500

2. 19th century marquetry centre table by L.W. Collman 1850 - 1870. £250

3. An early oak refectory table with a massive plank top, on six squared chamfered legs, 13½ft long, 2ft 6ins wide. £1,200

4. A good quality Victorian rosewood writing table. £145

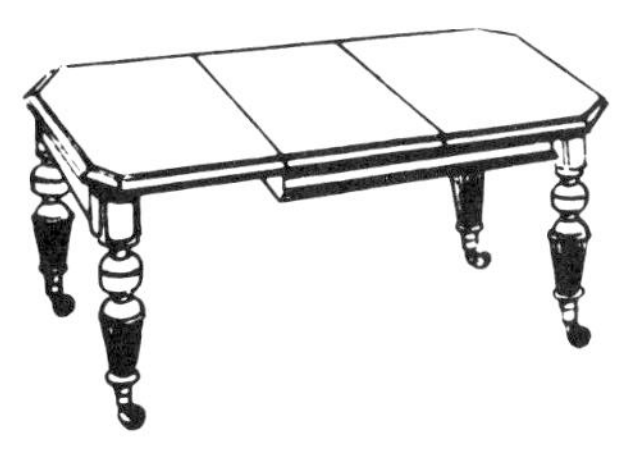

5. Victorian mahogany telescopic dining table with a loose centre leaf. £17.50

6. Early 19th century mahogany extending dining table on spirally reeded legs terminating in brass cup castors. £145

1. Regency period extending dining table in mahogany with an unusual split pedestal action. £325

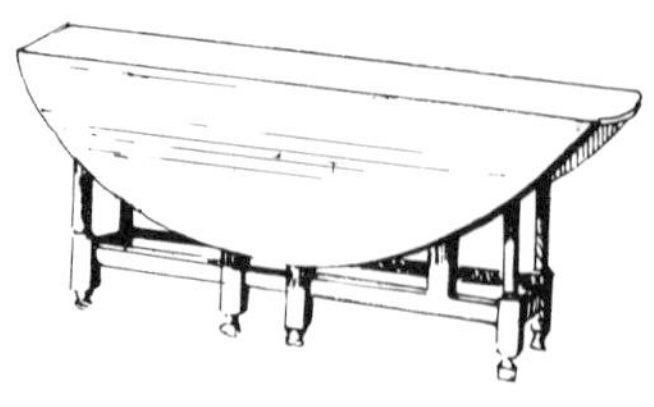

2. 18th century Irish wakes table in cherry wood, with a double gate action. £300

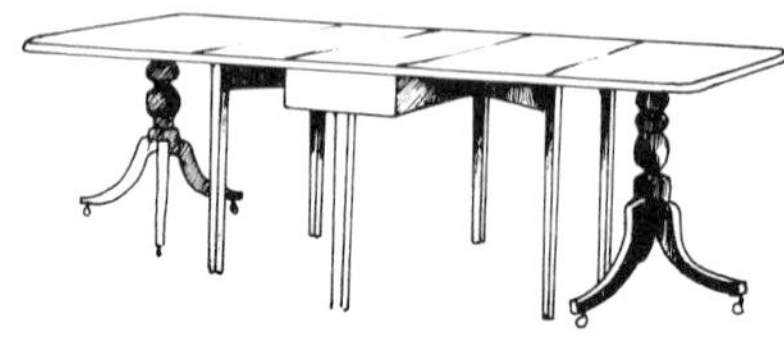

3. An unusual American mahogany extension dining table in the style of Duncan Phyle. £1,200

4. A good honey colour walnut refectory table of the mid 17th century. £400

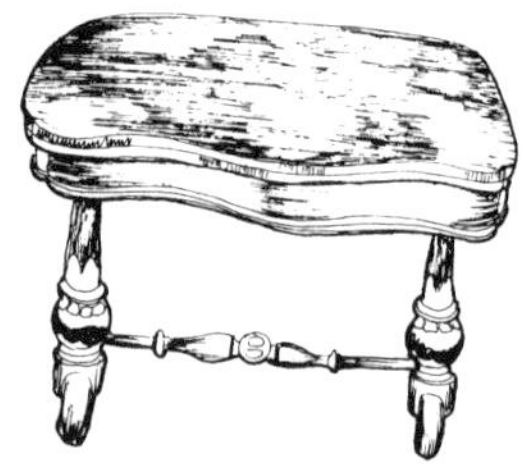

5. 19th century mahogany stretcher table with a serpentine shaped top. £75

6. A massive early Georgian oak refectory table on six turned legs, with a plank top and drawer at either end, 28 ft 8 ins long. £1,600

1. Regency two pillar mahogany dining table. £360

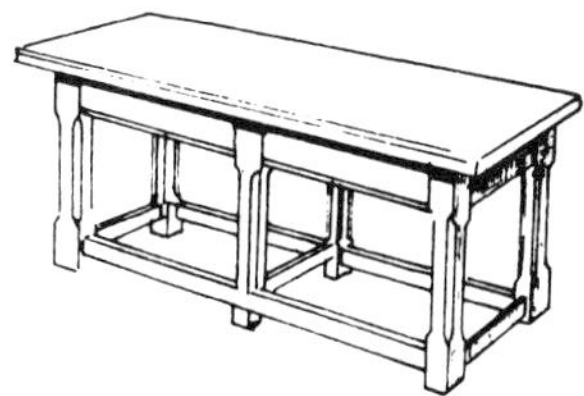

2. Good quality 17th century oak refectory table on six legs with stretchers. £280

3. A mahogany three pillar table in good original condition, 5 ft wide, 12 ft 9 ins long, circa 1830. £750

4. Late 18th century mahogany drop leaf dining table. £150

5. An exceptionally fine quality Regency period three pillar mahogany table, 12 ft long, with brass claw castors. £440

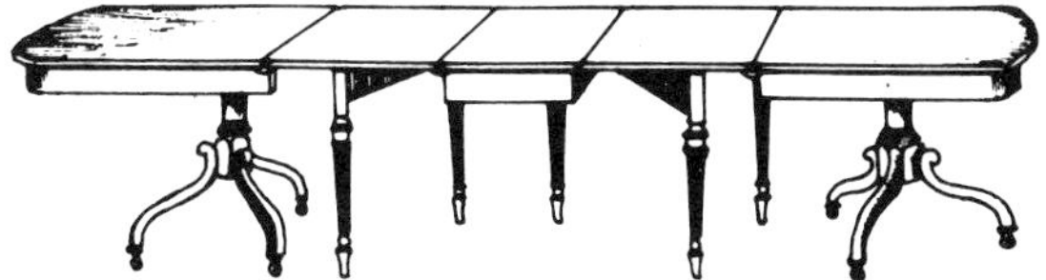

6. An extremely large early 19th century mahogany extending table with a gateleg centre section. £435

1. Late 18th century mahogany lowboy, 35ins wide. £180

2. Late 17th century oak lowboy crossbanded in walnut. £185

3. George III country made oak lowboy on square legs. £100

4. Late 18th century mahogany dressing table. £110

5. Fine George I fruitwood dressing table with the original brass handles. £155

6. A good quality George I walnut lowboy with a crossbanded top and drawers. £270

1. George I red walnut lowboy. £250

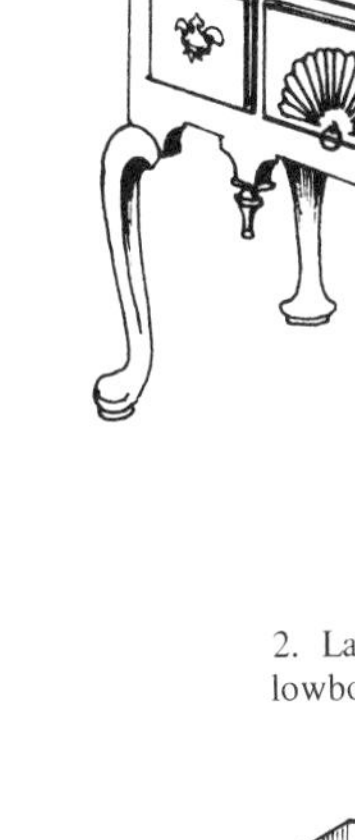

2. Late 17th century fruitwood lowboy in fine original condition. £400

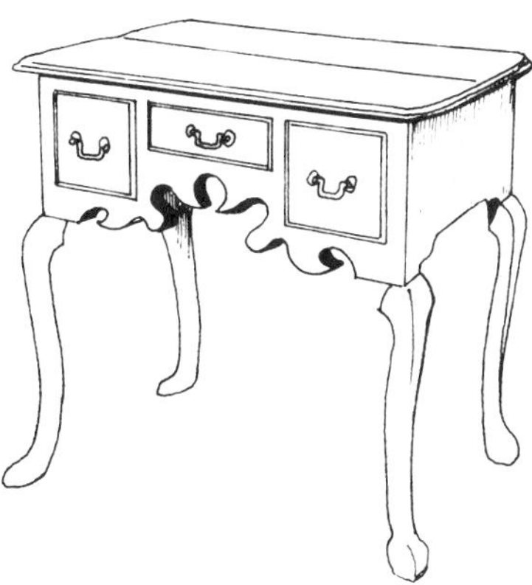

3. George II oak lowboy with a finely shaped frieze. £145

4. Early 18th century walnut lowboy with the original brasses. £260

5. 18th century country made oak lowboy. £115

6. Rare Queen Anne oak lowboy of faded honey colour, circa 1710, 32ins long, 28½ins high, 21½ins deep. £340

WORKBOXES AND GAMES TABLES

1. Late 18th century mahogany work table on fine fluted legs. £135

2. Small Regency rosewood games table with a reversible sliding top. £85

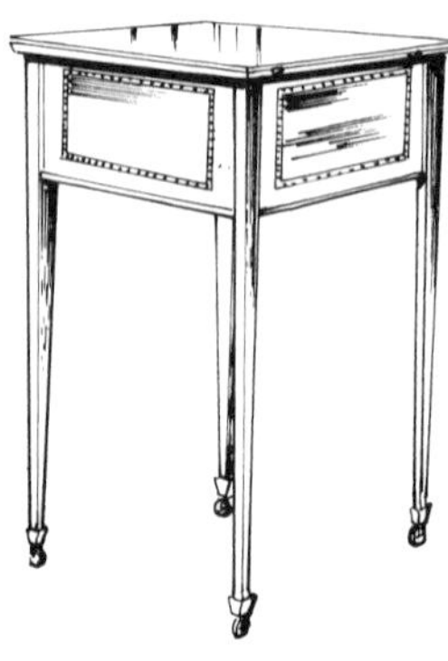

3. Edwardian mahogany and satinwood banded sewing table on square tapering legs with spade feet. £21

4. Early 19th century combined games and sewing table in rosewood. £155

5. Good quality 19th century combined games table and workbox in rosewood. £125

6. Victorian walnut workbox with a chessboard top and tripod base. £45

7. Good quality early Victorian mahogany sewing table with drop flaps and a U shaped centre support. £75

8. 18th century mahogany accounting table, 24 ins wide inlaid with marquetry panels. £100

9. Early 19th century mahogany work table with ormolu enrichments. £175.

1. A good quality Victorian papier mache work table with floral and gilt decoration. £175

2. A fine mahogany games table, circa 1800, with a tooled leather top which reverses to become a chessboard. £380

3. George III mahogany drop flap work table, circa 1800. £115

4. Victorian cone shaped rosewood sewing table on a tripod base. £29

5. A fine quality Regency mahogany work table. £175

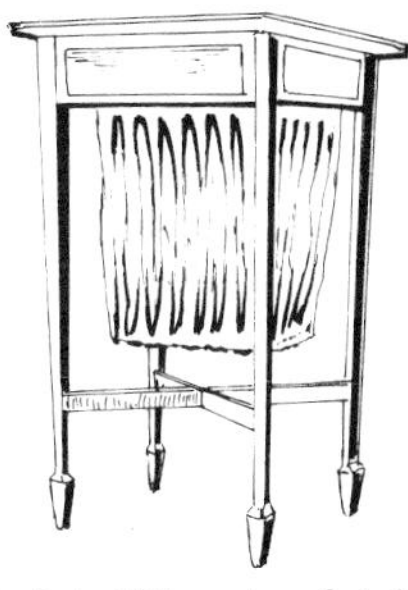

6. Late 18th century faded mahogany work table with a forward opening partitioned drawer, 18 ins wide, circa 1790. £245

7. Regency period games table on a centre column support with splayed feet. £165

8. Fine quality 19th century rosewood workbox. £75

9. A good Regency rosewood games table, circa 1820. £70

WORKBOXES AND GAMES TABLES

1. An early Victorian rosewood chess table on a platform base with scroll feet. £50

2. 19th century rosewood work table on a shaped platform base with scroll feet. £85

3. Regency period mahogany work table on a shaped platform base. £75

4. Good quality early Victorian burr walnut work table with a chess board top. £90

5. Good Regency period work table veneered in amboyna. £210

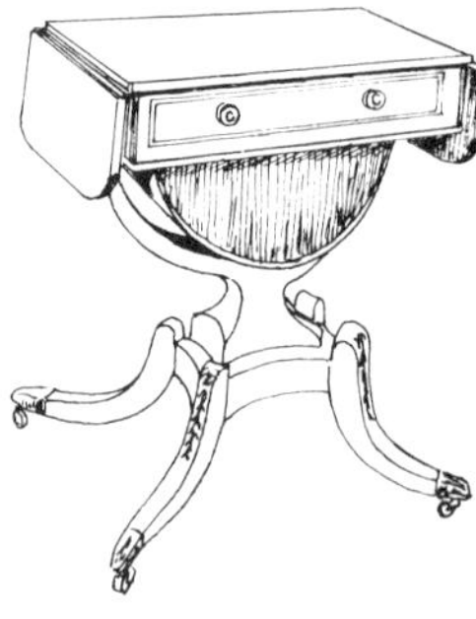

6. Regency mahogany work table with drop flaps and splay feet with brass castors. £135

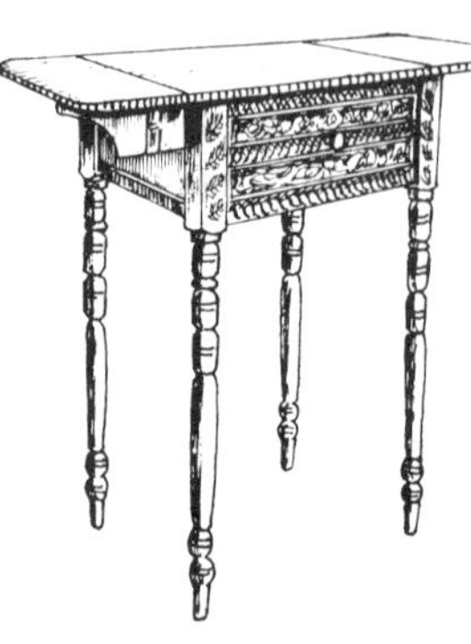

7. 19th century marquetry work table on fine turned legs. £130

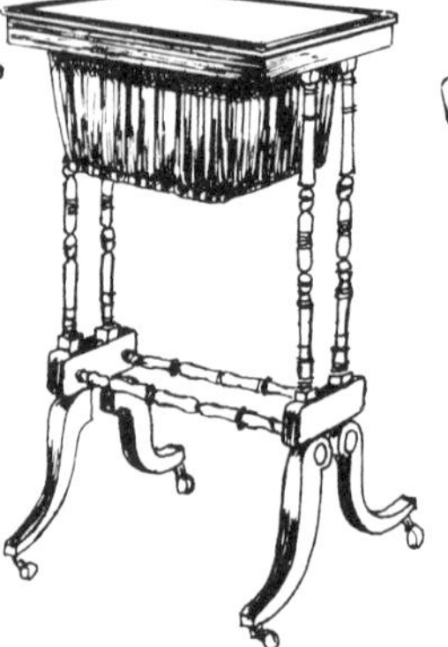

8. Early 19th century satinwood work table. £155

9. Early Victorian mahogany work table with drop flaps, three drawers and sliding bag. £70

1. Late 18th century partridge wood games table. £185

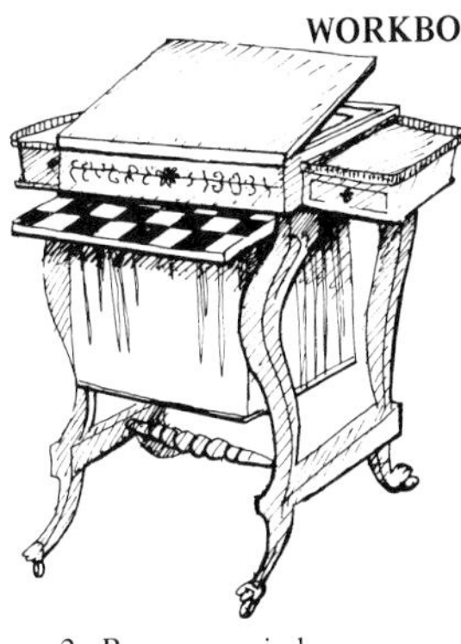

2. Regency period combined games table and work table in rosewood with inlaid brass decoration. £500

3. Early 19th century rosewood, card and games table with gilt paw feet. £150

4. Early 19th century mahogany sewing table on fine turned legs, with fitted top drawer. £85

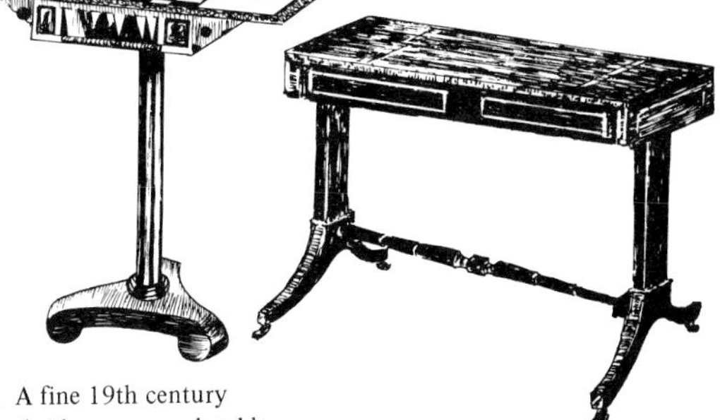

5. A fine 19th century Tunbridge ware work table with drop flaps. £155

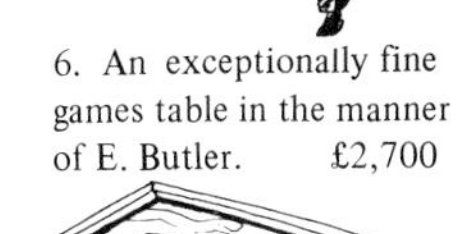

6. An exceptionally fine games table in the manner of E. Butler. £2,700

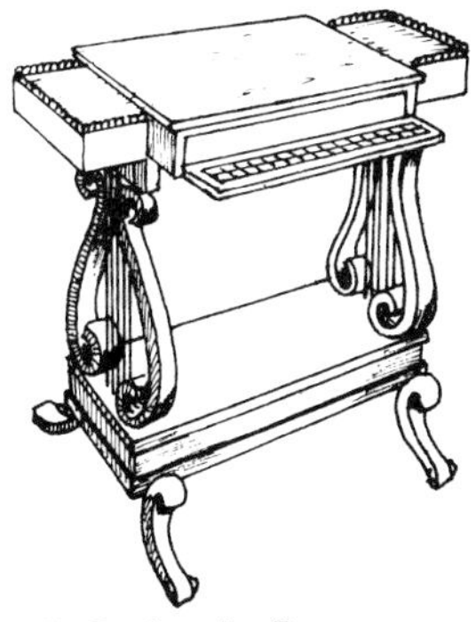

7. Good quality Regency period satinwood work table with lyre end supports and a pierced brass gallery. £205

8. An unusual Regency sewing table with a rising screen and adjustable reading slope. £225

9. Victorian mahogany work box with drawer. £27.50

TEAPOYS

1. Early 19th century mahogany teapoy. £85

2. A fine Victorian papier mache teapoy inlaid with mother of pearl. £120

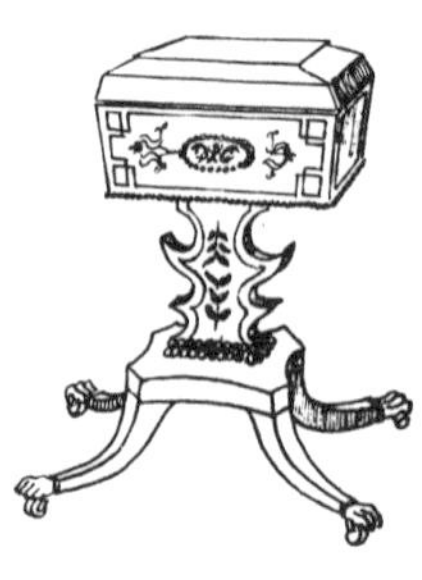

3. Regency brass inlaid rosewood teapoy on splayed feet with brass claw castors. £200

4. Early Victorian rosewood teapoy on a barley twist column with cabriole legs. £55

5. Good quality early Victorian papier mache teapoy. £135

6. Victorian mahogany teapoy on a carved tripod base. £50

7. Regency rosewood teapoy on a carved stretcher base. £65

8. Early 19th century rosewood teapoy inlaid with mother of pearl, on a platform base with bun feet. £60

1. Victorian pollard oak teapoy on a platform base with cabriole legs. £65

2. Victorian black lacquered teapoy on a shaped platform base. £65

3. A fine early 19th century rosewood teapoy. £85

4. William IV figured walnut teapoy on a shaped platform base with paw feet. £80

5. A fine early Victorian rosewood teapoy inlaid with mother of pearl. £120

6. Early 19th century Tunbridge ware teapoy on a ' U ' support with splay feet and brass claw castors. £200

7. A fine quality Regency brass inlaid rosewood teapoy. £185

8. Victorian papier mache teapoy. £75

CHESTS

1. Unusual mahogany chest of four drawers enclosed by a pair of finely figured mahogany doors, 3 ft 7 ins wide, circa 1795. £98

2. Small mahogany chest with brushing slide, only 33 ins wide, circa 1765. £335

3. An unusual Wellington chest in rosewood with six drawers on one side and shelves on the other. £125

4. Victorian mahogany chest of three long and two short drawers, 3 ft 7 ins wide. £8

5. Late 18th century finely figured mahogany chest of small proportions, 34½ ins wide, 29 ins high. £140

6. A good marquetry chest veneered on oak with red walnut, circa 1800, 50 ins wide, 38 ins high. £350

7. A Victorian mahogany bow front chest of three long and two short graduated cock beaded drawers, 3 ft 6 ins wide. £32

8. Fine Charles II chest with bone and ebony inlay, circa 1670. £430

1. Small late 18th century mahogany chest of drawers on ogee feet. £110

2. Victorian mahogany chest of drawers on short turned legs. £20

3. Good quality Victorian rosewood Wellington chest of seven drawers, 2 ft wide. £80

4. Small bow chest in dark plum colour Cuban mahogany with oak lined drawers, 33 ins wide, 19 ins deep, 26 ins high, circa 1745. £195

5. Victorian mahogany chest of three long and two short drawers, 3 ft 4 ins wide. £12

6. An attractive moulded front chest of drawers in walnut, circa 1740, 39 ins wide, 22 ins deep, 43 ins high. £145

7. George I mellow honey coloured walnut veneered chest, the top, sides and drawer fronts quartered and chevron crossbanded, circa 1725, 38 ins wide. £225

8. Late 18th century mahogany chest of superb quality and chestnut colour, 38 ins wide, circa 1785. £198

CHESTS

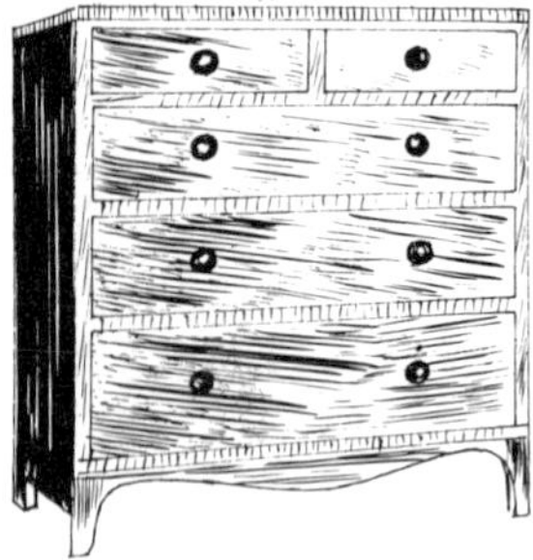

1. Mid 19th century mahogany chest of three long and two short graduated drawers, on splay feet. £28

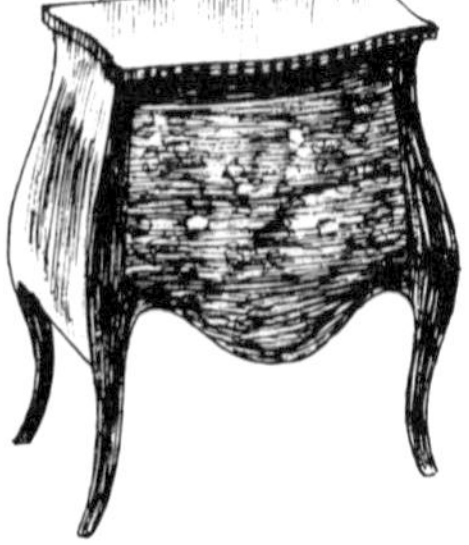

2. A finely grained serpentine chest of drawers, 4 ft wide, 2 ft 6 ins deep, 29½ ins high, circa 1800. £168

3. 19th century floral marquetry bombe shaped chest of two drawers. £330

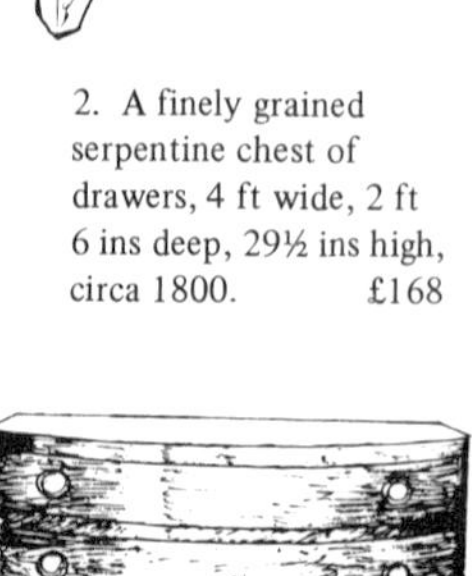

4. 19th century mahogany bow fronted chest of three long and two short drawers, 3 ft 4 ins wide. £25

5. George II bow front chest of drawers, 2 ft 11½ ins wide. £225

6. Rosewood Wellington chest, circa 1840, 53 ins high, 25½ ins wide. £95

7. A well figured late 18th century mahogany chest with slide, 33 ins wide. £180

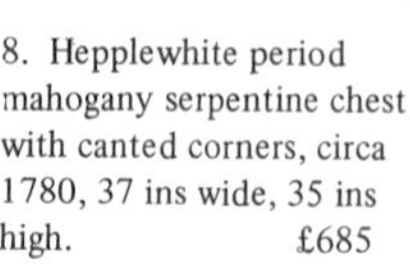

8. Hepplewhite period mahogany serpentine chest with canted corners, circa 1780, 37 ins wide, 35 ins high. £685

1. An Edwardian walnut chest of drawers. £4

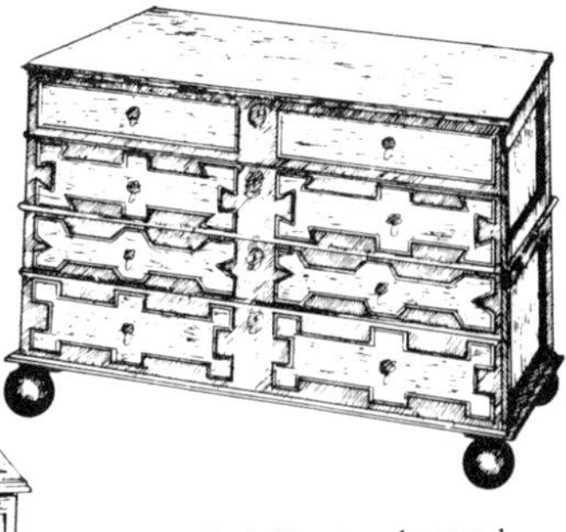

2. A Stuart cedarwood chest of drawers, 37 ins wide. £270

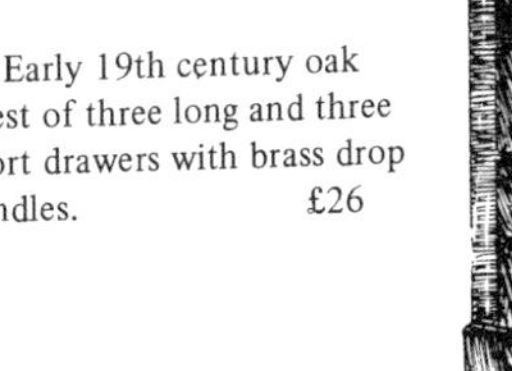

3. Early 19th century oak chest of three long and three short drawers with brass drop handles. £26

4. A Stuart period cedarwood, oak and walnut chest. £310

5. Queen Anne walnut chest of drawers, 36 ins wide of good colour. £300

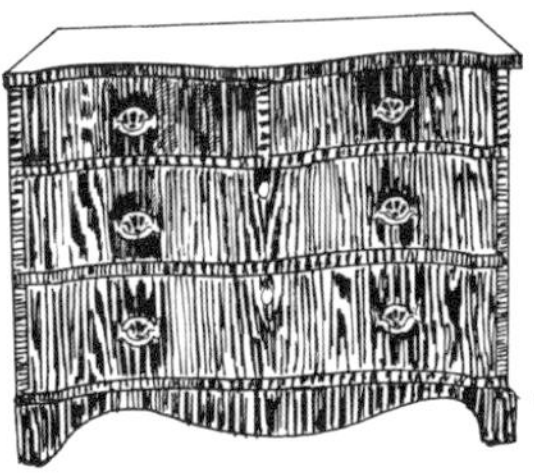

6. Early 19th century serpentine front chest of drawers in coromandel wood. £300

7. 18th century Dutch oak chest of good colour. £275

8. Early 19th century mahogany bow fronted chest of three long drawers on splay feet. £60

CHESTS

1. Magnificent oyster walnut chest of drawers of good colour, circa 1690, 38½ins wide. £550

2. Late 18th century mahogany chest on bracket feet with canted corners and a brushing slide, 3 ft 1 in wide. £225

3. 19th century stripped pine chest of drawers on turned legs. £17

4. Good quality George II figured walnut bachelors chest of small proportions. £1,400

5. Early 18th century oyster veneered walnut chest of drawers on bun feet. £275

6. Late 19th century mahogany chest of drawers with barley twist columns and bun feet. £10

7. George I chest of Cuban mahogany on bracket feet, with brass carrying handles. £200

8. Small early 19th century teak military chest with sunken brass handles and brass straps, only 2 ft 11 ins wide. £145

1. William and Mary oyster veneered and inlaid chest of drawers. £280

2. Georgian crossbanded walnut chest with a brushing slide. £380

3. Early 19th century marquetry chest of drawers decorated with floral sprays. £275

4. Late 18th century satinwood bow front chest of drawers with a brushing slide, crossbanded with tulip wood and with ebony and boxwood string inlay. £1,200

5. Early 19th century mahogany bow front chest of drawers on turned feet. £55

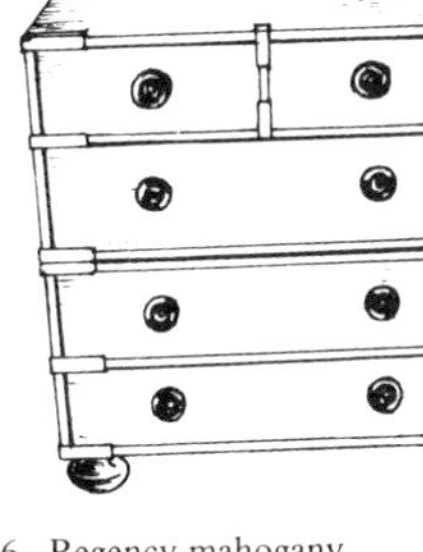

6. Regency mahogany military chest with sunken wooden knobs and brass straps, 3ft 3 ins wide. £90

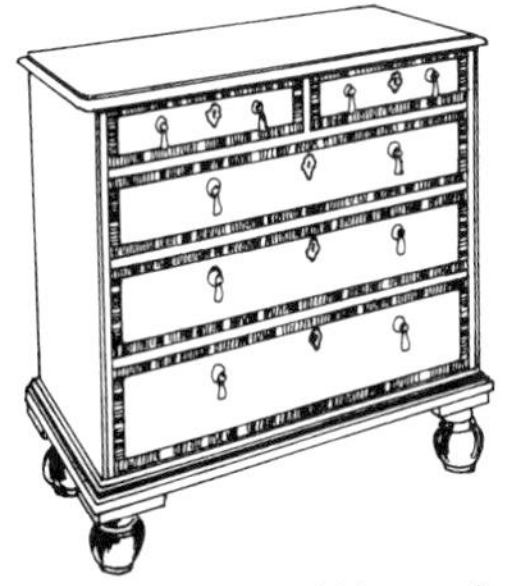

7. William and Mary period walnut crossbanded chest of two short and three long drawers. £470

8. 19th century mahogany chest of three long and two short drawers, on cabriole legs. £46

CHEST ON CHESTS

1. A fine Charles II walnut chest on stand with seaweed marquetry decoration, circa 1686. £825

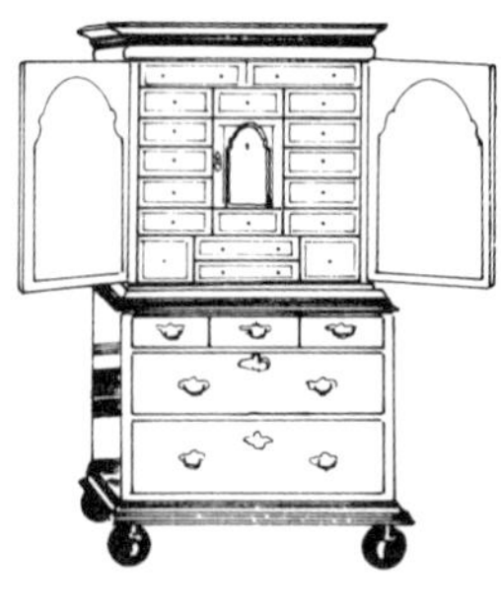

2. Queen Anne walnut feather banded cabinet on chest, the panelled door opening to reveal a multitude of small drawers. £720

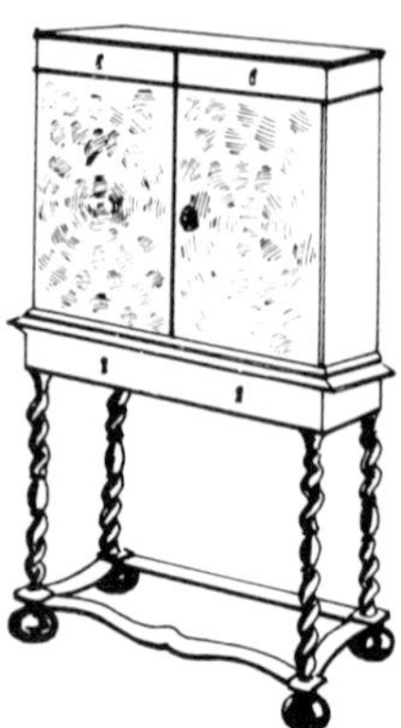

3. Late 17th century oyster shell walnut cabinet on barley twist supports with shaped stretchers. £240

4. 18th century mahogany chest on chest with canted corners, 3ft 6ins wide. £260

5. A fine quality Queen Anne walnut chest on chest of good colour. £640

6. Georgian mahogany chest on chest with a pull out slide. £385

7. Early Victorian mahogany chest on chest with boxwood string inlay and pressed brass handles. £80

8. Late 18th century mahogany chest on chest with a secretaire drawer, elaborate cornice and ogee feet. £900

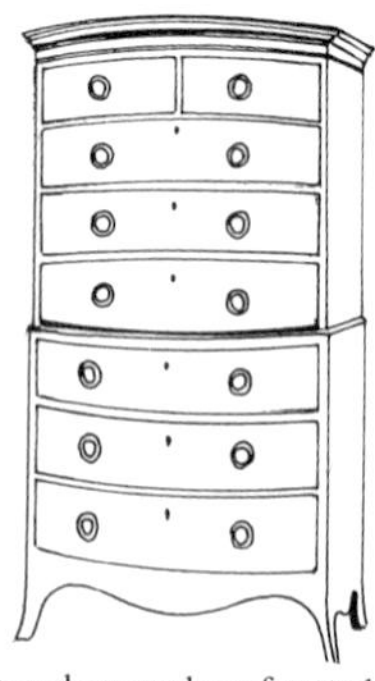

9. A fine mahogany bow fronted chest on chest with a shaped apron and splayed feet. £375

1. Late 17th century oak chest on stand in fine original condition. £275

2. A Charles II crested cabinet in red and gold with Oriental decoration, on a carved giltwood stand with eagle crest, acanthus and cherubs. £1,900

3. A fine quality 18th century walnut tallboy with fluted pilasters and a shaped apron. £810

4. A faded mahogany linen press with oak lined drawers and sliding trays, 50ins wide, circa 1800. £125

5. A fine William and Mary oyster veneered cabinet on stand with barley twist legs and cross stretchers. £425

6. George III mahogany tallboy on ogee feet, 3ft 6ins wide. £190

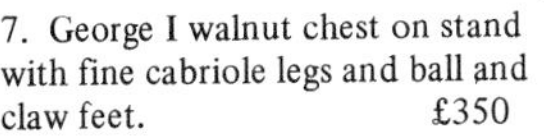

7. George I walnut chest on stand with fine cabriole legs and ball and claw feet. £350

8. An excellent Queen Anne mullberry wood chest on stand with onion shaped feet. £910

9. Queen Anne walnut chest on stand with oak lined drawers. £400

COMMODE CHESTS

1. A fine 18th century French provincial serpentine and bombe shaped commode with parquetry and marquetry decoration. £1,020

2. Good quality Louis XV period two drawer commode of various woods veneered on oak, with a shaped figured marble top. £3, 570

3. Early 19th century French bombe commode in kingwood and walnut, with fine ormolu mounts and a shaped marble top. £390

4. 19th century floral marquetry bombe shaped chest, with ormolu handles and escutcheons, only 28ins wide. £330

5. A profusely decorated Louis XVI style commode with a figured marble top.£725

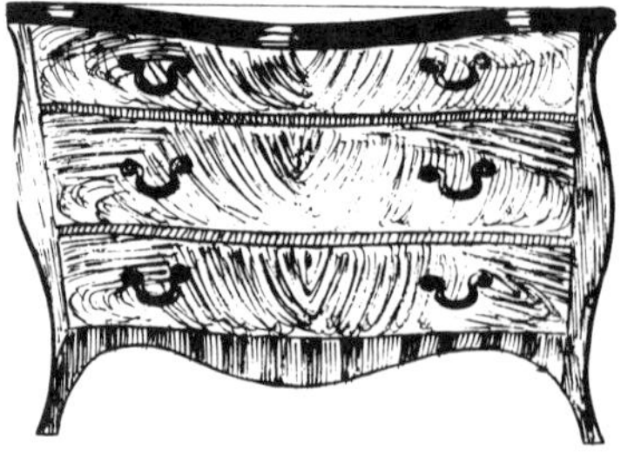

6. A fine quality Georgian figured mahogany commode with a fitted top drawer containing a mirror and assorted compartments. £750

1. A good quality Louis XV commode with ormolu handles and mounts. £1,950

2. Louis XVI walnut commode with a frieze drawer and three long drawers below, with a figured marble top. £385

3. 18th century Venetian two drawer commode painted with flowers on a green ground, 1.12 metres wide. £3,200

4. A good quality shaped front 19th century Continental marquetry commode. £1,250

5. George III mahogany serpentine fronted commode on splay feet, 42¼ins wide. 1,850 gns

6. 18th century Swedish three drawer commode veneered with walnut, 1.29 metres wide. £900

COMMODE CHESTS

1. George III serpentine front commode in satinwood. £510

2. A fine early 19th century French commode in kingwood and satinwood with rose marble top. £900

3. French provincial commode in oak, with the original metalwork, circa 1800. £145

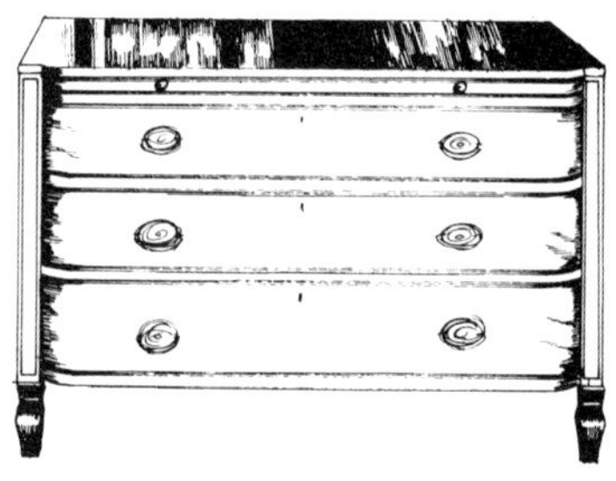

4. George III satinwood chest, 1.7m wide. £1, 050

5. George III bombe commode with a shaped grey marble top. £375

6. George III satinwood demi lune commode inlaid with urns. £510

1. A highly desirable 17th century walnut and holly commode. £1,100

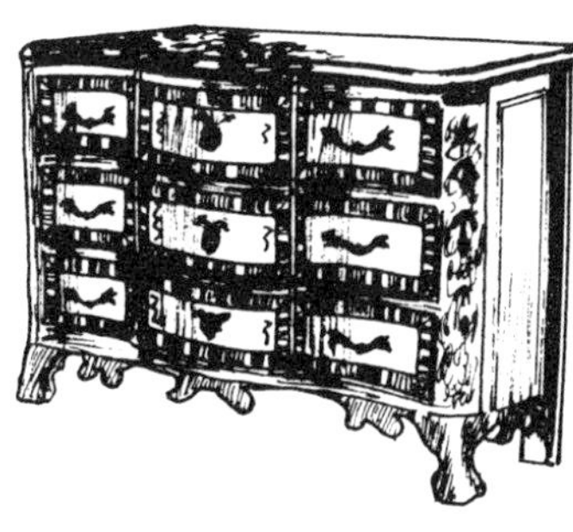

2. 18th century serpentine front commode inlaid with various woods. £850

3. 19th century French inlaid bombe shaped commode in kingwood. £550

4. Late 18th century Italian walnut commode. £425

5. Louis XV style commode in kingwood and rosewood with a shaped marble top and ormolu mounts. £410

6. A fine early 19th century kingwood parquetry commode with a figured marble top. £550

TRUNKS

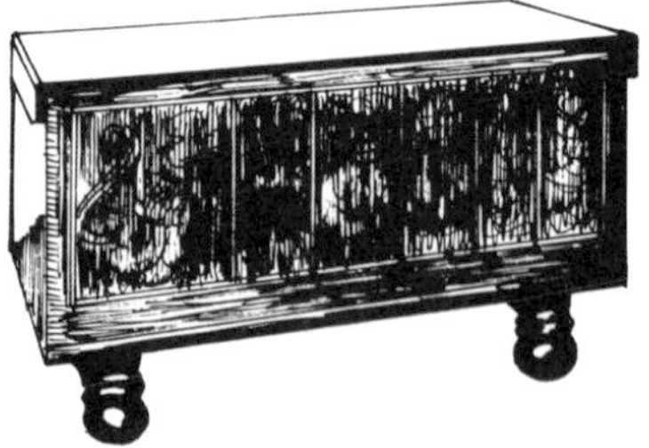

1. Fine early 16th century North Italian cassone, 5 ft 10 ins long, 2 ft 1 in high. £165

2. An early oak mule chest with geometric panels and a single drawer, 44 ins wide. £155

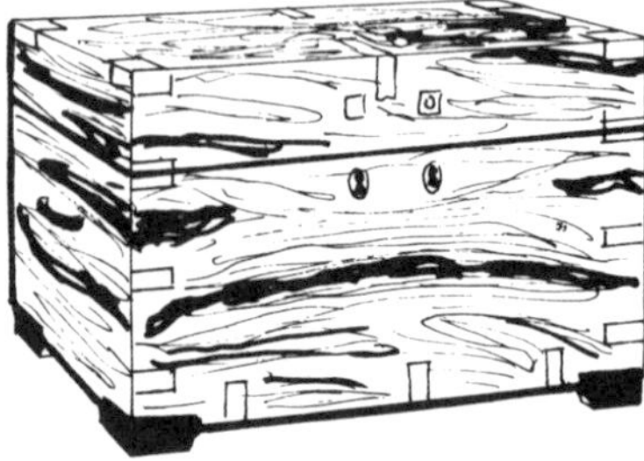

3. 19th century camphor wood trunk with brass straps and corners. £35

4. 18th century Spanish chestnut wood coffer, 5 ft 2 ins long, 1 ft 10 ins deep, 2 ft 9 ins high. £205

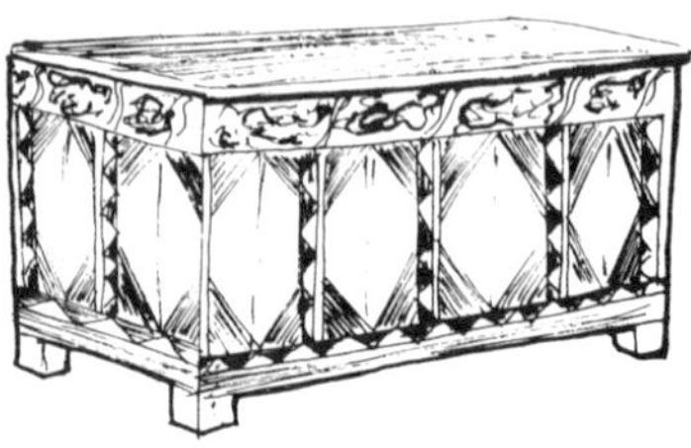

5. Late 17th century inlaid oak coffer. £78

6. 17th century oak coffer with primitive decoration, 49 ins long, 20 ins deep, 27½ ins high. £65

7. Pony skin coach trunk, circa 1790. £28

8. A large 18th century inlaid coffer. £88

1. An early French cupboard in walnut of good colour, circa 1600, 3 ft 4 ins high, 5 ft 6 ins long, 1 ft 6 ins deep. £425

2. 17th century Spanish chestnut wood coffer, 5 ft long, 2 ft deep, 2 ft 5 ins high. £260

3. Late 17th century oak mule chest with drawers at the base. £110

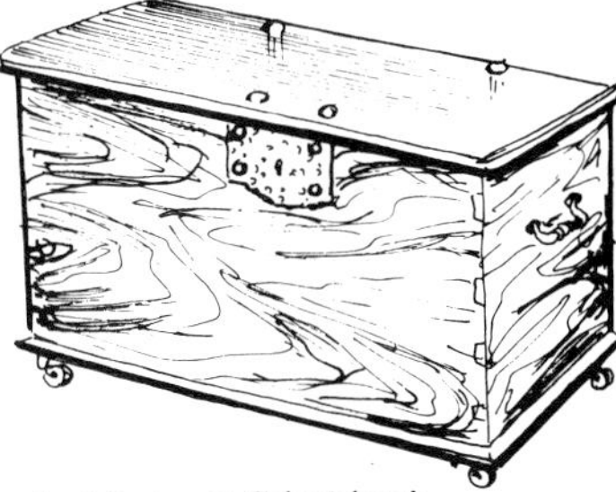

4. A Portugese Colonial teak coffer, circa 1800, 4 ft 6 ins long, 2 ft 1 in deep, 2 ft 3 ins high. £145

5. Late 17th century oak dower chest with a panelled front. £65

6. An excellent 14th century oak chest. £5,400

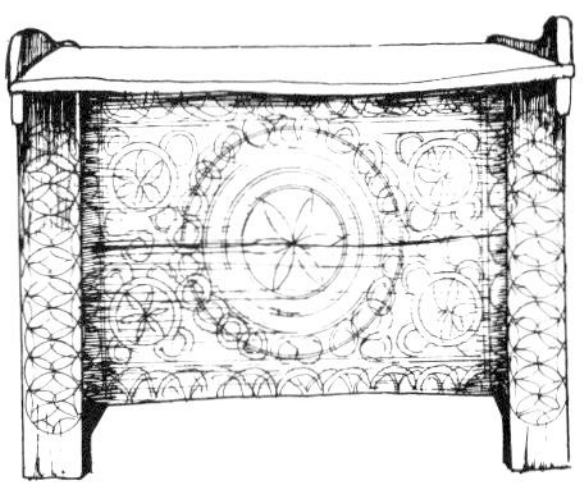

7. Mid 16th century Austrian oak coffer. £270

8. 16th century English oak coffer, 6 ft long, 1 ft 10½ ins deep, 2 ft 8 ins high. £320

1. A good quality late 17th century oak dower chest. £160

2. Early oak chest decorated with ebony and boxwood inlay with carved pilasters, initialled IMG, dated 1665, 58ins wide. £390

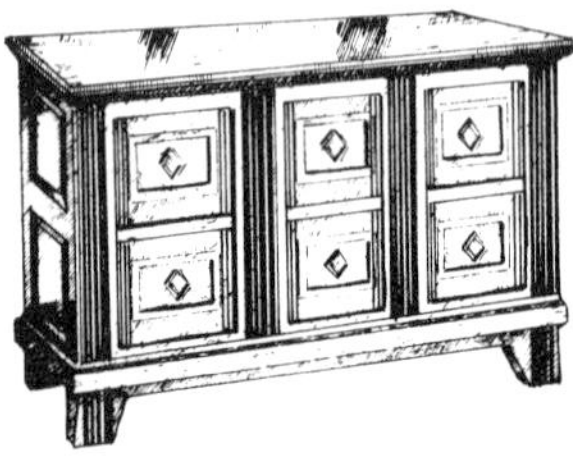

3. 17th century oak cupboard, 63ins wide. £460

4. Late 18th century elm dower chest. £35

5. 18th century Spanish carved walnut coffer. £170

6. A good 16th century English Gothic style coffer. £375

7. Late 18th century sealskin travelling case decorated with brass studs. £45

8. Victorian mahogany cellarette on bun feet. £45

1. 16th century Gothic oak coffer of good rich patina. £400

2. 16th century Italian cassone of carved walnut. £210

3. Early 18th century oak coffer. £125

4. George III mahogany silver chest with brass fittings. £120

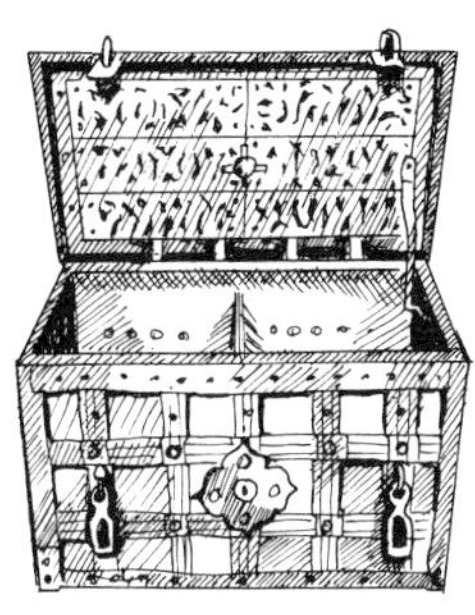

5. 17th century iron treasure chest. £165

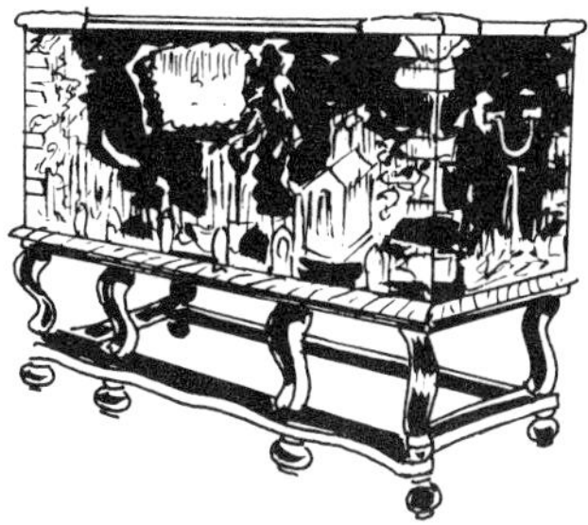

6. Late 17th century lacquered chest on stand. £425

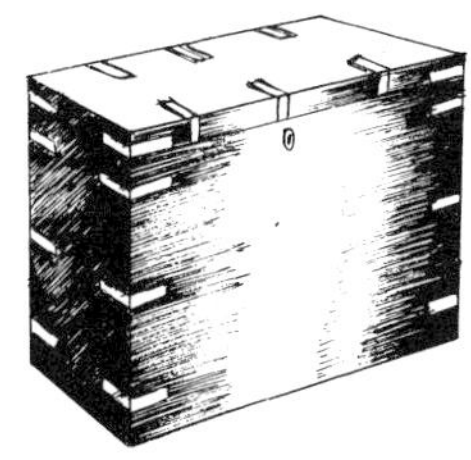

7. Victorian brass bound mahogany trunk. £28

8. George III panelled oak chest inlaid with fruitwood. £45

1. A fine 18th century oak cabinet of good colour. £550

2. Flemish oak cupboard of good colour and condition. £160

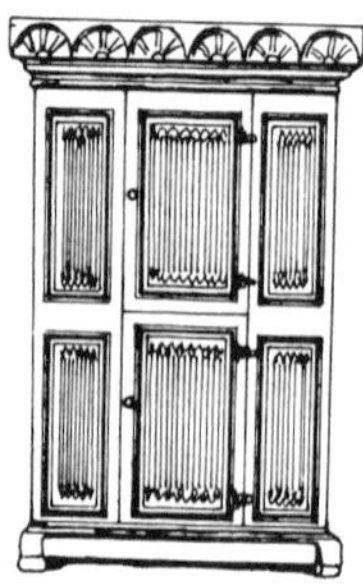

3. Late 18th century Continental mahogany wardrobe. £195

4. Late 18th century French armoire in oak with steel fittings. £205

5. Mid 17th century oak livery cupboard with fielded cupboard doors. £200

6. Rare George II portable cupboard in mahogany, 6ft 5ins tall, 13ins deep. £420

7. George I walnut cabinet veneered in oak, 3ft 8ins wide. £250

8. Early 19th century mahogany linen press in two sections, 3ft 2ins wide. £51

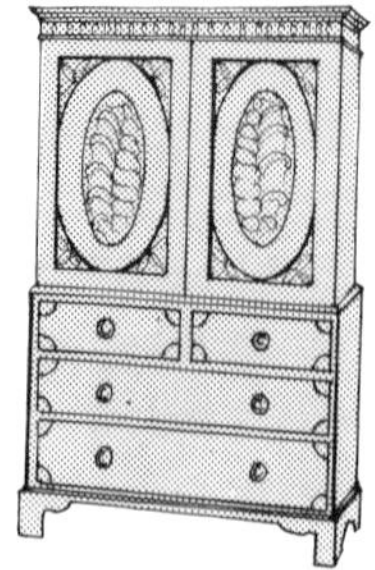

9. Late 18th century mahogany linen press with satinwood inlaid doors. £145

1. Unusual 19th century Continental painted wardrobe. £105

2. Early 19th century French walnut armoire. £185

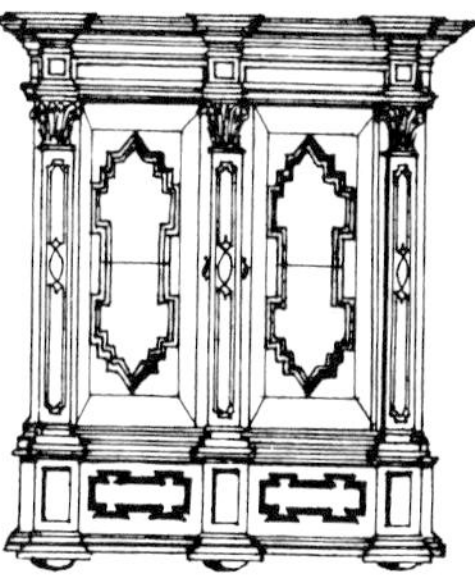

3. Victorian mahogany wardrobe on bun feet. £35

4. Victorian stripped pine wardrobe with a drawer at the base. £18

5. 18th century mahogany clothes press, 8ft 4ins high, 5ft 9ins wide. £180

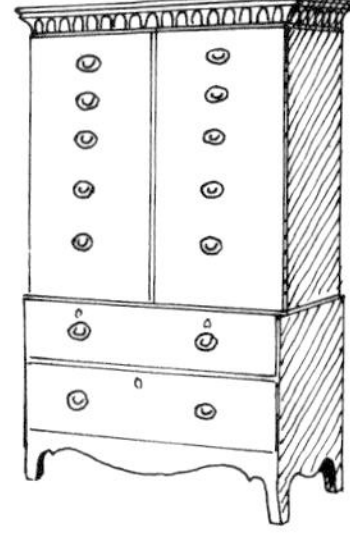

6. George III mahogany linen press with oak slides and oak lined drawers. £75

7. Early 18th century German armoire with two long drawers. £265

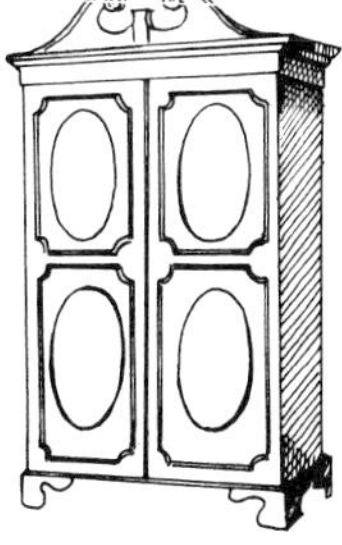

8. George III mahogany hanging wardrobe with a swan neck pediment. £110

9. A fine Georgian oak cupboard of good colour with four drawers in the lower section and brass loop handles. £100

CABINETS

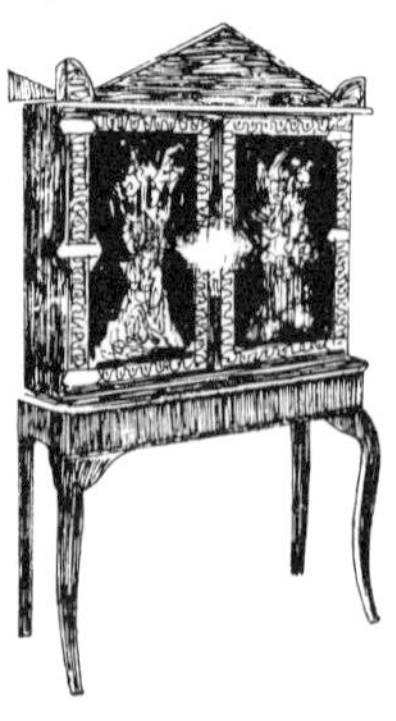

1. One of a pair of English Regency cabinets on stands with black japan and chinoiserie decoration and gilt mounts. £1,400

2. A fine Regency period rosewood cabinet, 4 ft wide. £310

3. A Regency ebonised cabinet with brass string inlay and a figured marble top. £100

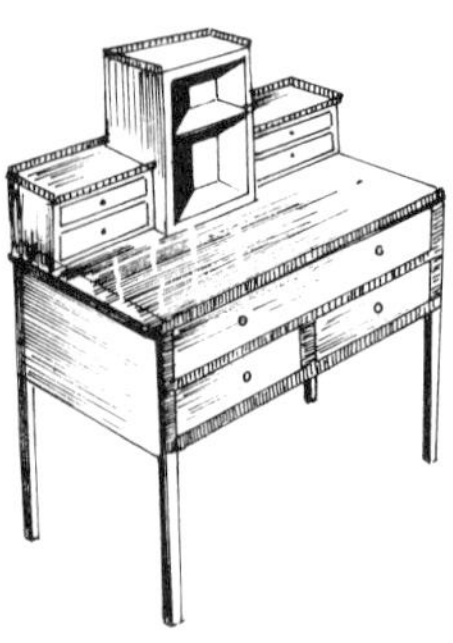

4. Late 18th century Sheraton cabinet in satinwood. £310

5. 17th century Flemish ebony cabinet inset with panels of Italian pietre dure and mounted in gilt brass. £2,400

6. An important 17th century Franco-Flemish ebony cabinet in the style of Jean Mace. £1,400

7. A gilt lacquer and shibayama work cabinet. £820

8. Good quality 19th century marquetry cabinet. £420

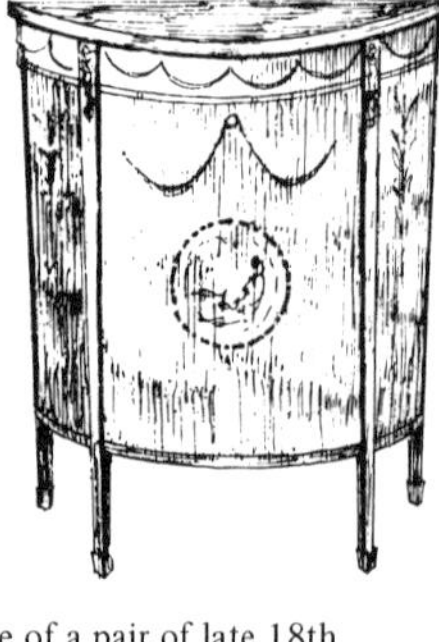

9. One of a pair of late 18th century side cabinets veneered with satinwood, inlaid with other woods and mounted with gilt metal. £4,725

1. An 18th century style cabinet in the Chinese taste, lacquered and engraved with brass strapwork. £170

2. A rare padouk wood cabinet with superbly carved ' sunburst ' panels, 47 ins wide, 76 ins high, circa 1770. £350

3. One of a pair of fine quality Victorian burr walnut dwarf cabinets. £410

4. Small Edwardian walnut cabinet with a glazed fall front and cupboard below, 1 ft 10 ins wide. £5

5. A superb porcelain mounted ebony cabinet with Meissen plaques depicting romantic scenes and court portraits. £5,800

6. A fruitwood marquetry cabinet by Louis Marjorelle. £300

7. An unusual mahogany collector's cabinet with assorted sized oak lined drawers numbered one to nine, 24 ins wide, 42 ins high, 19 ins deep, circa 1790. £105

8. Fine quality 19th century Italian cabinet. £630

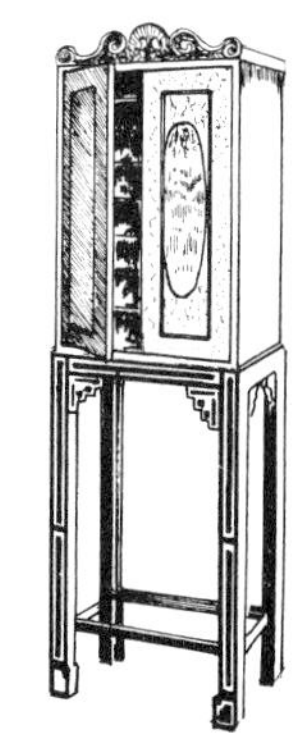

9. Early 19th century lacquered cabinet with gilt decoration. £115

COURT CUPBOARDS

1. 17th century oak court cabinet. £325

2. Small buffet in honey coloured oak, magnificently carved, with panels and door inlaid in various woods, circa 1765, 4 ft 8 ins long, 2 ft deep, 4 ft 4 ins high. £375

3. Elizabethan oak buffet. £200

4. English 16th century oak cupboard, 5 ft 7½ ins wide. 1,500 gns

5. Early 17th century Italian walnut cupboard with iron fittings. £205

6. An early oak tridarn of good colour. £280

7. A fine quality early 17th century oak livery cupboard. £730

8. A fine 17th century carved oak cupboard. £275

9. A reproduction carved oak cupboard, 4 ft 7 ins wide. £35

1. A fine James I oak court cupboard. £1,155

2. Continental cupboard with a fall front to the top compartment, 36 ins wide, 23 ins deep, 53 ins high, circa 1770. £135

3. A small Jacobean oak cupboard. £420

4. A mid 17th century oak buffet, 5 ft wide. £145

5. Late 17th century English oak court cupboard. £245

6. Mid 17th century oak cupboard chest made in two halves. £235

7. A fine early 18th century oak cupboard with fielded centre drawers. £210

8. 18th century elm bacon cupboard in the form of a settle. £90

9. A 16th century German Sacristey cupboard, 141 cm wide. £230

DRESSERS

1. A fine early Welsh dresser in honey coloured oak, with a plate rack, original cup hooks, three drawers and two cupboards, 68ins wide, circa 1780. £225

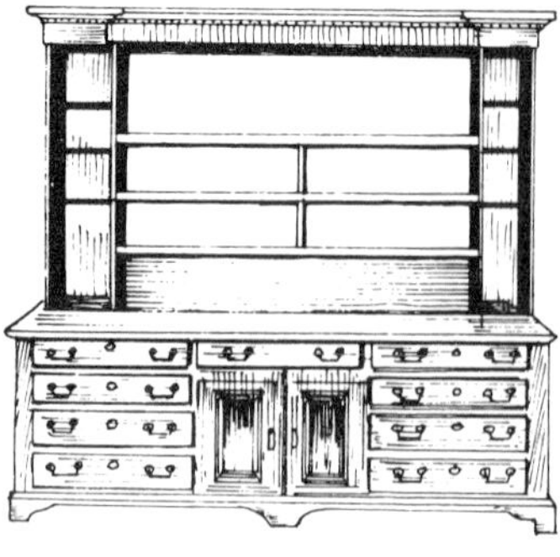

2. A good quality late 18th century oak dresser with centre panelled cupboard doors and nine drawers. £460

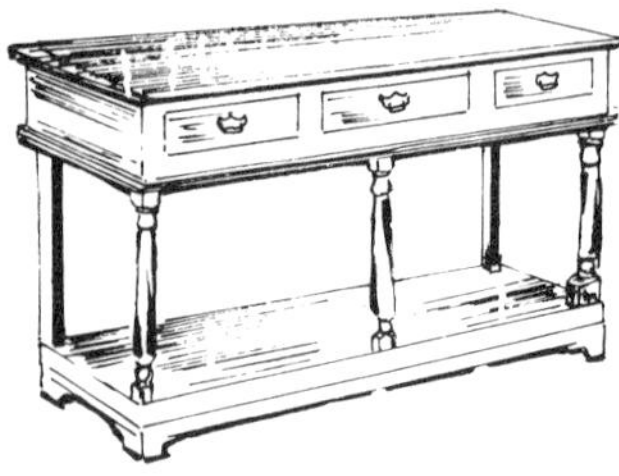

3. An 18th century oak dresser base with pot board. £170

4. Late 18th century oak and elm dresser with a pot board. £185

5. 18th century West of England oak dresser. £220

6. Late 19th century oak dresser with carved cupboard doors, 4ft 8ins wide. £43

1. A well proportioned mid 18th century finely figured oak dresser with three drawers crossbanded in mahogany, 6ft 1in wide, 1ft 5½ins deep, 6ft 8ins high. £238

2. An unusual late 18th century oak Welsh dresser with a central clock flanked by shelves. £275

3. An unusual early 18th century dresser base with the original handles, 5ft 2ins wide, 1ft 10½ins deep, 3ft high. £245

4. An 18th century oak dresser base of good colour and condition. £135

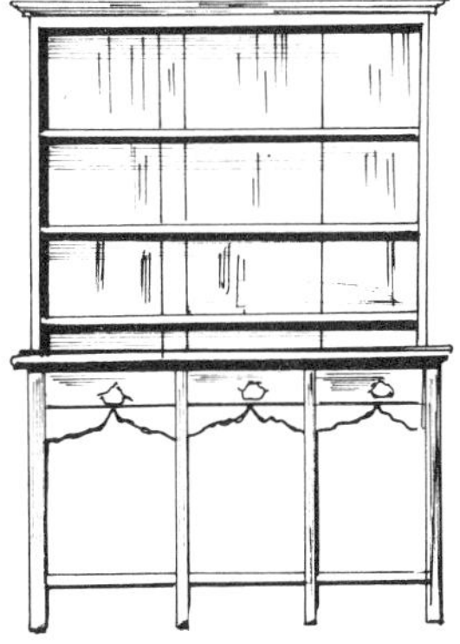

5. 18th century West of England oak dresser on square legs with stretchers. £220

6. A small Welsh dresser of good colour and patination, only 48ins wide, 74ins high. £275

DRESSERS

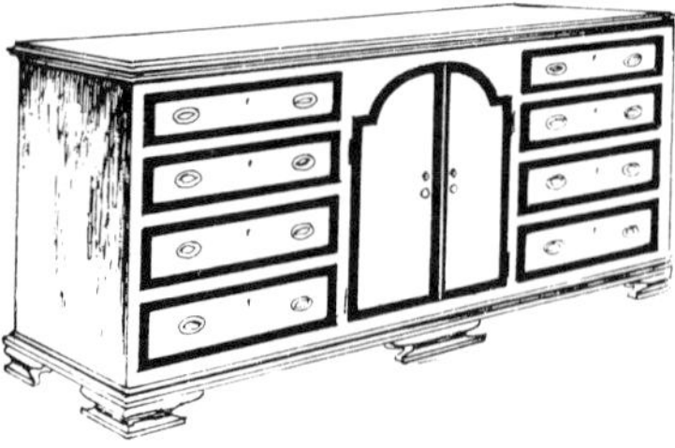

1. Late 18th century Lancashire oak dresser crossbanded with fruitwood, 6ft 2ins long. £250

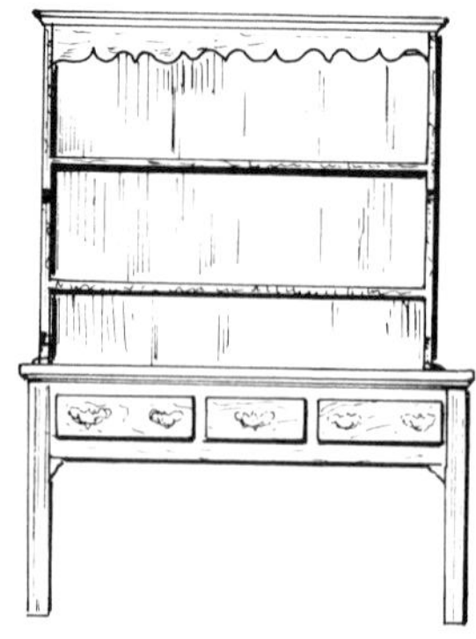

2. 18th century oak and elm dresser, 5ft 2ins long. £250

3. Fine 18th century dresser in oak crossbanded on the drawers. £225

4. Small late 18th century oak dresser with original brass drop handles and turned legs, 4ft 8ins wide. £210

5. Early 19th century oak dresser with drawers, cupboards and a shaped apron. £190

6. 18th century oak dresser with drawers, cupboards and a row of spice drawers on the top. £205

1. George III Welsh oak dresser with pot board only 4ft 7ins wide. £245

2. George III oak dresser of six drawers with brass loop handles and a centre cupboard. £195

3. A fine 18th century dresser of good honey colour, 7ft 3ins long. £280

4. An elaborate 18th century Welsh dresser in oak, of good patina with spice drawers and a shaped freize. £310

5. 18th century serving dresser, circa 1780. £148

6. A tall 18th century oak Welsh dresser with pot board, 4ft 8ins wide. £235

DRESSERS

1. Late 17th century oak dresser with pot board. £200

2. Rustic 18th century pine dresser with primitive silhouette legs to the base, two drawers and a pewter plate rack, 61ins wide. £185

3. Late 18th century oak dresser with drawers and cupboards. £230

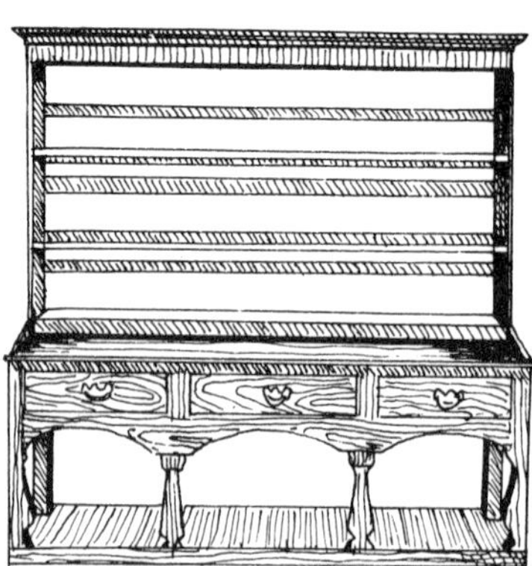

4. A fine early Georgian oak dresser of good honey colour. £240

5. A fine early 18th century oak buffet dated 1729, 75ins high, 49ins wide. £375

6. George III oak dresser of drawers and cupboards, 5ft 7ins wide. £210

1. Early Victorian pine dresser with a nicely shaped frieze and apron. £80

2. Late 18th century crossbanded oak serving dresser of a good mellow gold colour. £268

3. A large 17th century Welsh dresser in oak in good original condition, 8ft long. £335

4. Late 17th century oak dresser on turned legs. £210

5. A good 17th century oak moulded front dresser of three drawers, 7ft long. £285

6. A fine quality Georgian oak dresser of good honey colour. £250

BOOKCASES

1. Finely carved Victorian open fronted bookcase with adjustable shelves, 6 ft 6 ins wide. £70

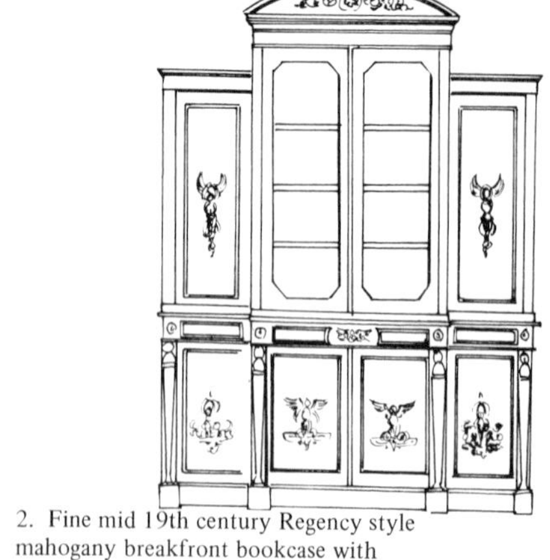

2. Fine mid 19th century Regency style mahogany breakfront bookcase with fine ormolu mounts, 7 ft 5 ins long, circa 1850. £725

3. Georgian mahogany breakfront bookcase 94 ins long, 97 ins high, circa 1800. £585

4. Sheraton mahogany breakfront bookcase circa 1780, 8 ft 6 ins high, 6 ft 7 ins long. £785

5. Mahogany breakfront bookcase, circa 1790, 7 ft 6 ins high, 8 ft long 1 ft 3 ins deep. £895

6. Exceptionally fine mahogany bookcase from the first half of the 18th century, 68 ins wide. £620

1. Early 19th century pine breakfront bookcase, 6 ft wide. £320

2. Regency period rosewood breakfront bookcase with the original grilles. £510

3. Georgian mahogany breakfront bookcase 8 ft 10 ins high, 7 ft 7 ins long. £700

4. An exceptionally fine quality finely figured mahogany breakfront bookcase. £2,300

5. Late 18th century stepped front bookcase, 8 ft long. £850

6. A fine quality 19th century mahogany bookcase with architectural mouldings. £290

1. Hepplewhite bookcase with crossbanded and panelled doors. £650

2. Regency rosewood bookcase with gilt enrichments and lions paw feet, 41ins wide. £230

3. Early 19th century mahogany bookcase with glazed doors. £185

4. An exceptionally fine William IV mahogany bookcase, 5.64 m. wide. £3,675

5. Georgian mahogany bookcase with astragal glazed doors to the upper section and inlaid panelled doors below, with bracket feet, 4ft wide. £130

6. Georgian mahogany breakfront library bookcase 86ins wide, 101ins high. £1,200

7. Victorian mahogany bookcase with three enclosed shelves, drawer and cupboard. £41

1. Regency mahogany bookcase with adjustable shelves and doors below with brass grilles. £280

2. Early 19th century ebony and amboyna wood breakfront bookcase. 5ft 6ins wide. £200

3. Late 18th century mahogany bookcase in the Chippendale style. £350

4. George III mahogany breakfront bookcase with astragal glazed doors, 10ft wide. £950

5. George III mahogany bookcase with fluted columns. £350

6. Late 18th century figured mahogany breakfront bookcase with adjustable doors and panelled cupboard doors. £600

7. George III mahogany bookcase with astragal glazed doors. £255

BOOKCASES

1. George III mahogany open bookcase with drawer, 30 ins wide. £156

2. Early 19th century mahogany breakfront bookcase with brass grilles on the centre doors, 6 ft 7 ins long. £170

3. Regency mahogany open bookcase inlaid with brass and with painted decoration on the panelled doors and back. £220

4. A set of Regency mahogany shelves. £38

5. Fine quality George III mahogany open bookshelves. £460

6. Small Edwardian inlaid mahogany open fronted set of two shelves with a compartment enclosed by a leaded glass door. £8

7. Early Victorian open bookcase in rosewood, 2 ft 2 ins wide. £45

8. Victorian mahogany hanging shelves, 3 ft 9 ins wide. £8

9. Victorian mahogany standing shelves. £25

1. Unusual Regency mahogany open bookcase with mirror above, 2 ft 11 ins wide. £145

2. Late George III breakfront bookcase in simulated rosewood and gilt, 61 ins long. £235

3. Exquisite small bookcase, circa 1800, the decoration refurbished as near to the original in faded green with floral enrichment, 10½ ins x 47 ins x 19½ ins. £145

4. Regency rosewood dwarf bookcase with a figured marble top. £485

5. Edwardian mahogany three tier revolving bookstand. £25

6. Regency bookcase in finely grained mahogany with brass feet. £395

7. 19th century mahogany bookcase with an adjustable shelf and panelled cupboard doors. £30

8. Regency rosewood open bookcase with a figured marble top and ormolu decoration. £185

9. A fine Regency figured mahogany bookcase having panelled doors with drawers above and below. £225

CHINA CABINETS

1. A good quality Edwardian inlaid burr walnut music cabinet. £23

2. Edwardian mahogany specimen table on square tapering legs, with boxwood string inlay. £55

3. A small Edwardian mahogany display cabinet with an astragal glazed door, 2ft wide. £17.50

4. 19th century heart shaped specimen table in satinwood with floral marquetry decoration. £160

5. Oriental hardwood cabinet with applied leaf moulding. £44

6. Small Edwardian mahogany display cabinet with boxwood string inlay. £38

7. 19th century music cabinet with a brass gallery. £17

8. Edwardian mahogany specimen table with shaped legs. £35

9. Victorian burr walnut display cabinet with ormolu mounts. £60

1. A fine quality Victorian burr walnut display cabinet with a pierced brass gallery and ormolu mounts. £70

2. A good early 19th century marquetry specimen table with ormolu mounts. £110

3. George III ebonised display cabinet with brass string inlay and ormolu mounts. £180

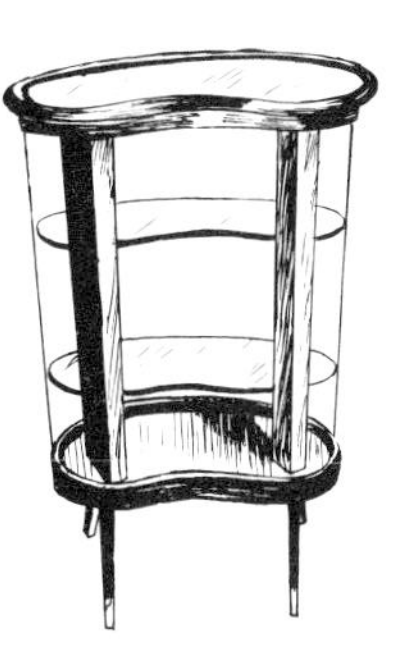

4. An unusual Edwardian kidney shaped specimen cabinet in mahogany, with boxwood string inlay. £45

5. Edwardian inlaid mahogany hanging cabinet with two shelves enclosed by glazed doors, 2ft 6ins wide. £51

6. A fine 19th century boulle display cabinet with ormolu decoration. £115

7. Late Victorian ebonised display cabinet with boxwood string inlay. £25

8. 19th century mahogany specimen table on cabriole legs with ormolu mounts. £75

9. Early 19th century ebonised display cabinet with a figured marble top. £115

CHINA CABINETS

1. Edwardian mahogany and satinwood, hand painted floral decorated display cabinet on tapering legs, 2ft 6ins wide. £68

2. An early good quality, Dutch marquetry kettle shaped display cabinet. £1,350

3. An Edwardian, mahogany and fruitwood inlaid, shaped front china display cabinet, 36ins wide. £300

4. Vernis Martin style French vitrine with ormolu mounts, circa 1860. £465

5. Edwardian inlaid mahogany china cabinet, 4ft 6ins wide. £72

6. Edwardian mahogany china cabinet on cabriole legs, with a drawer at the base. £25

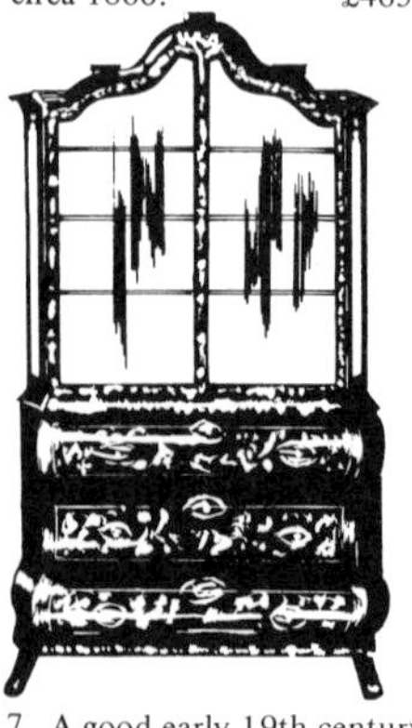

7. A good early 19th century Dutch marquetry display cabinet. £1,050

8. 19th century display cabinet on turned and tapering fluted legs, 3ft 4ins wide. £51

9. A fine Edwardian satinwood china display cabinet. £263

1. Heavily carved Oriental hardwood display cabinet from the 19th century. £100

2. French display cabinet with Vernis Martin panels and ormolu mounts, circa 1860, 4ft 8ins wide. £1,350

3. Fine quality ormolu mounted rosewood vitrine with marquetry panels, circa 1870, 63ins high, 27 ins wide. £540

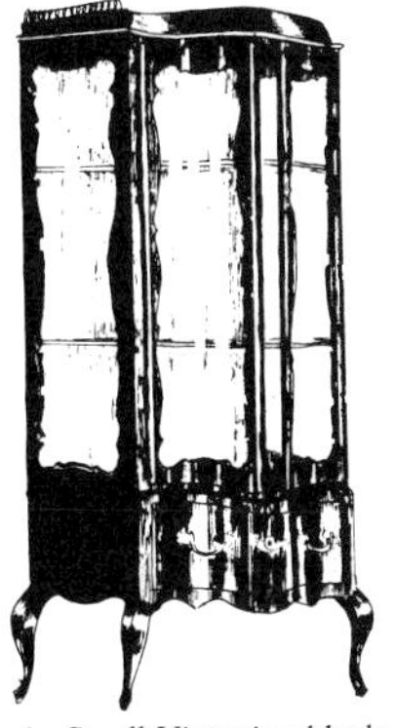

4. Small Victorian black painted china cabinet. £40

5. 19th century French marquetry cabinet with fine ormolu mounts and a marble top, circa 1840, 4ft 8ins wide, 4ft 8ins high. £1,250

6. Edwardian inlaid mahogany china cabinet with astragal glazed doors and tapered legs with spade feet. £40

7. Louis XV vitrine with Vernis Martin panels and ormolu mounts. £2,000

8. Early 19th century French bijouterie strung with ivory and edged with lignum. £240

9. Early 19th century marquetry chest mounted with a matching display cabinet. £890

CHINA CABINETS

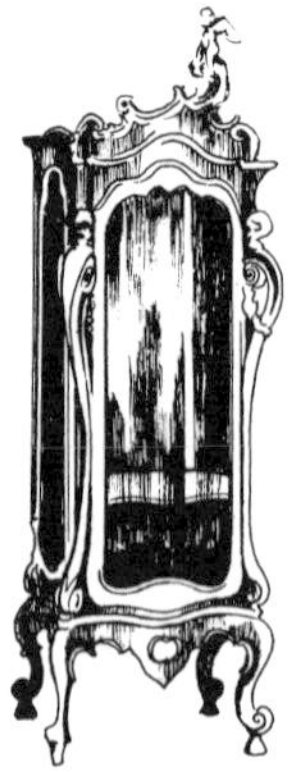

1. Mid 19th century French walnut cabinet on cabriole legs. £235

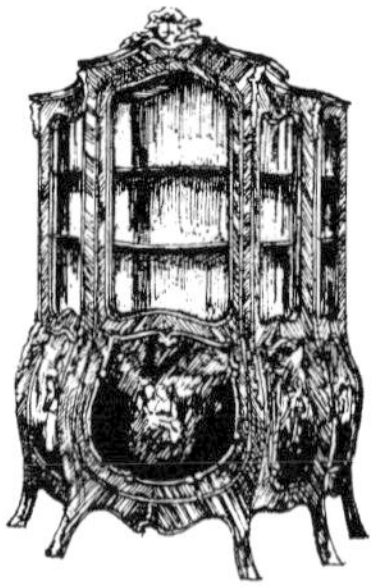

2. An exceptionally fine Louis Philippe cabinet with Vernis Martin panels. £420

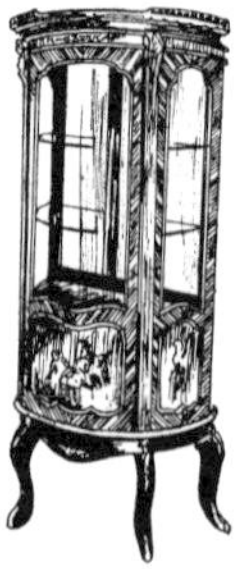

3. Early 19th century French display cabinet in kingwood with Vernis Martin panels. £420

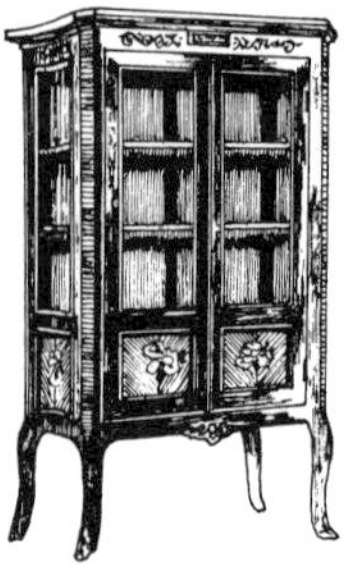

4. A fine 19th century French display cabinet inlaid with marquetry flowers. £380

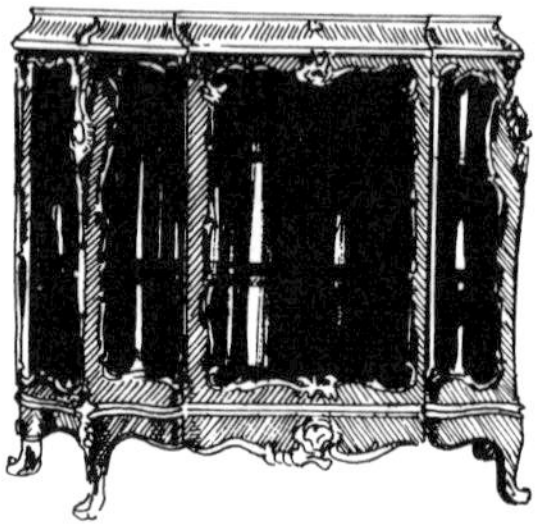

5. 19th century display cabinet veneered in kingwood, with ormolu decoration. £450

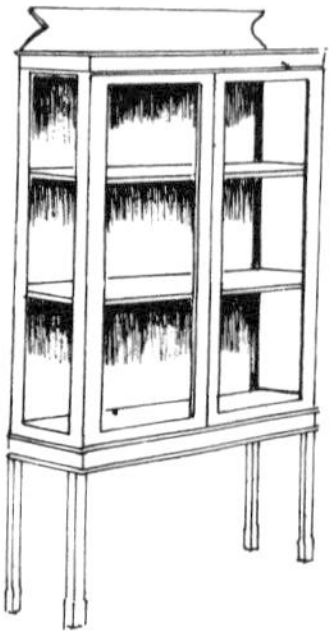

6. Edwardian mahogany display cabinet with boxwood string inlay. £32

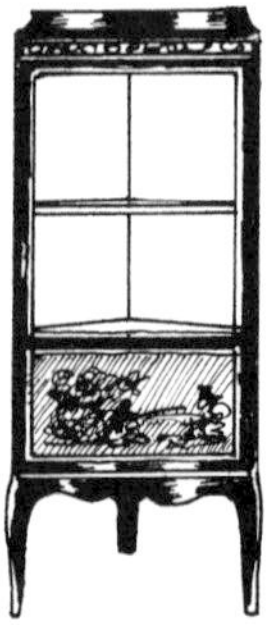

7. A superb early 18th century French display cabinet with a hand painted scene on the door. £310

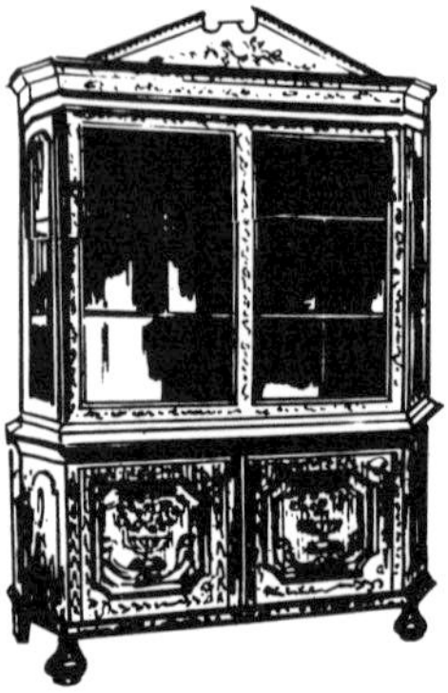

8. A fine mid 18th century marquetry vitrine. £540

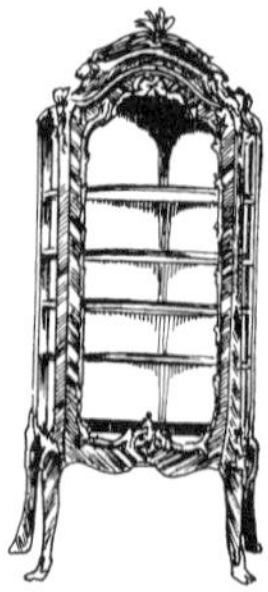

9. A nicely proportioned 19th century French display cabinet in kingwood. £300

1. 18th century Dutch marquetry display cabinet. £900

2. A fine 19th century kingwood vitrine decorated with painted panels signed L.O. Oliver. £900

3. Early 19th century French walnut display cabinet with ebony inlay. £200

4. Edwardian inlaid mahogany display cabinet. £60

5. A fine quality Edwardian inlaid mahogany display cabinet with astragal glazed doors. £155

6. A fine 19th century French display cabinet inlaid with various coloured woods. £475

7. Small Edwardian mahogany display cabinet, 2ft 1ins wide. £27

8. A good late 18th century Dutch marquetry display cabinet. £675

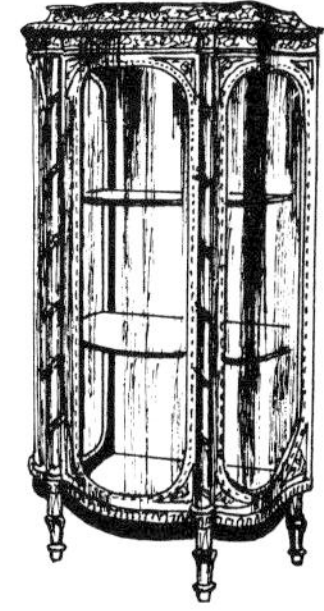

9. A fine 19th century gilt display cabinet. £285

1. 19th century burr walnut credenza with bowed glass ends and a panelled centre door with inlaid decoration, ormolu mounts and banding. £175

2. A fine 19th century giltwood credenza with a figured, shaped marble top. £310

3. 19th century walnut and rosewood credenza with ormolu mounts, 6ft 1in long, 3ft 5ins high. £550

4. Victorian ebonised credenza with glazed ends and a panelled cupboard centre door with gilt decoration. £55

5. Victorian breakfront burr walnut credenza with marquetry decoration and fine ormolu mounts. £180

6. Victorian burr walnut credenza inlaid with boxwood, with bowed glass ends and ormolu mounts. £200

1. Victorian ebonised credenza with ivory and ormolu decoration, a mirror back and glass shelves, 6ft 6ins wide. £80

2. An exceptionally fine quality Victorian burr walnut credenza with heavy ormolu mounts and boxwood inlay. £570

3. Small Victorian inlaid walnut breakfront credenza with ormolu decoration. £145

4. 19th century Italian gilded credenza with gesso ornamentation and a shaped marble top. £400

5. 19th century boulle credenza with serpentine glazed ends and ormolu mounts. £370

6. 19th century credenza in burr walnut with rosewood banding and ormolu mounts, 6ft wide. £500

CHIFFONIERS

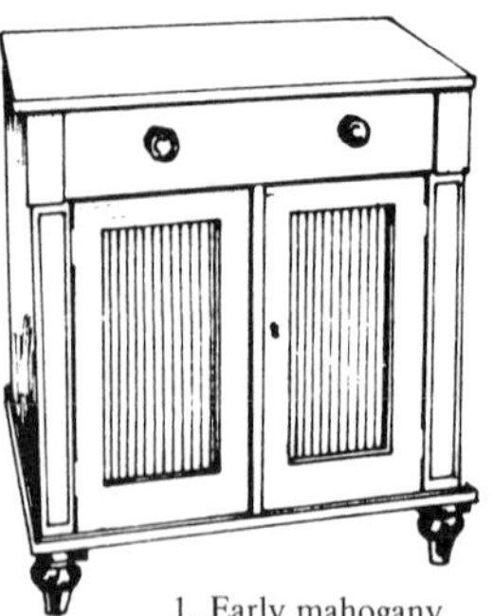
1. Early mahogany chiffonier with brass string inlay. £215

2. George III chiffonier veneered in satinwood with a pierced brass gallery. £315

3. Small early 19th century mahogany chiffonier, 24ins wide, 54ins high. £140

4. A good quality Victorian mahogany chiffonier, 3ft 1ins wide. £50

5. An unusual Regency chiffonier in mahogany with sunray pleated door panels, 39ins wide. £185

6. Regency mahogany chiffonier with bookshelves above and brass grilles to the panelled doors. £175

1. Victorian shaped front walnut veneered chiffonier with a drawer and cupboards. £14

2. Late Regency mahogany chiffonier cabinet, 36ins wide. £68

3. An attractive and finely figured mahogany chiffonier only 2ft 2½ins wide, 4ft 1ins high. £115

4. Regency period rosewood chiffonier with brass string inlay. £245

5. Victorian shaped front chiffonier in mahogany, 3ft 4ins wide. £7.50

6. A nicely proportioned Regency period brass inlaid rosewood chiffonier with a pierced brass gallery. £235

CHIFFONIERS

1. Early 19th century mahogany cabinet with mirrored doors. £155

2. Regency mahogany brass inlaid rosewood chiffonier with a pierced brass gallery. £290

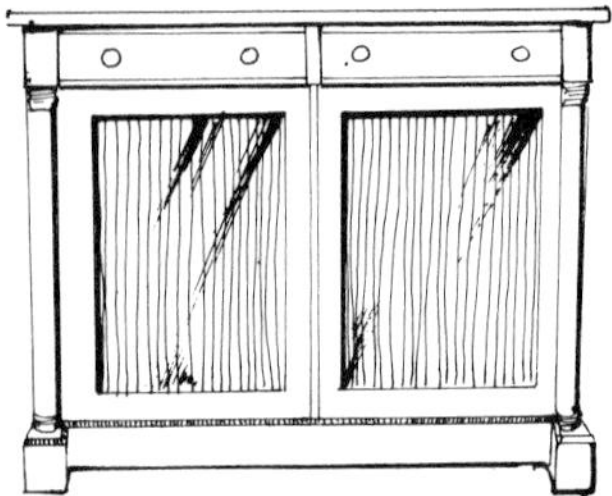

3. 19th century rosewood cabinet with brass capitals and pleated silk panels, 3ft 3ins wide, circa 1815. £98

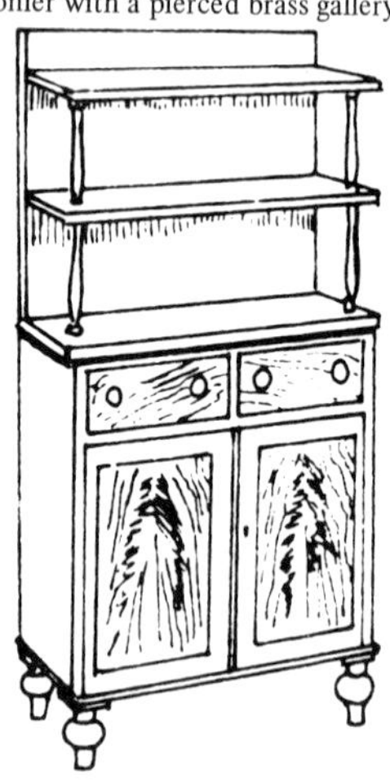

4. Regency figured mahogany chiffonier. £120

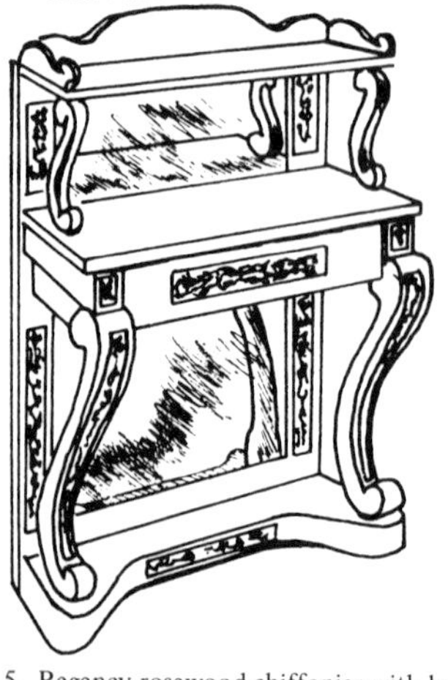

5. Regency rosewood chiffonier with brass inlay and a white marble top. £190

6. 19th century mahogany chiffonier with a fitted writing drawer, 2ft 9ins wide, circa 1825. £108

1. Regency rosewood chiffonier with brass grille on the panelled door. £225

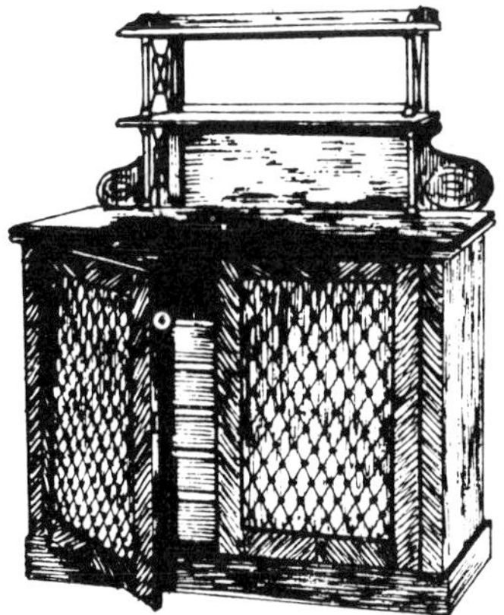

2. A fine Regency mahogany chiffonier with brass grille to the doors backed by green silks. £275

3. A Victorian mahogany chiffonier. £11

4. A small Regency mahogany hall stand of superb quality with a mirror back and brass inlay, 22ins wide. £185

5. Early 19th century rosewood cupboard with a figured marble top. £90

6. A fine Regency rosewood chiffonier with reeded columns and brass grille to the doors. £210

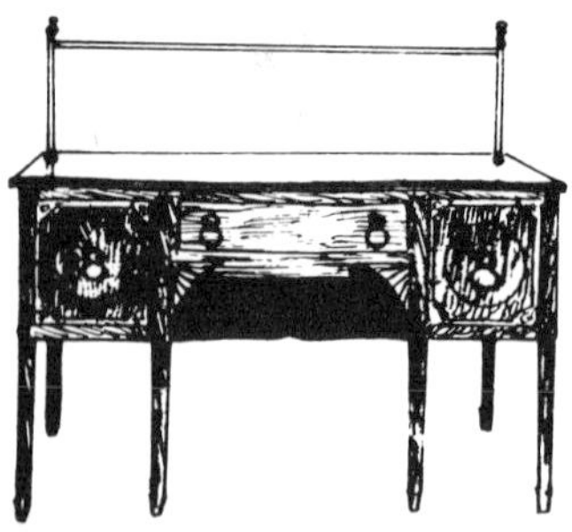

1. A good quality Sheraton mahogany serpentine front sideboard, 5ft wide. £450

2. Victorian mahogany pedestal sideboard with four drawers and two cupboards. £30

3. Late 19th century sideboard in ebony and amboyna, embellished with 24 porcelain plaques, 6ft wide, 8ft 2½ins high, 18ins deep. £475

4. Mid Victorian mahogany pedestal sideboard with a mirror back in a carved frame. £25

5. A fine early Victorian pedestal sideboard with ebony string inlay and paw feet. £40

6. Mahogany bow front sideboard on six tapered legs with spade feet, inlaid with ebony and boxwood stringing, 63ins long, circa 1790. £485

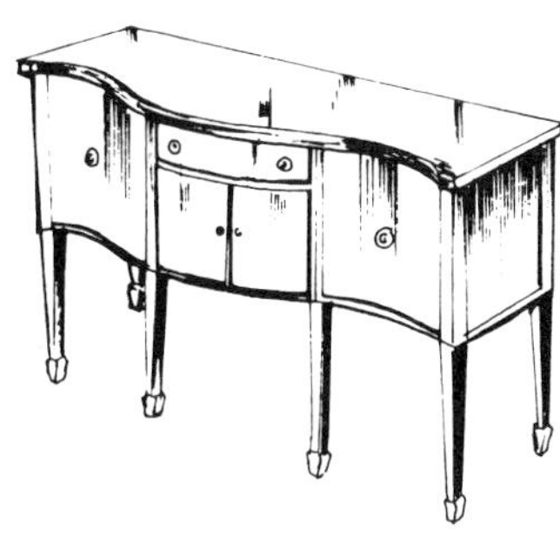

1. A reproduction Georgian style serpentine fronted sideboard in mahogany, 5ft wide.£66

2. Small George III serpentine front mahogany sideboard only 50ins wide, with two deep drawers. £375

3. Edwardian inlaid rosewood sideboard with a mirrored back, drawers, galleries and cupboards. £24

4. An unusual concave sideboard in figured mahogany, 3ft ½in wide, circa 1800. £165

5. Edwardian ebonised sideboard with a central cupboard flanked by shaped shelves. £12

6. George III mahogany sideboard of double serpentine shape inlaid with boxwood stringing, circa 1800. £300

1. Small George III mahogany sideboard in excellent condition, on tapered legs with spade feet, circa 1790. £435

2. Early 19th century mahogany sideboard on fine turned legs. £95

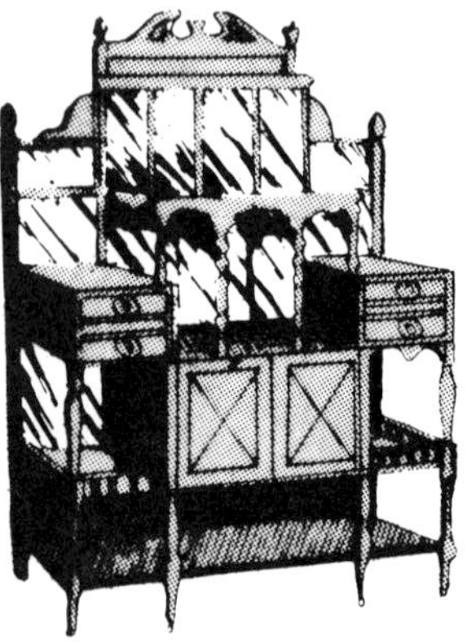

3. Late 19th century mahogany sideboard with bevelled mirrors, galleries, drawers and cupboards. £16

4. Edwardian carved mahogany sideboard with a bevelled mirror back, two drawers and two cupboards. £7.50

5. Small breakfront mahogany sideboard, circa 1780, 4ft 4ins wide. £385

6. A small attractive early 19th century breakfront cabinet in mahogany, 40ins long. £205

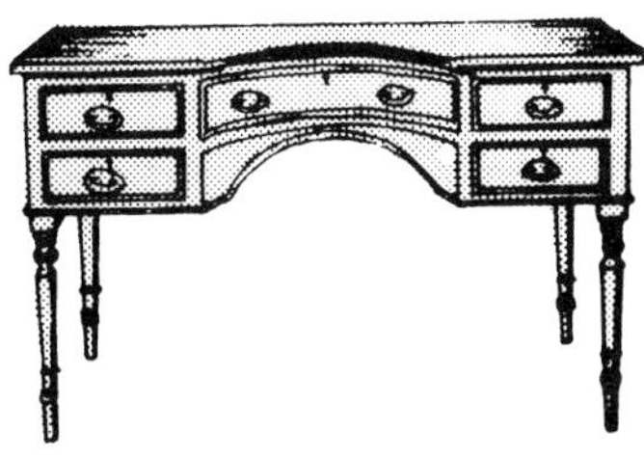

1. A fine George III mahogany sideboard with a concave centre and fine turned legs. £225

2. Early 19th century mahogany breakfront sideboard on turned legs with a recessed tambour in the centre. £235

3. A late 19th century walnut sideboard with a shaped marble top and mirror back. £27.50

4. An unusually small Regency bowfronted sideboard only 48ins wide. £400

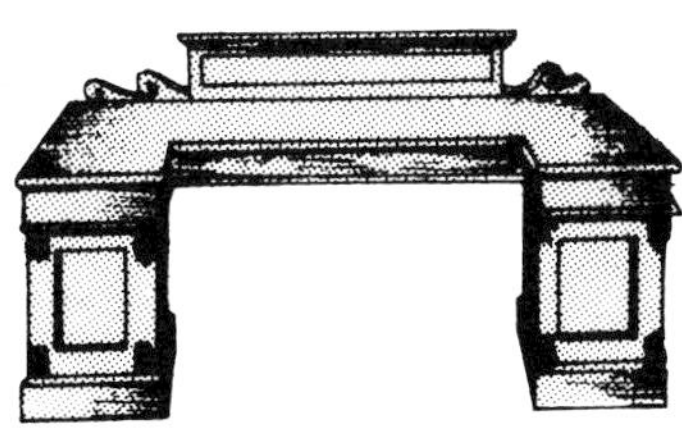

5. An early Victorian pedestal sideboard with a cellerette drawer. £32

6. Late 18th century Sheraton style mahogany sideboard, 60ins long. £310

CORNER CABINETS

1. Late 18th century mahogany hanging corner cupboard. £65

2. 18th century red lacquered corner cabinet with shaped shelves. £140

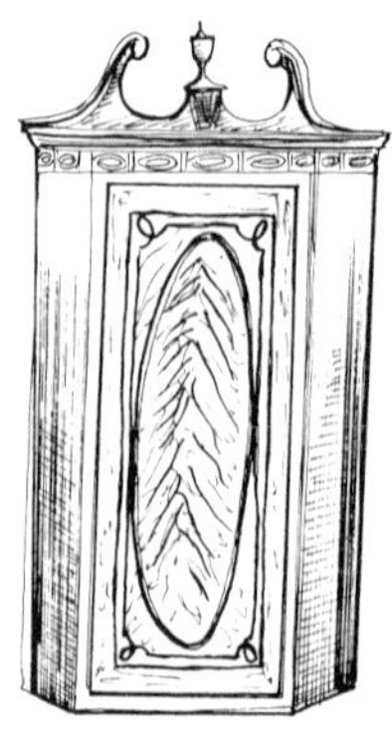

3. A fine quality Sheraton corner cupboard of rich chestnut colour, 57ins high, circa 1785. £185

4. Louis Philippe corner display shelves with pierced brass galleries and a white marble top. £90

5. 18th century mahogany corner cupboard with shelves above. £70

6. Victorian stripped pine corner cupboard with glazed doors. £22

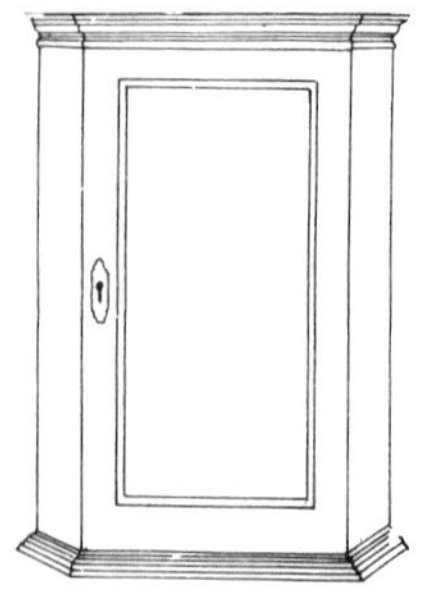

7. George III mahogany corner cupboard with shaped shelves. £65

8. A good quality 18th century Dutch walnut corner cupboard with satinwood inlay. £385

1. George III walnut veneered corner cabinet with a swan neck pediment. £90

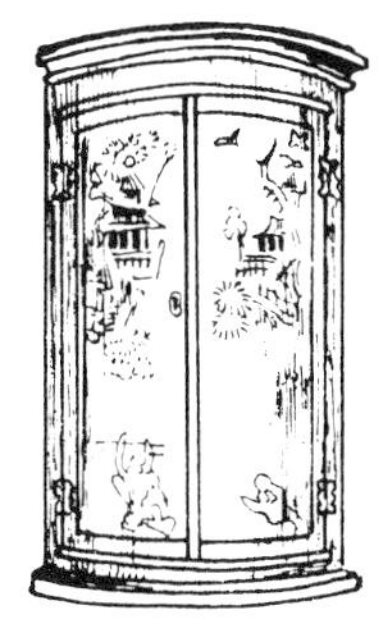

2. Early 18th century japanned corner cupboard decorated with Chinese domestic scenes. £100

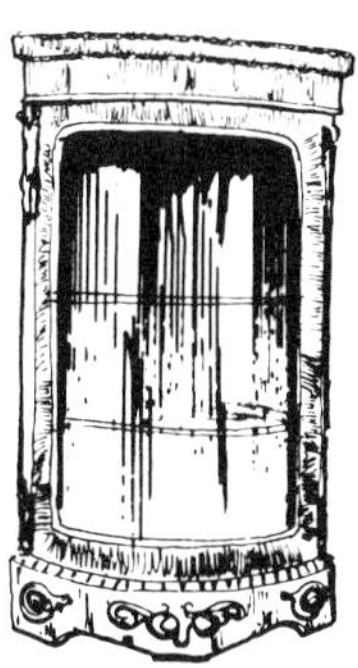

3. One of a pair of Victorian burr walnut corner cabinets with ormolu mounts. £280

4. George III mahogany corner cupboard with a broken arch pediment. £70

5. Late 18th century Sheraton style mahogany corner cupboard. £85

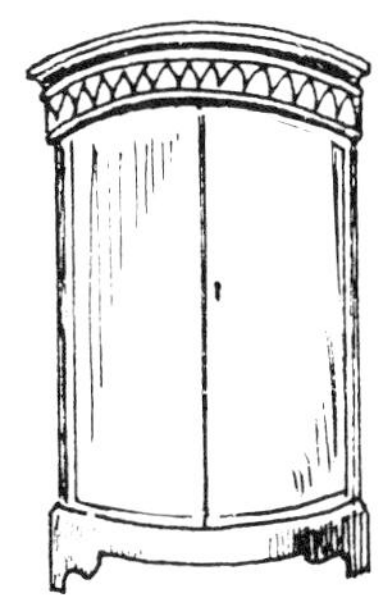

6. George III mahogany bowfronted corner cupboard. £140

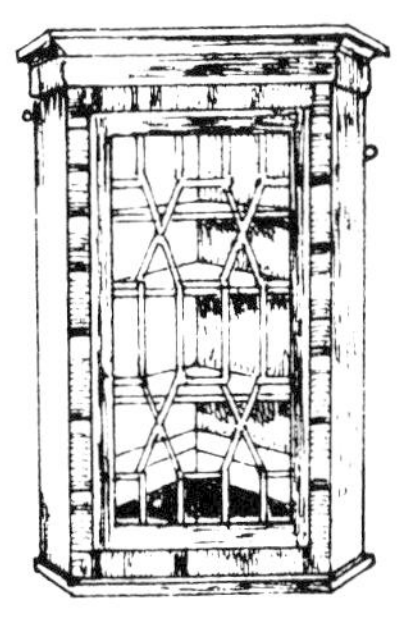

7. Late 18th century Sheraton mahogany corner cupboard with an astragal glazed door. £80

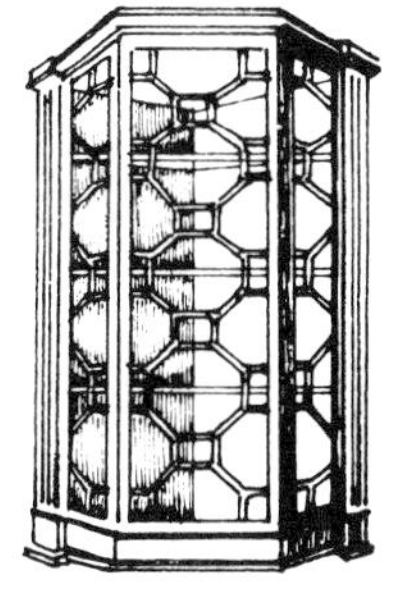

8. A fine early 18th century corner display cabinet with astragal glazed doors and fluted pilasters. £140

CORNER CABINETS

1. Edwardian inlaid rosewood corner cabinet with a multitude of galleries and mirrors. £40

2. An Edwardian mahogany corner display cabinet. £15

3. Edwardian inlaid mahogany corner cupboard. £60

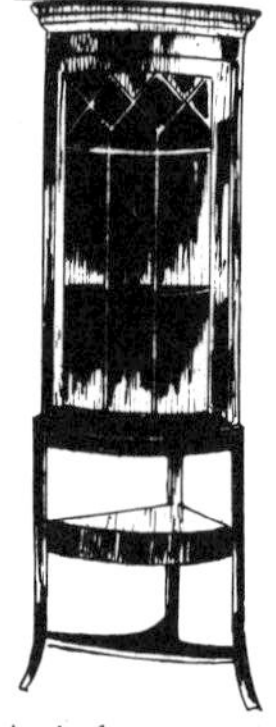

4. A nicely proportioned George III mahogany corner display cabinet. £235

5. Reproduction carved oak corner cupboard. £28

6. A good 18th century stripped pine corner cupboard with three shelves and a dentil cornice. £110

7. 19th century Sheraton style inlaid mahogany corner display cupboard with a conch shell on the lower section. £130

8. George III stripped pine corner cupboard with shaped shelves. £120

1. Late 18th century Sheraton style figured mahogany corner cupboard with satinwood inlay. £380

2. Early 18th century corner cupboard with fielded and panelled cupboard doors. £135

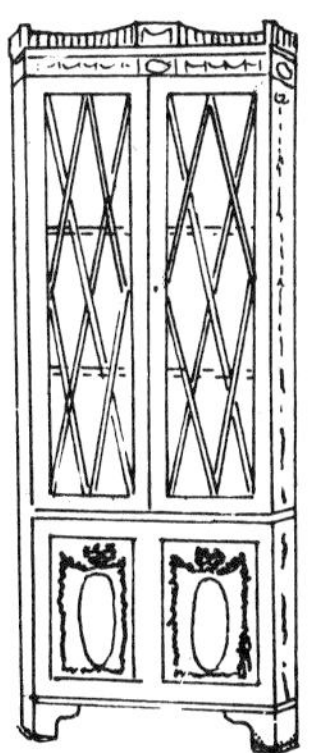

3. George III mahogany corner cupboard with diamond glazed doors. £240

4. 18th century oak corner cupboard with panelled doors. £95

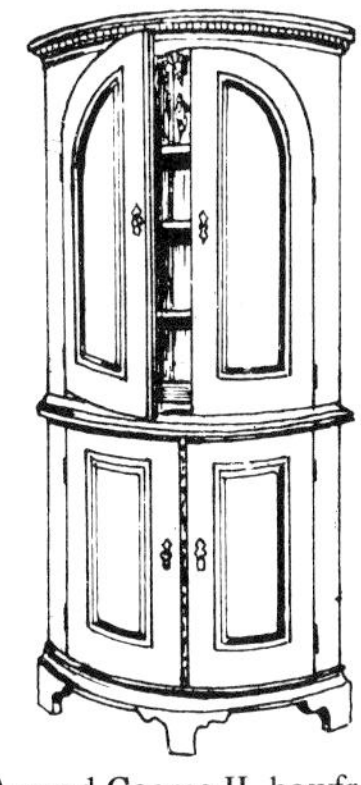

5. A good George II bowfronted corner cupboard in mahogany, with bracket feet. £265

6. George III figured mahogany bowfronted corner cupboard. £125

7. 18th century oak corner cupboard of good colour. £130

8. An excellent 18th century walnut and marquetry corner cupboard. £440

1. Small late 18th century mahogany washstand, on finely turned legs, 16ins x 14ins x 32ins high. £65

2. An extremely fine quality chinoiserie japanned dressing table. £1,500

3. Late 18th century mahogany washstand with a 14ins square top when closed. £45

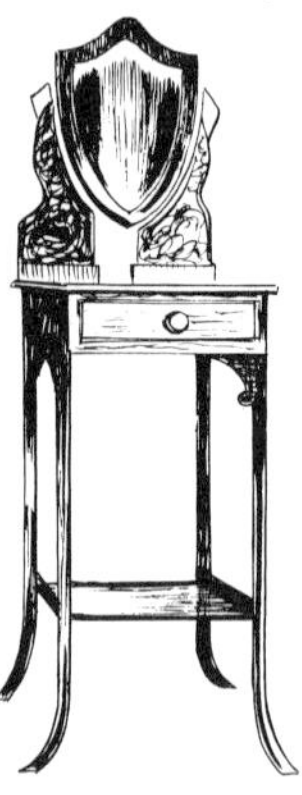

4. Late Victorian mahogany shaving stand with boxwood string inlay. £17.50

5. Georgian mahogany enclosed washstand with a fitted exterior extending mirror and tambour top opening to form a dressing table with an unusual side drawer containing three small drawers and bottle compartments, 16ins wide, 32½ins high, 17ins deep, circa 1760. £195

6. Late 19th century mahogany washstand with boxwood string inlay. £75

7. Late 19th century mahogany washstand with a tiled back and marble top. £12

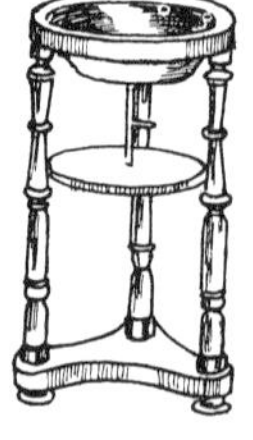

8. Early 19th century mahogany washstand. £40

9. Late Victorian walnut washstand with a figured marble top. £9

1. Late 19th century walnut washstand with a white marble top. £8

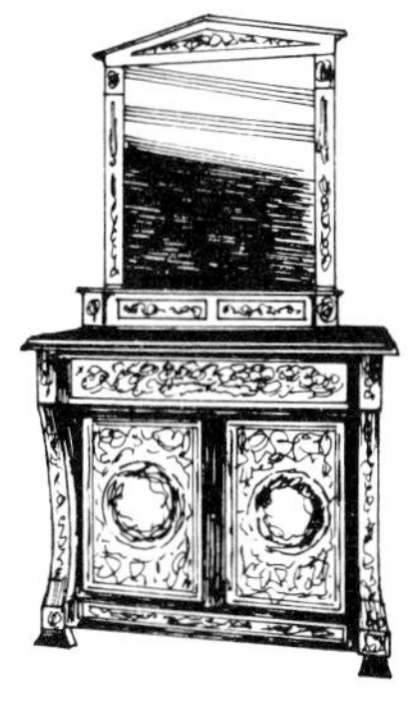

2. 19th century marquetry corner washstand. £175

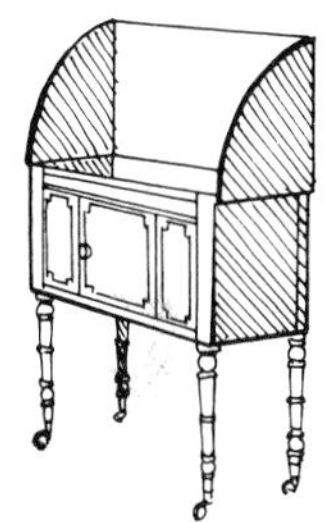

3. George III mahogany washstand. £38

4. George III mahogany toilet cabinet. £75

5. 19th century mahogany washstand. £18

6. A good quality George III serpentine front dressing table in satinwood. £145

7. Late Victorian walnut dressing table. £13

8. A good Sheraton style folding top satinwood dressing table with an adjustable mirror and ebony string inlay. £150

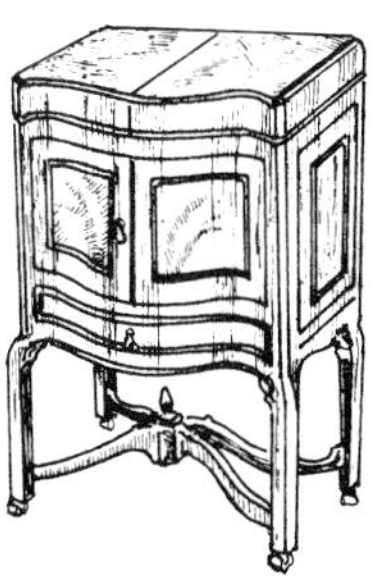

9. Late 18th century Chippendale style folding top mahogany washstand. £100

COMMODES AND POT CUPBOARDS

1. Edwardian mahogany bedside cupboard. £3.50

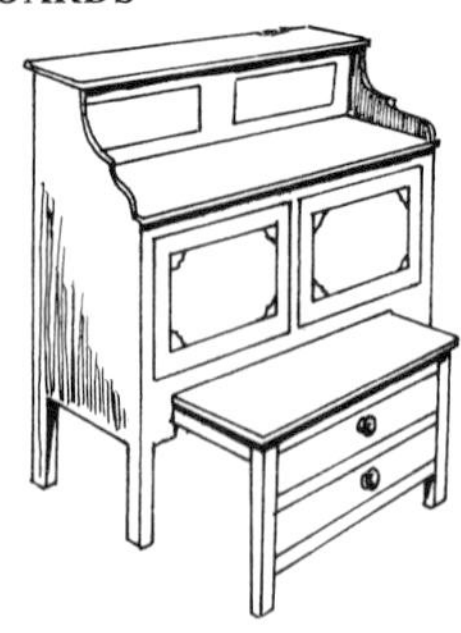

2. Early 19th century mahogany bedside cupboard with boxwood string inlay. £60

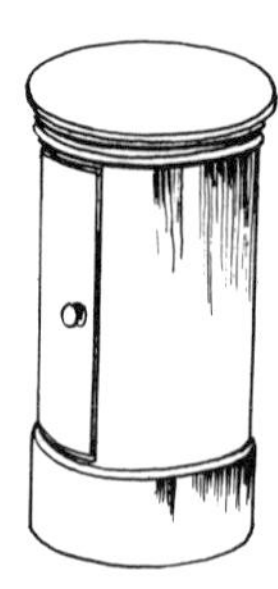

3. Victorian mahogany pot cupboard. £14

4. Late 18th century mahogany tray top commode. £60

5. George III mahogany bedroom steps with a pot cupboard and bidet drawer. £75

6. George III mahogany bedside cupboard. £30

7. Victorian mahogany one step commode on short turned legs. £4

8. A late 18th century mahogany pot cupboard with an open shelf and drawer. £45

9. Victorian commode with a pull out step. £9

1. Early 19th century mahogany night commode on turned legs with brass cup castors. £60

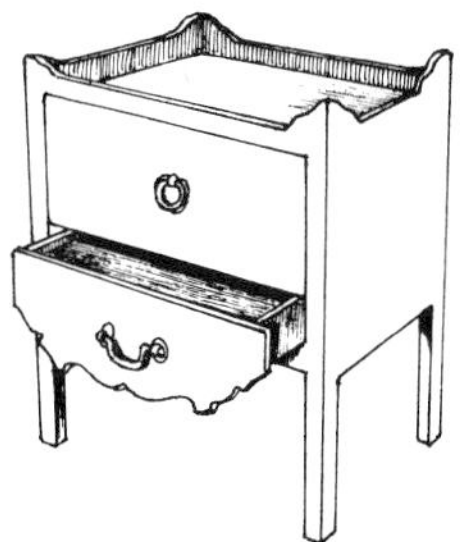

2. Late 18th century mahogany tray top commode on square legs chamfered on the inside edge. £55

3. George III mahogany commode with a lift up top and pressed brass handles. £35

4. A good Victorian mahogany pot cupboard with a figured marble top. £16

5. Victorian burr walnut bedside cupboard. £5

6. 18th century mahogany pot cupboard with a fretted frieze. £45

7. Victorian mahogany three step commode. £40

8. A nicely proportioned Edwardian mahogany bedside cupboard with satinwood banding. £10

9. George III satinwood tray top commode. £125

WHATNOTS

1. Victorian walnut whatnot with a brass rail. £32

2. William IV rosewood whatnot with barley twist supports and shaped shelves. £45

3. A small Georgian mahogany whatnot 36 ins high, circa 1810. £95

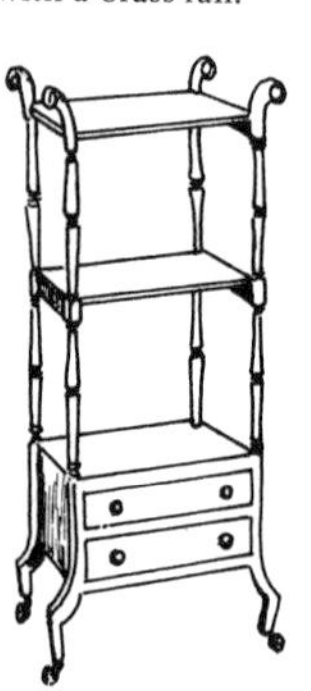

4. Late 18th century mahogany whatnot with two drawers at the base. £100

5. Early 19th century mahogany whatnot with brass string inlay and brass cup castors. £135

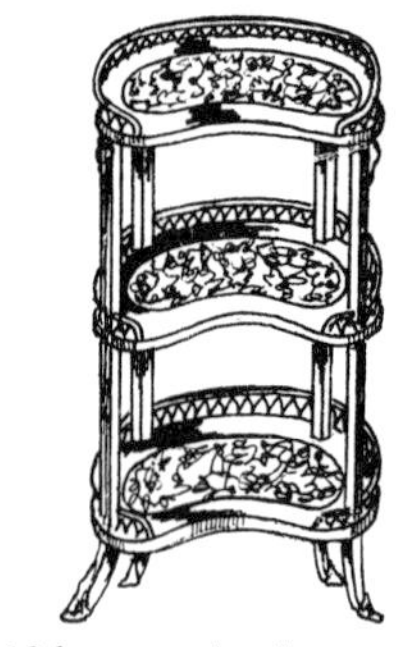

6. 19th century boulle etagere with pierced brass galleries. £90

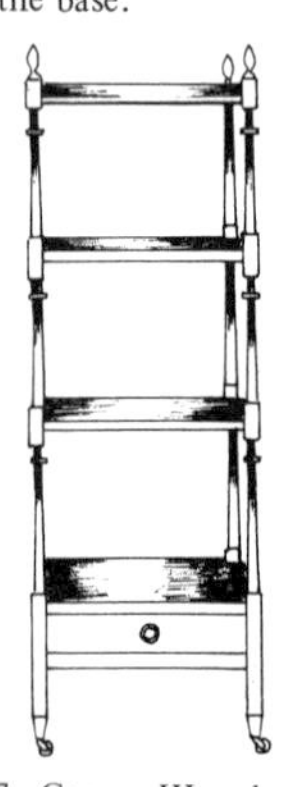

7. George III mahogany whatnot of slender proportions. £135

8. Early Victorian burr walnut whatnot with barley twist supports. £48

9. An unusual George III double canterbury - whatnot in medium colour mahogany, 14 ins square, 40 ins high. £195

1. Late 18th century mahogany whatnot with cupboard, 58 ins high, circa 1780. £125

2. Victorian burr walnut whatnot with shaped shelves and a fretwork gallery. £35

3. George III mahogany whatnot 20 ins wide, 18 ins deep, 49 ins high. £110

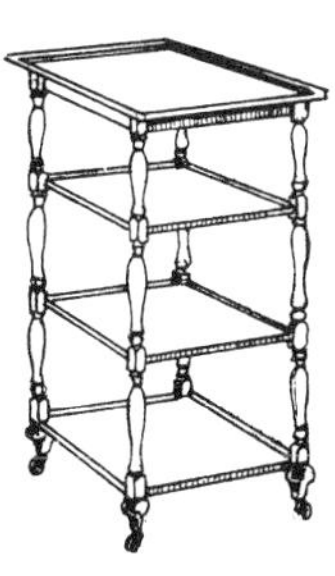

4. Early 19th century mahogany four tier whatnot with turned supports. £50

5. George III mahogany whatnot with a drawer at the base. £85

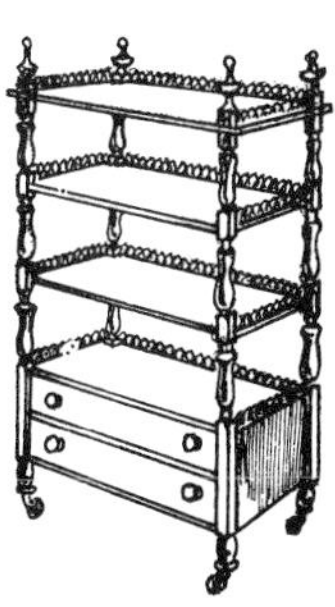

6. Good quality Regency rosewood whatnot. £100

7. Victorian inlaid walnut whatnot with a fretwork gallery. £27. 50

8. Victorian burr walnút corner whatnot inlaid with boxwood. £20

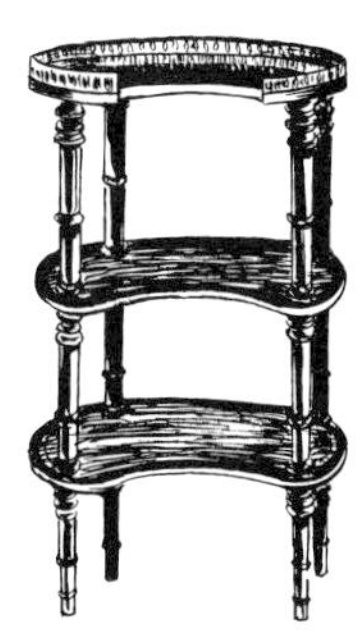

9. Regency mahogany whatnot with brass string inlay and a pierced brass gallery. £45

CANTERBURYS

1. Victorian walnut music canterbury fitted with a drawer, 23ins wide. £42

2. An unusual Regency canterbury in rosewood. £85

3. William IV mahogany music canterbury. £60

4. A fine Regency rosewood music canterbury. £80

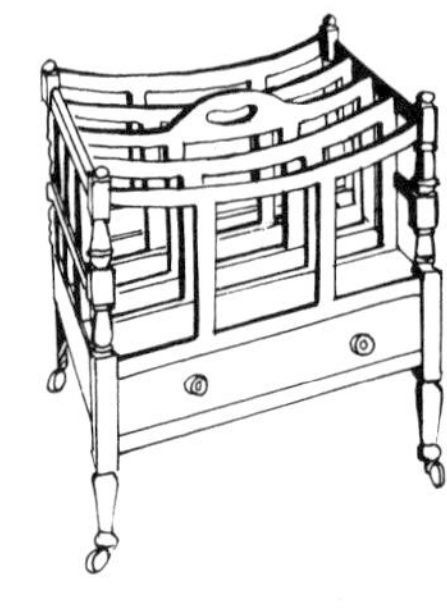

5. George III mahogany canterbury with flat splats and a drawer in the base. £125

6. An exceptionally fine quality Sheraton satinwood canterbury. £750

7. Early 19th century music canterbury on short turned legs with brass castors. £110

8. Regency mahogany music canterbury on turned legs. £80

1. Early 19th century mahogany music canterbury. £95

2. Regency mahogany music canterbury. £90

3. Small Victorian burr walnut canterbury with shaped partitions. £60

4. A fine early Victorian burr walnut music canterbury with fretted supports and a concave drawer at the base. £50

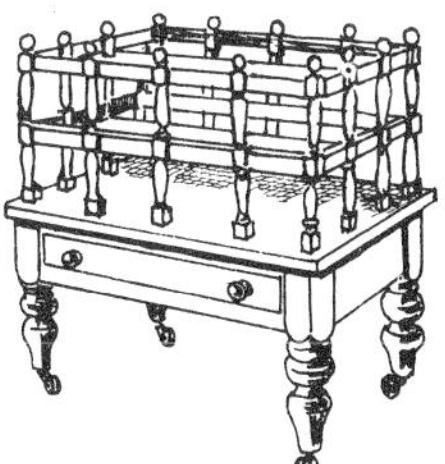

5. George III mahogany canterbury on turned legs with brass cup castors. £100

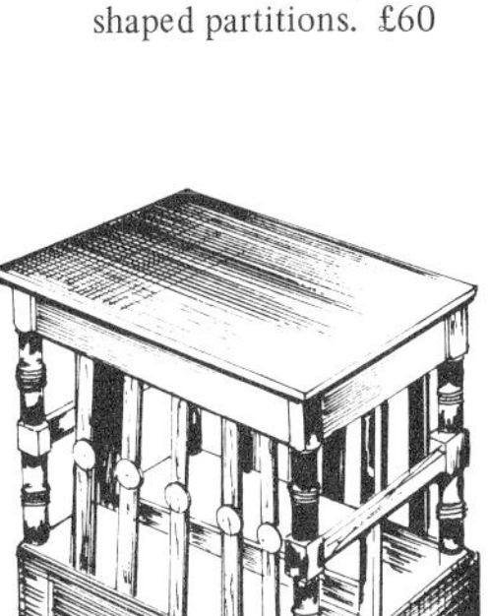

6. Regency rosewood canterbury with an unusual lidded top, 19ins x 15ins, circa 1820. £135

7. A fine Victorian ebonised canterbury. £35

8. A good George III mahogany canterbury. £130

1. William IV mahogany cellarette on fine turned legs. £100

2. An exceptionally fine quality late 18th century mahogany wine cooler inlaid with satinwood, on square tapering legs with brass castors. £360

3. A fine octagonal cellarette in mahogany, 18 ins wide, 24 ins high, circa 1795. £295

4. Late 18th century octagonal cellarette on short splayed legs. £135

5. Late 18th century domed top inlaid satinwood cellarette. £185

6. Early 19th century finely grained mahogany wine cooler on lions paw feet. £120

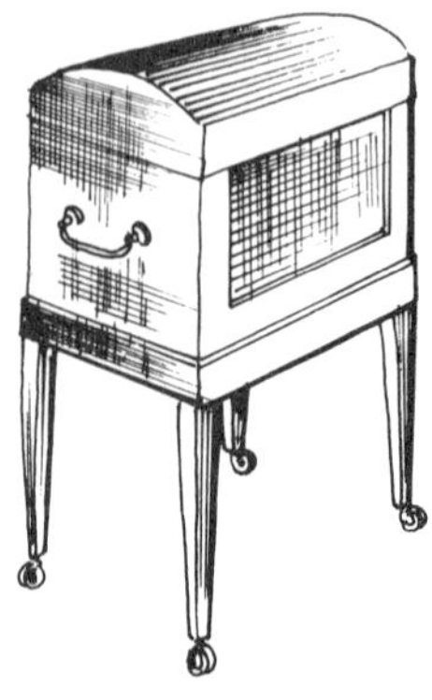

7. George III mahogany wine cooler on square tapering legs. £120

8. A good late 18th century Hepplewhite style mahogany cellarette on short turned legs with brass castors. £185

9. Late 18th century Sheraton style mahogany wine cooler on fine turned legs. £155

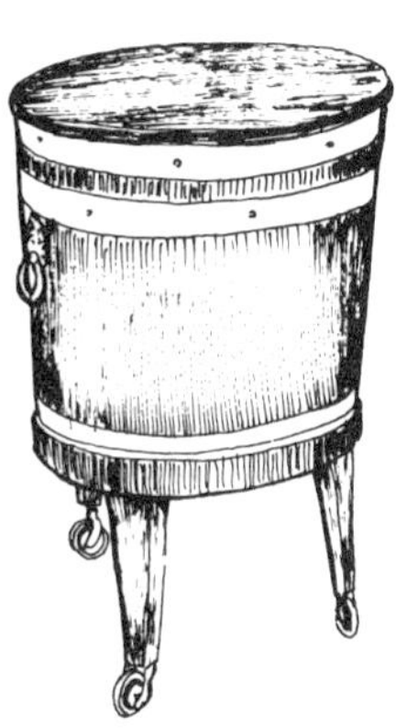

1. Late 18th century mahogany oval brass bound cellarette, complete with the original stand. £235

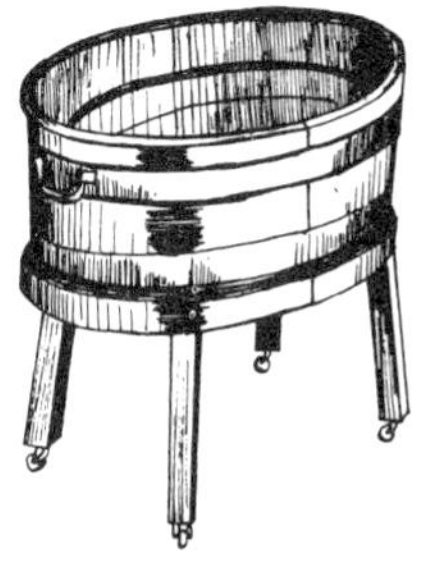

2. Late 18th century brass bound cellarette with brass carrying handles. £165

3. George III mahogany domed top wine cooler with brass carrying handles. £195

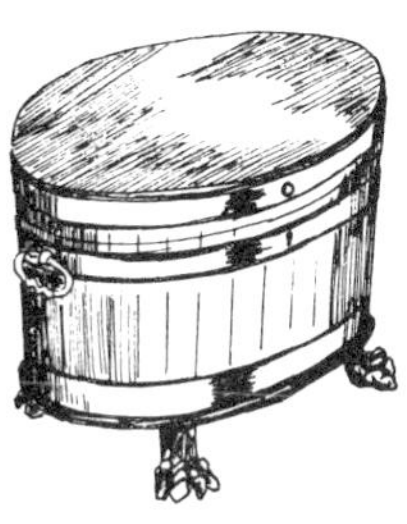

4. Small George III mahogany brass bound cellarette on paw feet. £150

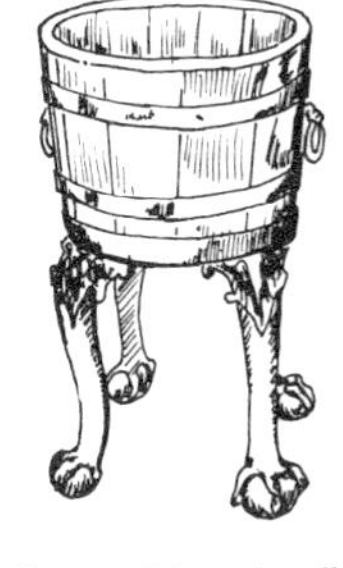

5. Chippendale style cellarette in mahogany on finely carved legs with ball and claw feet. £205

6. George II mahogany wine waiter on ogee feet. £155

7. Fine 18th century mahogany hexagonal wine cooler with brass bindings and handles. £260

8. 19th century Dutch marquetry wine cooler on cabriole legs. £95

9. A fine 19th century mahogany wine cellarette, cross banded and inlaid with satinwood, holly, ebony and boxwood, on a detachable mahogany stand of a later date. £120

PEDESTALS AND STANDS

1. Edwardian mahogany two tier plant stand. £3.50

2. A fine early 19th century Regency gilt and gesso torchere. £125

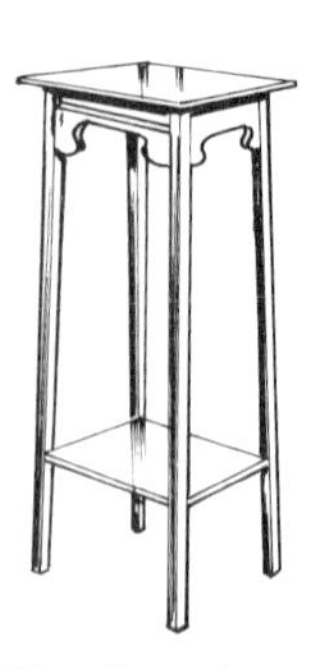

3. Edwardian mahogany and satinwood banded two tier plant stand. £6.50

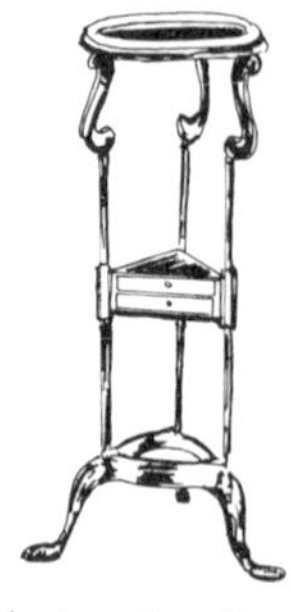

4. A good quality mahogany basin stand, circa 1760. £120

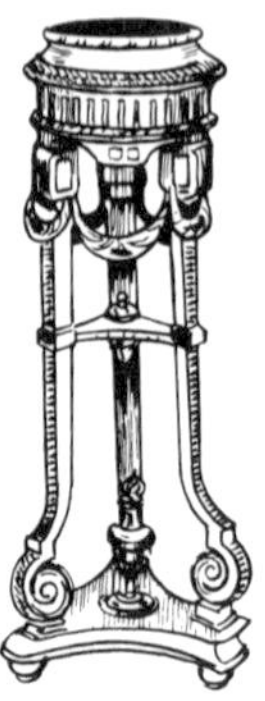

5. 19th century carved and gilded jardiniere in the style of Robert Adam. £200

6. Pair of early 18th century walnut torcheres, 3ft 8ins high. £440

7. A fine French Empire black and white marble column with ormolu mounts. £200

8. Edwardian mahogany jardiniere stand. £12.50

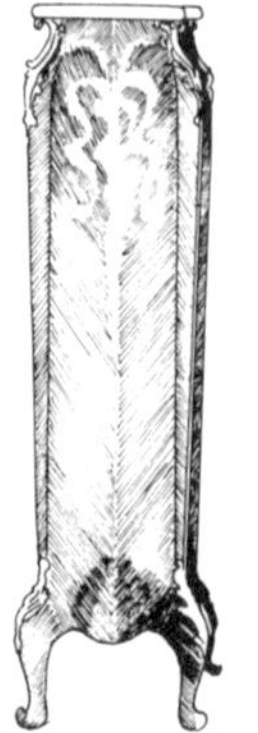

9. A 19th century kingwood and marquetry plinth with ormolu mounts and a marble top. £240

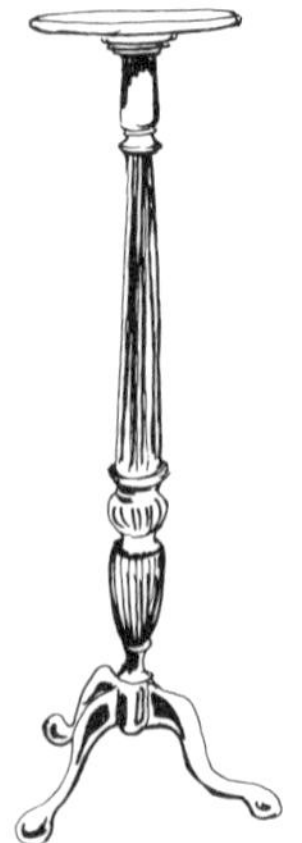

10. 19th century carved and fluted torchere on a tripod base, 4ft 6ins high. £18

11. Edwardian inlaid mahogany two tier plant stand. £12.50

BLACKAMOOR FIGURES

1. Pair of finely carved Regency walnut torcheres with simulated malachite and marble bases. £500

2. A small early 19th century carved wood blackamoor table inlaid with various woods, 20ins high. £110

3. An excellent pair of blackamoor figures with the original attractive colouring, 6ft 2ins high. £950

DUMB WAITERS

1. George III mahogany dumb waiter, circa 1790. £170

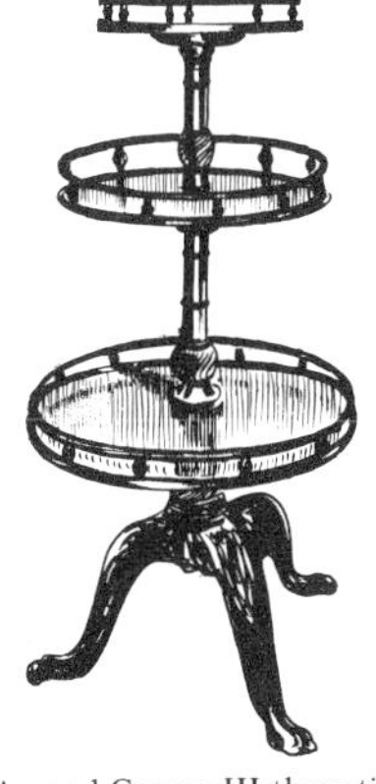

2. A good George III three tier mahogany dumb waiter on a tripod base with ball and claw feet. £400

3. Late 18th century mahogany three tier dumb waiter. £160

4. George III mahogany dumb waiter on a tripod base with pad feet. £175

5. Early 19th century two tier dumb waiter on a tripod base with brass castors. £240

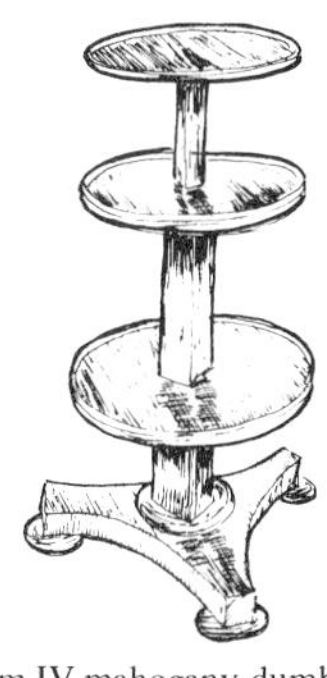

6. William IV mahogany dumb waiter, 42ins high. £120

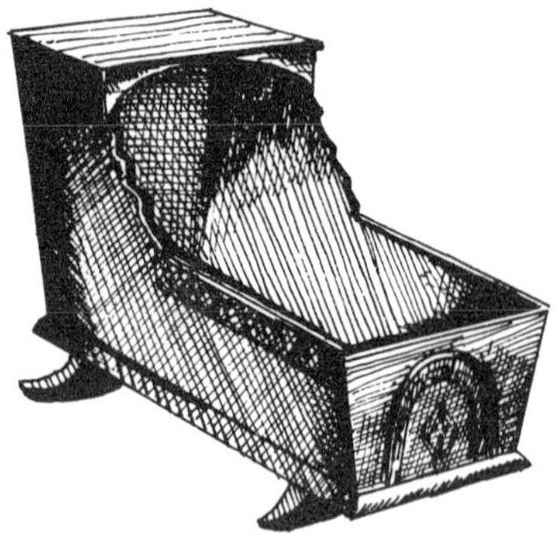

1. Late 17th century oak cradle. £75

2. Late 18th century mahogany and canework crib. £85

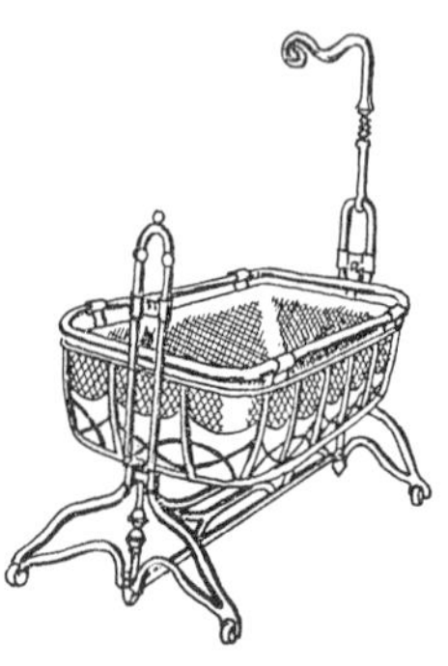

3. A Victorian brass crib. £40

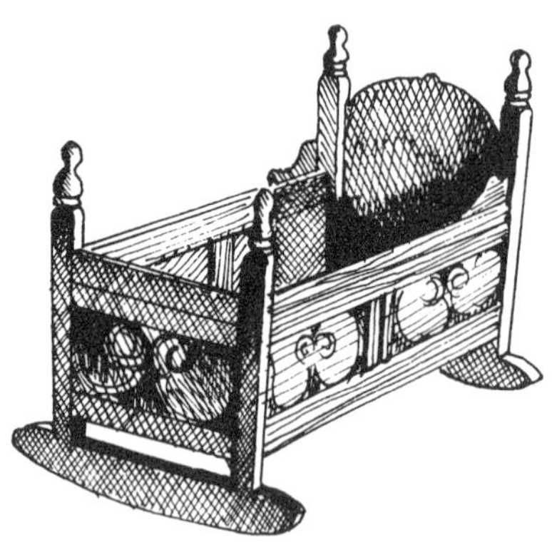

4. 17th century oak box cradle. £60

5. 17th century Continental oak crib. £75

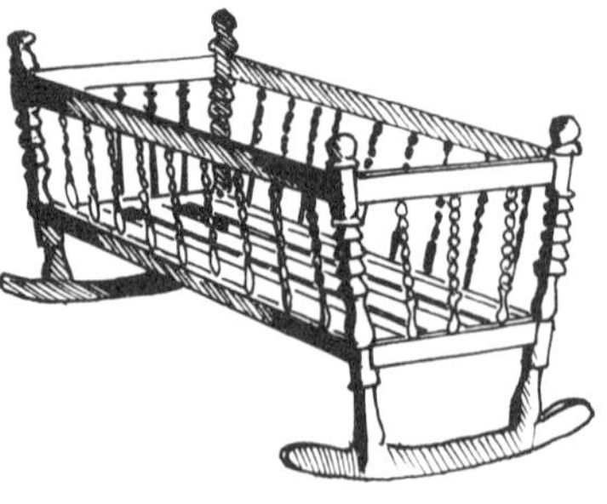

6. Late 18th century mahogany crib. £45

1. Late 18th century mahogany four post bed, 53ins wide. £200

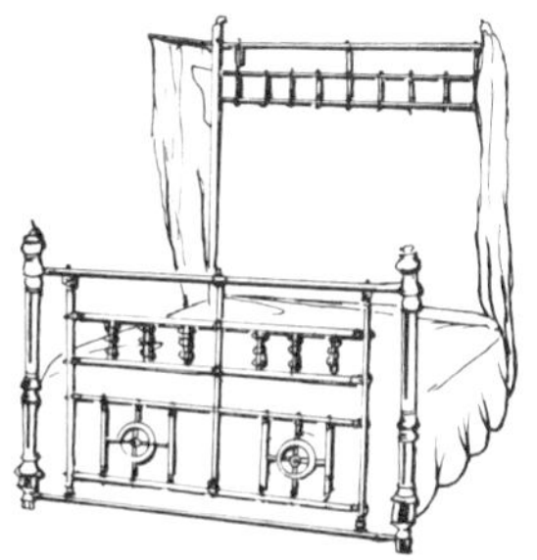

2. Victorian brass bed, 4ft 6ins wide. £65

3. A fine quality 19th century lacquered and gilt bed. £190

4. An extremely fine inlaid mahogany Edwardian bed with painted panels, 4ft wide. £65

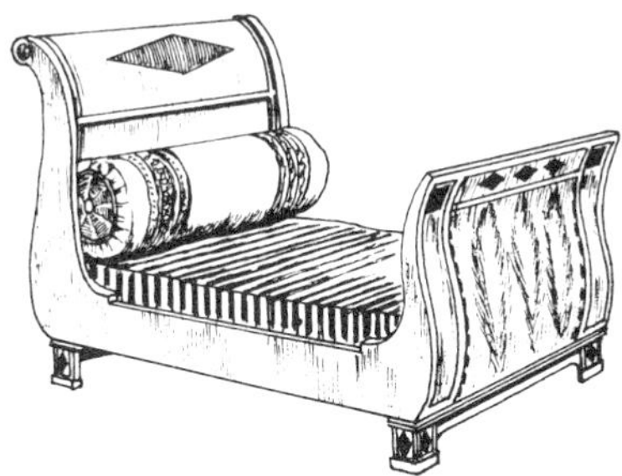

5. Early 19th century inlaid mahogany scroll end bed. £110

6. Magnificent carved rosewood four poster bed. £1,150

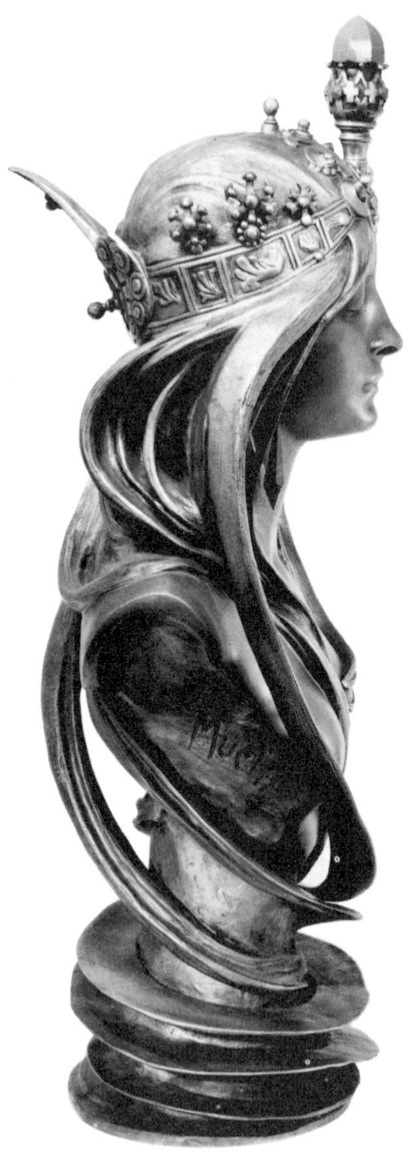

An important gilt bronze bust by Alphonse Mucha, signed, 27½ins high. £11,000

(Sotheby's Belgravia, 3-11-71 – World auction record for a piece of Art Nouveau)

Wedgwood's copy, No 22 of the Portland Vase, the Beaufort Codington copy. £20,000

(Sotheby & Co., 30-11-71 – World auction record for any English ceramic)

A very finely cast Archaic bronze cauldron (ting), 9¼ins high, Shang dynasty. £16,000

(Sotheby & Co., 14-3-72)

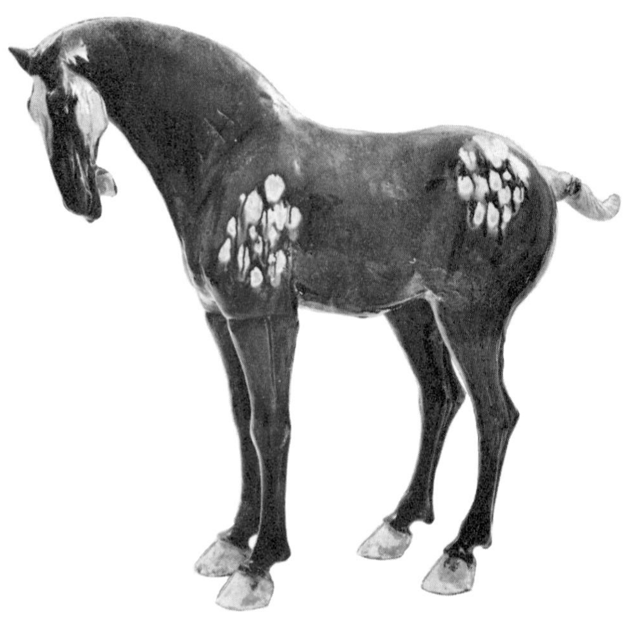

A brilliantly glazed pottery figure of a fereghan horse, T'ang dynasty. £33,000

(Sotheby & Co., 14-12-71 – World auction record for a T'ang ceramic)

A very fine Ming dynasty blue and white Palace bowl. £18,000

(Sotheby & Co., 14-3-72)

A rare and very finely modelled T'ang dynasty glazed pottery figure of a polo pony. £28,000

(Sotheby & Co., 14-3-72)

An extremely rare enamelled armorial goblet by Beilby of Newcastle. £3,100

(Sotheby & Co., 6 -12 -71)

One of a set of six James II single light wall sconces, 1687. £26,000

(Sotheby & Co., 20-4-72)

A large and very rare T'ang dynasty silver dish, 12ins diameter. £40,000

(Sotheby & Co., 29-2-72 – World auction record for a T'ang work of art)

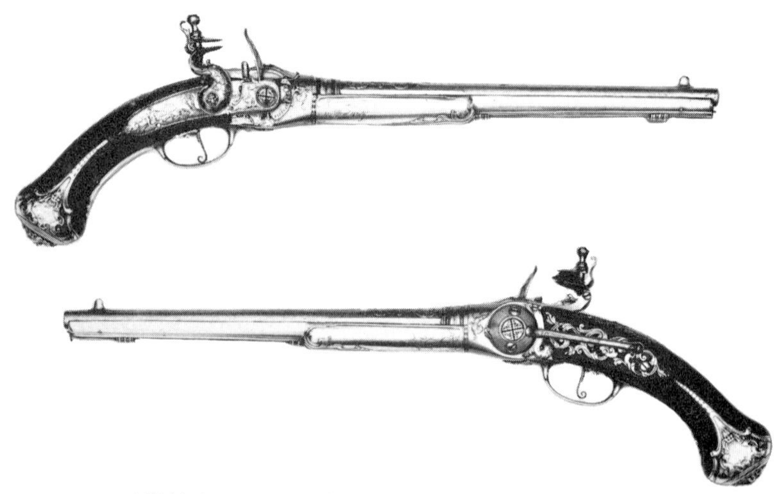

A highly important pair of flintlock breech - loading repeating pistols by Michele Lorenzoni of Florence, early 18th century. £60,000

(Sotheby & Co., 17-7-72 – World auction record for a pair of pistols)

A superb, heavy early Charles II silver gilt twelve sided, covered porringer, c. 1661. £26,000

(Sotheby & Co., 8-6-72)

A very rare pair of Louis XV ormolu mounted Mennecy figures. £9,000

(Sotheby & Co., 11-4-72)

An important set of twelve Japanese inro, depicting the signs of the Zodiac, by Koma Kwansai II and Masaharu. £14,000

(Sotheby & Co., 14-6-72 – Record outside Japan for inro)

A fine small ebony veneered repeating bracket clock, No 99 made by Thomas Tompion. £16,000

(Sotheby & Co., 22-5-72)

Benin Bronze head of an Oba. £29,000

Modigliani 'Tete'. £72,000

(Sotheby & Co., 7-12-71 – World auction record for any piece of African art)

(Sotheby & Co., 28-6-72 – World auction record for sculpture by the artist)

An important Hawaiian light brown wood 'sfick' God (Aumakua). £5,000

(Sotheby & Co., 7-12-71)

The Sutton Cup - a highly important Elizabeth I cup and cover of silver gilt and rock crystal, maker's mark Son & Cross probably for Isaac Sutton, 1573. £36,000

(Sotheby & Co., 8-6-72)

A highly important Louis XVI ormolu-mounted black lacquer secretaire a abattant by J.H. Riesener. £72,000

(Sotheby & Co., 26 -11 -71 –World auction record for a piece of lacquer furniture)

Colour print by Sharaku, Danjuro V in the role of Takemura Sadanoshin in a play performed in 1794. £4,600
(Sotheby & Co., 28-6-72 – Record price outside Japan for a Japanese colour print)

A fine portrait of Shah Abul Ma'ali by Ustad Dust Musawwir, Mughal, c.1550-60. £6,000

(Sotheby & Co., 11-4-72)

Portrait of a dog with the Aldrovandi Coat of Arms on his collar by Il Guercino. £110,000

(Sotheby & Co., 12-7-72 – World auction record for the artist)

The Roseate Spoonbill from a copy of the first issue of Audubon's 'The Bird's of America' which sold for £62,000.

(Sotheby & Co., 26 -6 -72)

Goya - one of the set of 33 etchings with aquatint entitled 'La Tauromaquia', first edition of 1816, which fetched £18,000.

(Sotheby & Co., 13 -7 -72)

Frasonard - portrait of Ann Francois d'Harcourt, Duc de Beuvion. £340,000

(Sotheby & Co., 8-12-71 – World auction record for a French work of art)

Thomas Gainsborough - Mr and Mrs John Gravenor and his two daughters Elizabeth and Anne. £280,000

(Sotheby & Co., 19-7-72 – World auction record for any British work of art)

Albrecht Durer's engraving of St. Eustace. £7,500

(Sotheby & Co., 13-7-72)

'A boy in the act of drinking' by Annibale Carracci from the Thomas Lawrence and Ellesmere collections. £40,000

(Sotheby & Co., 11-7-72 – World auction record for the artist)

Amadeo Modigliani 'La Rousse au Pendentif', 36¼ x 23½ ins. £115,000

(Sotheby & Co., 28-6-72 – World auction record for the artist)

Rene Magritte 'Au Seuil de la Liberte'. £55,000

(Sotheby & Co., 12-4-72 – World auction record for the artist)

1. A Victorian Officer's blue cloth spiked Helmet of the 1st Volunteer Battalion, The Yorkshire Regiment. £32

2. A rare Baden (Ersatz) pressed steel Infantryman's Picklehaube. £28

3. A Victorian Officer's green cloth spiked Helmet of the 1st A. Battalion, The North York Rifle Volunteers. £30

4. A Wurttemberg Dragoon Officer's Picklehaube. £40

5. A good Victorian Officer's blue cloth Helmet of the 108th Madras Infantry. £44

6. A scarce Imperial German Gendarmerie Picklehaube of Mecklenberg Strelitz. £33

7. A scarce Victorian O.R.'s blue cloth spike Helmet of the 2nd Admin. Battalion Aberdeenshire Rifle Volunteers. £26

8. A rare Swedish O.R.'s Picklehaube modelled on the Prussian 1842 Pattern. £56

9. A Victorian Officer's black cloth spiked Helmet of the 2nd Volunteer Battalion, The Scottish Rifles. £30

1. A Victorian Officer's blue cloth Helmet of the 1st Volunteer Battalion The Royal West Kent Regiment. £41

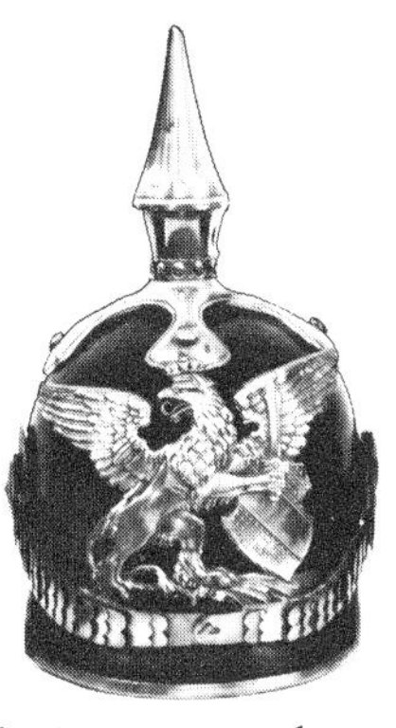

2. A very rare early Baden O.R.'s Picklehaube circa 1870. £110

3. A Victorian Volunteer Artillery Officer's blue cloth Helmet of the 1st Essex Volunteer Artillery. £35

4. A scarce Victorian Officer's blue cloth spiked Helmet of the 3rd Admin. Battalion Lanark Rifle Volunteers. £32

5. A fine Victorian Officer's blue cloth Helmet of the 6th Volunteer Battalion, The Royal Scots. £56

6. A fine Victorian Officer's black cloth spiked Helmet of the 1st Forfarshire Rifle Volunteers Corps. £31

7. A rare Prussian Officer's Picklehaube of an N.C.O.'s School. £40

8. An Officer's blue cloth ball topped Helmet of the Aberdeenshire Artillery Volunteers. £36

9. A Prussian Reservist's Infantry Officer's Picklehaube. £34

1. An early 17th century Morion, the skull forged from two pieces of iron. £91

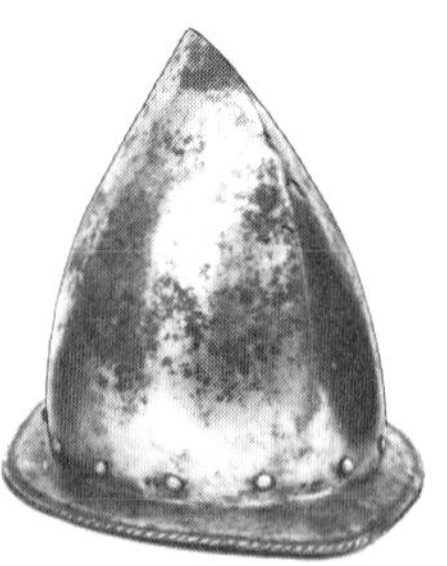

2. A tall early 17th century Cabasset of North Italian manufacture. £75

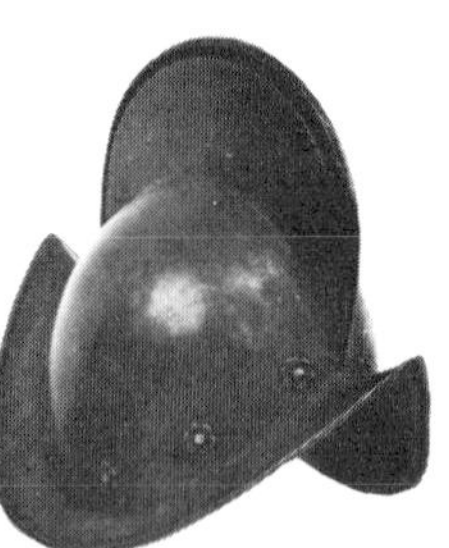

3. A good mid 17th century 'Spanish' form Morion of German manufacture. £80

4. A rare Officer's brown fur Busby of the Fifeshire Artillery. £35

5. A good Officer's feather bonnet of the Royal Highlanders (Black Watch). £56

6. A good Victorian Officer's brown fur Busby of the Royal Artillery Volunteers. £25

7. A scarce Victorian Officer's Shako of the Renfrew Militia. £37

8. A fine Victorian Officer's Lance Cap of the 9th Royal Lancers. £102

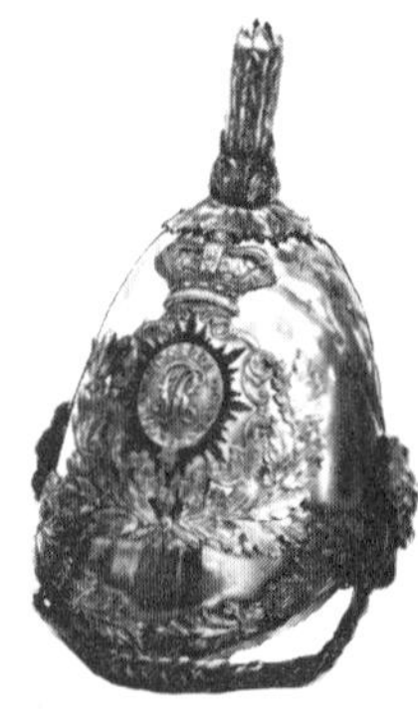

9. Crimea War. An Officer's Albert Pattern Cavalry Helmet of the 5th Dragoon Guards. £63

1. A Cromwellian Lobster Tailed Helmet 'Pot' of North German or Dutch manufacture. £100

2. A heavy Cromwellian Helmet, the skull forged from two pieces of iron. £90

3. A Cromwellian Lobster Tailed Helmet. £70

4. A 19th century Bavarian Cuirassiers Helmet circa 1870. £52

5. An Officer's Gilt Helmet of the Afghan Cavalry. £30

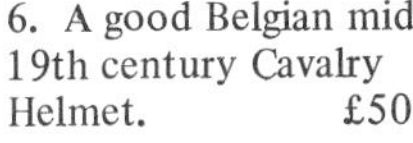

6. A good Belgian mid 19th century Cavalry Helmet. £50

7. An R.A.F. Officer's Parade Helmet, leather skull with moleskin trimmings. £27

8. A Victorian Officer's Busby of The Madras Artillery of brown bearskin. £32

9. A Victorian Officer's 1870 Pattern Shako of The Royal Military College Sandhurst. £22

1. A rare 1817 Pattern Officer's Roman style Helmet of The Life Guards. £260

2. A Victorian Officer's silvered Helmet with gilt fittings of The Lothians and Berwickshire Yeomanry Cavalry. £95

3. A fine Victorian Officer's Albert Pattern silvered Helmet, The Glasgow Yeomanry, circa 1860. £136

4. A fine Victorian Officer's Albert Pattern silvered Helmet of the Glasgow Yeomanry circa 1860. £125

1. A very rare Roman bronze Cavalry Helmet, 4th to 3rd century B.C., height 8¼ins, the skull made in two halves, each half bearing large flattened hemispherical boss and frontal boss with traces of milling. The small curled hook at the rear once retained the large protective leather cape. £500

1. An interesting old Bowie type knife, single edged blade 7ins by Tiffany, New York. £150

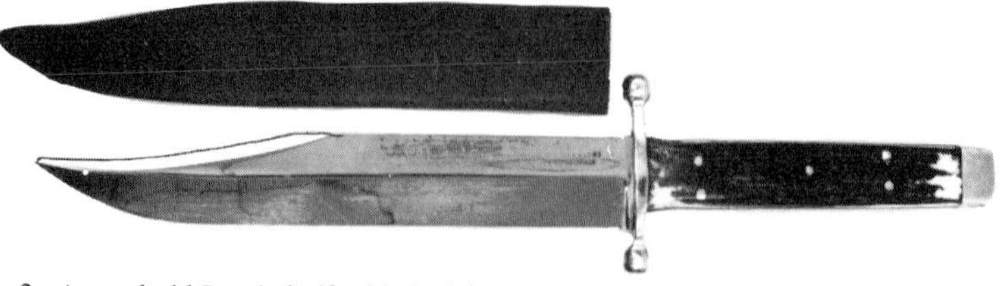

2. A good old Bowie knife, blade 8¼ins stamped V.R. Joseph Rodgers and Sons, 6 Norfolk Street Sheffield. £32

3. Victorian Bowie knife, clipped back blade 7¼ins by Woodhead, Howard Street, Sheffield. £32

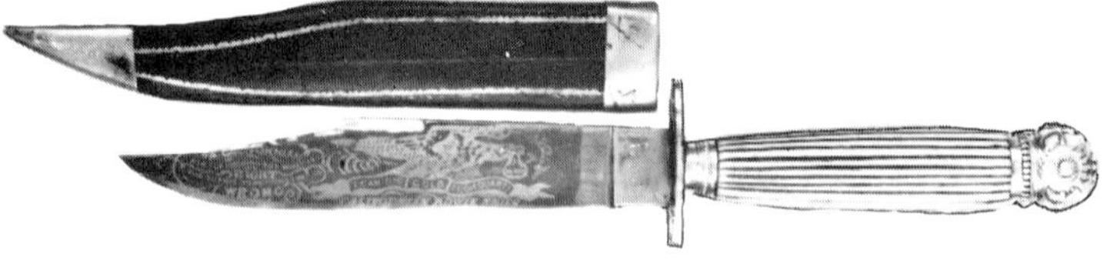

4. A V.S. Bowie knife by Woodhead, Howard Street, Sheffield, H.M. Silver (1870) ferrule to base of grip. £52

5. A fine Victorian Scottish Officer's dirk of The 1st Lanarkshire Militia together with a broadsword. £120

6. A Victorian Bowie knife by E.M. Dickenson, etched Klondyke. £30

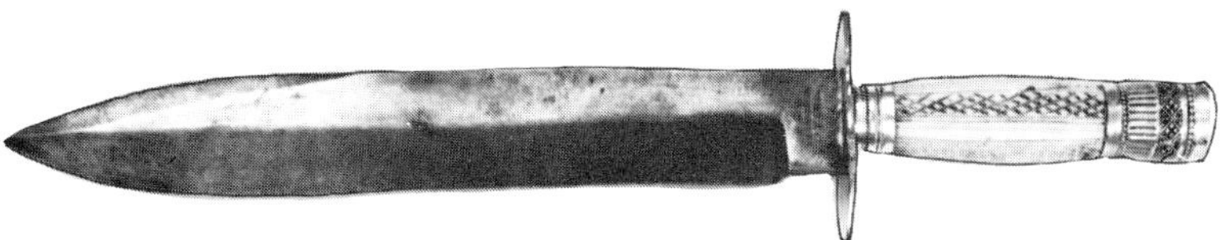

1. A good old Bowie type knife, blade 10ins, stamped 'V.R.' G. Beardshaw, cast steel Sheffield. £26

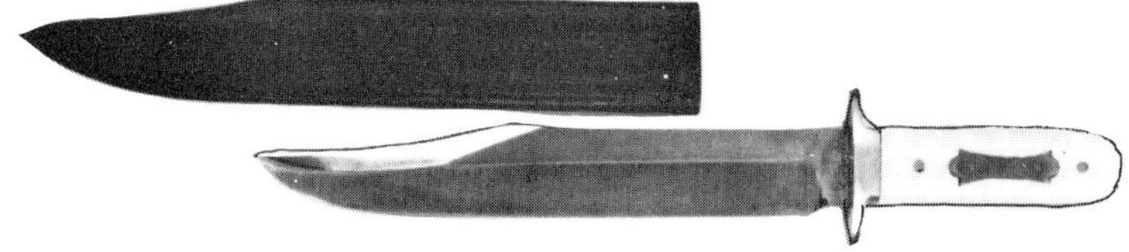

2. A good old U.S. Bowie knife by Tiffany, Broadway, New York U. S. A. £64

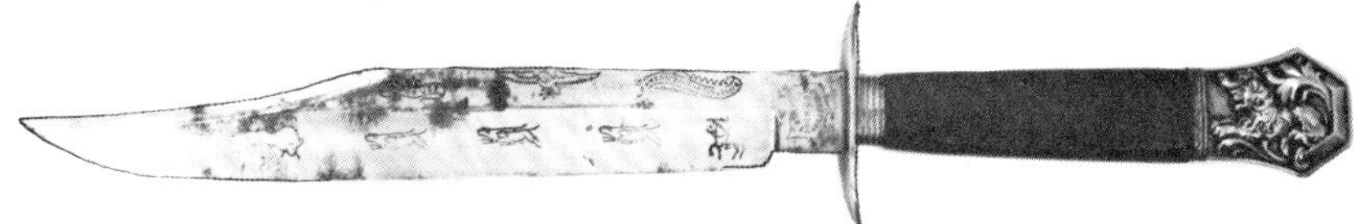

3. An old Bowie knife with impressed design of huntsman and dog, buffalo, eagle, I'm for Use and 'American Hunting Knife' by John Coe, Sheffield. £110

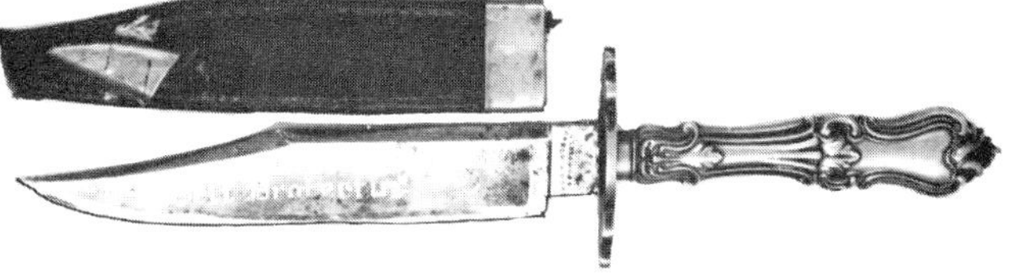

4. A Victorian Bowie knife, clippped back blade 7ins, by Hobson etched 'Self Protector'. £27

5. A good large Bowie knife of pure form, broad clipped back blade, 10ins. £36

6. An impressive Victorian Romantic dagger, 21½ins overall. £50

1. A good Bali dagger Kris, black and white watered straight double edged blade with central ridge 15ins. £52

2. A Madura Kris, blade 13ins, with fine black and white smooth watering. £50

3. A good Bali dagger Kris, black and white watered straight double edged blade 15ins. £55

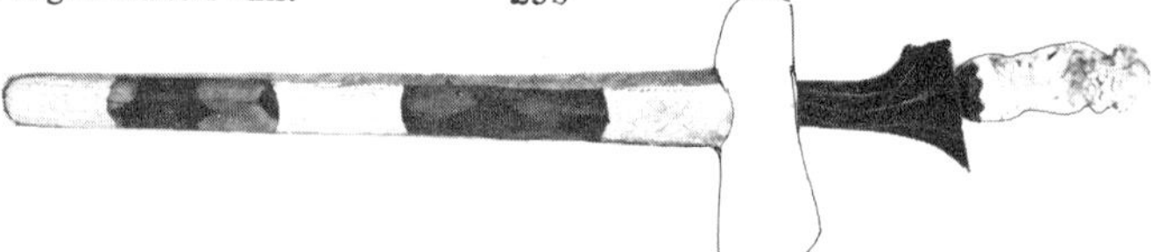

4. A fine and rare Bali Kris, blade 14ins having entirely different watering on either side. £150

5. An unusual Bali dagger Kris, straight double edged blade 14ins. £38

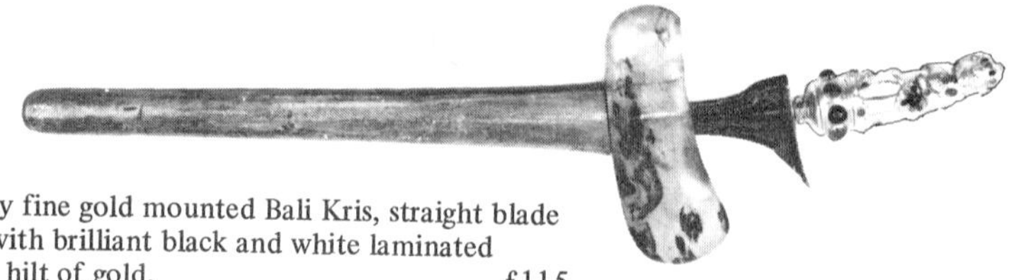

6. A very fine gold mounted Bali Kris, straight blade 15½ins with brilliant black and white laminated watering hilt of gold. £115

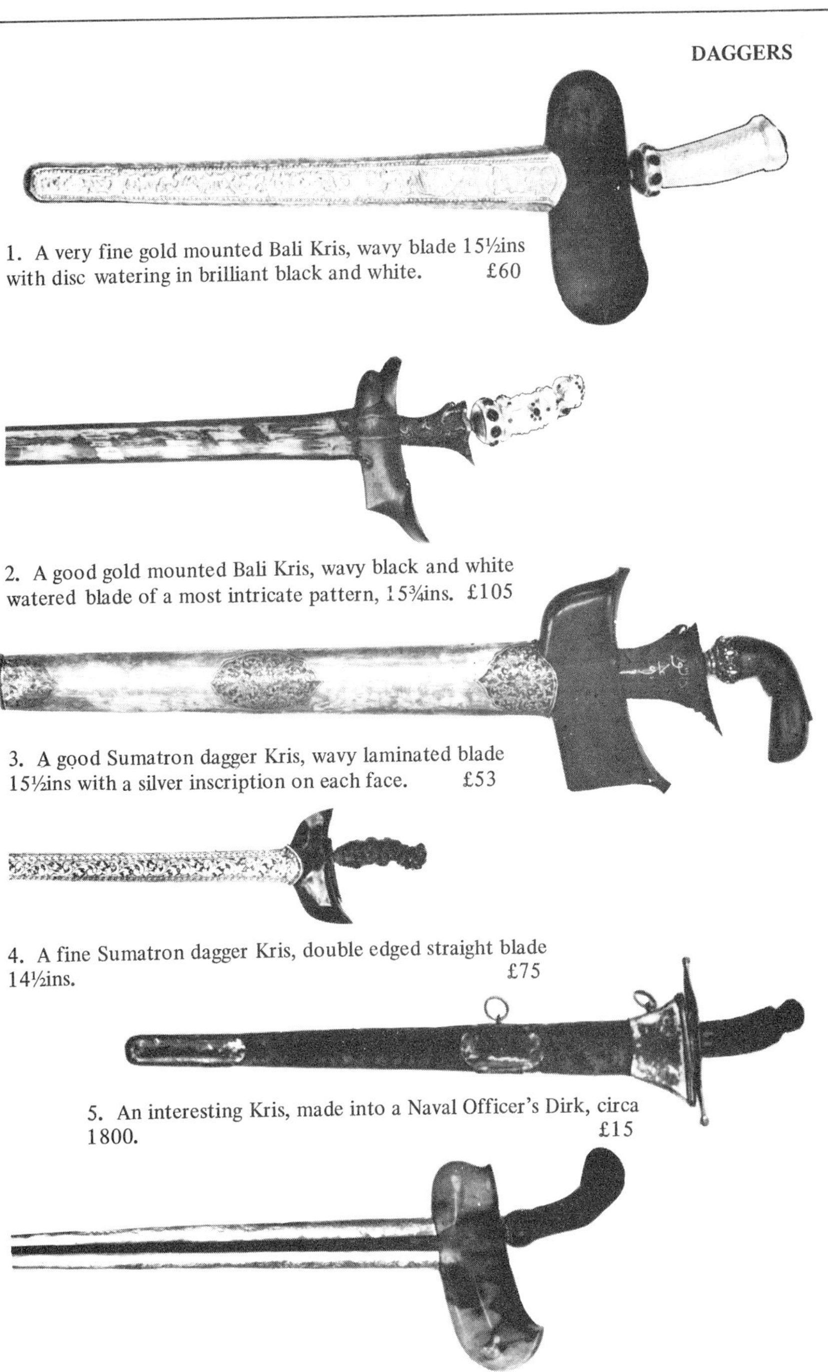

1. A very fine gold mounted Bali Kris, wavy blade 15½ins with disc watering in brilliant black and white. £60

2. A good gold mounted Bali Kris, wavy black and white watered blade of a most intricate pattern, 15¾ins. £105

3. A good Sumatron dagger Kris, wavy laminated blade 15½ins with a silver inscription on each face. £53

4. A fine Sumatron dagger Kris, double edged straight blade 14½ins. £75

5. An interesting Kris, made into a Naval Officer's Dirk, circa 1800. £15

6. A good central Japanese Kris, straight blade 12½ins. £12

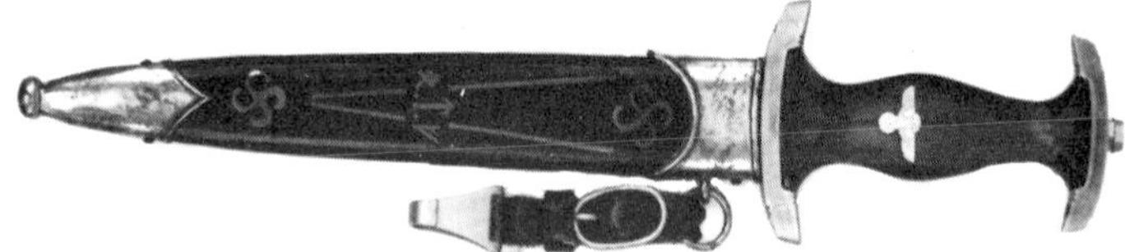

1. A very rare Nazi S.A. 'Funeral' ceremonial dagger by Horster. £130

2. A Serbo Croation Army Officer's dagger, plated blade 9ins. £26

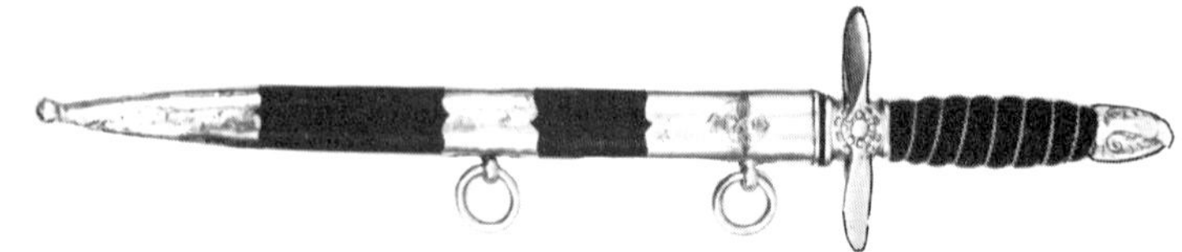

3. A scarce Serbo Croation Air Force Officer's dagger. £38

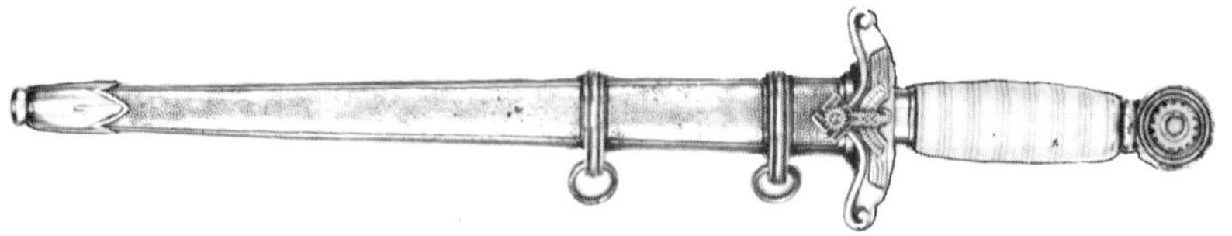

4. A very rare Nazi Teno Officer's dagger, blade 11ins by Eickhorn. £125

5. A Georgian Naval Officer's dirk, blued blade 6¼ins. £26

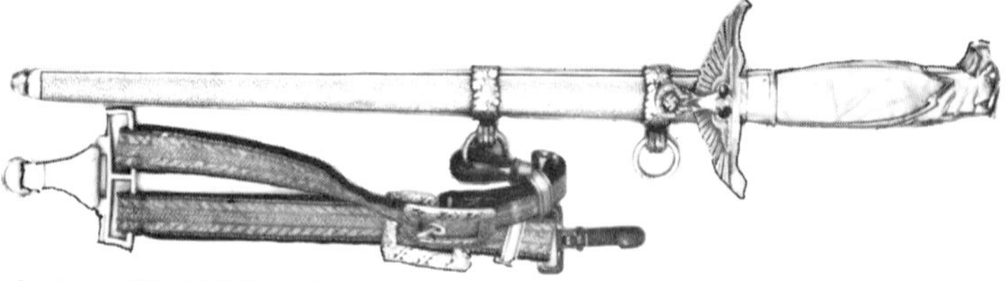

6. A rare Nazi Diplomat's dagger by Alcoso with the original hanging straps. £100

1. A World War II Japanese Naval Officer's dirk, single edged blade 8ins. £15.50

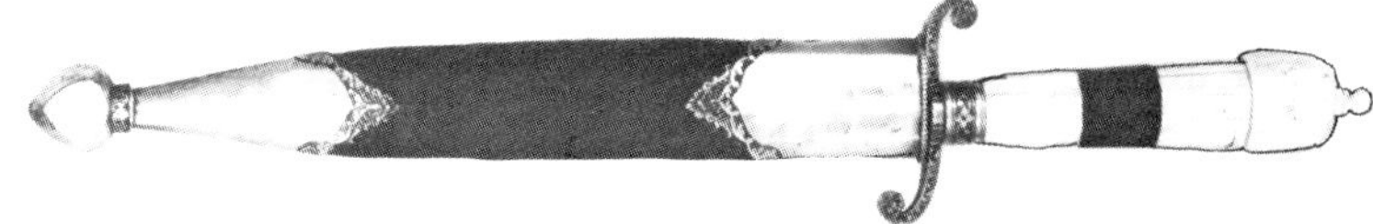

2. An Indian Bowie knife, single edged slightly clipped back blade 9¾ins. £30

3. An Imperial Russian Naval dirk, cruciform section blade 7¾ins. £16

4. A good Georgian Naval Officer's dirk, tapered blade 7ins of flattened diamond section. £25

5. A fine Georgian Naval Officer's dirk, blade 11ins etched with anchor, trophy of arms etc., by Firman, London. £39

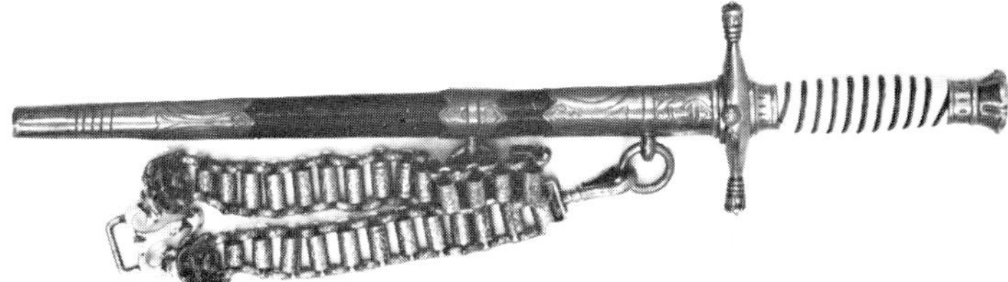

6. A scarce Turkish W.W.I. Naval Officer's dirk, four sided, deeply fullered blade 10 ins. £35

DAGGERS

1. A good nielloed silver mounted Russian dagger Kindjal, double edged shallow diamond sectioned blade 15ins. £85

2. A fine nielloed and gilded Russian silver dagger Kindjal, double edged blade 15ins. £72

3. A good Russian dagger Kindjal, straight multi fullered blade 15ins. £29

4. A good 18th century silver mounted hunting knife, double edged straight blade, 11½ins. £60

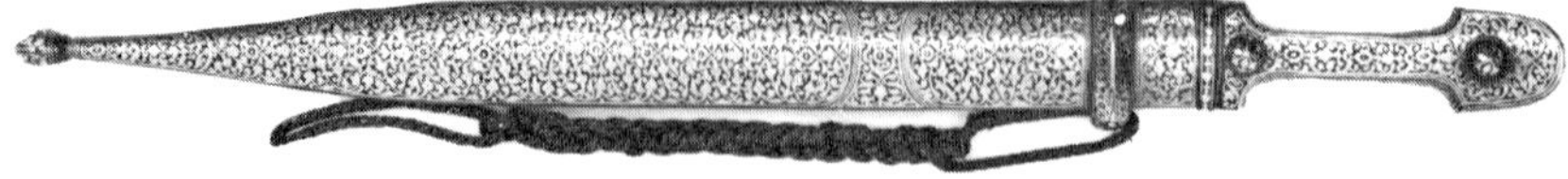

5. A very fine Cossack dagger Kindjal, triple fullered blade 14ins. £105

6. A fine Cossack dagger Kindjal, triple fullered blade 12½ins, scroll etched within fullers. £65

7. A silver mounted Cossack dagger Kindjal, double edged deeply offset fullered blade 15¾ins. £54

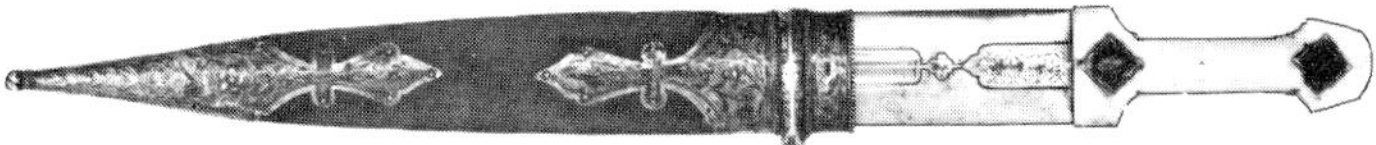

1. A good Russian (American) dagger Kindjal, double edged multi fullered blade 11½ins. £36

2. A fine Nielloed Russian silver dagger Kindjal, double edged and fullered blade 13½ins. £60

3. A fine Cossack dagger Kindjal, finely ground double edged blade 13½ins. £105

4. An early 18th century Scottish Highland dirk, triple fullered broadly clipped back blade, 16ins. £46

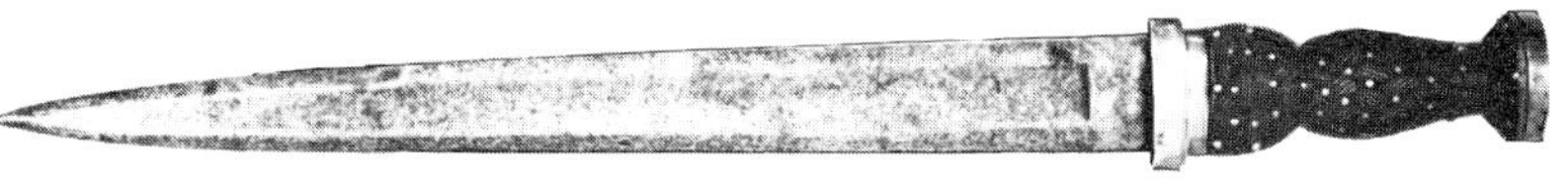

5. A good Scottish 18th century dirk circa 1760, blade 14½ins. £85

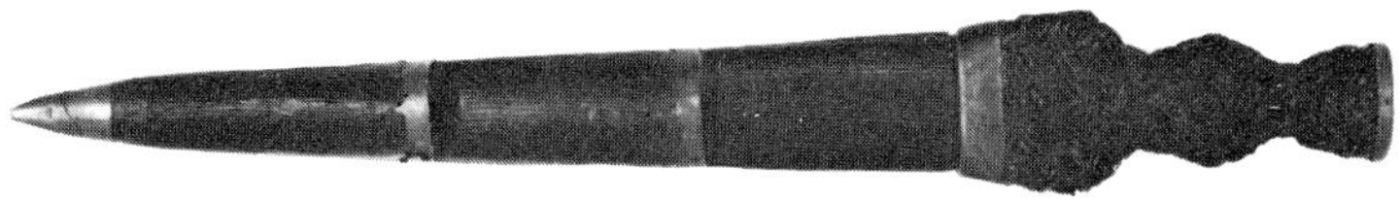

6. An early 18th century pewter Scottish Highland dirk, shortened double edged blade 9¾ins. £50

7. A very fine and most desirable Scottish Georgian Officer's dirk circa 1800, blade 15ins with broad fuller. £180

DAGGERS

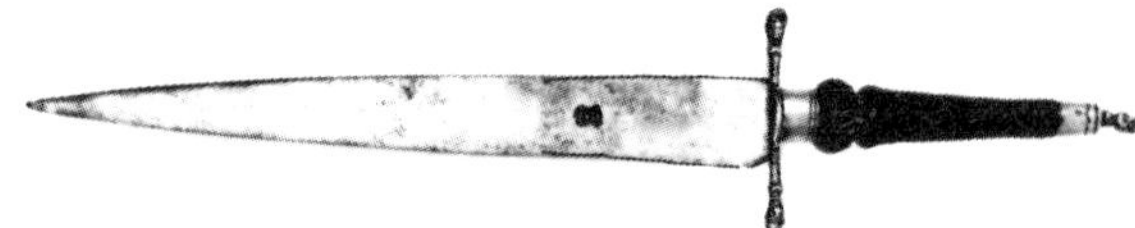

1. A good Plug bayonet circa 1700, single edged blade 11½ins, inlaid with two copper armourer's marks. £62

2. An early 18th century Plug bayonet, straight single edged clipped back blade 13½ins. £34

3. A decorative Indian Naval Midshipman's type dirk, foliate etched blade 15ins by Manton and Co, Calcutta. £25

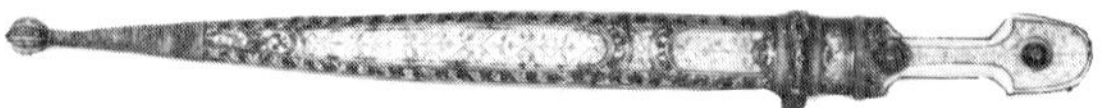

4. An unusually fine and small Cossack dagger, Kindjal double edged blade 9ins. £65

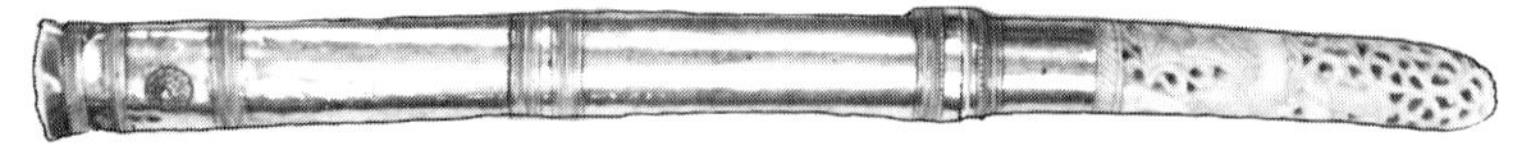

5. A good Burmese knife D.H.A., single edged blade 9½ins. £30

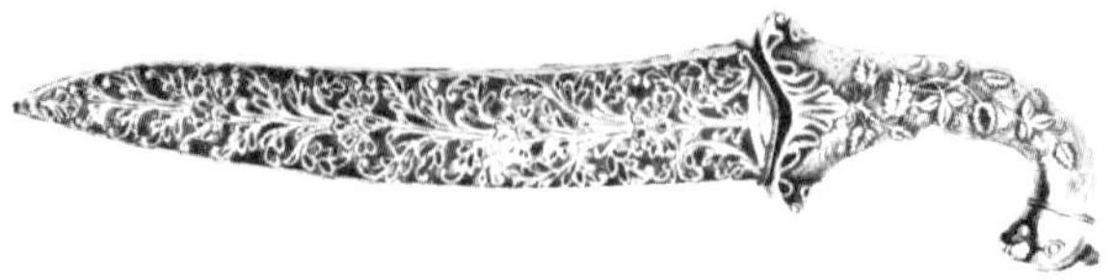

6. A good Indian dagger, Khanjar, curved blade 9ins well chiselled with hunters and elephants. £39

7. A fine Indo Persian dagger, Kard, slightly re-curved single edged watered blade 9ins. £50

1. A late 18th century Scottish Highland dirk, single edged double fullered scalloped back blade 11½ins. £32

2. A fine mid 18th century Scottish Highlander's dirk, single edged scalloped and slightly clipped back blade 11ins. £44

3. A good mid 19th century H.M. silver mounted Scottish dirk by F.A. Lyon, Leith Street, Edinburgh. £75

4. A fine Victorian Officer's dirk of the 78th Highlanders (Seaforths) blade 11ins. £90

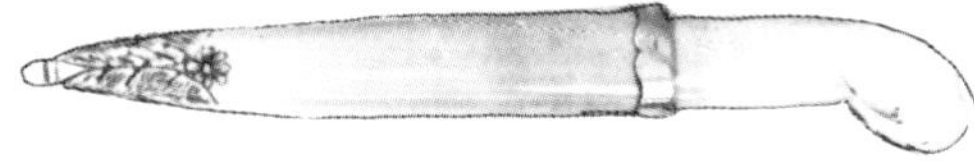

5. A good Scandinavian Filching knife, the hilt and sheath of Walrus ivory. £26

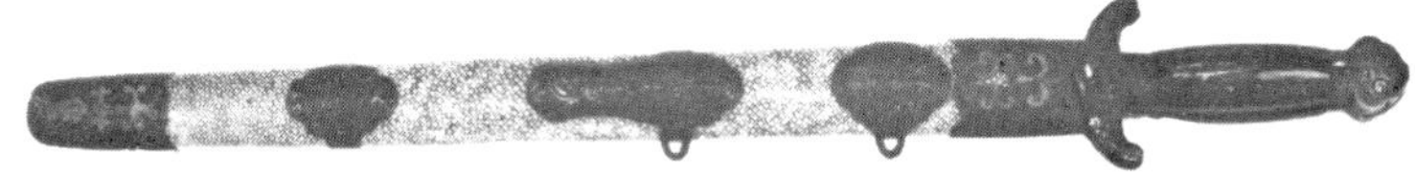

6. A good Chinese double sword, double edged blades 17ins. £22

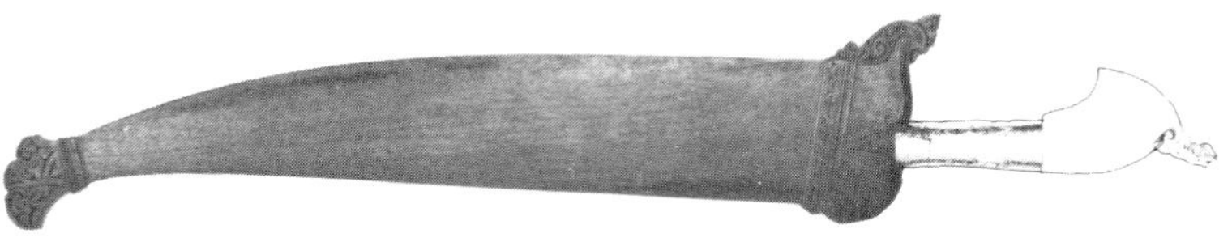

7. A good Moro sword Barong, leaf shaped blade 17½ins. £27

1. A Victorian Burmese Bowie knife 14ins, clipped back slightly curved blade 8½ins. £10

2. A good Malayan knife Bade-Bade, blade 10ins. £29

3. A good scroll embossed silver mounted Malayan knife Bade-Bade, blade 6½ins. £21

4. A fine Arab silver mounted Jambiya, curved blade 8ins with central rib. £40

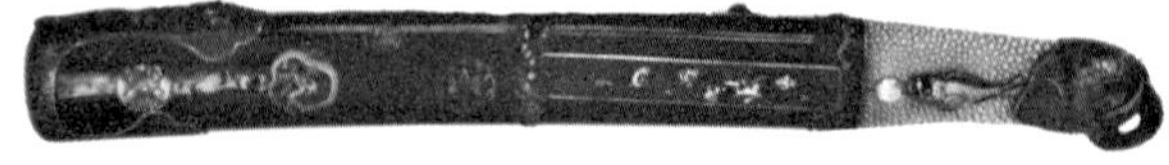

5. A Japanese dagger Aikuchi, blade 8½ins. £42

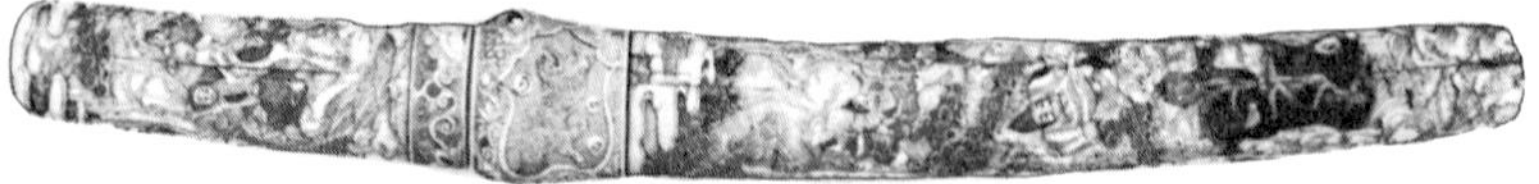

6. A good Japanese carved bone dagger 16½ins, blade 9ins, intricately carved overall. £50

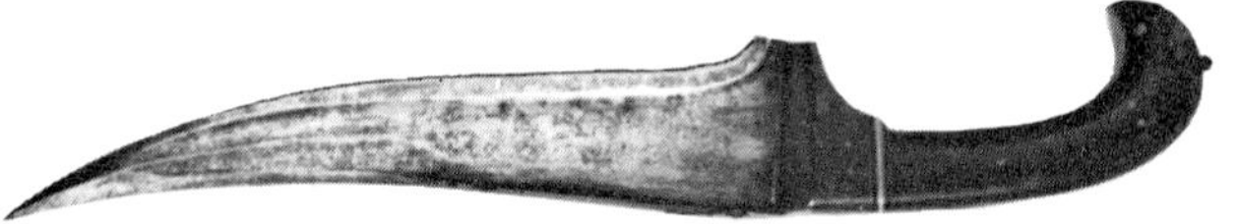

1. A good Indian dagger, re-curved 'T' sectioned fullered blade 8½ins. £10

2. A scarce Australian model 1943, S.M.L.E., machete bayonet. £28

3. A fine silver mounted Kukri, blade 13½ins with simple engraved decoration. £24

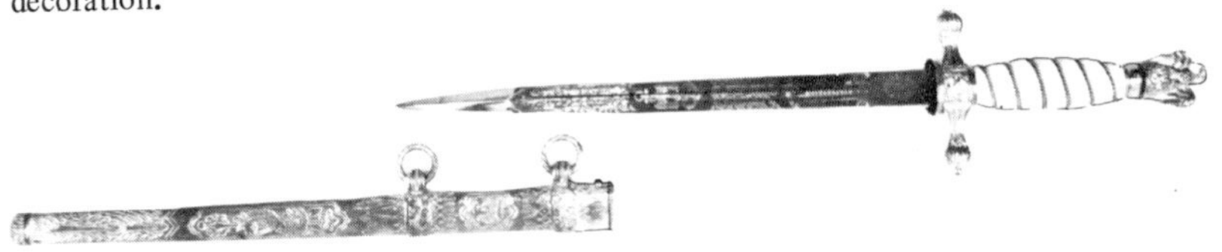

4. A fine Nazi Naval Officer's presentation dirk, the blade blued and gilt with Nazi Eagle and fouled anchor. £190

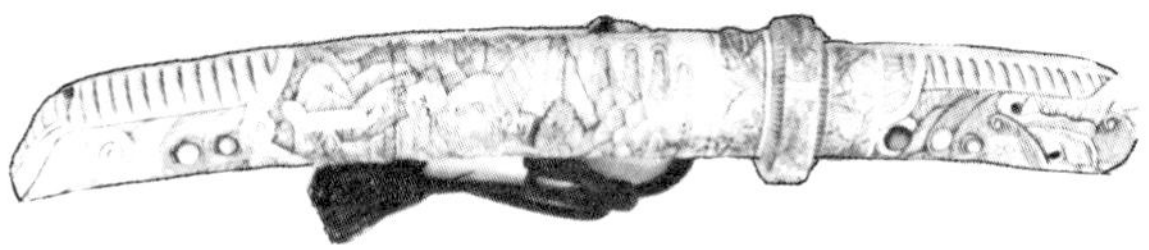

5. A Japanese carved bone dagger Tanto, blade 6ins, the hilt carved as a marine master's head. £34

6. A good Japanese carved bone dagger 14½ ins, blade 8 ins, nicely carved overall. £56

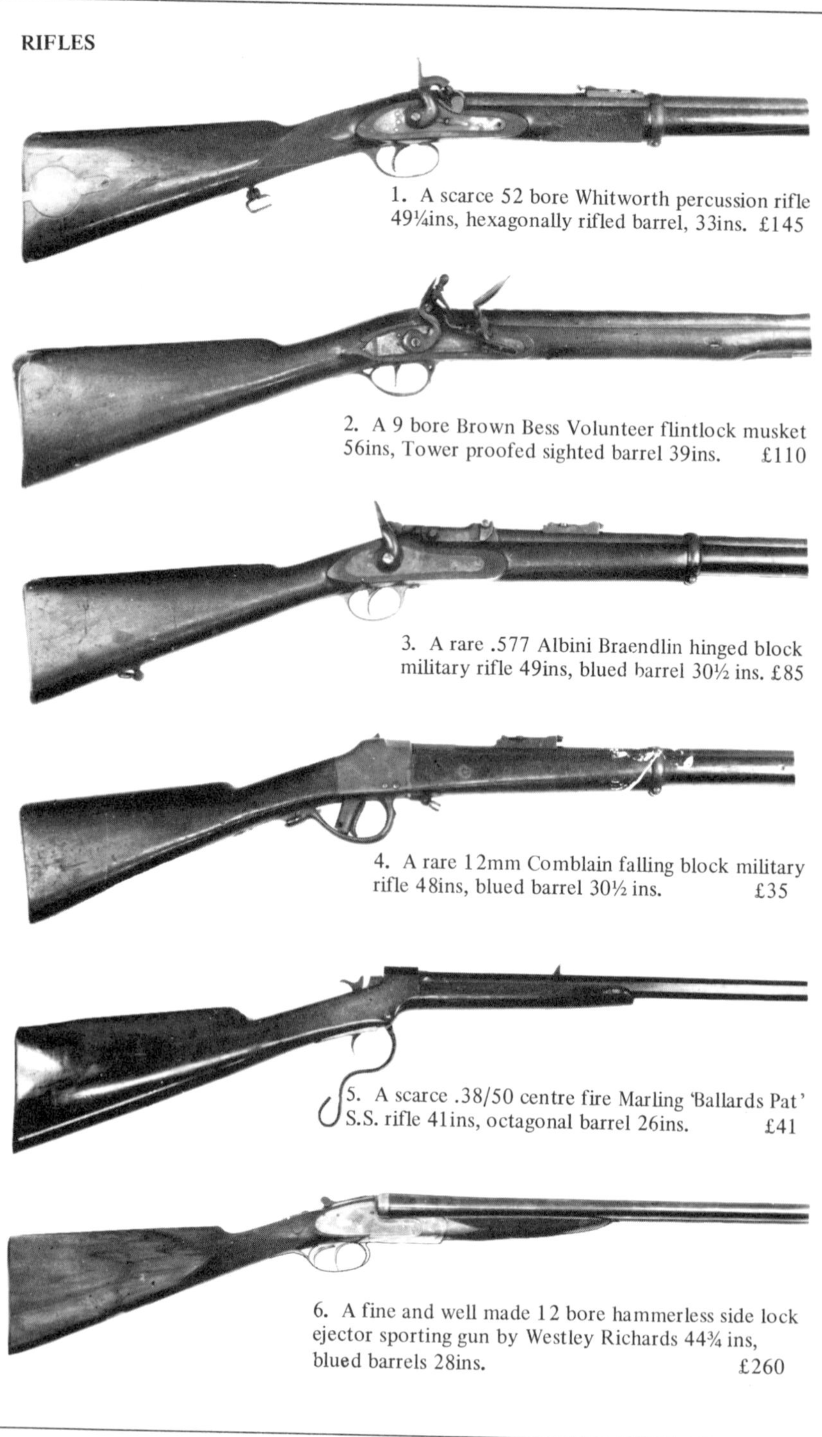

1. A scarce 52 bore Whitworth percussion rifle 49¼ins, hexagonally rifled barrel, 33ins. £145

2. A 9 bore Brown Bess Volunteer flintlock musket 56ins, Tower proofed sighted barrel 39ins. £110

3. A rare .577 Albini Braendlin hinged block military rifle 49ins, blued barrel 30½ ins. £85

4. A rare 12mm Comblain falling block military rifle 48ins, blued barrel 30½ ins. £35

5. A scarce .38/50 centre fire Marling 'Ballards Pat' S.S. rifle 41ins, octagonal barrel 26ins. £41

6. A fine and well made 12 bore hammerless side lock ejector sporting gun by Westley Richards 44¾ ins, blued barrels 28ins. £260

1. A good and scarce .44 Winchester model 1873 full tube magazine rifle 43¼ins, round barrel 24½ins. £180

2. A scarce 1.15mm Werndle military rifle 50ins, blued barrel 33ins. £22

3. A massive well made 8 bore Snider single barrelled sporting gun 52ins, browned barrel 32¼ins. £27

4. An interesting .50ins Peabody patent 1862 single shot rifle 54¾ins, blued barrel 36ins. £40

5. An extremely rare .44 ins rimfire Winchester 1866 3rd model rifle 46¼ins, round barrel 27ins. £185

6. A massive well made 4 bore Snider single barrelled sporting gun 53ins, barrel 32½ins. £65

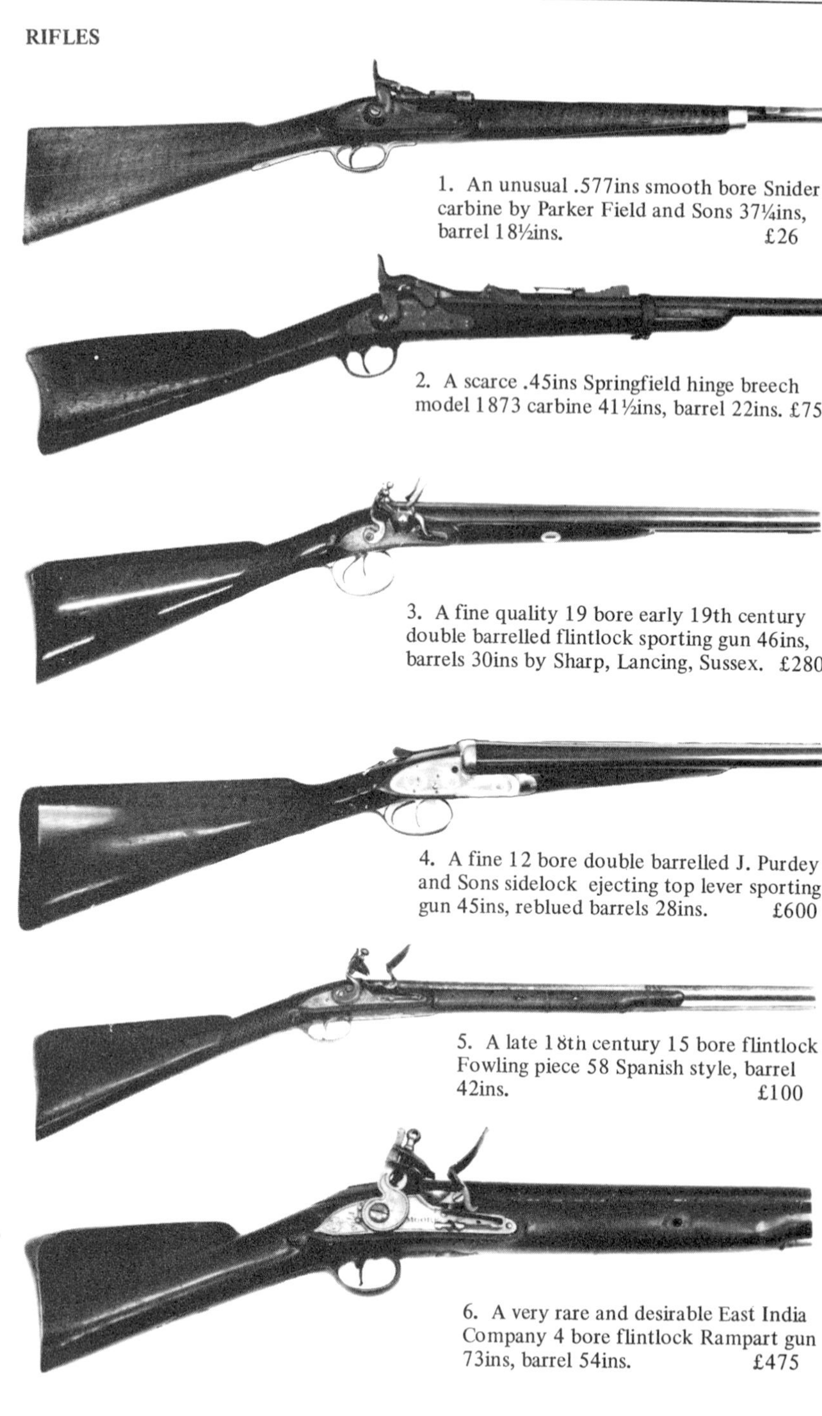

1. An unusual .577ins smooth bore Snider carbine by Parker Field and Sons 37¼ins, barrel 18½ins. £26

2. A scarce .45ins Springfield hinge breech model 1873 carbine 41½ins, barrel 22ins. £75

3. A fine quality 19 bore early 19th century double barrelled flintlock sporting gun 46ins, barrels 30ins by Sharp, Lancing, Sussex. £280

4. A fine 12 bore double barrelled J. Purdey and Sons sidelock ejecting top lever sporting gun 45ins, reblued barrels 28ins. £600

5. A late 18th century 15 bore flintlock Fowling piece 58 Spanish style, barrel 42ins. £100

6. A very rare and desirable East India Company 4 bore flintlock Rampart gun 73ins, barrel 54ins. £475

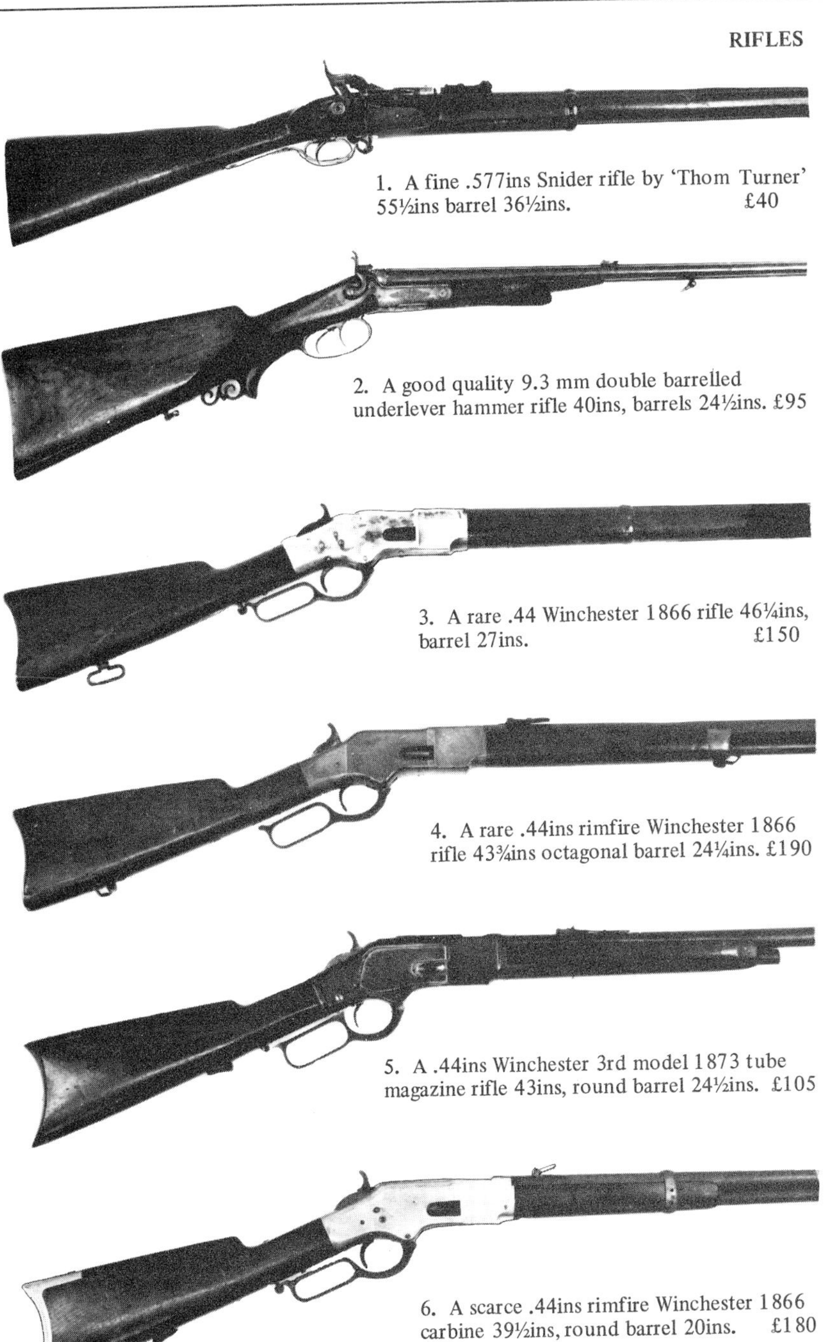

1. A fine .577ins Snider rifle by 'Thom Turner' 55½ins barrel 36½ins. £40

2. A good quality 9.3 mm double barrelled underlever hammer rifle 40ins, barrels 24½ins. £95

3. A rare .44 Winchester 1866 rifle 46¼ins, barrel 27ins. £150

4. A rare .44ins rimfire Winchester 1866 rifle 43¾ins octagonal barrel 24¼ins. £190

5. A .44ins Winchester 3rd model 1873 tube magazine rifle 43ins, round barrel 24½ins. £105

6. A scarce .44ins rimfire Winchester 1866 carbine 39½ins, round barrel 20ins. £180

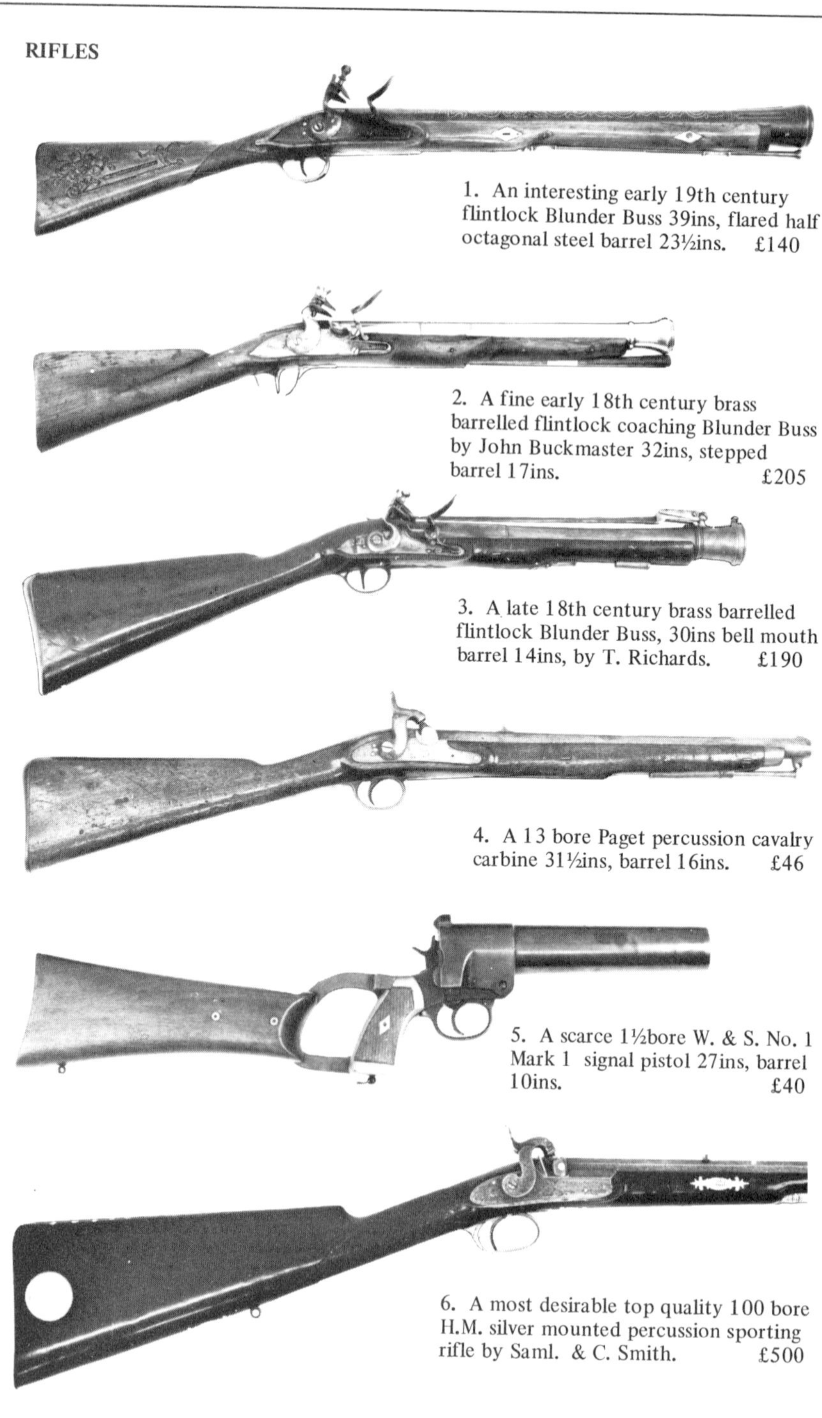

1. An interesting early 19th century flintlock Blunder Buss 39ins, flared half octagonal steel barrel 23½ins. £140

2. A fine early 18th century brass barrelled flintlock coaching Blunder Buss by John Buckmaster 32ins, stepped barrel 17ins. £205

3. A late 18th century brass barrelled flintlock Blunder Buss, 30ins bell mouth barrel 14ins, by T. Richards. £190

4. A 13 bore Paget percussion cavalry carbine 31½ins, barrel 16ins. £46

5. A scarce 1½bore W. & S. No. 1 Mark 1 signal pistol 27ins, barrel 10ins. £40

6. A most desirable top quality 100 bore H.M. silver mounted percussion sporting rifle by Saml. & C. Smith. £500

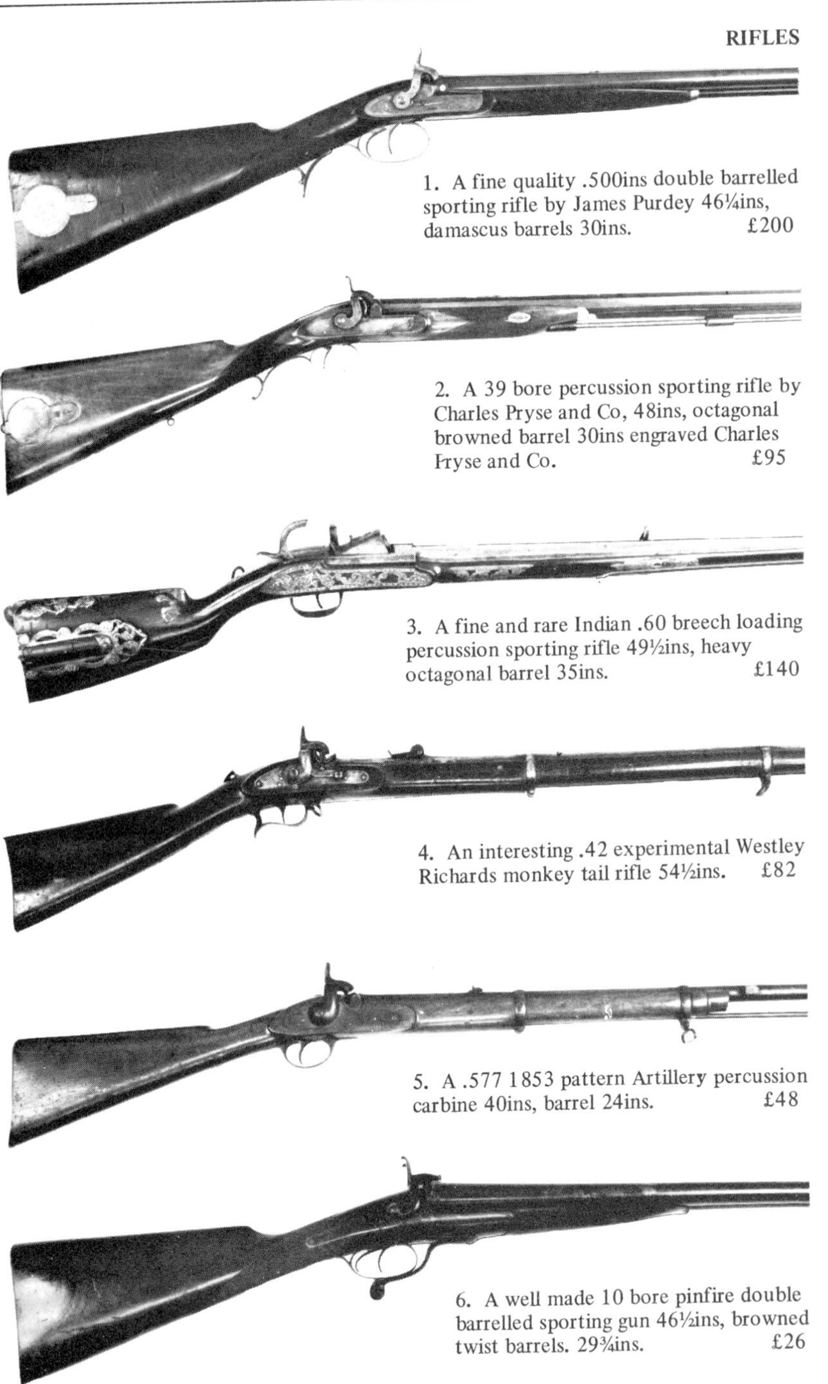

1. A fine quality .500ins double barrelled sporting rifle by James Purdey 46¼ins, damascus barrels 30ins. £200

2. A 39 bore percussion sporting rifle by Charles Pryse and Co, 48ins, octagonal browned barrel 30ins engraved Charles Fryse and Co. £95

3. A fine and rare Indian .60 breech loading percussion sporting rifle 49½ins, heavy octagonal barrel 35ins. £140

4. An interesting .42 experimental Westley Richards monkey tail rifle 54½ins. £82

5. A .577 1853 pattern Artillery percussion carbine 40ins, barrel 24ins. £48

6. A well made 10 bore pinfire double barrelled sporting gun 46½ins, browned twist barrels. 29¾ins. £26

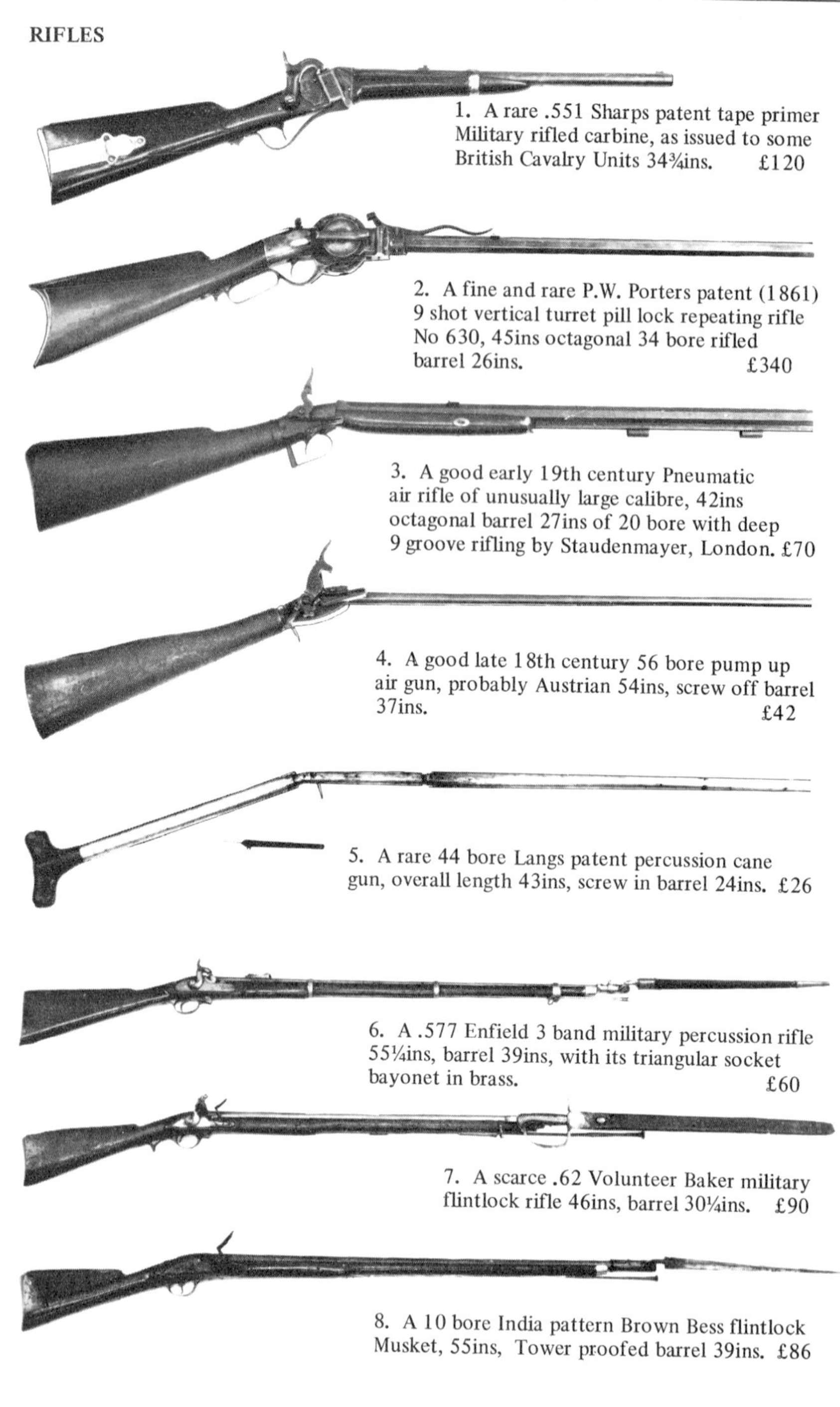

1. A rare .551 Sharps patent tape primer Military rifled carbine, as issued to some British Cavalry Units 34¾ins. £120

2. A fine and rare P.W. Porters patent (1861) 9 shot vertical turret pill lock repeating rifle No 630, 45ins octagonal 34 bore rifled barrel 26ins. £340

3. A good early 19th century Pneumatic air rifle of unusually large calibre, 42ins octagonal barrel 27ins of 20 bore with deep 9 groove rifling by Staudenmayer, London. £70

4. A good late 18th century 56 bore pump up air gun, probably Austrian 54ins, screw off barrel 37ins. £42

5. A rare 44 bore Langs patent percussion cane gun, overall length 43ins, screw in barrel 24ins. £26

6. A .577 Enfield 3 band military percussion rifle 55¼ins, barrel 39ins, with its triangular socket bayonet in brass. £60

7. A scarce .62 Volunteer Baker military flintlock rifle 46ins, barrel 30¼ins. £90

8. A 10 bore India pattern Brown Bess flintlock Musket, 55ins, Tower proofed barrel 39ins. £86

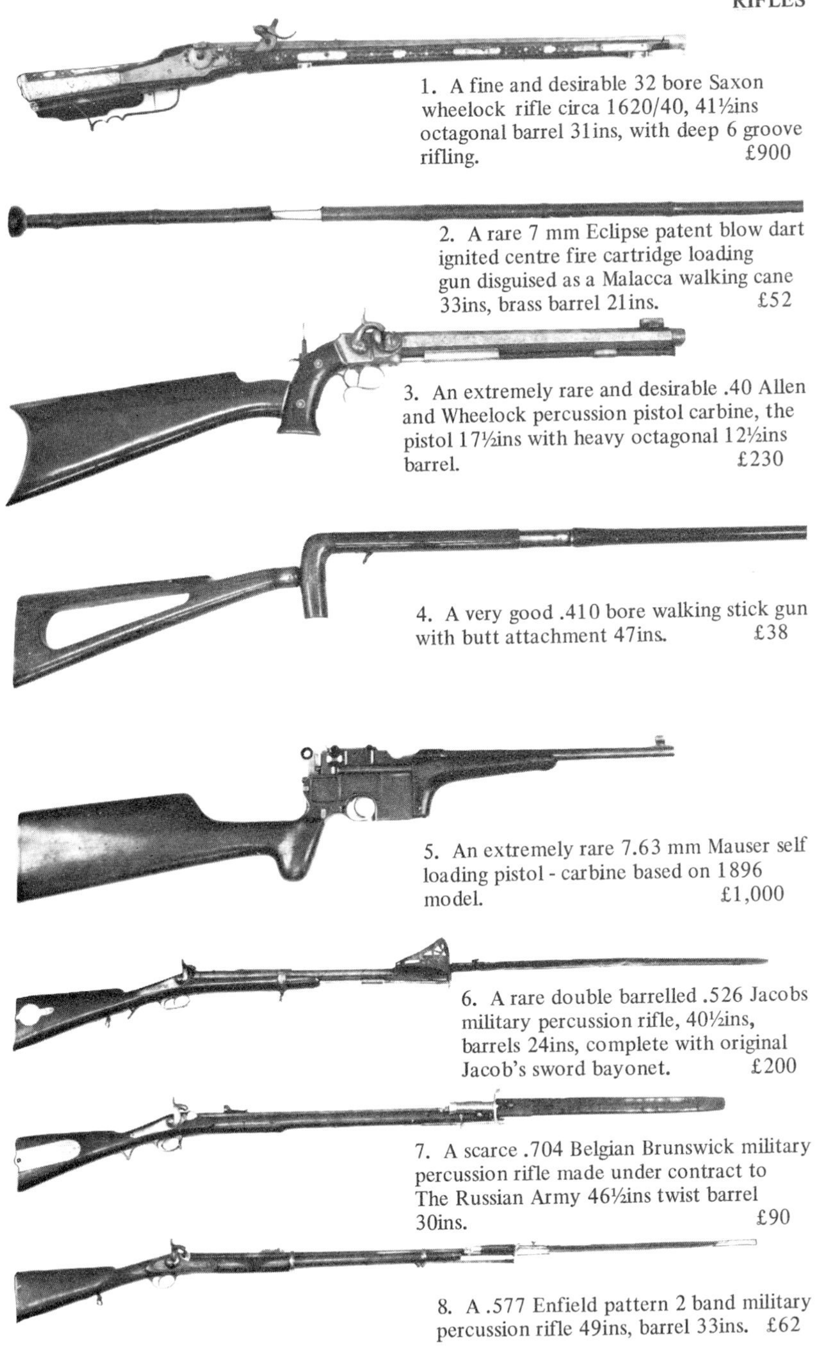

1. A fine and desirable 32 bore Saxon wheelock rifle circa 1620/40, 41½ins octagonal barrel 31ins, with deep 6 groove rifling. £900

2. A rare 7 mm Eclipse patent blow dart ignited centre fire cartridge loading gun disguised as a Malacca walking cane 33ins, brass barrel 21ins. £52

3. An extremely rare and desirable .40 Allen and Wheelock percussion pistol carbine, the pistol 17½ins with heavy octagonal 12½ins barrel. £230

4. A very good .410 bore walking stick gun with butt attachment 47ins. £38

5. An extremely rare 7.63 mm Mauser self loading pistol - carbine based on 1896 model. £1,000

6. A rare double barrelled .526 Jacobs military percussion rifle, 40½ins, barrels 24ins, complete with original Jacob's sword bayonet. £200

7. A scarce .704 Belgian Brunswick military percussion rifle made under contract to The Russian Army 46½ins twist barrel 30ins. £90

8. A .577 Enfield pattern 2 band military percussion rifle 49ins, barrel 33ins. £62

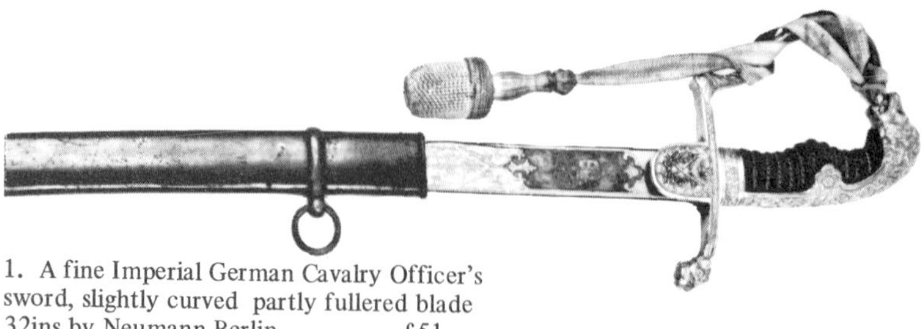

1. A fine Imperial German Cavalry Officer's sword, slightly curved partly fullered blade 32ins by Neumann Berlin. £51

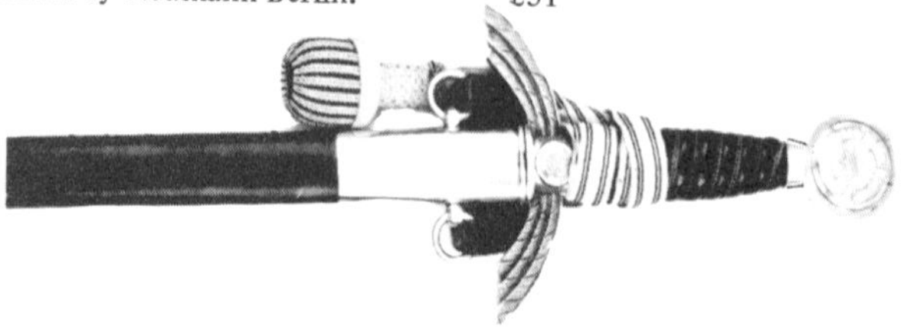

2. A good Nazi Army Officer's sword, slightly curved blade 34ins (mint) by Alcoso. £32

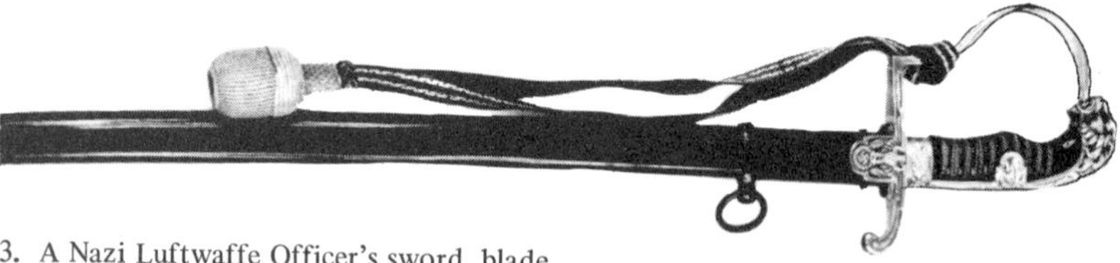

3. A Nazi Luftwaffe Officer's sword, blade 28½ins by Eickhorn. £43

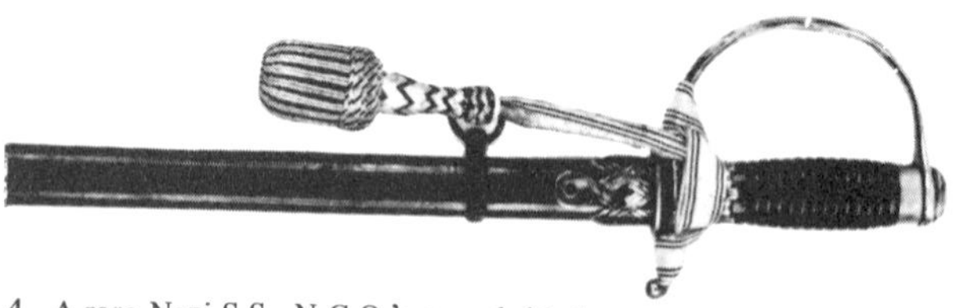

4. A rare Nazi S.S. N.C.O.'s sword, blade 31ins by Krebs. £70

5. A rare Nazi Police Officer's presentation boy service sword, blade 32½ins by Weyersberg. £76

1. A scarce mid 18th century British Military brass hilted hanger, slightly curved blade 25ins by Dawes of Birmingham. £35

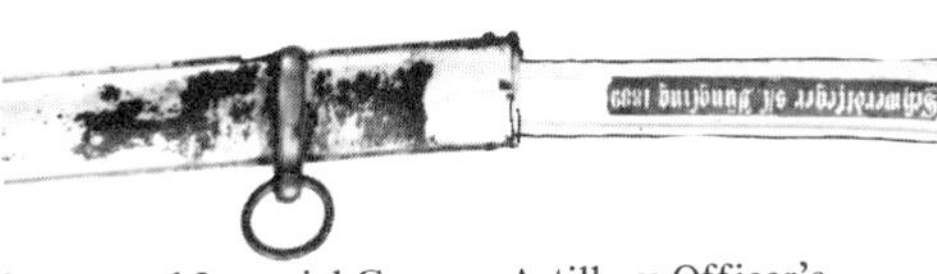

2. A good Imperial German Artillery Officer's sword curved pipe backed, clip back blade 36ins by W.K.C. £47

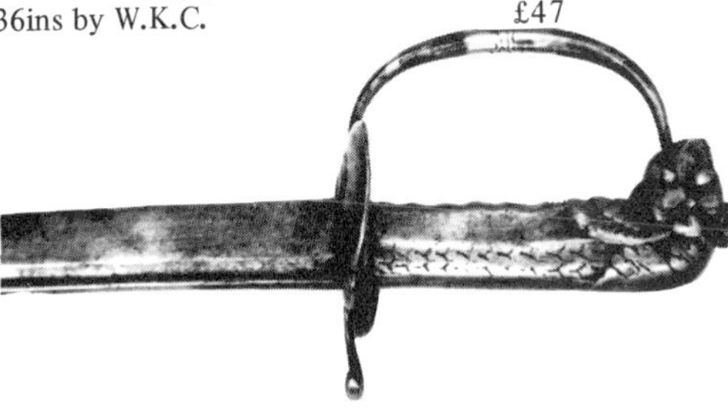

3. A late 17th century hanger, single edged fullered blade, 27ins. £36

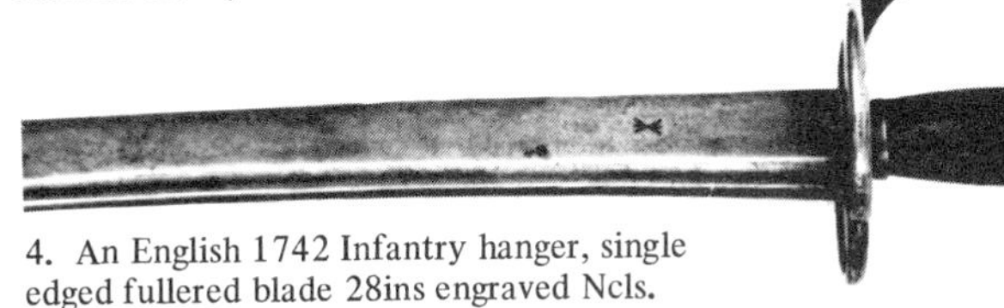

4. An English 1742 Infantry hanger, single edged fullered blade 28ins engraved Ncls. Deakin. £65

5. A desirable 1742 General Pattern Infantry Private's brass hilted hanger, dated 1762. £56

1. A scarce mid 18th century British Military brass hilted hanger, slightly curved blade 24½ins. £40

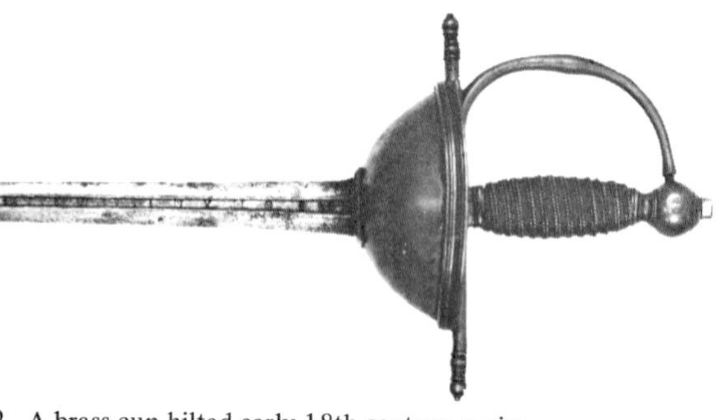

2. A brass cup hilted early 18th century rapier, blade 36½ins. £85

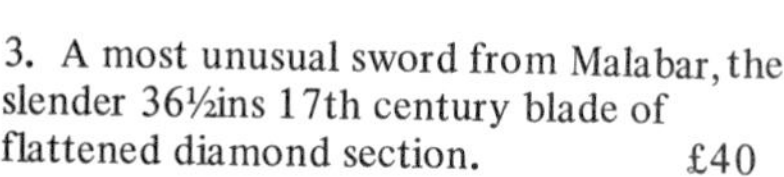

3. A most unusual sword from Malabar, the slender 36½ins 17th century blade of flattened diamond section. £40

4. A rare 1796 pattern heavy Cavalry Officer's sword, straight single edged blade 35ins. £42

5. A fine late 18th century Prussian Officer's model 1732/97 Cavalry backsword (Kurassierpallasch). £135

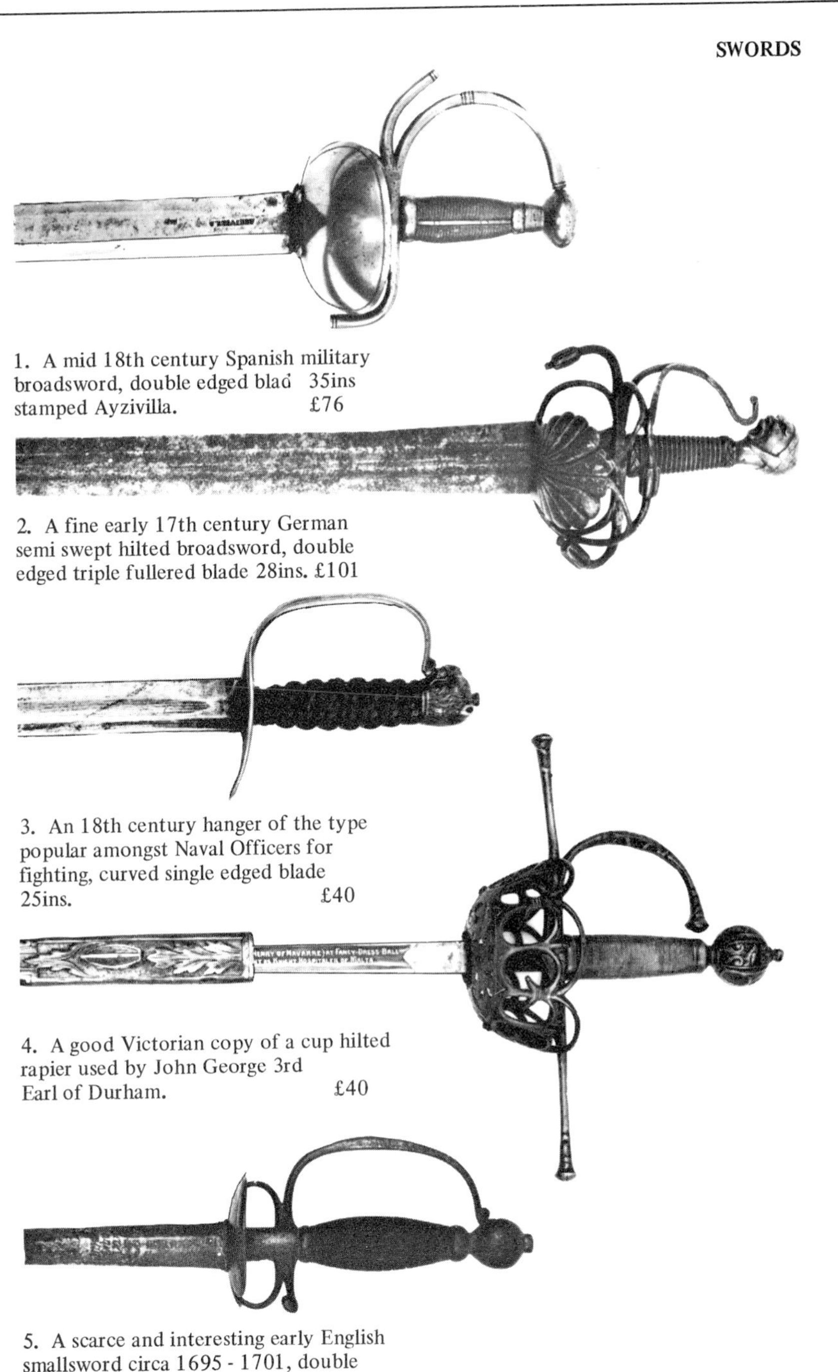

1. A mid 18th century Spanish military broadsword, double edged blad 35ins stamped Ayzivilla. £76

2. A fine early 17th century German semi swept hilted broadsword, double edged triple fullered blade 28ins. £101

3. An 18th century hanger of the type popular amongst Naval Officers for fighting, curved single edged blade 25ins. £40

4. A good Victorian copy of a cup hilted rapier used by John George 3rd Earl of Durham. £40

5. A scarce and interesting early English smallsword circa 1695 - 1701, double edged blade 29ins. £70

SWORDS

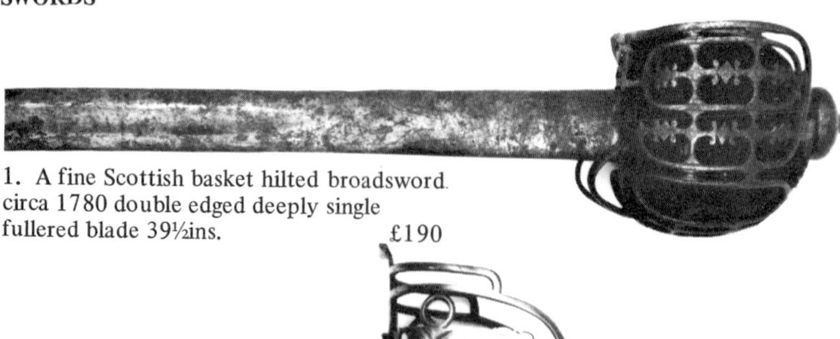

1. A fine Scottish basket hilted broadsword circa 1780 double edged deeply single fullered blade 39½ins. £190

2. A late 19th century Military Issue Scottish broadsword plain straight double edged blade by Mole. £45

3. A post 1902 Scottish Officer's broadsword of The Argyll and Sutherland Highlanders. £47

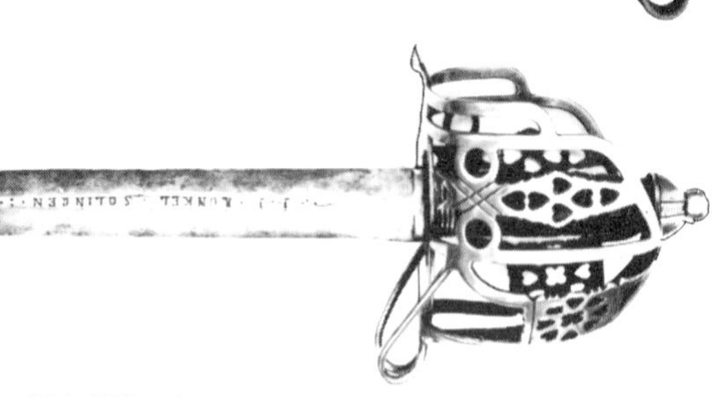

4. A Scottish Officer's basket hilted broadsword circa 1800, double edged blade 33ins. £60

5. A good fine early 18th century Military Scottish broadsword, broad straight double edged blade 34¾ins. £150

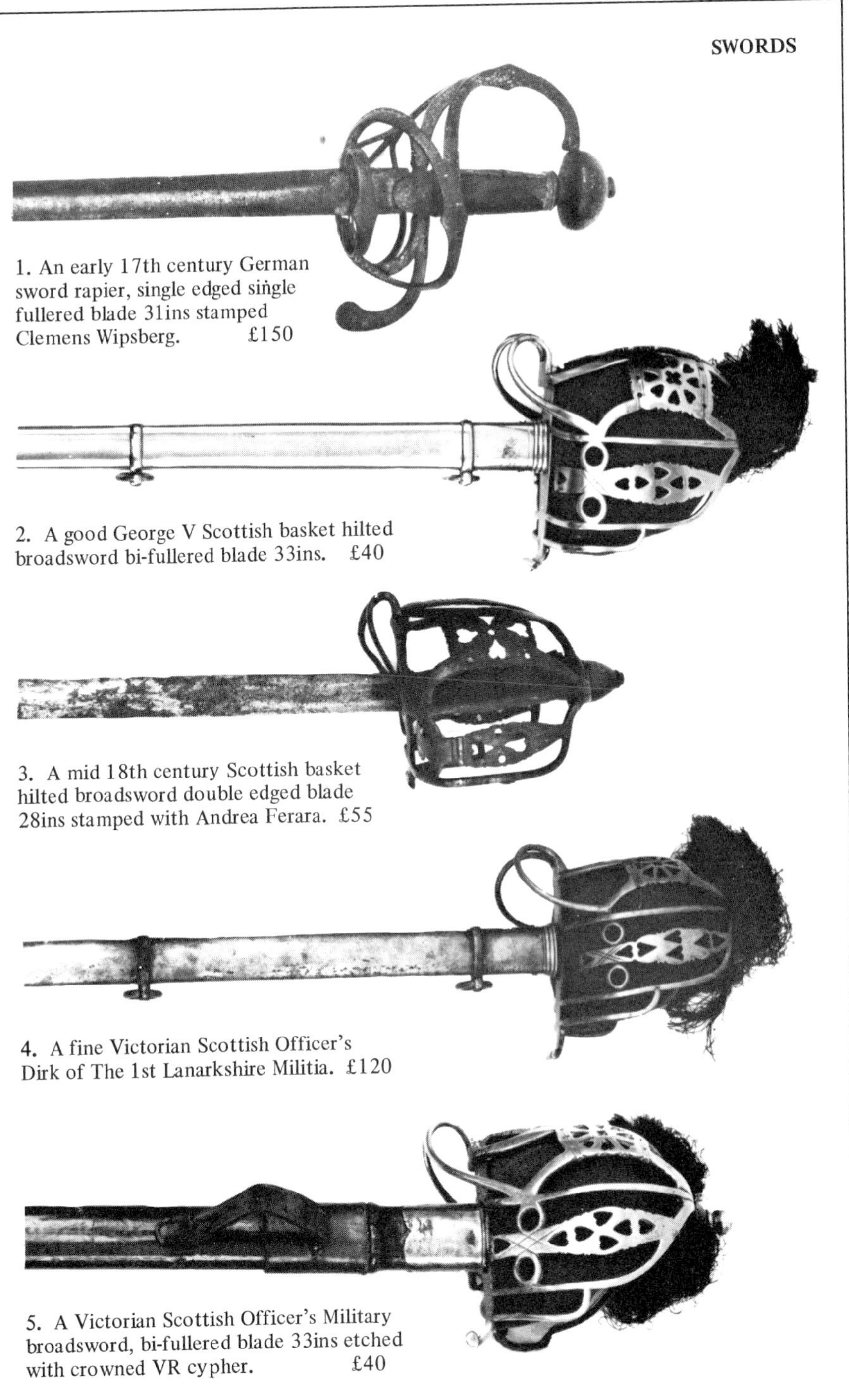

1. An early 17th century German sword rapier, single edged single fullered blade 31ins stamped Clemens Wipsberg. £150

2. A good George V Scottish basket hilted broadsword bi-fullered blade 33ins. £40

3. A mid 18th century Scottish basket hilted broadsword double edged blade 28ins stamped with Andrea Ferara. £55

4. A fine Victorian Scottish Officer's Dirk of The 1st Lanarkshire Militia. £120

5. A Victorian Scottish Officer's Military broadsword, bi-fullered blade 33ins etched with crowned VR cypher. £40

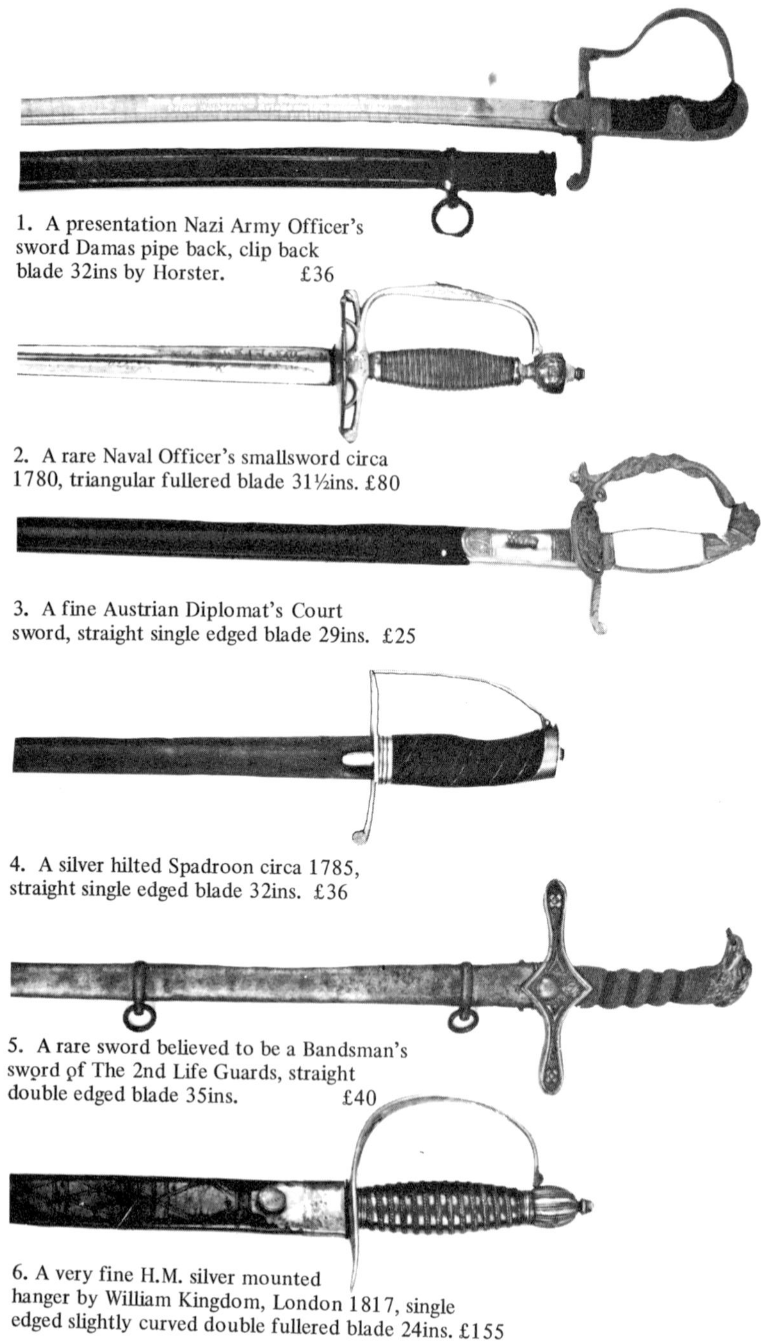

1. A presentation Nazi Army Officer's sword Damas pipe back, clip back blade 32ins by Horster. £36

2. A rare Naval Officer's smallsword circa 1780, triangular fullered blade 31½ins. £80

3. A fine Austrian Diplomat's Court sword, straight single edged blade 29ins. £25

4. A silver hilted Spadroon circa 1785, straight single edged blade 32ins. £36

5. A rare sword believed to be a Bandsman's sword of The 2nd Life Guards, straight double edged blade 35ins. £40

6. A very fine H.M. silver mounted hanger by William Kingdom, London 1817, single edged slightly curved double fullered blade 24ins. £155

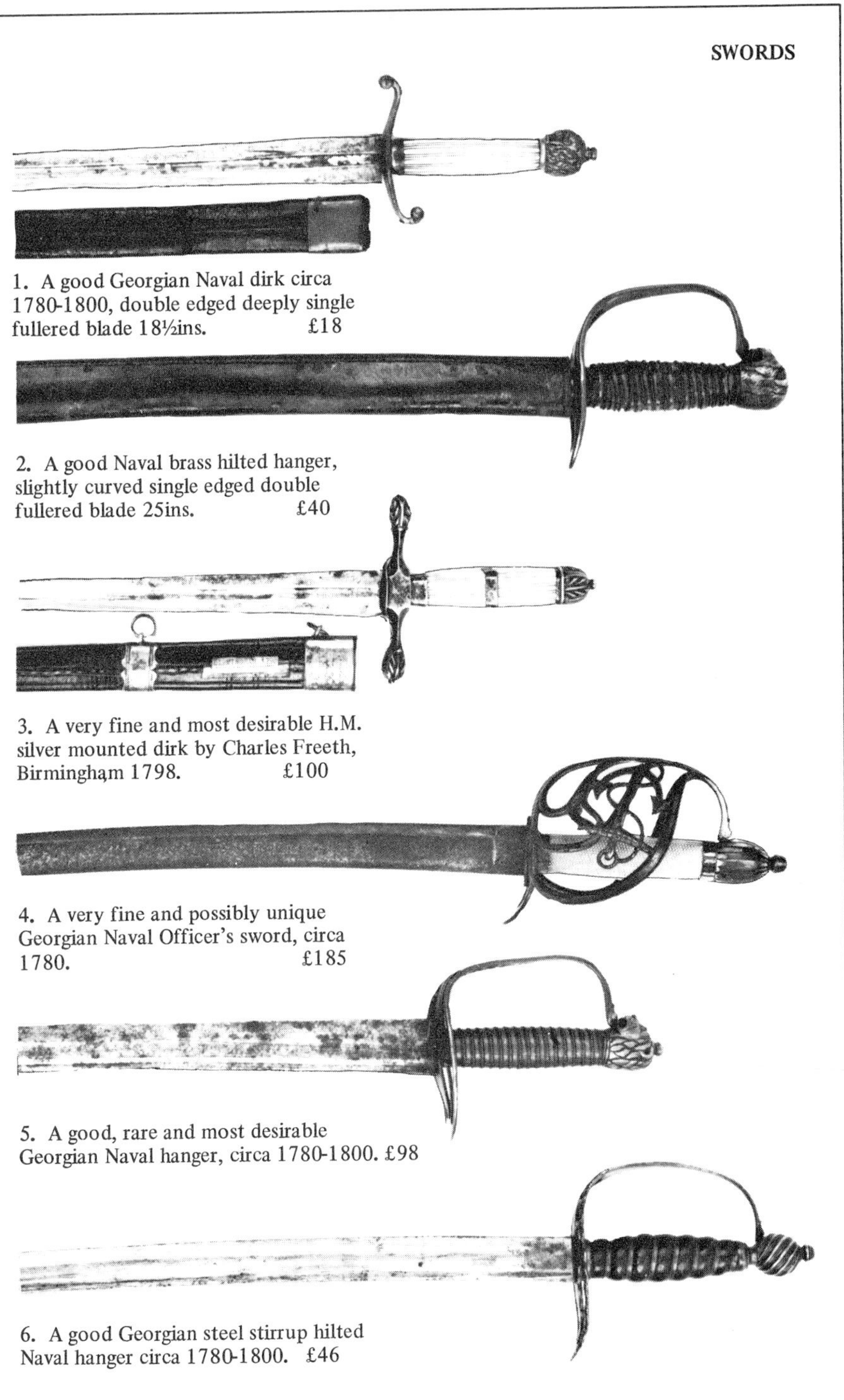

1. A good Georgian Naval dirk circa 1780-1800, double edged deeply single fullered blade 18½ins. £18

2. A good Naval brass hilted hanger, slightly curved single edged double fullered blade 25ins. £40

3. A very fine and most desirable H.M. silver mounted dirk by Charles Freeth, Birmingham 1798. £100

4. A very fine and possibly unique Georgian Naval Officer's sword, circa 1780. £185

5. A good, rare and most desirable Georgian Naval hanger, circa 1780-1800. £98

6. A good Georgian steel stirrup hilted Naval hanger circa 1780-1800. £46

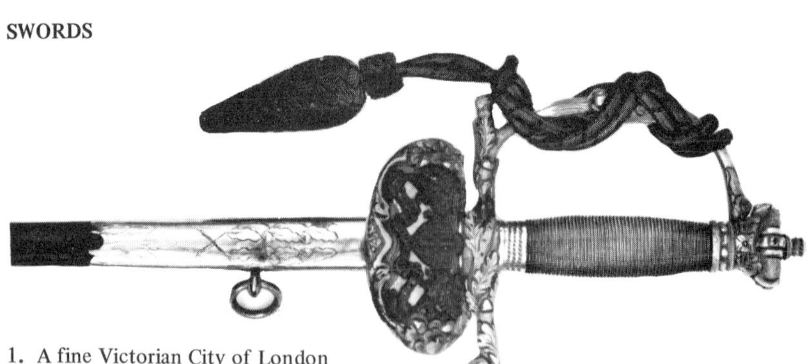

1. A fine Victorian City of London Sheriff's sword, blade 30ins etched with London's City Arms. £36

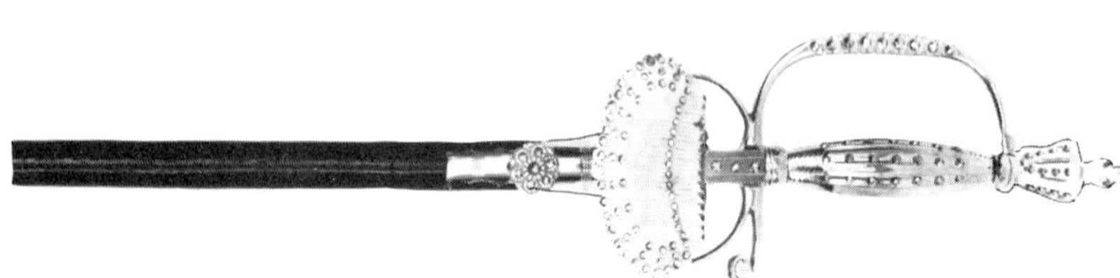

2. A Court sword, plain blade 30¾ins of triangular section. £31

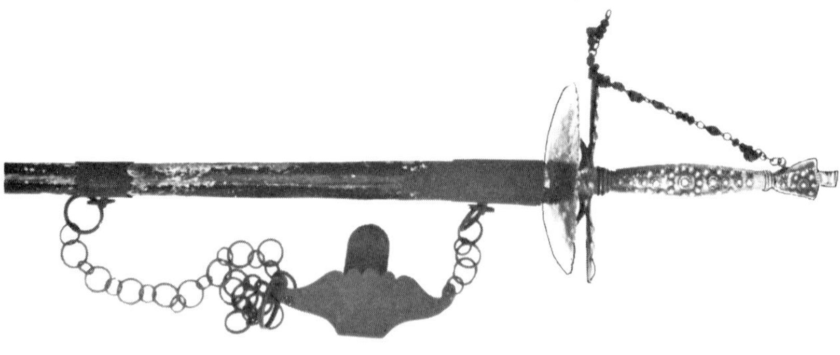

3. A good Georgian Court sword, trefoil section blade 30½ins. £25

4. An early 19th century French presentation sword, single edged slightly fullered blade 29¼ins with broad fuller. £150

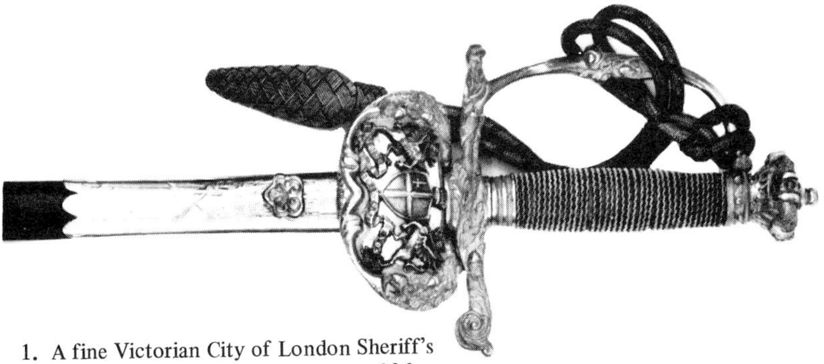

1. A fine Victorian City of London Sheriff's sword, blade 30ins. £36

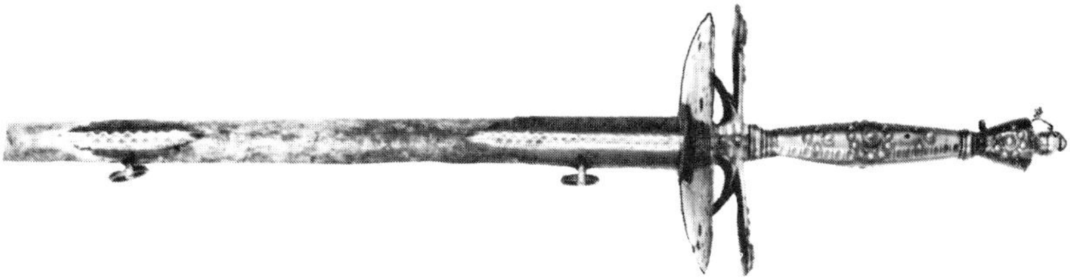

2. A good Georgian Court sword, trefoil sectioned blade 31½ins etched with scrolls and Firmin. £29

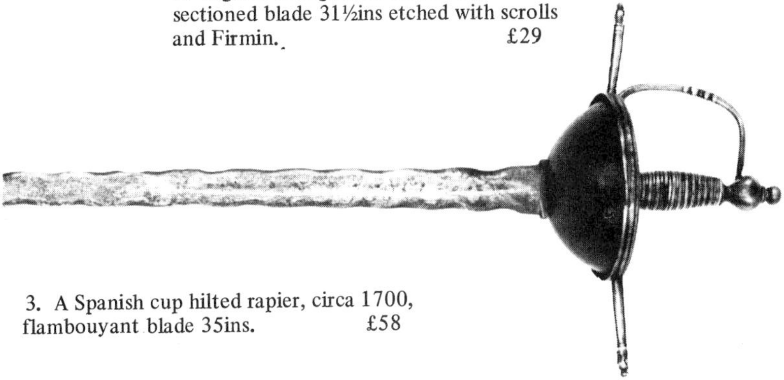

3. A Spanish cup hilted rapier, circa 1700, flambouyant blade 35ins. £58

4. A scarce Japanese sword Tachi 18ins probably made for a boy, blade 9½ins. £26

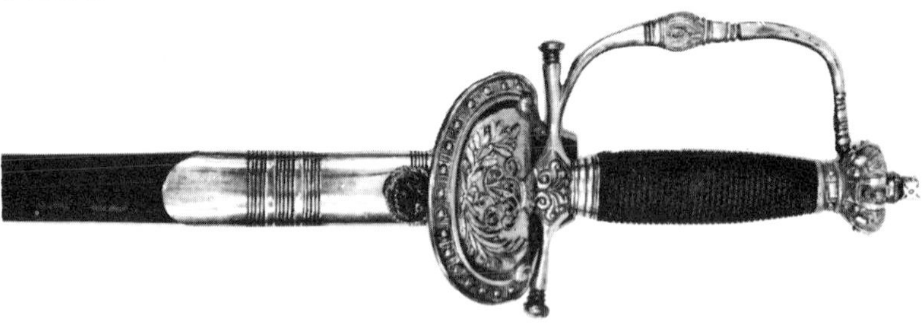

1. A good Victorian Court sword, blade 30ins etched with the crowned Royal Cypher amid foliage. £26

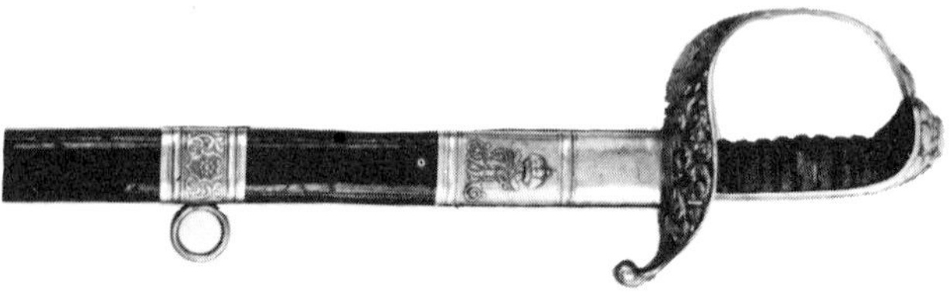

2. An Imperial Austrian sword, slightly curved fullered single edged blade 29ins. £20

3. A fine and rare early 17th century sword stick, flattened diamond section rapier blade 41½ins signed Martinus Me Fecit. £80

4. A good pair of Japanese swords Daisho comprising Wakizashi blade 16½ins Bo-Hi Tsure-Hi, Maru-Dome, Ryo-Chiri, Mokume-Hada O-Kissaki Patinated Shakudo Habaki Mokko Nanako Tsuba with gilt Mons of the Fujiwara family. £260

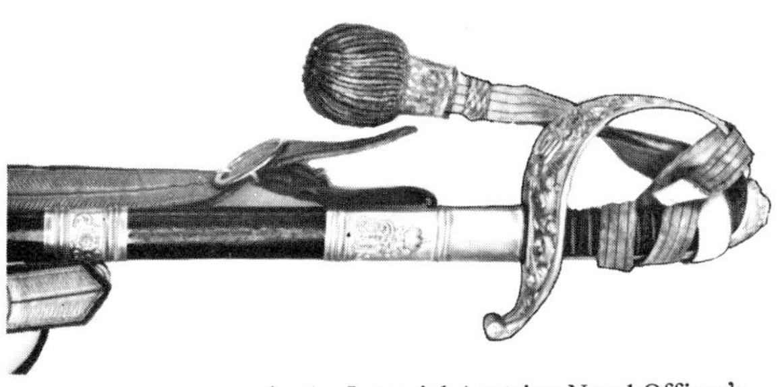

1. An Imperial Austrian Naval Officer's sword, slightly curved plain plated blade 28ins by Weyersberg. £30

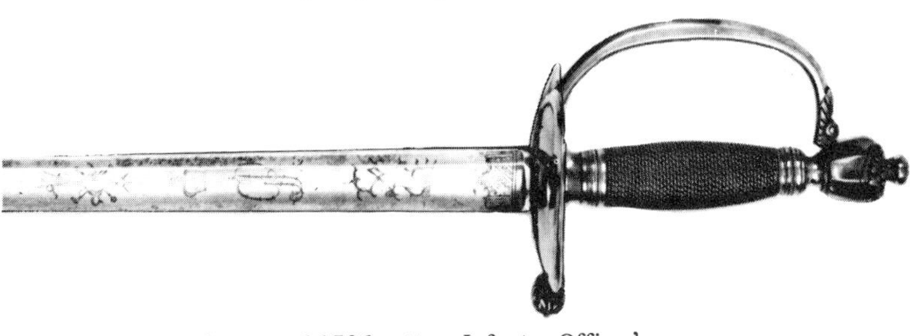

2. A good 1796 pattern Infantry Officer's sword, blade 32½ins engraved crowned G.R. £28

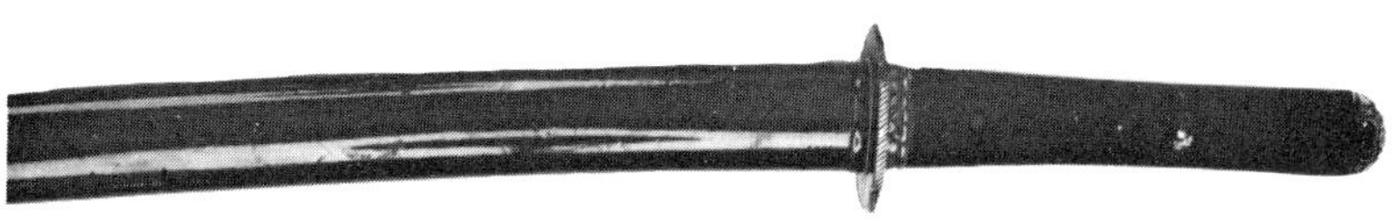

3. A very fine and attractive silver mounted Japanese shortsword Wakizashi, blade 22½ins. £64

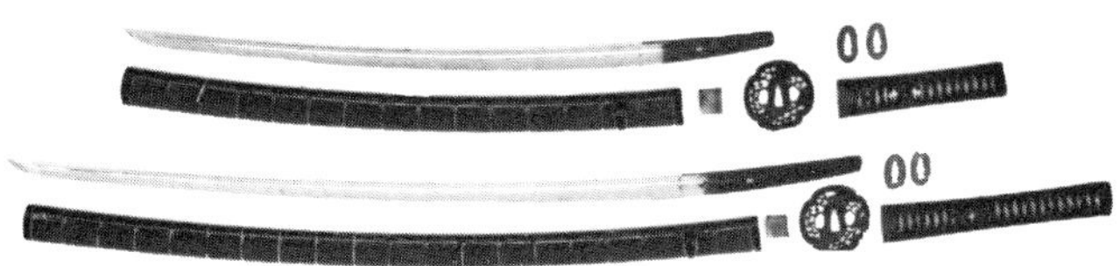

4. A good Daisho of Japanese swords in 16th century style, probably of 18th century manufacture, Katana, Shinogi-Zukuri 25½ins, of slender tapering form, unsigned, one Mekugi Ana. Alternatively Ichibon and Nibon Sugi Yakiba, Ayasugi Hada, Bo-Hi Ni Tsure-Hi, Kaki Toshi, Hisaki Agari, Kata-Chiri Kaen Boshi Chu Kissaki. £860

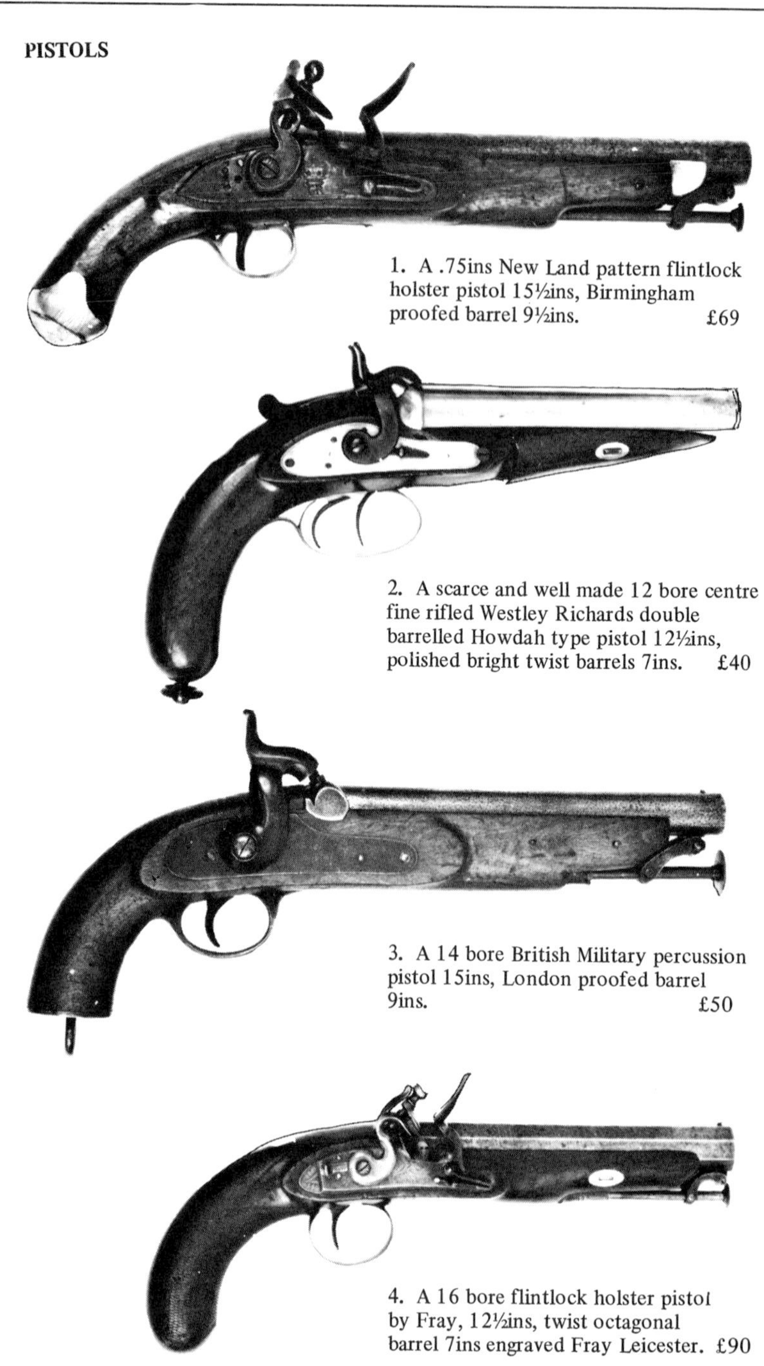

1. A .75ins New Land pattern flintlock holster pistol 15½ins, Birmingham proofed barrel 9½ins. £69

2. A scarce and well made 12 bore centre fine rifled Westley Richards double barrelled Howdah type pistol 12½ins, polished bright twist barrels 7ins. £40

3. A 14 bore British Military percussion pistol 15ins, London proofed barrel 9ins. £50

4. A 16 bore flintlock holster pistol by Fray, 12½ins, twist octagonal barrel 7ins engraved Fray Leicester. £90

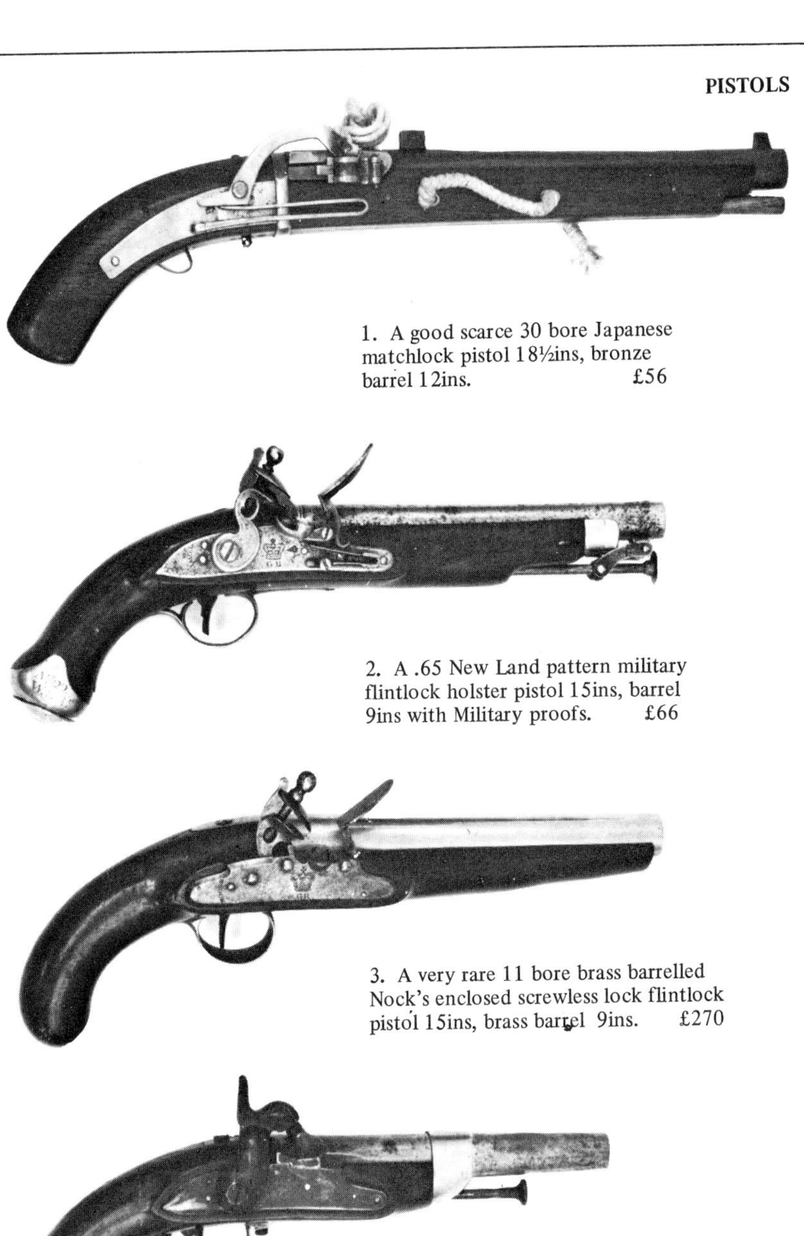

1. A good scarce 30 bore Japanese matchlock pistol 18½ins, bronze barrel 12ins. £56

2. A .65 New Land pattern military flintlock holster pistol 15ins, barrel 9ins with Military proofs. £66

3. A very rare 11 bore brass barrelled Nock's enclosed screwless lock flintlock pistol 15ins, brass barrel 9ins. £270

4. A French 15 bore Military percussion holster pistol 14ins barrel 8ins, converted from Model 1822 flintlock. £70

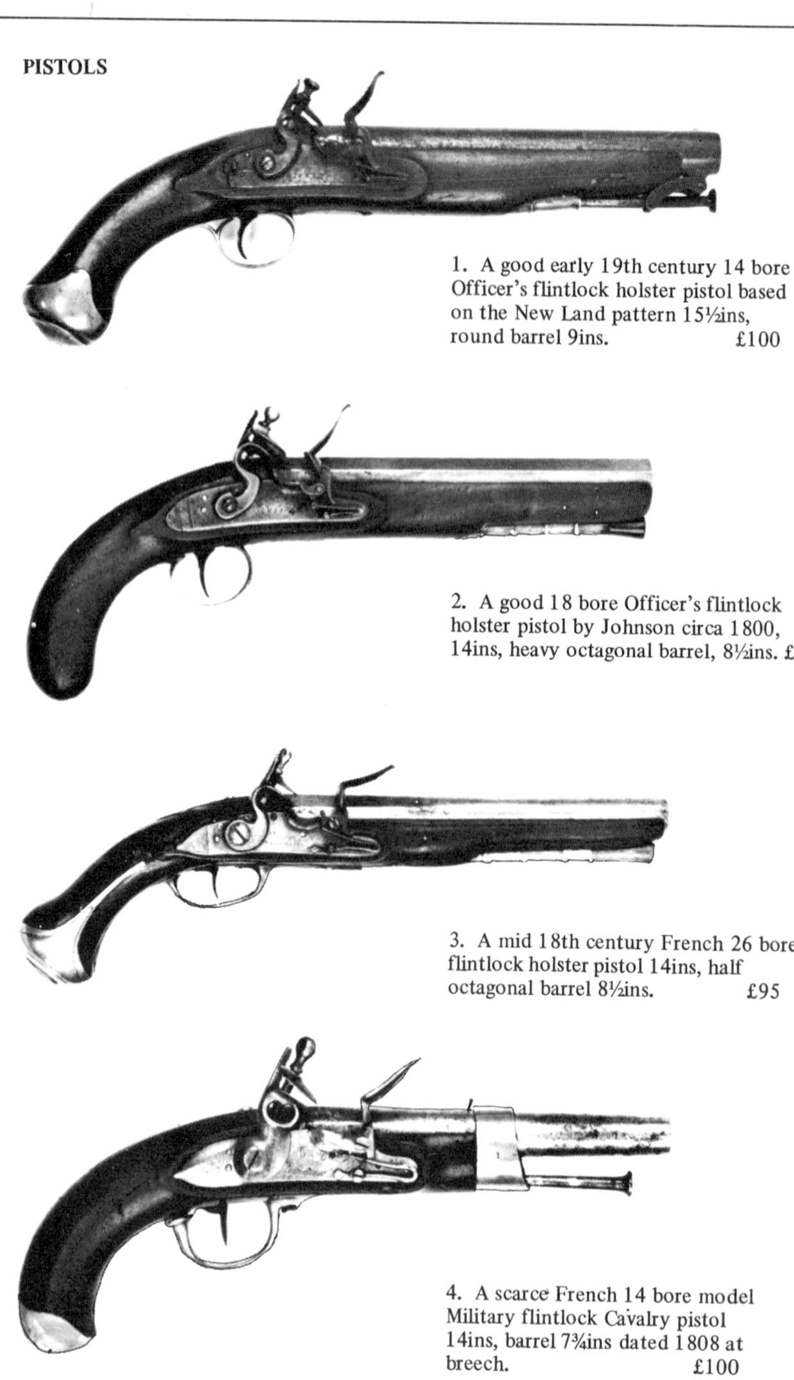

1. A good early 19th century 14 bore Officer's flintlock holster pistol based on the New Land pattern 15½ins, round barrel 9ins. £100

2. A good 18 bore Officer's flintlock holster pistol by Johnson circa 1800, 14ins, heavy octagonal barrel, 8½ins. £80

3. A mid 18th century French 26 bore flintlock holster pistol 14ins, half octagonal barrel 8½ins. £95

4. A scarce French 14 bore model Military flintlock Cavalry pistol 14ins, barrel 7¾ins dated 1808 at breech. £100

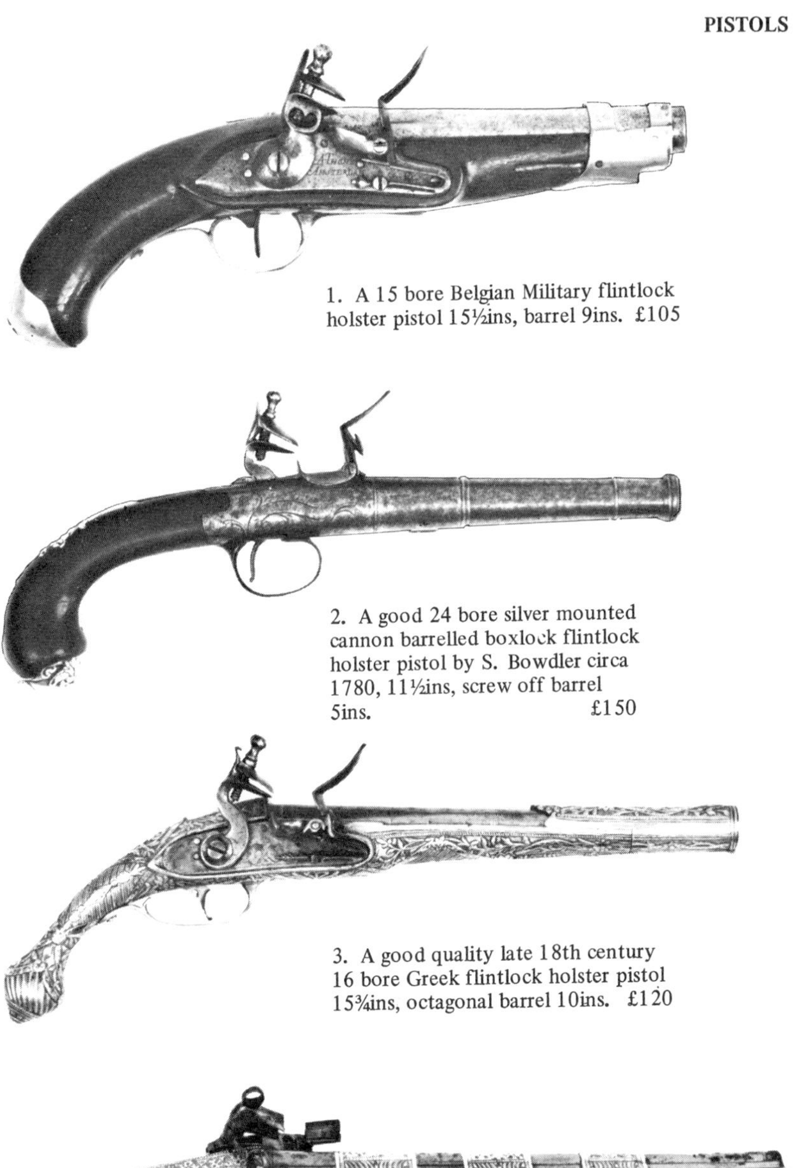

1. A 15 bore Belgian Military flintlock holster pistol 15½ins, barrel 9ins. £105

2. A good 24 bore silver mounted cannon barrelled boxlock flintlock holster pistol by S. Bowdler circa 1780, 11½ins, screw off barrel 5ins. £150

3. A good quality late 18th century 16 bore Greek flintlock holster pistol 15¾ins, octagonal barrel 10ins. £120

4. A rare double barrelled side by side 36 bore Russian Cossack Miquelet flintlock holster pistol circa 1800, 17ins, barrels 11ins. £275

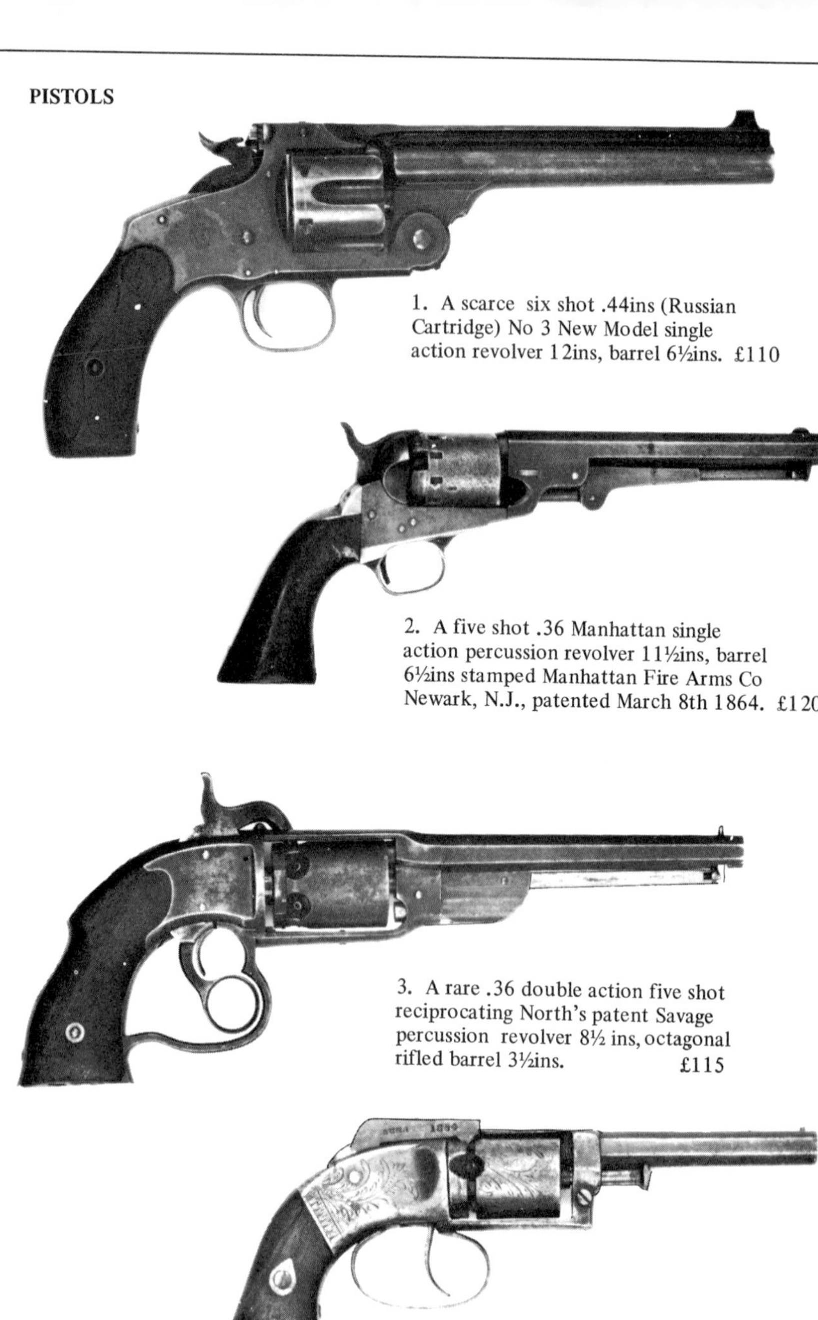

1. A scarce six shot .44ins (Russian Cartridge) No 3 New Model single action revolver 12ins, barrel 6½ins. £110

2. A five shot .36 Manhattan single action percussion revolver 11½ins, barrel 6½ins stamped Manhattan Fire Arms Co Newark, N.J., patented March 8th 1864. £120

3. A rare .36 double action five shot reciprocating North's patent Savage percussion revolver 8½ ins, octagonal rifled barrel 3½ins. £115

4. A scarce Ell's patent five shot self cocking percussion revolver 8½ins, octagonal rifled barrel 3½ins. £68

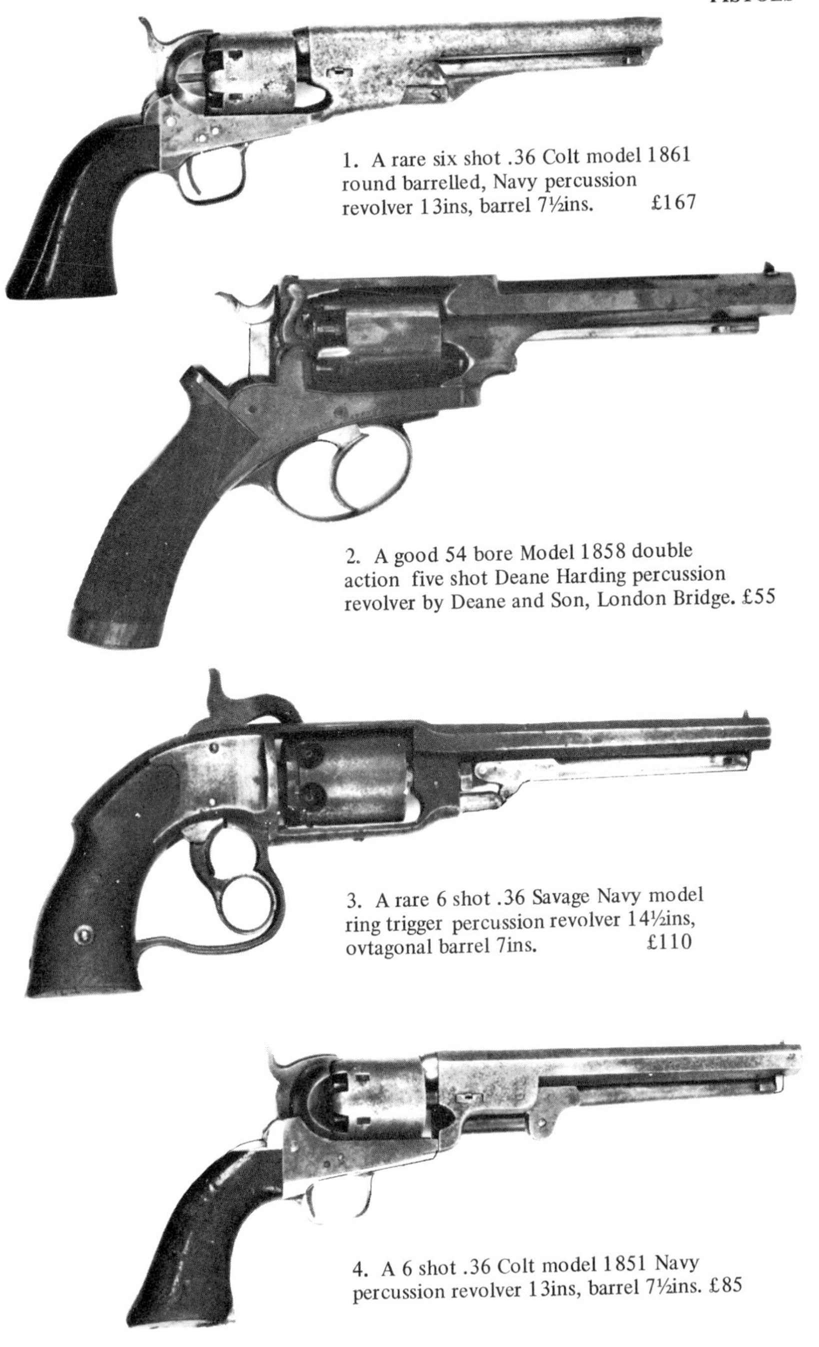

1. A rare six shot .36 Colt model 1861 round barrelled, Navy percussion revolver 13ins, barrel 7½ins. £167

2. A good 54 bore Model 1858 double action five shot Deane Harding percussion revolver by Deane and Son, London Bridge. £55

3. A rare 6 shot .36 Savage Navy model ring trigger percussion revolver 14½ins, ovtagonal barrel 7ins. £110

4. A 6 shot .36 Colt model 1851 Navy percussion revolver 13ins, barrel 7½ins. £85

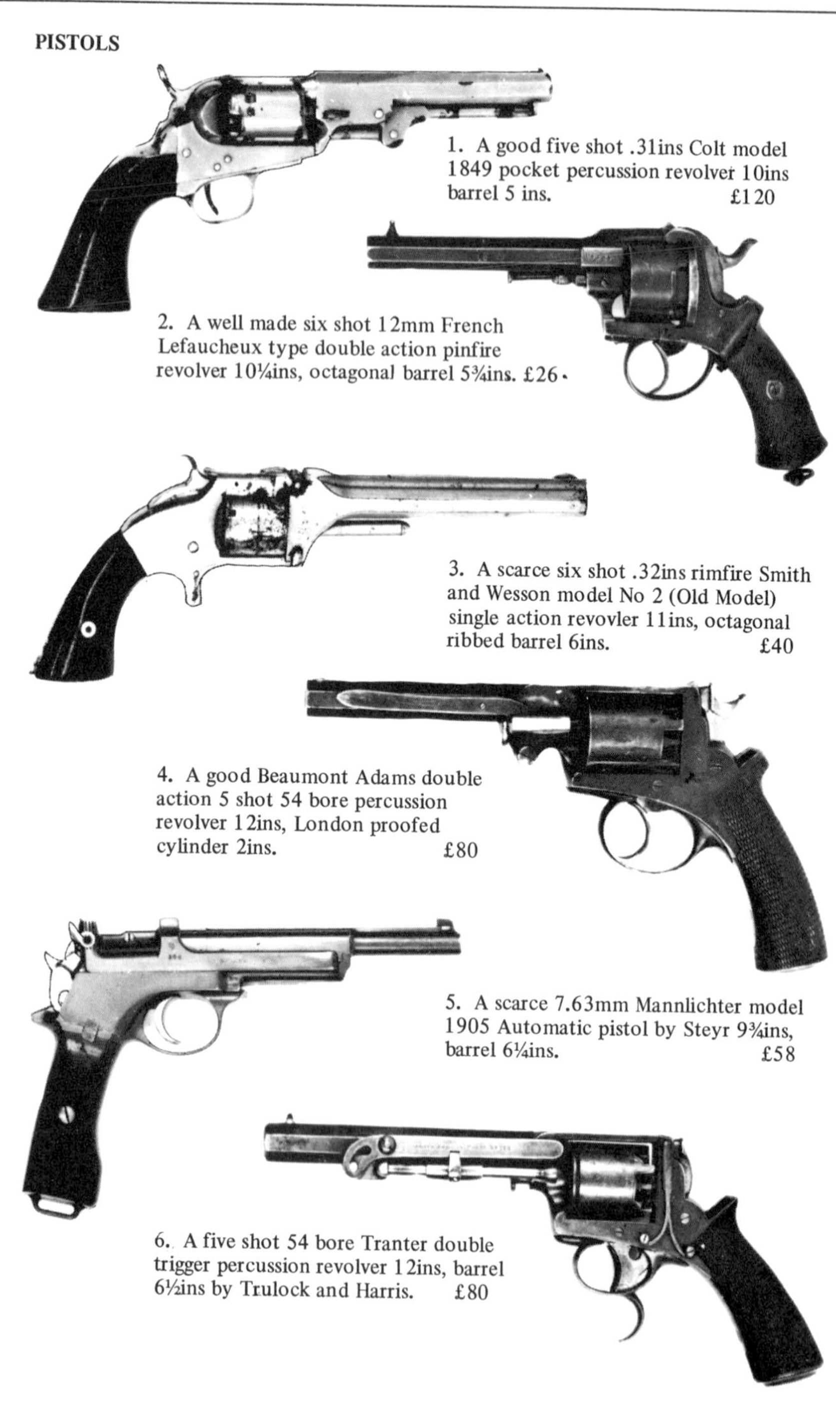

1. A good five shot .31ins Colt model 1849 pocket percussion revolver 10ins barrel 5 ins. £120

2. A well made six shot 12mm French Lefaucheux type double action pinfire revolver 10¼ins, octagonal barrel 5¾ins. £26

3. A scarce six shot .32ins rimfire Smith and Wesson model No 2 (Old Model) single action revovler 11ins, octagonal ribbed barrel 6ins. £40

4. A good Beaumont Adams double action 5 shot 54 bore percussion revolver 12ins, London proofed cylinder 2ins. £80

5. A scarce 7.63mm Mannlichter model 1905 Automatic pistol by Steyr 9¾ins, barrel 6¼ins. £58

6. A five shot 54 bore Tranter double trigger percussion revolver 12ins, barrel 6½ins by Trulock and Harris. £80

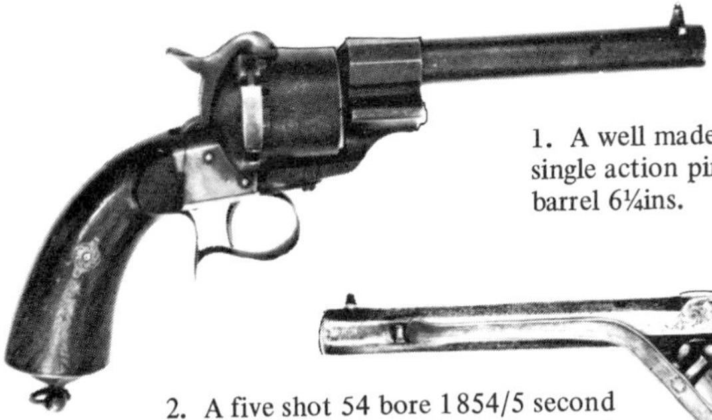

1. A well made 6 shot 11mm Lefaucheux single action pinfire revolver 11½ins, barrel 6¼ins. £40

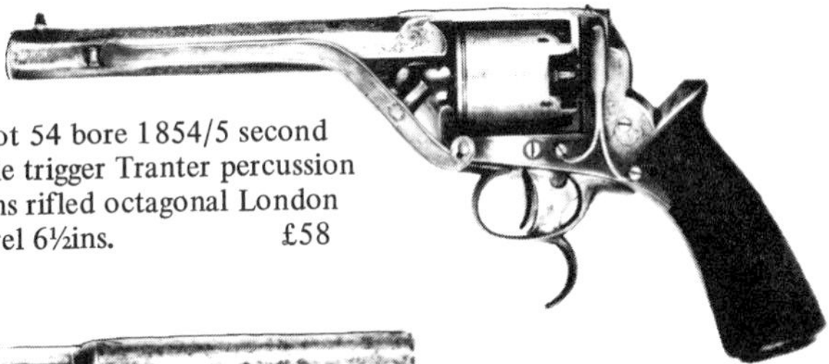

2. A five shot 54 bore 1854/5 second model double trigger Tranter percussion revolver 12ins rifled octagonal London proofed barrel 6½ins. £58

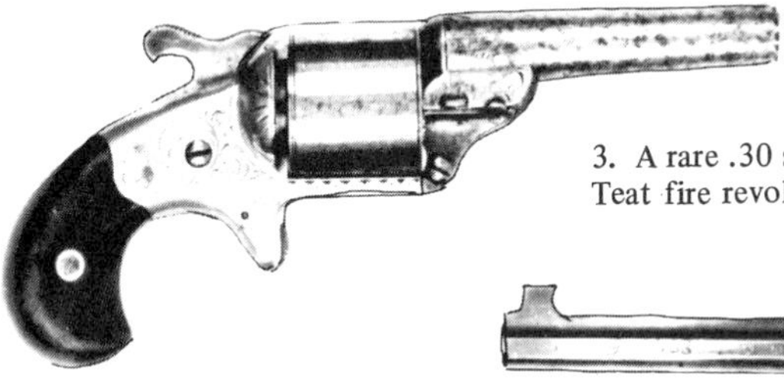

3. A rare .30 six shot Moore's patent Teat fire revolver 7¼ins, barrel 3¼ins. £65

4. A rare and desirable 8 shot .38ins Webley Poserry Automatic revolver model 1902, 10½ins, barrel 6ins. £205

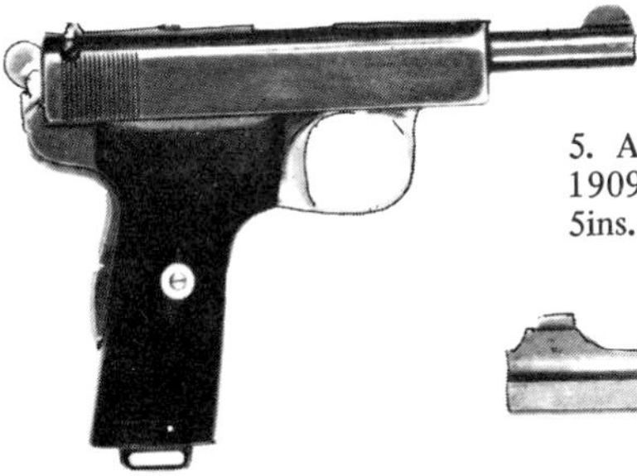

5. A scarce 9mm W. and S. model 1909 automatic pistol 8¼ins, barrel 5ins. £44

6. A scarce 6 shot .455ins (Cordite) Webley Fosberry automatic revolver 10½ins, barrel 6 ins. £125

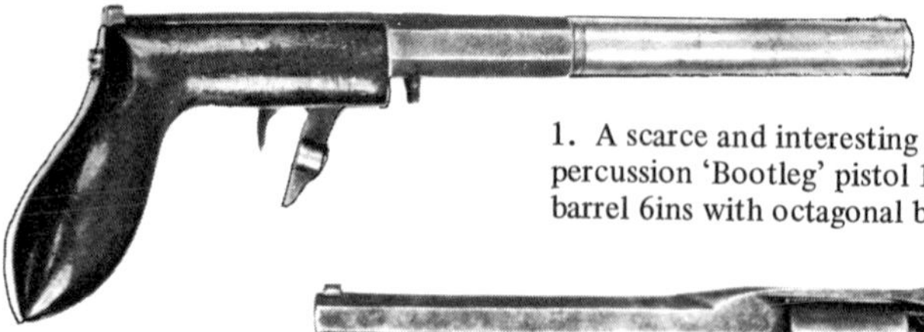

1. A scarce and interesting .36 underlever percussion 'Bootleg' pistol 10¼ins, rifled barrel 6ins with octagonal breech. £42

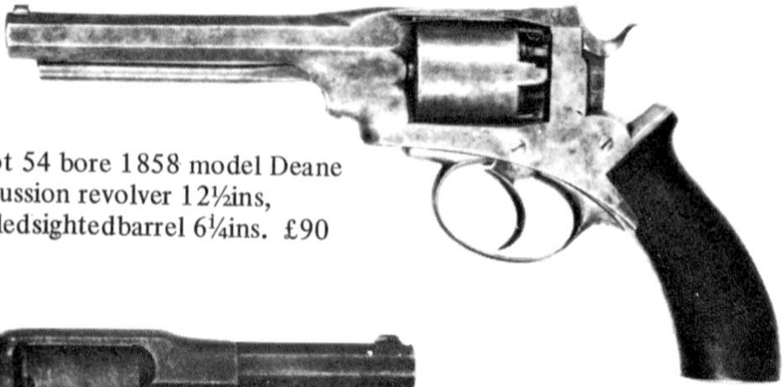

2. A five shot 54 bore 1858 model Deane Harding percussion revolver 12½ins, octagonal rifledsightedbarrel 6¼ins. £90

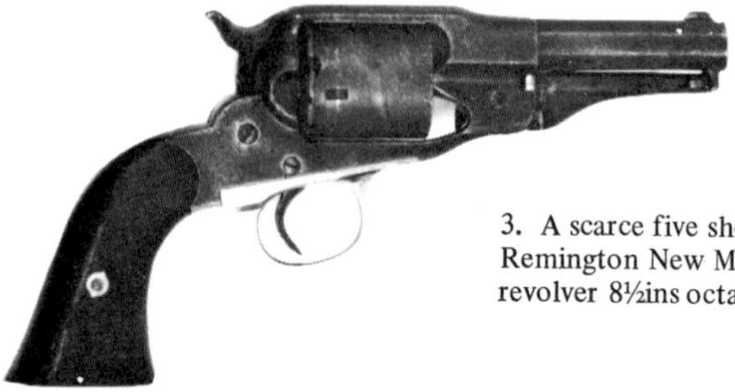

3. A scarce five shot .38ins rimfire Remington New Model 1863 single action revolver 8½ins octagonal barrels 3½ins. £50

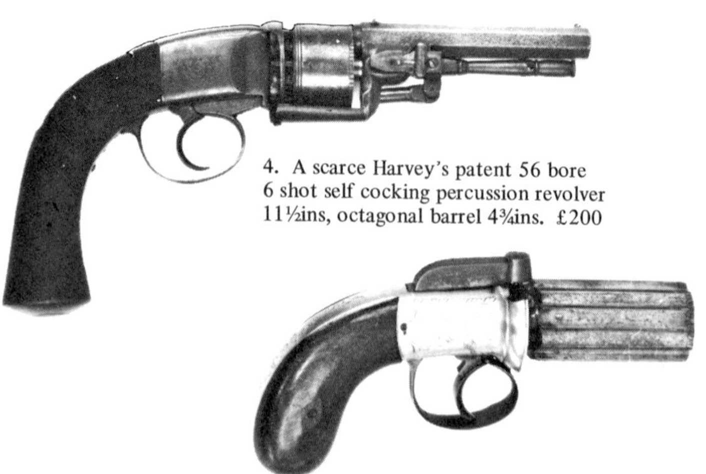

4. A scarce Harvey's patent 56 bore 6 shot self cocking percussion revolver 11½ins, octagonal barrel 4¾ins. £200

5. A 6 shot 120 bore top snap percussion pepperbox revolver 7ins, barrels 2½ins. £68

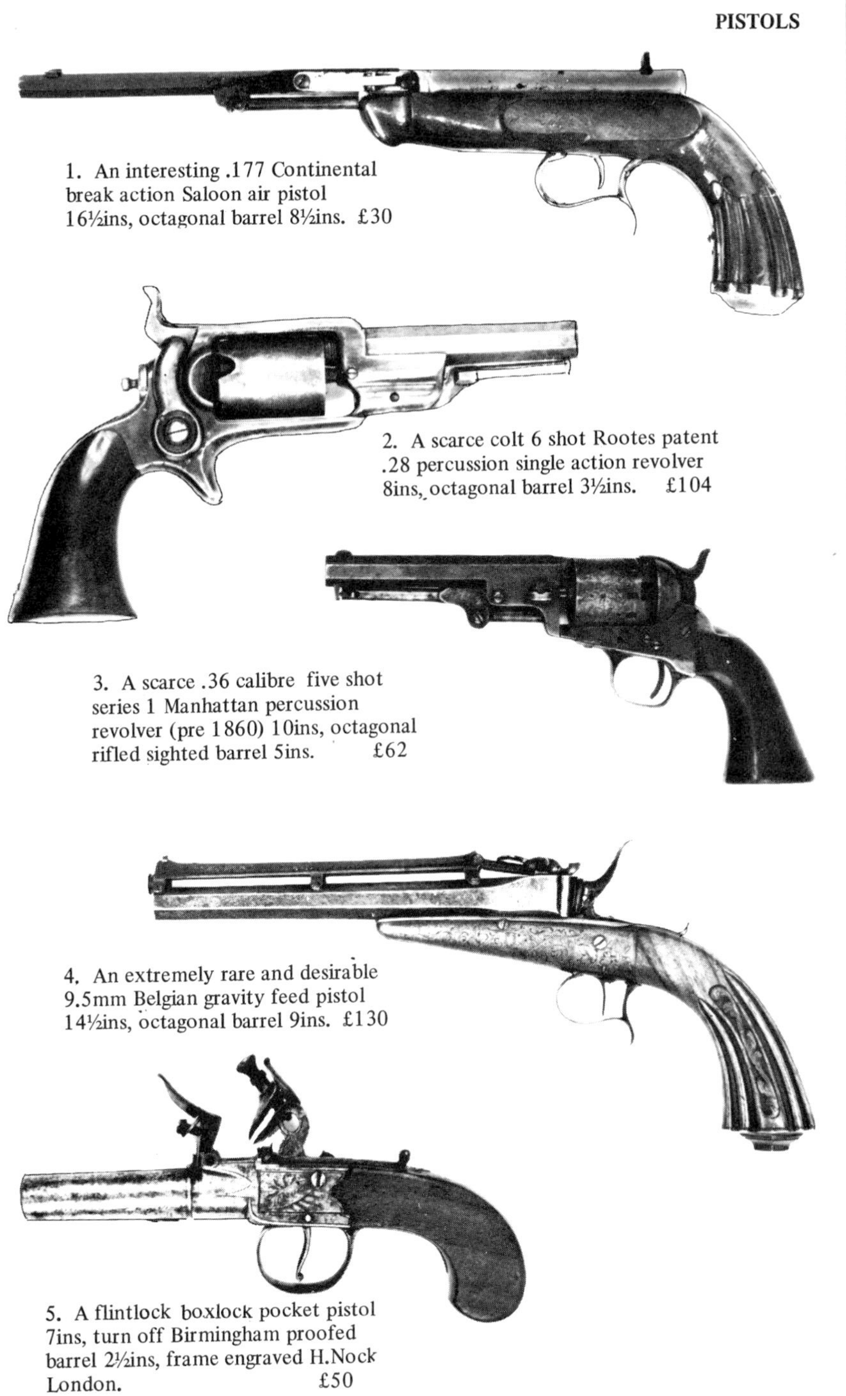

1. An interesting .177 Continental break action Saloon air pistol 16½ins, octagonal barrel 8½ins. £30

2. A scarce colt 6 shot Rootes patent .28 percussion single action revolver 8ins, octagonal barrel 3½ins. £104

3. A scarce .36 calibre five shot series 1 Manhattan percussion revolver (pre 1860) 10ins, octagonal rifled sighted barrel 5ins. £62

4. An extremely rare and desirable 9.5mm Belgian gravity feed pistol 14½ins, octagonal barrel 9ins. £130

5. A flintlock boxlock pocket pistol 7ins, turn off Birmingham proofed barrel 2½ins, frame engraved H.Nock London. £50

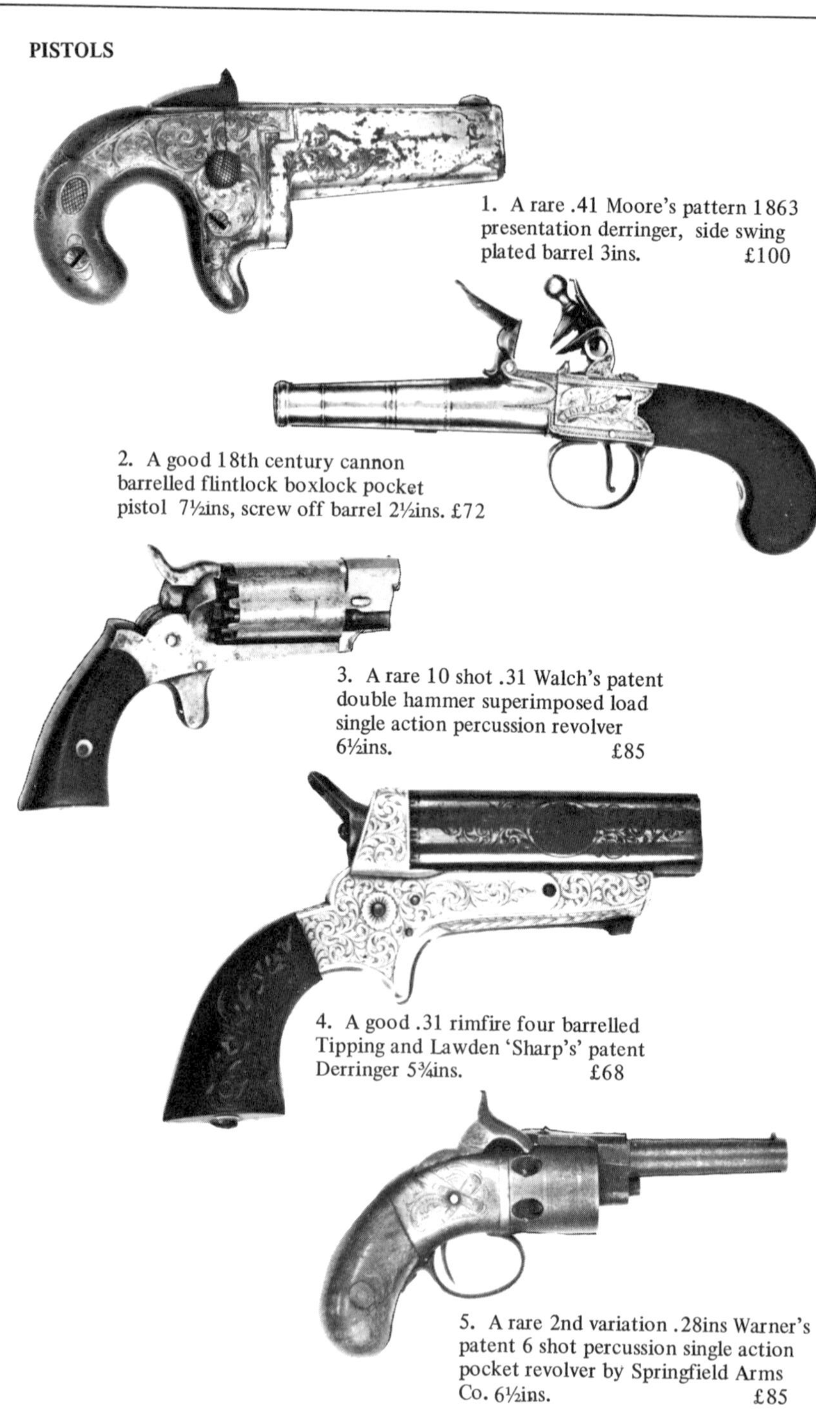

1. A rare .41 Moore's pattern 1863 presentation derringer, side swing plated barrel 3ins. £100

2. A good 18th century cannon barrelled flintlock boxlock pocket pistol 7½ins, screw off barrel 2½ins. £72

3. A rare 10 shot .31 Walch's patent double hammer superimposed load single action percussion revolver 6½ins. £85

4. A good .31 rimfire four barrelled Tipping and Lawden 'Sharp's' patent Derringer 5¾ins. £68

5. A rare 2nd variation .28ins Warner's patent 6 shot percussion single action pocket revolver by Springfield Arms Co. 6½ins. £85

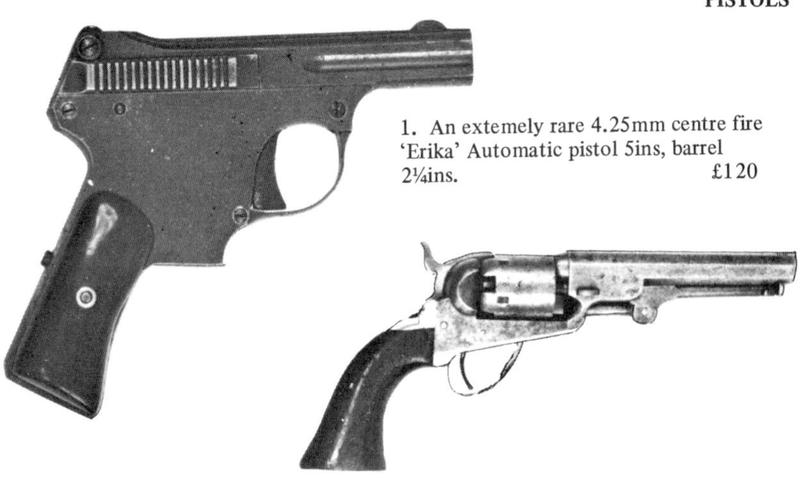

1. An extemely rare 4.25mm centre fire 'Erika' Automatic pistol 5ins, barrel 2¼ins. £120

2. A five shot Colt model 1849 pocket percussion revolver 10ins, barrel 5ins. £75

3. A good 88 bore six shot top snap percussion pepperbox revolver 8ins. £80

4. A fine flintlock boxlock pocket pistol 9ins, screw off rifled barrel 1¾ins. £135

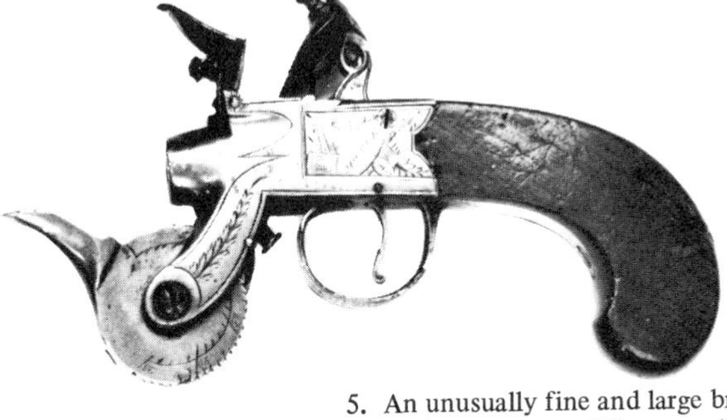

5. An unusually fine and large brass framed flintlock boxlock eprouvette 6½ins overall by Monck. £125

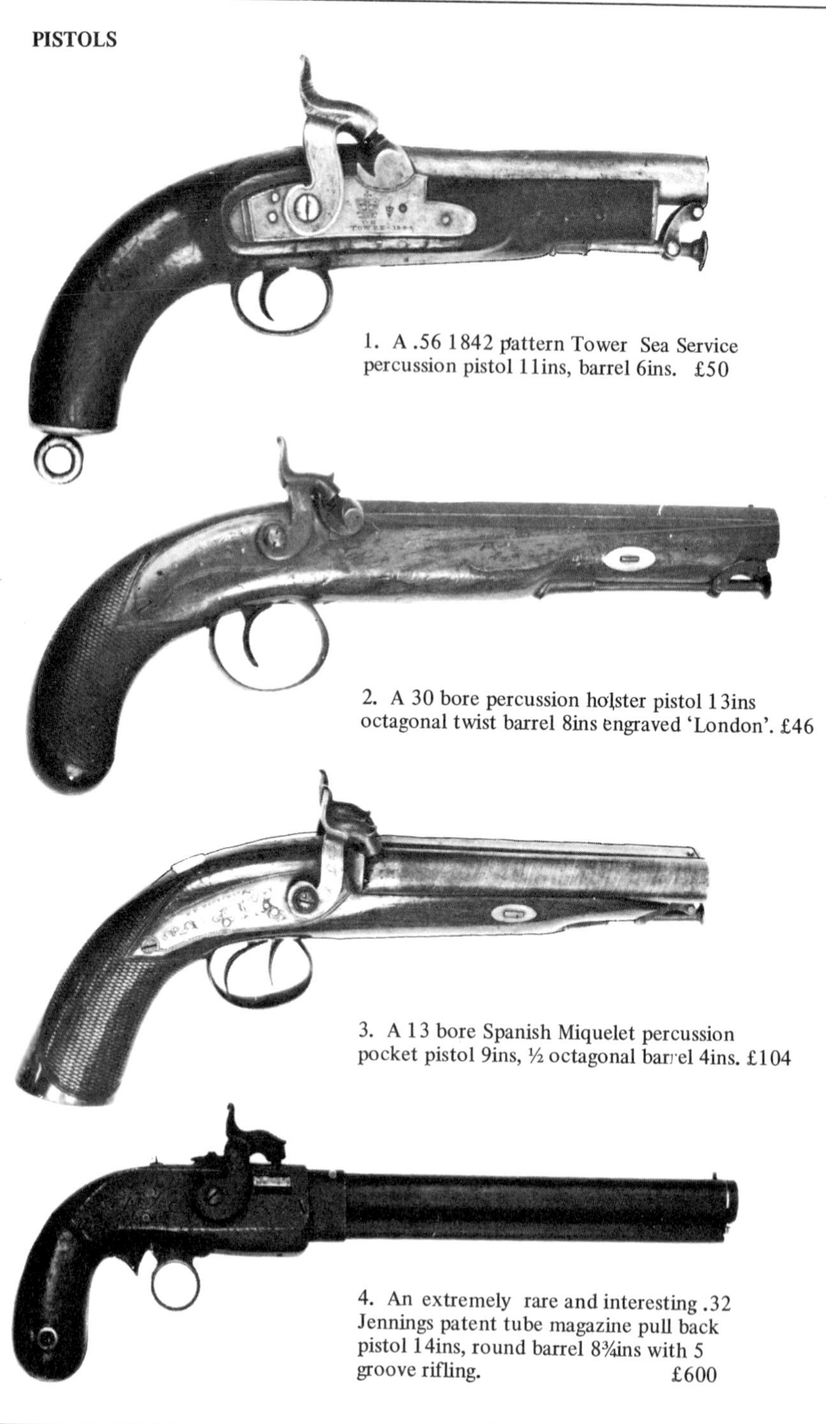

1. A .56 1842 pattern Tower Sea Service percussion pistol 11ins, barrel 6ins. £50

2. A 30 bore percussion holster pistol 13ins octagonal twist barrel 8ins engraved 'London'. £46

3. A 13 bore Spanish Miquelet percussion pocket pistol 9ins, ½ octagonal barrel 4ins. £104

4. An extremely rare and interesting .32 Jennings patent tube magazine pull back pistol 14ins, round barrel 8¾ins with 5 groove rifling. £600

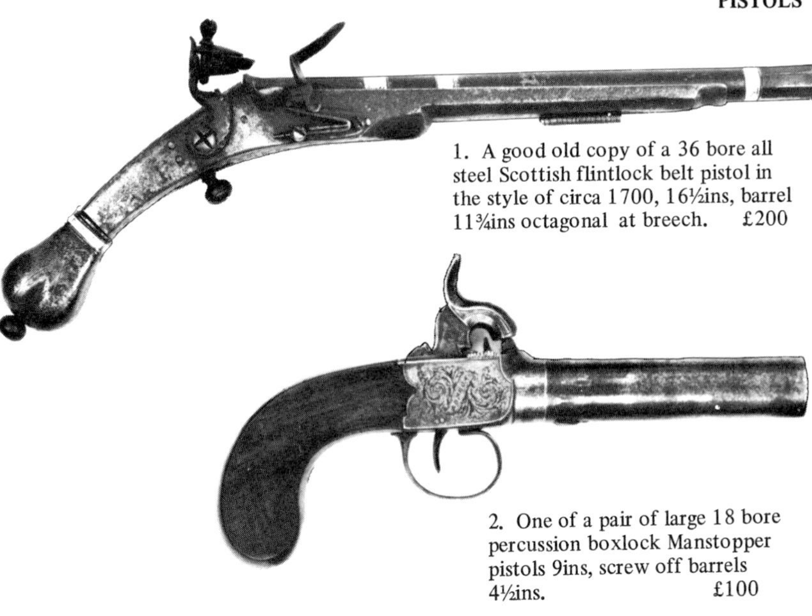

1. A good old copy of a 36 bore all steel Scottish flintlock belt pistol in the style of circa 1700, 16½ins, barrel 11¾ins octagonal at breech. £200

2. One of a pair of large 18 bore percussion boxlock Manstopper pistols 9ins, screw off barrels 4½ins. £100

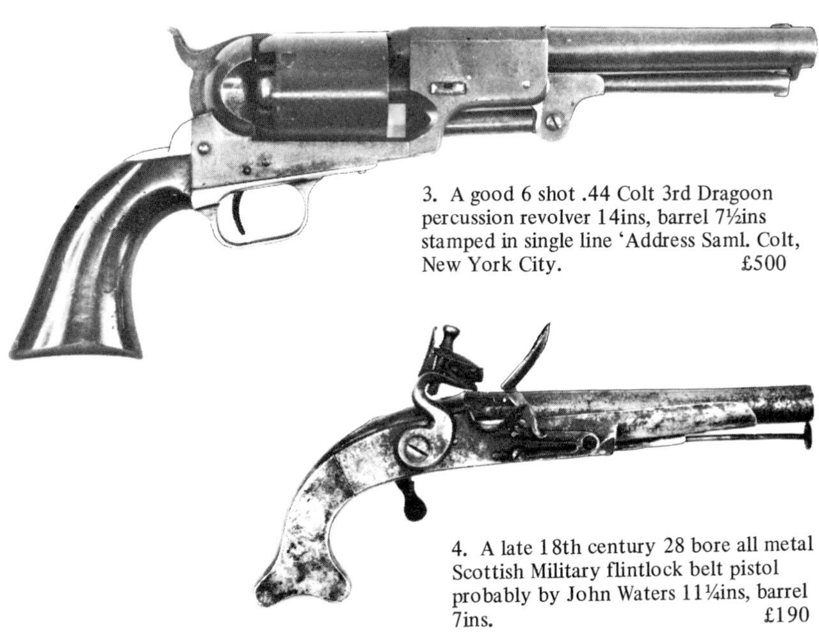

3. A good 6 shot .44 Colt 3rd Dragoon percussion revolver 14ins, barrel 7½ins stamped in single line 'Address Saml. Colt, New York City. £500

4. A late 18th century 28 bore all metal Scottish Military flintlock belt pistol probably by John Waters 11¼ins, barrel 7ins. £190

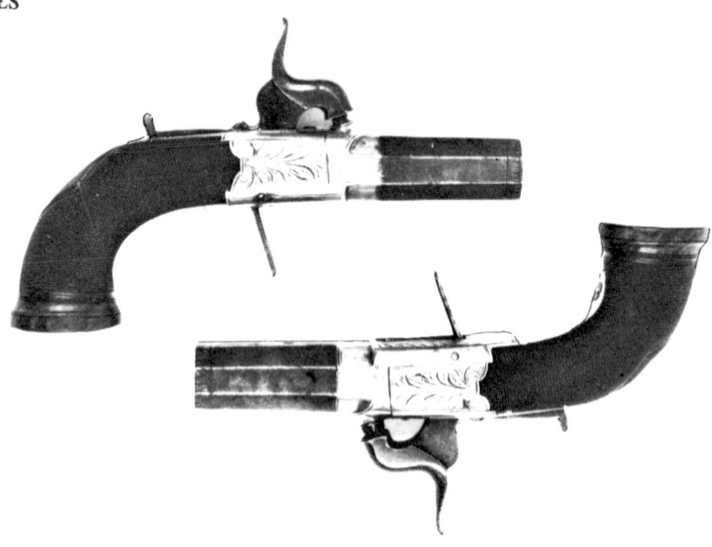

1. A good pair of brass framed boxlock percussion pocket pistols 5½ins, octagonal turn off barrels 1½ins, fern tip engraved muzzles with traces of original blueing. £105

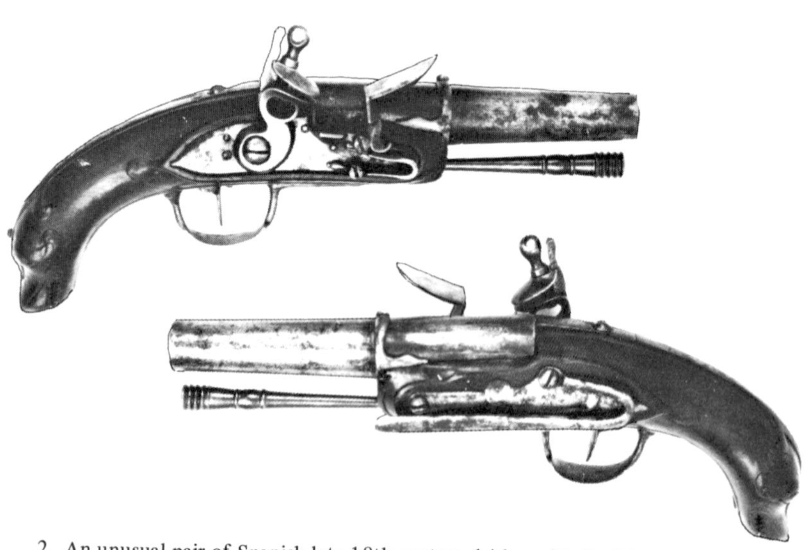

2. An unusual pair of Spanish late 18th century 14 bore flintlock belt pistols 10½ins, barrels 5¾ins halfstocked, with sweeping butts terminating in carved dog's heads. £310

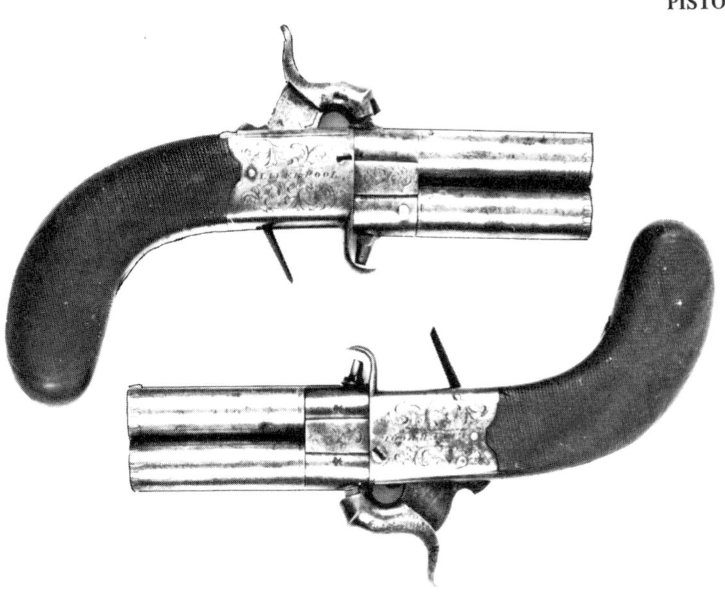

1. A pair of double barrelled turnover percussion boxlock pocket pistols 6½ins, screw off barrels 2ins scroll engraved frames with maker's mark T. Wilson and Co., Liverpool. £140

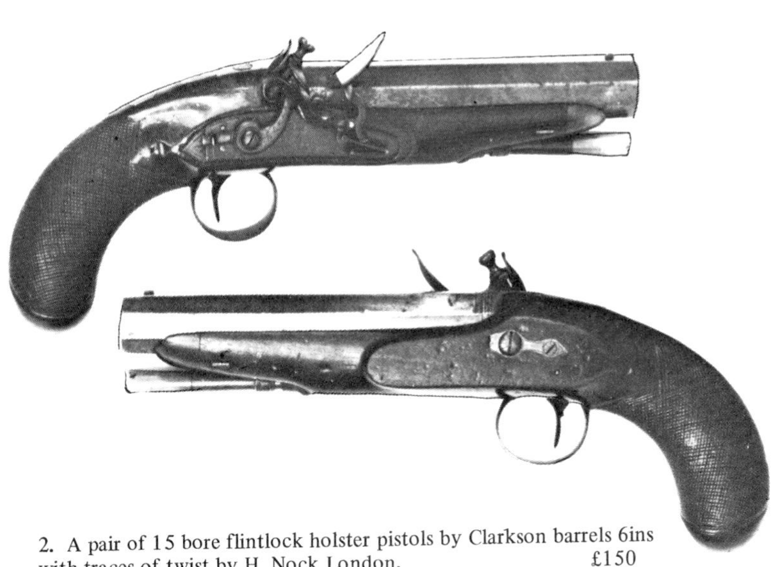

2. A pair of 15 bore flintlock holster pistols by Clarkson barrels 6ins with traces of twist by H. Nock London. £150

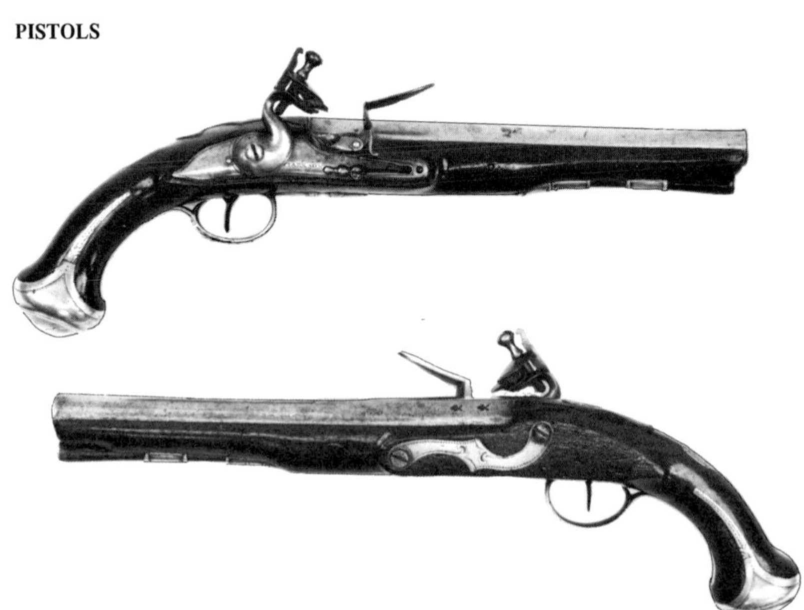

1. A good pair of 18 bore flintlock holster pistols by Clarkson circa 1760, 15½ins barrels octagonal at breech 9¼ins. £350

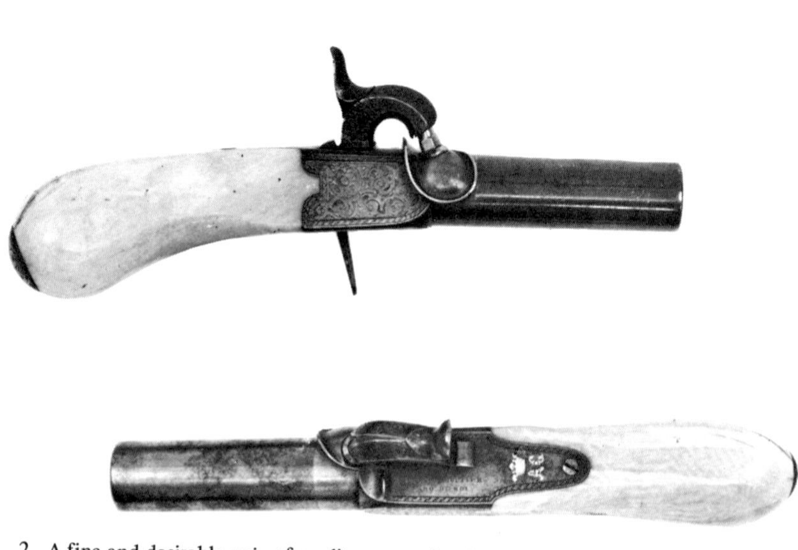

2. A fine and desirable pair of quality percussion boxlock pocket pistols by Le Page 7ins, barrels 2½ins, entirely scroll chiselled frame hammers and mounts. £185

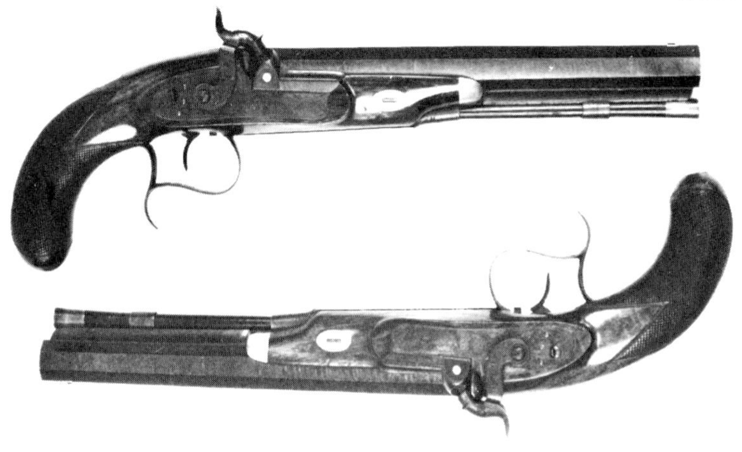

1. A good crisp pair of 36 bore percussion duelling pistols by Williams circa 1840, 15½ins, heavy octagonal twist barrels 9¾ins browned and engraved Williams 67 Threadneedle Street London. £400

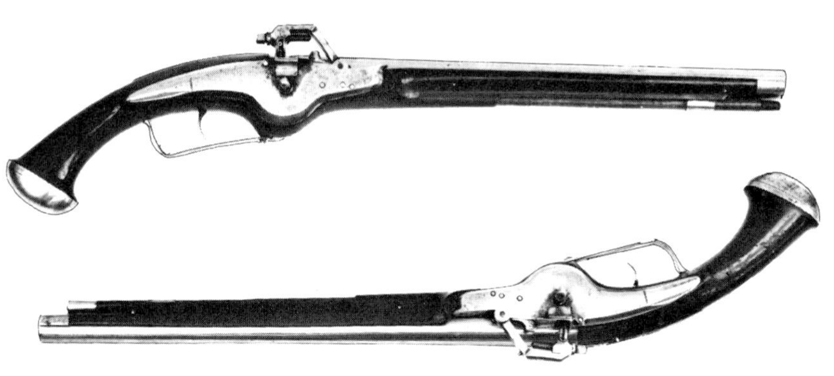

2. A good brace of 16 bore mid 17th century Swedish Military wheelock pistols 24½ins and 25ins overall, barrels 16½ins with full length top rib for sighting stamped with 'P' at breech. £1,100

1. A fine Officer's gilt Albert Shako plate of the 51st (2nd Yorkshire, West Riding) Light Infantry Regiment. £35

2. A scarce Officer's helmet plate of the 19th (St Pancras) County of London Regiment.£25

3. A rare Officer's gilt and silver star shaped Shako badge of the 58th Regiment of Foot (Rutlandshire). £39

4. A helmet plate from the Royal West Kent Regiment. £15

5. An Officer's gilt helmet plate of The Royal Warwickshire Regiment. £15

6. An·Officers gilt badge of the 38th Regiment. £25

7. A helmet plate of Gibralter castle. £15

8. A helmet plate of The Lothian Regiment. £48

9. A silver star shaped Shako badge of the 15th Regiment of Foot. £40

1. A rare Officer's copper gilt Shako plate of The Royal Artillery, 1812 -16 pattern. £60

2. A very rare O.R.'s brass Shako plate of The Royal Artillery, 1812 - 16 pattern. £50

3. A rare Officer's copper gilt Shako plate 1812 - 16 pattern of the 21st (Royal North British Fusiliers) Regiment. £79

4. Gilt badge from the Durham Light Infantry. £18

5. A rare Officer's copper gilt Shako plate 1812 -16 pattern of the 57th (West Middlesex) Regiment of Foot. £80

6. An Officer's gilt badge of the 5th European Bengal Regiment. £18

7. A Victorian Officer's helmet plate of the Royal Scots. £18

8. An Officer's gilt badge of the 53rd Regiment of Foot (Shropshire). £30

9. An Officer's gilt badge for the Albert Shako 1844 - 55 The Royal West Middlesex Militia. £17

SHOULDER BELT PLATES

1. A good Georgian Officer's embossed oval and silver shoulder belt plate of The West Kent Light Infantry. £35

2. A Georgian engraved oval brass shoulder belt plate of the 3rd Edinburgh Volunteers. £28

3. A Georgian Officer's engraved oval copper gilt shoulder belt plate of The Royal Colchester Volunteers. £46

4. A Georgian oval brass shoulder belt plate of The Ross and Cromarty Rangers. £20

5. A Georgian engraved oval brass shoulder belt plate of the Caithness Local Militia. £26

6. A Georgian copper gilt shoulder belt plate of The York Volunteer Cavalry. £50

7. A Georgian Officer's silvered shouldered belt plate of The 60th Regiment. £40

8. A rare Georgian Officer's copper gilt shoulder belt plate of The 83rd Regiment of Foot. £70

9. A fine Georgian Officer's silver shoulder belt plate of The Royal Edinburgh Light Dragoons. £45

1. An early Victorian Officer's rectangular gilt shoulder belt plate of the 59th (2nd Nottinghamshire) Regiment. £36

2. A Victorian Officer's copper gilt rectangular shoulder belt plate of The Royal Artillery. £26

3. A Victorian Officer's copper gilt rectangular shoulder belt plate of The 51st Light Infantry Regiment. £12

4. A fine Officer's shoulder belt plate of The 39th Regiment of Foot (Dorsetshire). £30

5. An Officer's copper gilt shoulder belt plate of The 9th Regiment of Foot (The East Norfolk) £22

6. A copper gilt shoulder belt plate of The 34th Regiment of Foot (Cumberland) circa 1832. £28

7. A rare Georgian copper gilt shoulder belt belt plate of The Grenadier Guards, circa 1815. £44

9. An Officer's copper gilt shoulder belt plate of The 68th Regiment (Durham Light Infantry) £25

8. An Officer's copper gilt shoulder belt plate of The 70th Regiment of Foot (Surrey) pre 1855. £28

1. A good and scarce .41 rimfire Colt No 3 Derringer Pistol, 4¾ ins, all original blued barrel 2½ins, No 814c, plain rosewood grips to birdshead butt, large Colt on barrel and emblem and calibre on left frame, original plating overall. Contained in its original pocket size leatherette case. £70

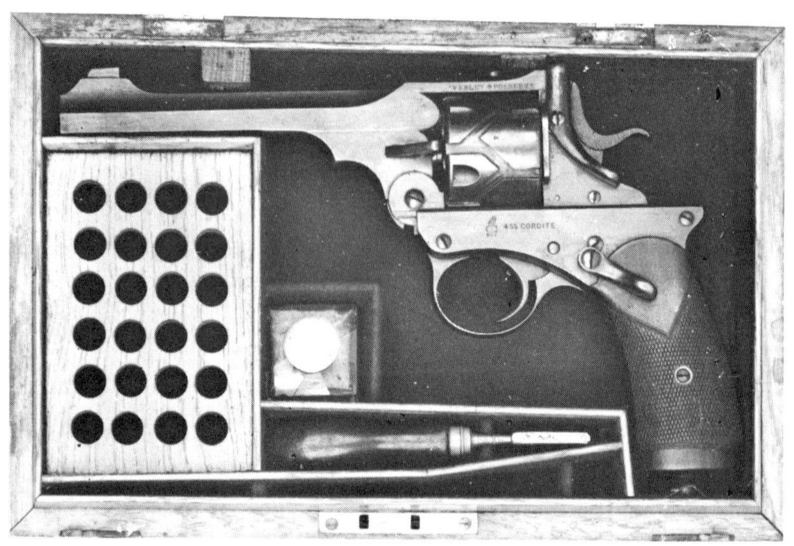

2. A scarce six shot .455ins (cordite) Webley Fosbery automatic revolver, model 1902, 11ins, barrel 6ins no. 1049, chequered wood grips, side safety. Contained in its oak pistol case with compartments, screwdriver, glass, oil bottle and cartridge tray. £180

1. A scarce over and under turnover percussion boxlock pocket pistol 6ins, barrels 2¼ins by W.M. and J.N. Rigby, finely scroll chiselled lockplates and mounts, barrels numbered 1 and 2, diced wood butt with silver escutcheon at base, in its fitted lined mahogany case. £210

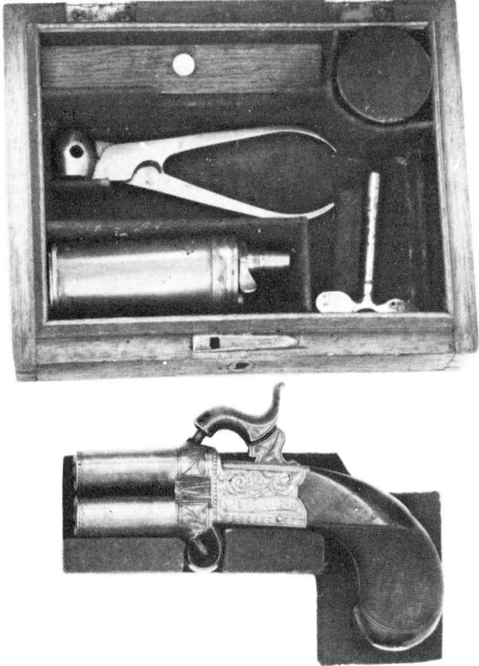

2. An 80 bore six shot open frame double action pin fire revolver 11ins round rifled barrel 6ins, scroll engraved frame, bag shaped two piece chequered grip. In its blue baize lined oak case with rod, turnscrew, oil bottle, cartridge board and key. £48

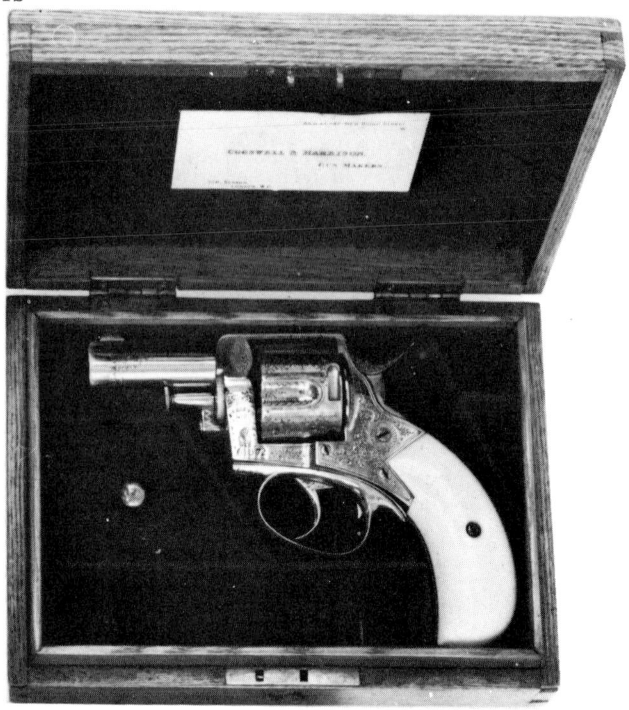

1. A five shot .45ins presentation 'British Bulldog' Webley no. 2 revolver 6½ins, barrel 2½ins no. 61072, plain ivory grips to birds head butt, gate loading, and swing ejector rod, plated overall and foliate engraved. Backstrap engraved 'Cogswell and Harrison, 226 Strand, 142 New Bond Street, London. £52

2. A pair of extremely rare and interesting Continental ,15ins indoor percussion target pistols 12ins, screw off twist barrels 3ins, the octagonal frames numbered 1 and 2 are continuations of the barrels, in their original baize lined mahogany case. £185

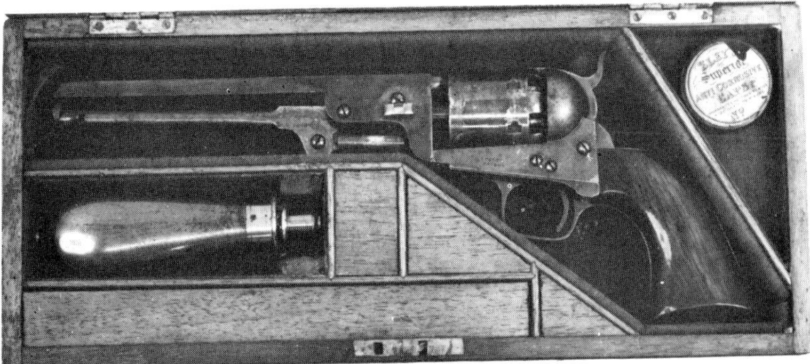

1. A six shot .36 Colt model 1851 Navy percussion revolver 13ins, barrel 7½ins no. 24834, most blueing and case hardening, probably a contemporary factory re-finish. £240

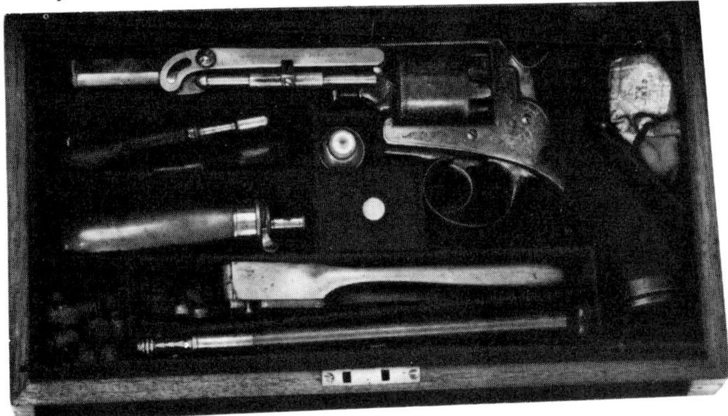

2. A fine and desirable 5 shot .45 double action percussion revolver 12ins octagonal rifled sighted barrel 6½ins, fully engraved on top strap 'George Gibbs Bristol'. £220

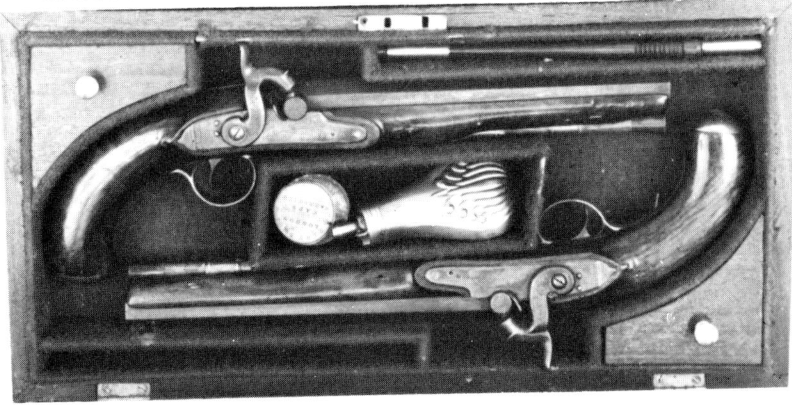

3. A pair of 16 bore percussion holster pistols 14½ins octagonal barrels 9ins with Tower private proofs by Jno. Jones and Son London. £225

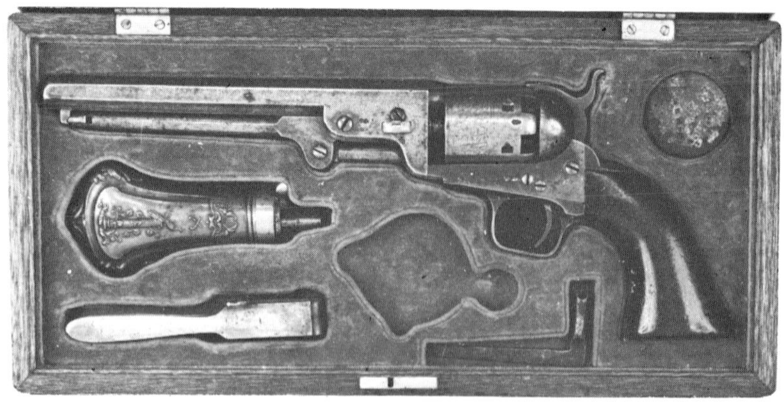

1. A desirable six shot .36 Colt model 1851 Navy percussion revolver 13ins barrel 7½ins no. 39437, in it's Continental close fitted pale blue velvet lined case with attractive shaped, embossed copper flask depicting a peacock on a pedestal, crossed pistols etc. £245

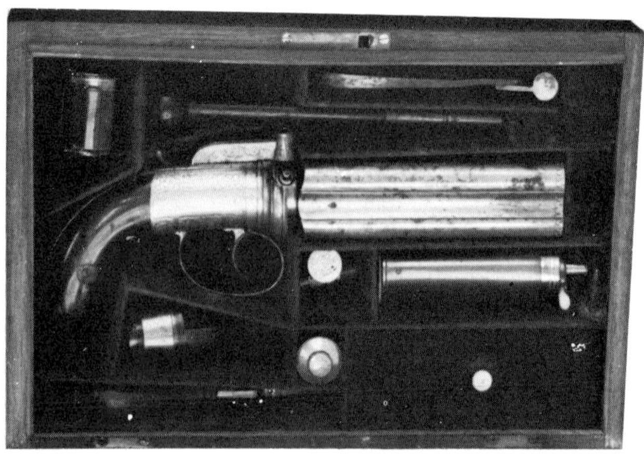

2. A fine and most desirable 34 bore 4 shot top snap percussion pepperbox revolver 11ins, flutted cylinder 6ins fern tip engraved at muzzle. £300

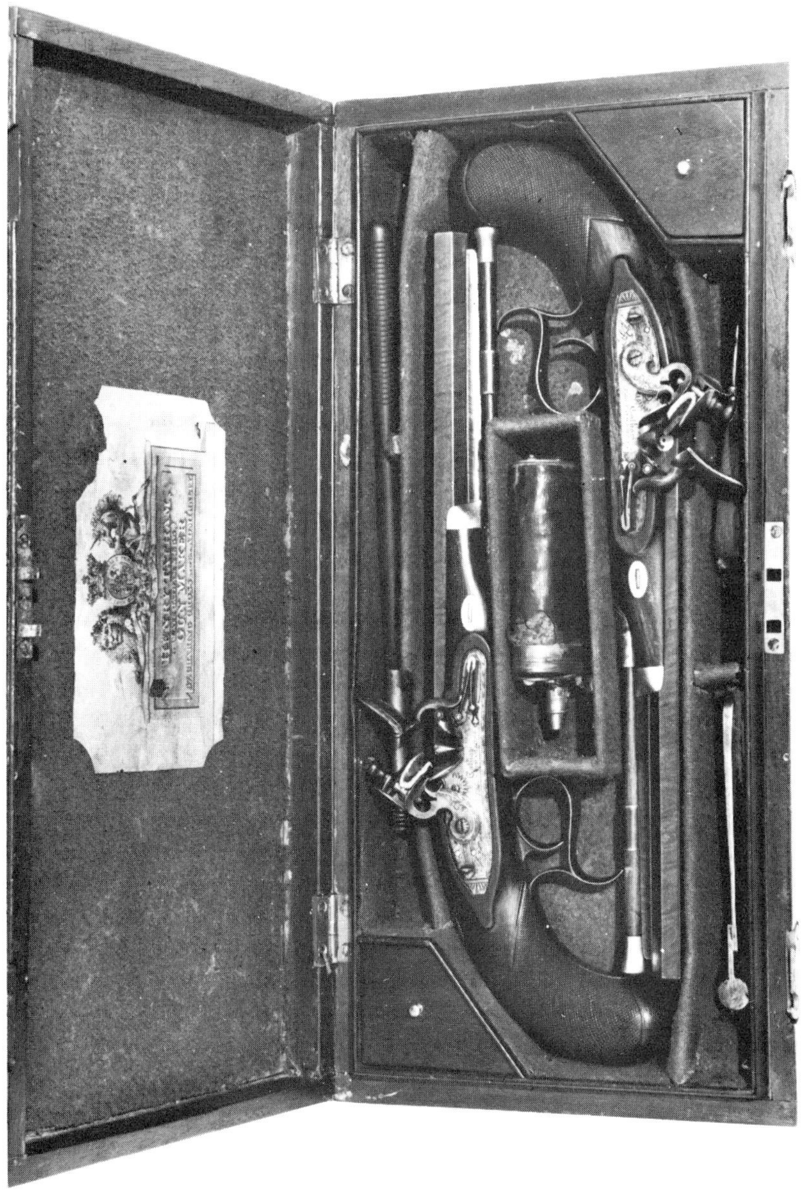

1. An extremely fine pair of 23 bore flintlock duelling pistols 14½ins, browned octagonal twist barrels 9½ins with plat touch holes and rectangular poincon embossed 'Tatham London', in their original fitted mahogany case with makers trade label. £700

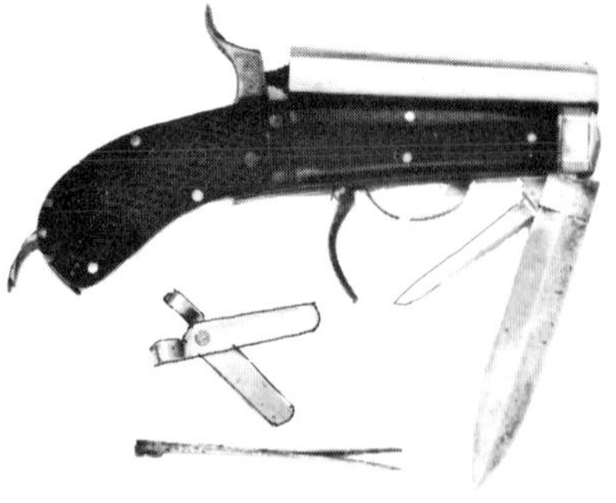

1. A good .28 Rodgers percussion knife pistol 6½ ins closed. £66

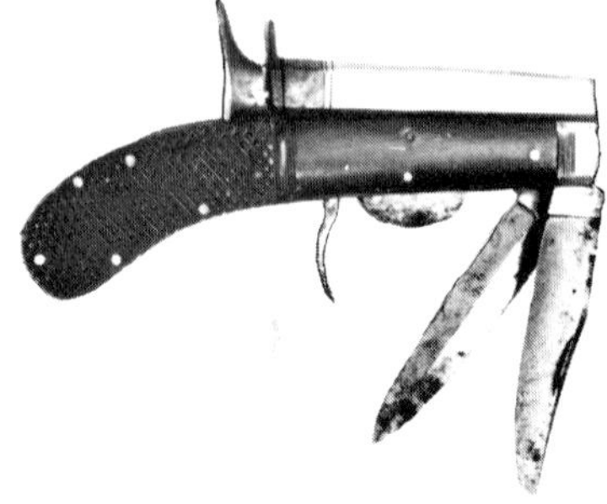

2. A good .25 rimfire Unwin and Rodgers knife pistol 6½ ins long. £42

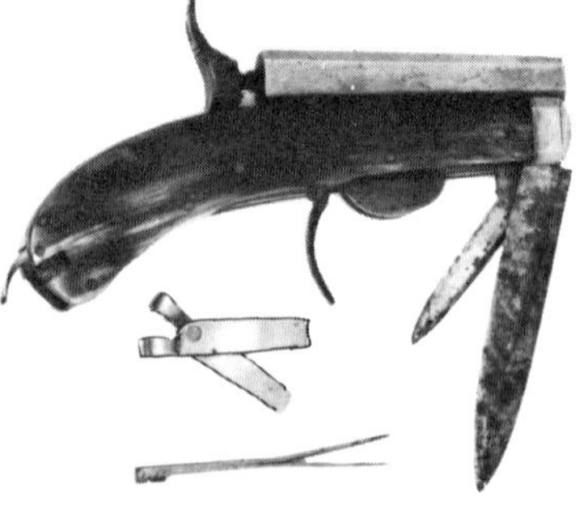

3. A good .28 Unwin and Rodgers percussion knife pistol. £66

4. A large and good quality multi bladed penknife by Harrison Bros. and Horson. £70

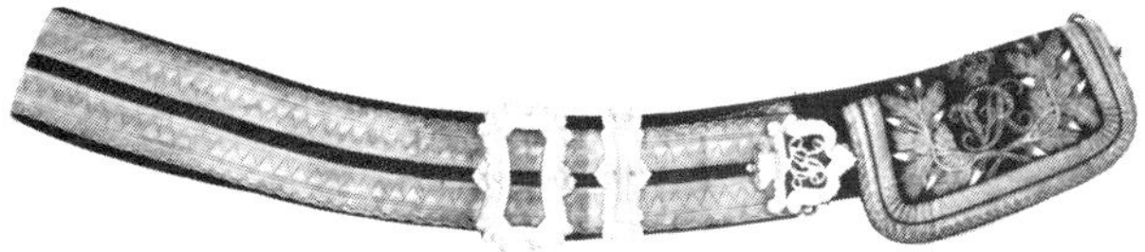

1. A fine Victorian Officer's full dress bullion pouch and belt of the Oxford Hussars Yeomanry. £24

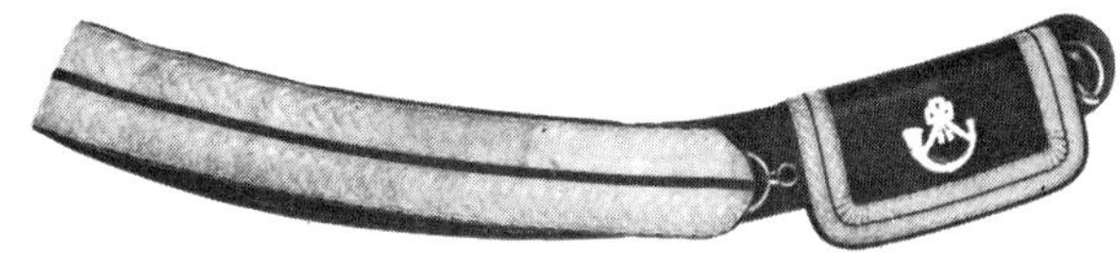

2. An Officer's pouch and belt of the Sherwood Rangers Yeomanry Cavalry. £19

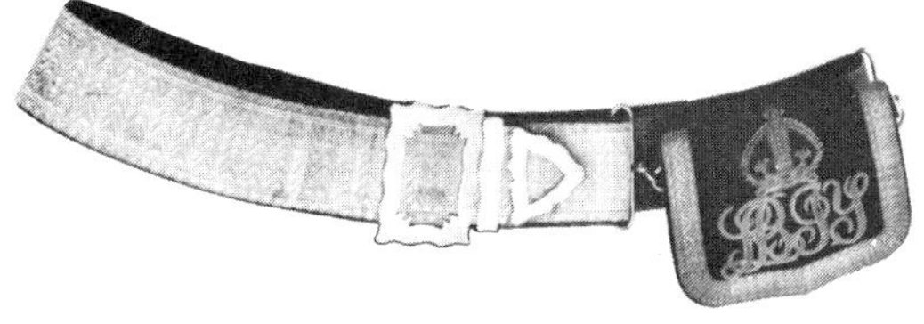

3. A good post 1901 Officer's full dress pouch of The Lothian and Berwickshire Imperial Yeomanry. £25

4. A good Officer's flap pouch of The West Somerset Yeomanry. £27

5. A scarce Post 1902 Officer's shoulder belt and pouch of the Staffordshire Yeomanry. £21

1. An interesting Victorian painted truncheon bearing the crowned arms of The London and Birmingham Railway. £34

2. A North American Indian Plains club I - Wata - Jinga. 21ins long. £55

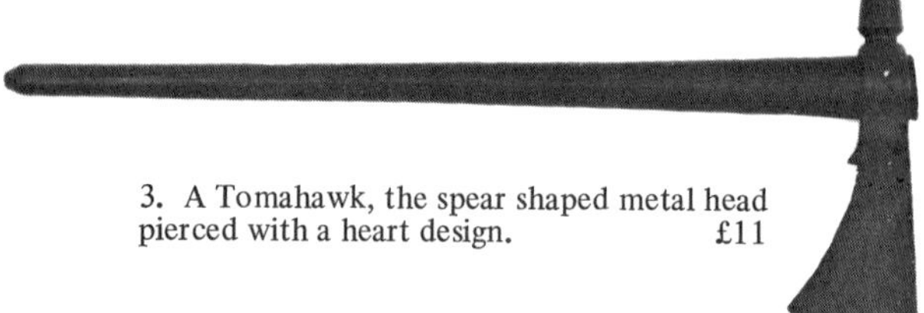

3. A Tomahawk, the spear shaped metal head pierced with a heart design. £11

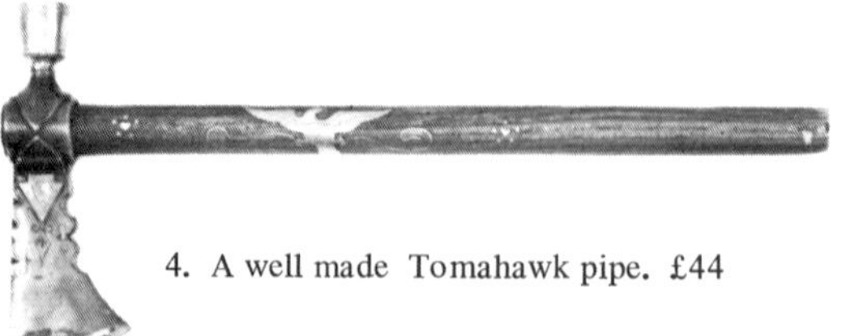

4. A well made Tomahawk pipe. £44

5. A Skean Dhu, blade 3¼ins with scalloped edge. £32

6. A scarce Springfield model 1885 entrenching tool, spade blade 8ins. £13

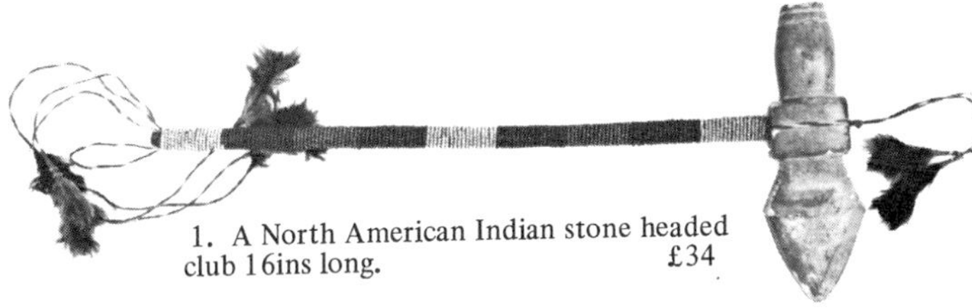

1. A North American Indian stone headed club 16ins long. £34

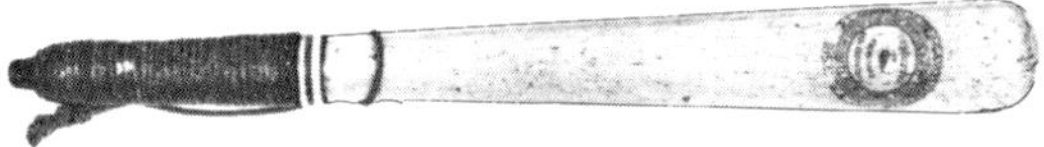

2. An interesting old truncheon made from a whale bone marlin spike, 17ins long. £50

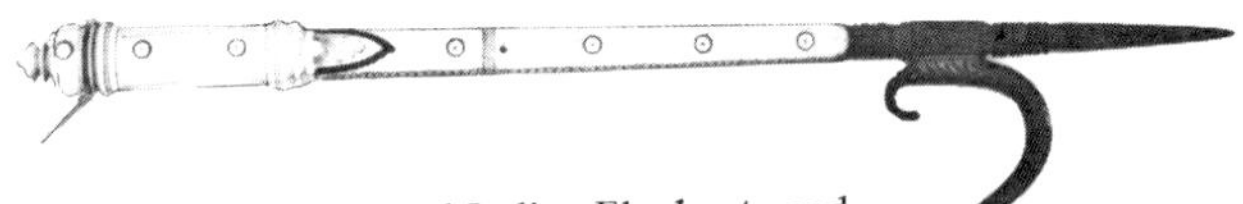

3. A very good Indian Elephant goad, Ankus, the haft of ivory. £60

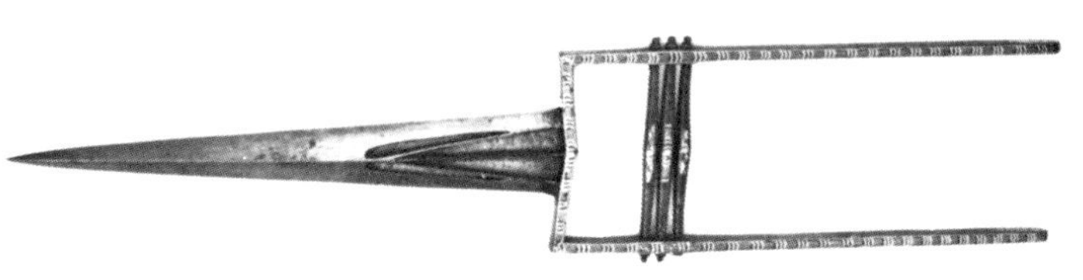

4. A good heavy Indian stabbing dagger, Katar. £12

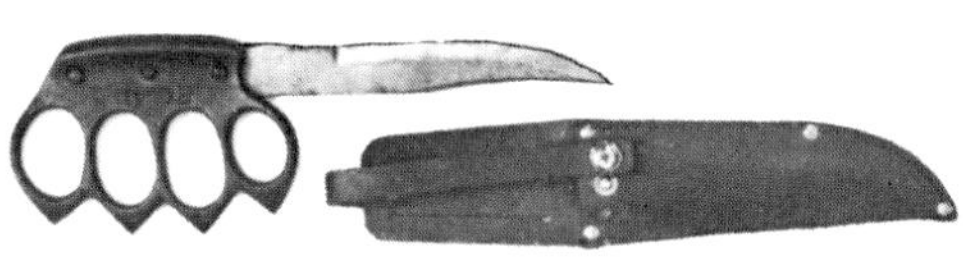

5. A scarce World War I, U.S. trench knife. £27

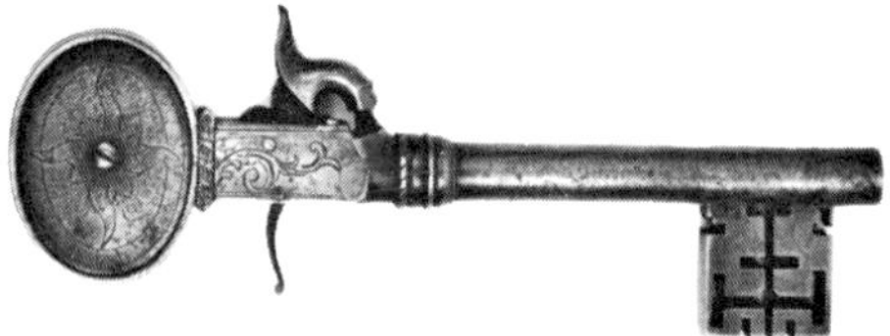

1. A very well made percussion key pistol, circa 1850 in style, 7½ins long. £140

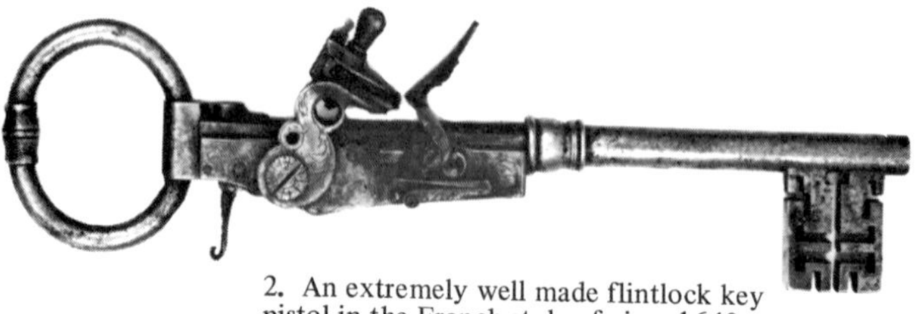

2. An extremely well made flintlock key pistol in the French style of circa 1640, 11ins long. £270

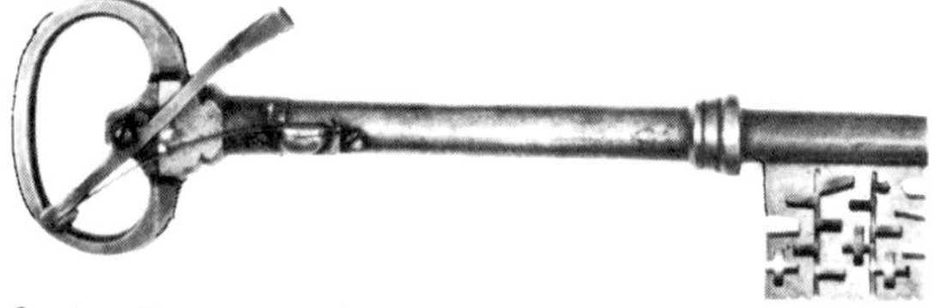

3. A well constructed example of a 16th century style matchlock key pistol with pan cover. £52

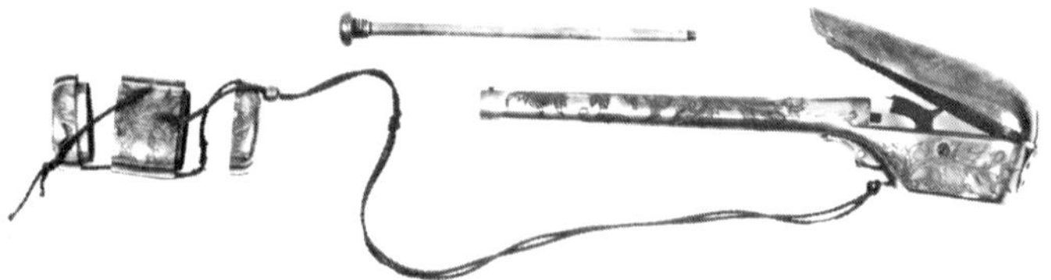

4. A very rare and most desirable Japanese percussion pistol and accessories disguised as a pen case and inro. £220

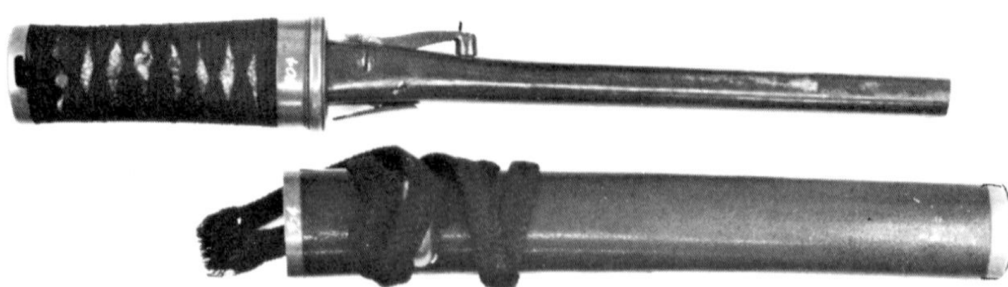

5. A good scarce 28 bore Japanese Tanju Aikuchi, 15½ins long. £200

1. A very fine old flintlock hunting dirk pistol, single edged blade 14ins long. £210

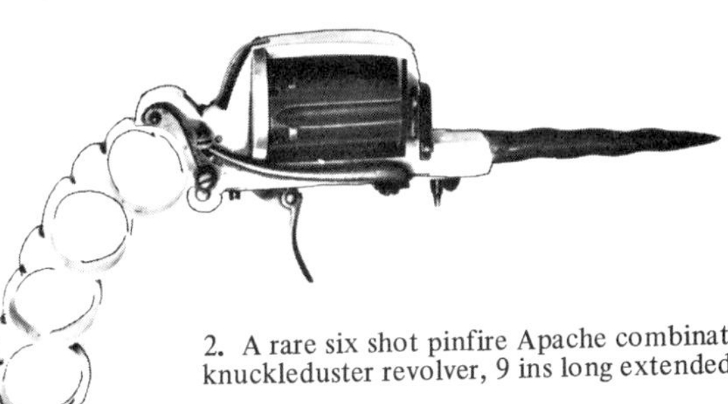

2. A rare six shot pinfire Apache combination knuckleduster revolver, 9 ins long extended. £170

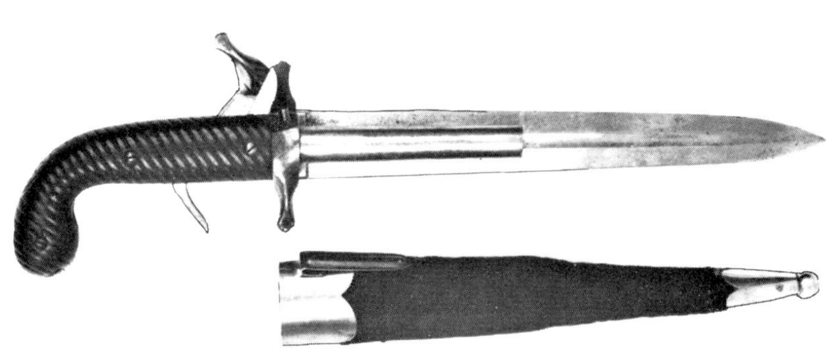

3. A good and rare double barrelled 80 bore percussion dagger pistol. £190

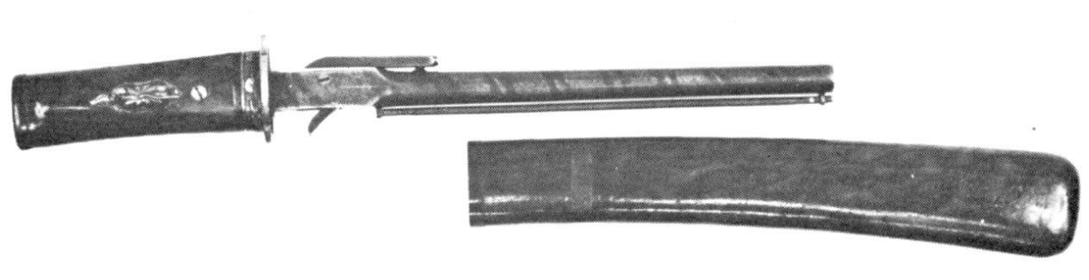

4. A rare Japanese Tanju - Aikuchi 80 bore boxlock percussion pistol cleverly disguised and mounted as a dagger Tanto, 15½ins overall. £250

A highly important Louis XVI black lacquer secretaire a abattant by Martin Carlin, from the Hillingdon collection. 120,000 gns

(Christie's, 29-6-72)

An important Louis marquetry secretaire a abattant by Roger Vandercruse Lacroix. 32,000 gns

(Christie's, 28 -6 -72)

A fine and large English striking, perpetual calendar carriage clock by M. F. Dent. 13,000gns

(Christie's, 26-10-71 – A record price for a carriage clock)

14th century Chinese wine jar. 210,000 gns

(For years it had stood unrecognised in the hall of a house on the continent, as an umbrella stand.)

(Christie's 5 -6 -72 – Highest price paid at auction for any work of art other than a painting)

A very rare pair of Lund's Bristol polychrome vases. 2,900 gns

(Christie's, 17-7-72)

A finely carved wooden doll. 800gns

(Christie's, 10-11-71 –Highest price paid at auction for an 18th century doll)

A very fine Webb cameo double overlay vase. 2,800 gns

(Christie's, 11-7-72)

An important German Solnhofer-stone Armorial supporter, second quarter 16th century. 6,500 gns
(Christie's, 20-6-72)

A superb Delftware Royalist charger with a standing portrait of George I. 1,350 gns

(Christie's, 17-7-72)

A fine and rare Chelsea Botanical plate of the Hans Sloane type. 2,700 gns

(Christie's, 17-1-72 –Record price)

A highly important early 17th century English snaphaunce pistol. 10,000gns

(Christie's, 27-10-71)

A superb Louis XV rectangular, enamelled gold snuff box by Jean-Francois Garand, from the collection of the late Mr. Charles Engelhard. 46,000 gns

(Christie's, 28-6-72)

One of a highly important pair of George II square salvers by Paul De Lamerie, 1749, from the collection of the late Mr. Charles Engelhard. £16,000

(Christie's, 5-7-72)

An important walnut longcase clock by Joseph Knibb. 16,000 gns

(Christie's, 16-3-72 – A record for a longcase clock)

A George II Royal Race prize teapot by James Kerr of Edinburgh, 1736, from the collection of the late Mr. Charles Engelhard. £38,000

(Christie's, 5-7-72)

An important English chased gold snuff box by George Michael Moser, from the collection of the late Mr. Charles Engelhard. 23,000 gns

(Christie's, 28-6-72 –Highest price paid at auction for an English snuff box)

MISCELLANEA

2. Wooden shoe with brass and copper pique, circa 1870. £22

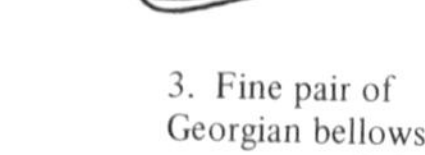

3. Fine pair of Georgian bellows. £12

1. A fine Stevengraph entitled‘ The Immaculate.’ £600

4. A good Naga wooden shield 48 ins long. £44

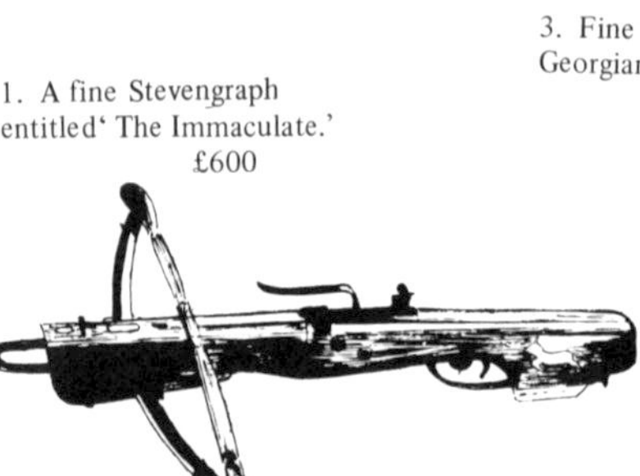

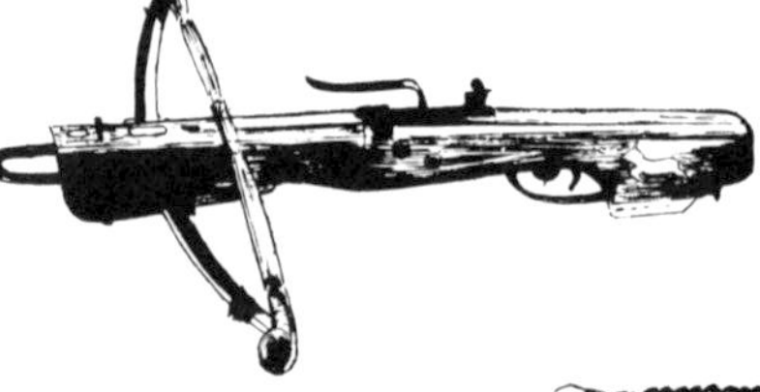

5. A good 18th century German hunting crossbow 31½ ins long,with a heavy bow 27 in span, scroll brass trigger guard, set trigger, adjustable rearsight. £260

6. George IV tipstaff, London 1827, maker A.D., 5½ ins long. £100

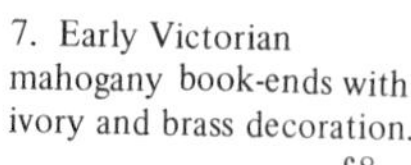

7. Early Victorian mahogany book-ends with ivory and brass decoration. £8

8. 18th century Scottish Highlands woolwinder. £15

9. Victorian walnut framed firescreen containing a decorative woolwork picture. £15

10. A fine Scottish Officer’s full dress Badger Headed sporran with six badger hair tassels. £42

1. A good Officer's sporran of the Seaforth Highlanders. £26

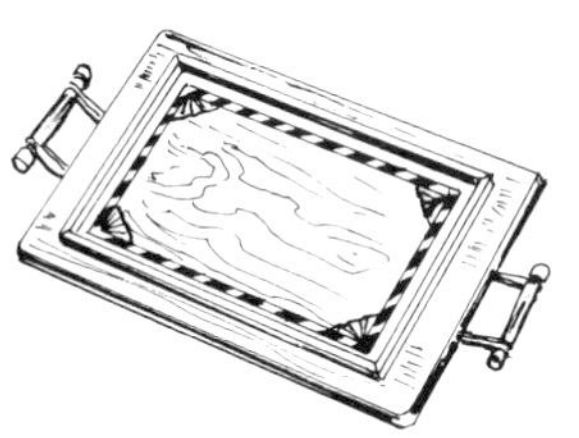

2. 19th century walnut butler's tray. £12

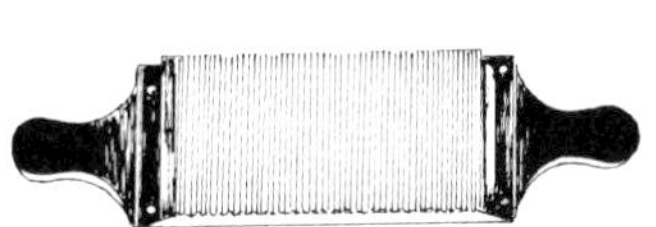

3. London made pill rolling slab. £14

4. A large wooden bread peel. £8

5. A magnificently engraved Nautilus shell 7 ins across. £150

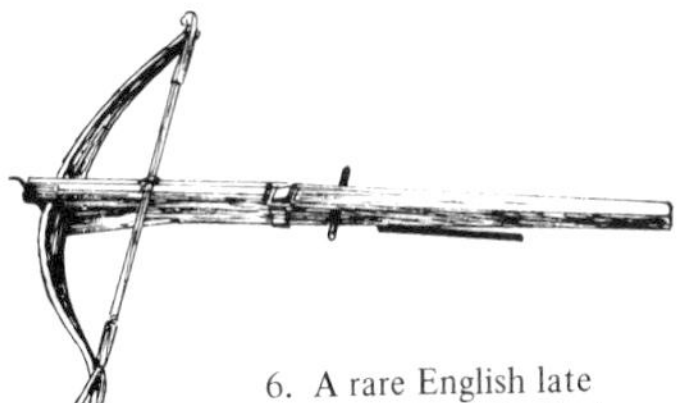

6. A rare English late 16th century Elizabethan crossbow. £170

7. A fine early Victorian ceremonial truncheon, 7¼ins long, painted with ' Royal Arms' in gilt. £16

8. 16th century Austrian rococo style fire screen. £25

9. A rare Nazi trumpet banner of the Adolf Hitler School. £50

10. A 19th century English china garden seat. £70

MISCELLANEA

1. A Tammany Hall mechanical bank. £20

2. A good old rare North American Indian feather war bonnet, the radiate crown approximately 16 ins wide, the brim of woven coloured beads in a geometric pattern and with glass centered green rosettes surmounting mauve, white and red woven tassels. £185

3. Mid 17th century pear shaped vase in Chinese cloisonne enamels, 20½ ins high. 400 gns

4. Chinese hornbill casque carved with figures, 17.8 cm long. £380

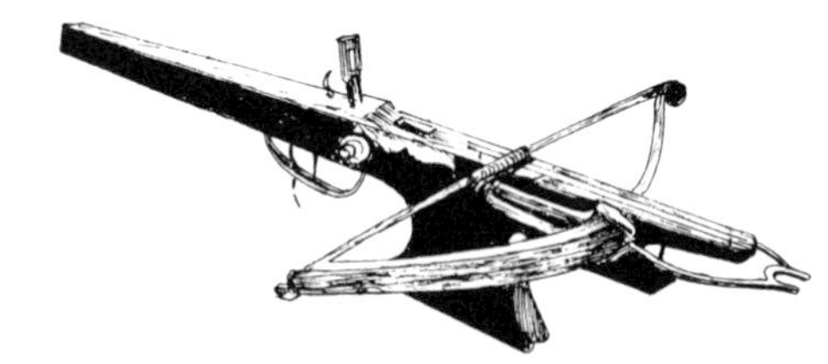

5. A German target crossbow circa 1770, 37 ins long. £75

6. Splendid copper, brass and wrought iron three dimensional weather cock, 40 ins high overall. £250

7. A rare late Georgian Battalion Regimental colour of the Coldstream Guards, 6 ft x 6 ft. £84

8. A scarce 'Old Bill' car radiator mascot. £25

1. 26th dynasty ancient Egyptian carved alabaster figure of the Ibis headed God Thoth, 6¼ ins high. £94

2. 18th century mahogany bookbinders press 14 ins x 10 ins x 16 ins, circa 1780. £28

3. Georgian mahogany candle stand. £25

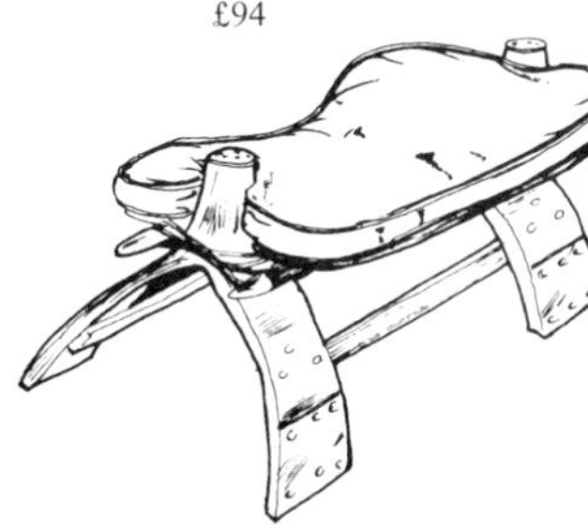

4. Oriental camel stool with a leather cushion. £12

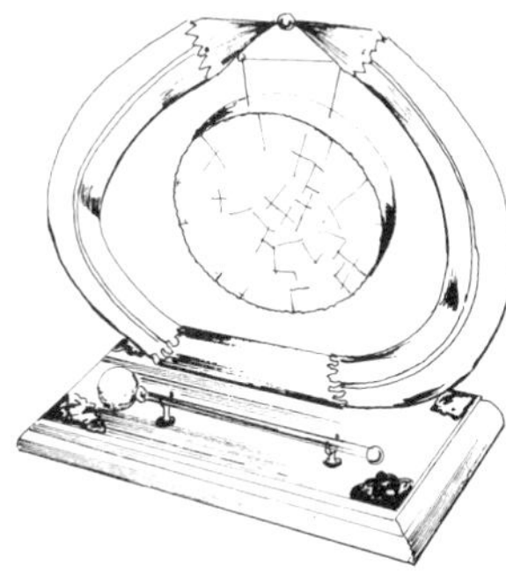

5. Burmese carved ivory tusk supported brass gong. £10

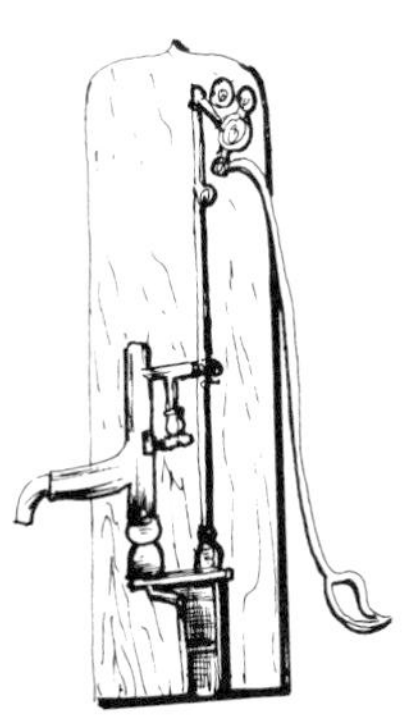

6. Highly polished brass, steel and lead farmhouse kitchen water pump. £68

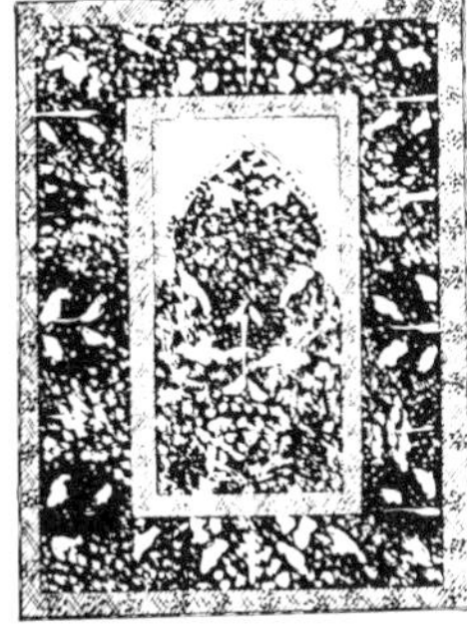

7. An exceptionally fine Ravar rug. £375

8. A fine pair of Battersea enamel candlesticks. £100

MISCELLANEA

1. 'Cultured pearl' in alabaster, and white and green marble on a plinth, total height 58ins. £170

2. 19th century cast iron doorstop. £8.50

3. Louis XV gold etui enamelled in green and yellow, fitted with scissors, knife and pen by Jean Ducrollay of Paris, 1745-50. £2,700

4. Portugese pottery nef in rich brown and cream glaze, supported on waves with walrus, dolphins and other sea creatures, 18ins high. £120

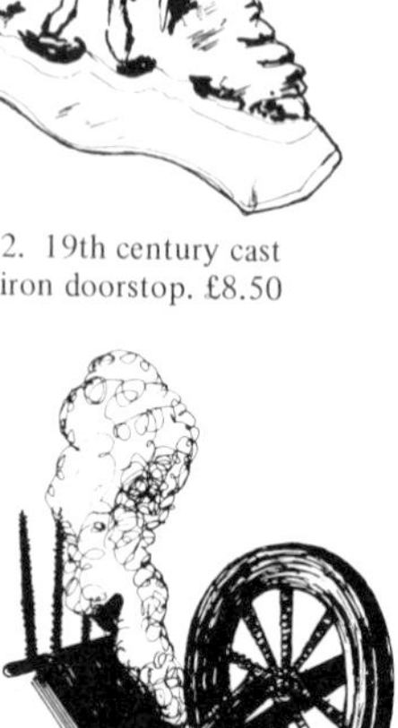

5. 17th century oak spinning wheel with ivory finials to the turnings, 40ins high. £58

6. Egyptian brown and green faience figure of a Pharaoh with a Ureaus symbol on his forehead, 21st dynasty, 5¼ins high. £80

7. A Ptolemaic mummy mask. £135

8. A 19th century Oriental soapstone figure. £12

9. Head of an Egyptian Official in black and pink granite from the New Kingdom, 19th dynasty, 29.2cm high. £1,470

1. A Ch'ien Lung cloisonne incense burner 26ins high. £250

2. A limestone bas-relief from Tel El-Amara. £1,600

3. 19th century soapstone figure. £10

4. A fragment from an Assyrian relief of the 8th century B.C. £210

5. A fine French etui with six fittings including a knife, scissors, pencil, ivory slide, spoon and bodkin, circa 1740. £630

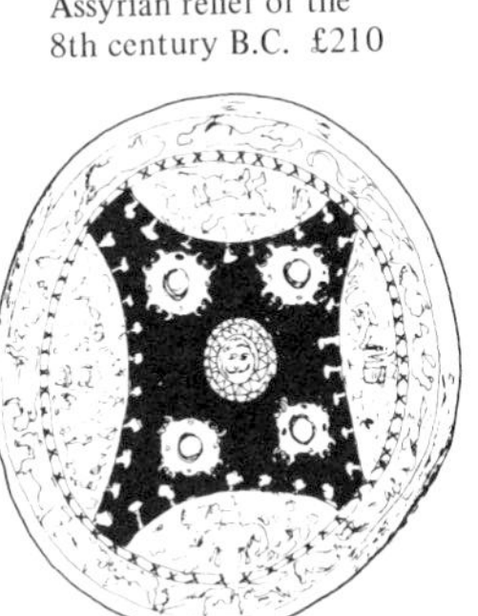

6. A fine Indo-Persian painted shield Dhal. £35

7. Victorian cast iron doorstop depicting a lion. £12

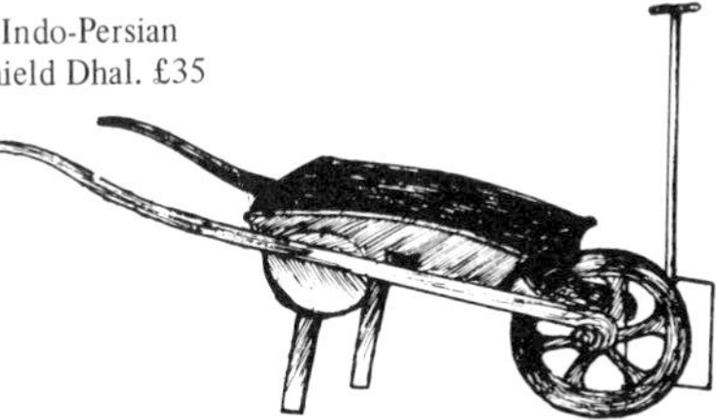

8. Ceremonial oak wheelbarrow complete with spade. £110

DOLLS AND TOYS

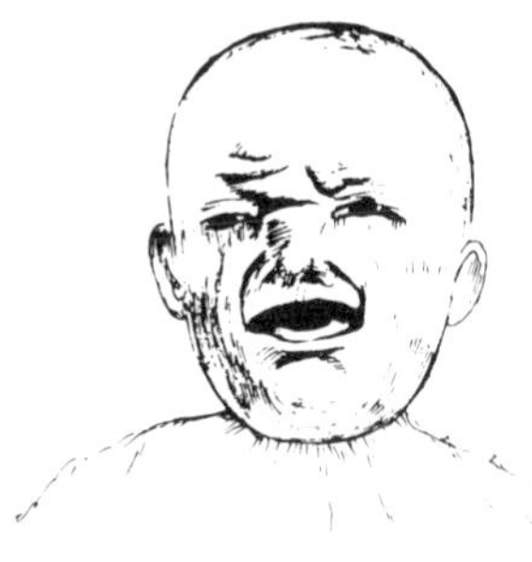

1. A 19th century American character doll. £45

2. A wind up Victorian toy complete with the original box. £50

3. Small late 19th century French doll. £20

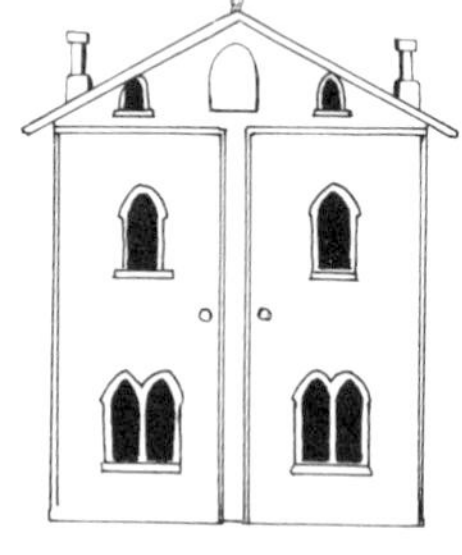

4. Victorian dolls' house 31ins wide. £40

5. Small Victorian doll with the original clothes. £30

6. 19th century black painted wood and wire birdcage 21ins long. £45

7. A fine Victorian rocking horse. £75

1. 19th century German bisque headed doll. £20

2. An excellent carved wooden doll, circa 1740. £840

3. Victorian mechanical toy of a chef peeling a carrot. £35

4. A dignified 19th century French doll. £180

5. A Simon and Halbig doll, 28ins high. £45

6. Small Victorian dolls' house with a hinged front, 14ins high. £38

7. Late 19th century dolls' house. £45

1. A rare pair of Cary celestial and terrestrial globes, dated 1799-1815. £1,050

2. An important celestial globe by Cary, dated 1790, 52ins high. £450

3. Pair of George III globes by W. & J. Cary of London with a compass in the stretchers. £750

4. A Smiths celestial globe, circa 1840. £150

5. A fine early 19th century globe with a mahogany stand, 2ft 7ins high. £195

6. A small Regency period terrestrial globe, 14ins diameter. £110

1. A fine First World War Edison Bell phonograph complete with cylinder records. £255

2. An early 19th century singing bird in a brass cage. £165

3. Victorian polyphone with eight 10 inch discs. £85

4. A fine automaton figure 'The Photographer'. £472.50

5. An exceptionally fine 19th century French automaton group. £800

6. A 19th century bisque headed automaton doll. £350

7. 19th century 'penny in the slot' polyphone. £410

8. 19th century Swiss musical box in a rosewood case. £225

1. 17th century viola of the Brescian school. £3,400

2. A bugle and sword carried at Waterloo by Lord Gantley. £200

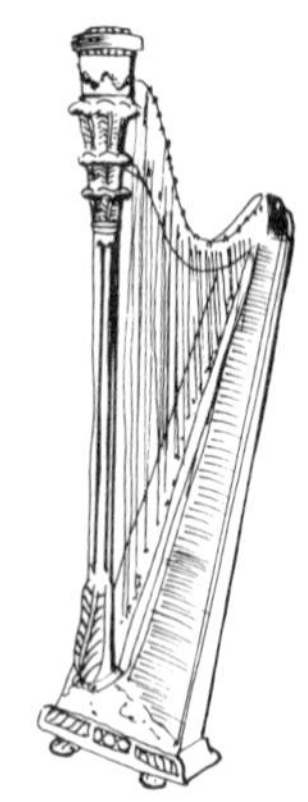

3. French harp by Renault of Paris, circa 1775. £180

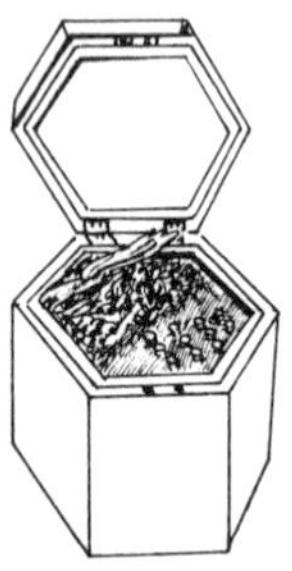

4. Victorian concertina in a mahogany box. £6

5. 19th century sidedrum. £12

6. The Lady Blunt violin by Stradivari. £84,000

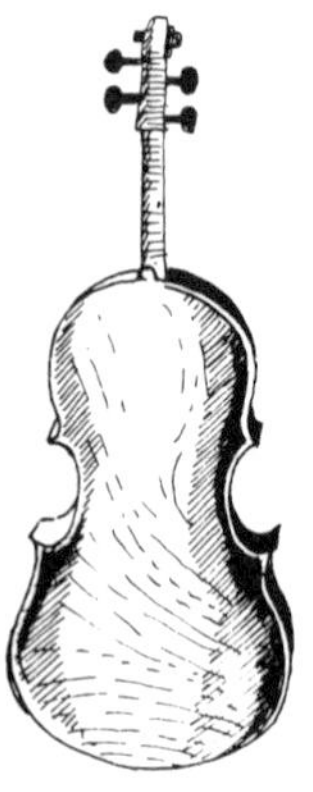

7. 19th century cello by Jules Remy of Paris. £300

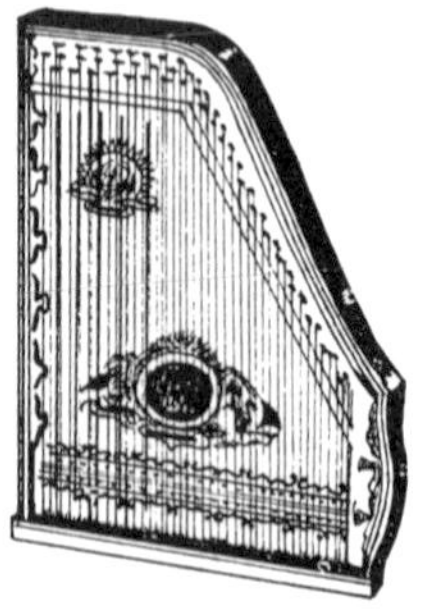

8. A Victorian zither. £12

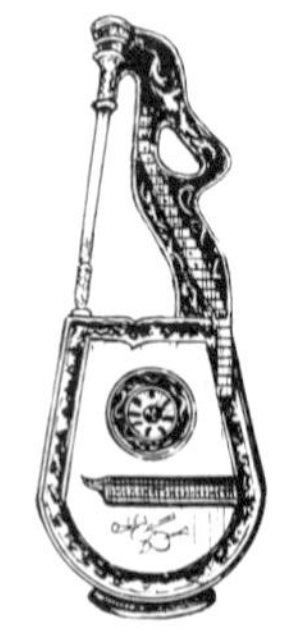

9. Early 19th century Dutch harp by Edward Lights. £150

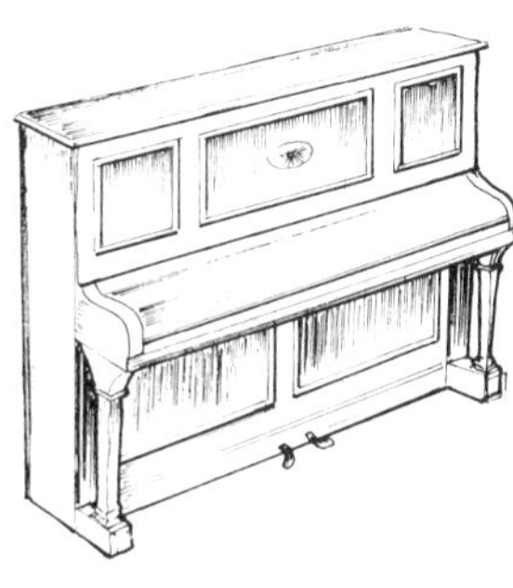

1. Edwardian inlaid mahogany piano. £15

2. Regency upright grand piano by Broadwoods of London. £148

3. A Victorian organ in a rosewood case. £32

4. An exceptionally fine piano by Garrati of Rome, circa 1880, with eleven painted panels and heavily decorated with ormolu. £1,050

5. An exceptionally fine late 19th century Erard grand piano profusely decorated with ormolu. £4,200

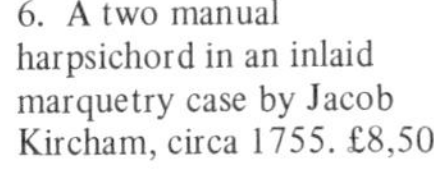

6. A two manual harpsichord in an inlaid marquetry case by Jacob Kircham, circa 1755. £8,500

7. Mid 18th century mahogany cased spinet by Joseph Harris of London. £400

8. George III four octave spinet by John Broadwood and Sons, London. £345

MIRRORS

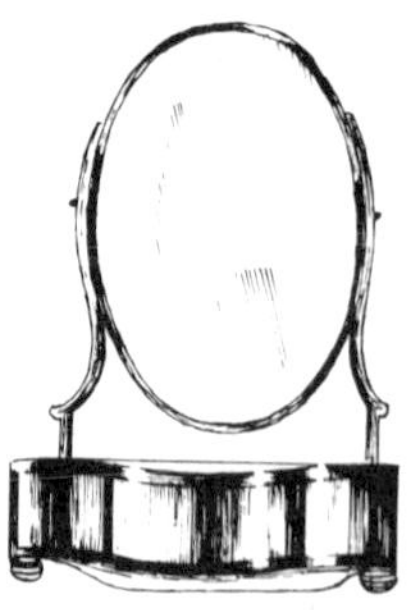

1. Late 18th century mahogany toilet mirror. £65

2. George III mahogany swing mirror. £55

3. Victorian swing mirror with barley twist supports. £4

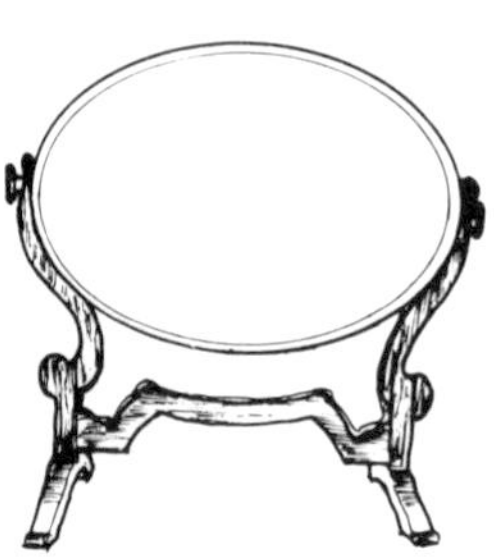

4. Late 18th century mahogany framed swing mirror. £35

5. Dresden china mirror, circa 1860, 2ft 8ins high. £295

6. 19th century rosewood dressing table mirror with a drawer in the base. £6

7. William IV carved wood and gilded mirror, 34insx 52ins. £145

8. Regency water gilt convex mirror with original glass and in mint condition, circa 1810, overall height 30ins, diameter 20ins. £120

9. An exceptionally fine Chinese Chippendale wall mirror, 3ft tall, 2ft 6ins wide. £1,360

1. Victorian walnut veneered dressing table mirror. £3.50

2. A large Victorian mahogany framed swing mirror. £10

3. Late 18th century mahogany dressing table mirror with drawers in the base. £40

4. 18th century mahogany swing mirror with shaped drawers in the base. £55

5. 19th century shield shaped scroll wall mirror of carved gilt wood, circa 1820, 26ins high, 17ins wide. £65

6. Sheraton shield shaped wall mirror. £55

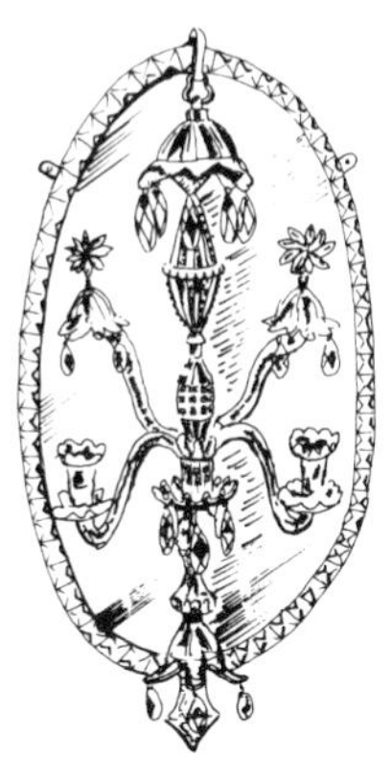

7. One of a pair of Irish glass girandoles from about 1785, 31½ ins high. 3,200gns

8. Mid 18th century mahogany fret mirror with carved and gilded Ho Ho bird, circa 1760. £78.50

9. An exceptionally fine gilt overmantel mirror in the manner of Thomas Johnson, 6ft 10ins tall. £1,900

1. Late 18th century Chippendale gilt mirror (in need of restoration). £380

2. Georgian mahogany toilet mirror with three drawers at the base supported on ogee feet. £60

3. 19th century reproduction mahogany framed wall mirror surmounted by a gilt bird. £40

4. One of a pair of late 18th century carved giltwood mirrors. £285

5. Edwardian carved oak overmantel, 4 ft 10ins wide. £12.50

6. George III mahogany cheval mirror, 5ft 6ins high. £90

7. Regency period convex mirror with the original gold leaf, circa 1820, 35ins high, 22ins wide. £65

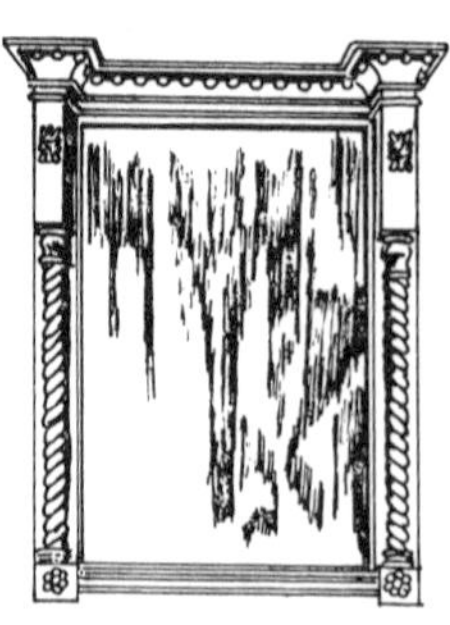

8. 19th century gilded wall mirror, 3ft high. £20

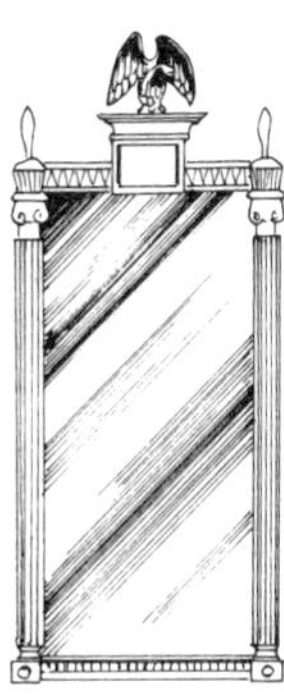

1. Late 18th century gilt mirror with the original glass and Verre Iglamise panel. £165

2. 18th century lacquered dressing table mirror with a fitted compartment below. £95

3. Victorian brass and bevelled mirror firescreen. £4

4. Good quality George III carved giltwood mirror. £100

5. 19th century gilt and white Adam style wall mirror with a convex centre glass. £90

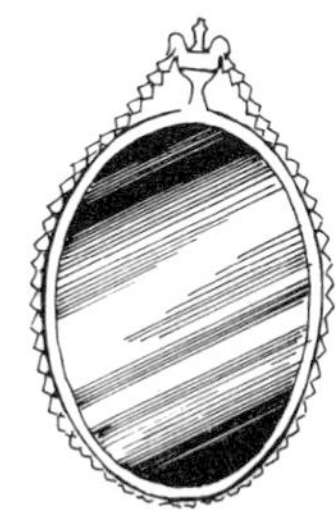

6. 18th century mirror by C. Carton. £135

7. Victorian gilded mirror with gesso ornamentation. £40

8. George II carved giltwood mirror of excellent proportions. £360

9. 19th century mahogany cheval mirror supported on paw feet. £20

1. An exceptionally fine famille rose stylised elephant. 12,500gns

2. Ming dynasty jar in blue and white porcelain, 15th century, 5¼ins diameter. £4,000

3. A fine Chien Lung famille rose charger. £130

4. An 18th century Chinese porcelain punch bowl painted in the characteristic famille rose palette. £400

5. 19th century Canton vase, 24ins tall. £35

6. An 18th century Chinese export punch bowl with Hogarth's 'A Midnight Modern Conversation' on one side and a Chinese tea party scene on the other. £800

7. One of a pair of Chinese blue and white vases and covers from the 19th century, 10ins high. £24

8. K'ang Hsi famille rose saucer dish, 12ins diameter. £200

9. Very rare Chinese Ting Yao bottle from the 11th century A.D., 11¾ins high. £7,000

1. Chinese teapot and stand decorated by J.H. O'Neale, 7½ ins high. 520gns

2. Chien Lung famille rose charger with a colourful floral decorarion, 15ins diameter. £145

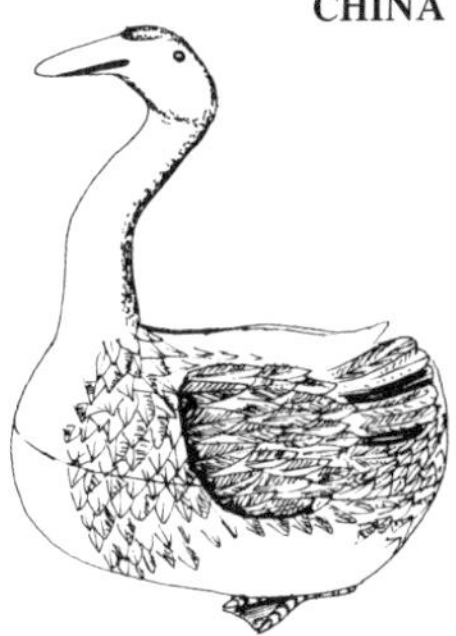

3. 18th century Chinese goose tureen, 12ins long. £6,900

4. One of a pair of Yung Cheng period bowls painted in the Ku Yueh-Hsuan style, 1723- 35, 12.2cm diameter. £13,000

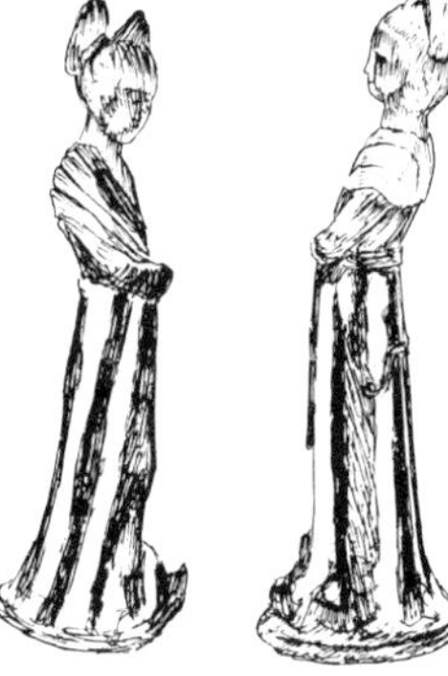

5. Pair of glazed pottery figures of ladies from the T'ang dynasty (618-906), 34.3 and 35.6cm high. £9,250

6. One of a pair of blue and white porcelain bowls decorated with the eight horses of Mu Wang. £560

7. One of a pair of jars and covers of the Yung Cheng period (1723-35) enamelled with colours within ruby coloured borders, 63.5cm high. £3,780

8. A fine K'ang Hsi dish richly decorated in gold, orange, green and blue, 15½ins diameter, (1662-1722). £94

9. 19th century Oriental blue and white jar and cover, 14ins high. £28

1. One of a pair of 19th century Cantonese vases, 17ins high. £330

2. T'ang dynasty figure of a woman playing polo, 15ins long. £28,000

3. 18th century Yuan celadon dish. £200

4. Heavy 19th century green ground Chinese dish with figure, bird and scenery decoration. £46

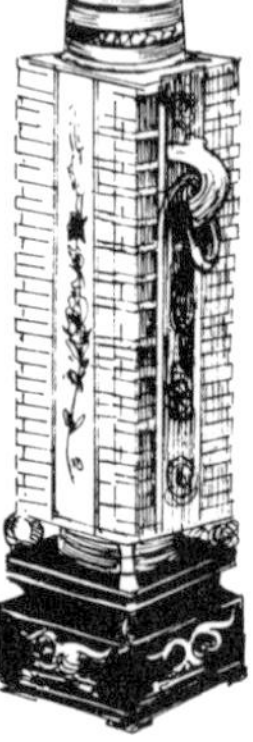

6. One of a pair of 19th century Chinese style salmon pink vases with gilt decoration, 9¾ins high. £36

5. Ch'eng Hua period porcelain bowl decorated in underglaze blue, 5.6cm diameter. £18,000

7. 19th century Japanese red and gilt two handled porcelain pot pourri with bird and figure decoration, 7ins tall. £13

8. K'ang Hsi period porcelain figures of Lung-Nu and Shan-Ts'ai, 55.7 cm and 44.5 cm high respectively. £3,800

9. Mid 14th century Chinese wine jar. £220,500

1. A small famille verte porcelain teapot, complete with lid, from the K'ang Hsi period, 4½ins high. £260

2. A fine pair of Japanese figure ornaments, circa 1899, 11½ins high. £45

3. An 18th century Chinese export bowl decorated with Hogarth panels. £3,800

4. A large famille rose bowl with a central medallion of a European figure on foot with hounds, from the Ch'ien Lung period, 13ins diameter. £330

5. 17th century Japanese Ko-Kutani porcelain dish with enamelled decoration, 36.1 cm diameter. £4,000

6. Chinese 18th century porcelain goose 14ins long (cracked on the base). £2,500

7. Japanese late 17th century Arita porcelain dish painted in blue with the Arms of Francois de Vicq and Aletta Pancras. £600

8. A T'ang dynasty figure of a horse, 28ins wide. £33,000

1. Meissen octagonal lilac ground cup and saucer. 190gns

2. One of a pair of Meissen brocaded Imari plates. £660

3. Figure of a Bustard by Johann Joachim Kandler 1706-1775, German, Meissen circa 1732, 84cm high. £13,125

4. A fine Meissen teapot decorated at Augsburg, 4½ins high. £4,500

5. Pair of Meissen figure groups 'The Seasons'. £250

6. A fine set of eight Meissen mid 18th century porcelain figures of soldiers in the Elector of Saxony's uniform, 11cm high. £5,040

2. One of a pair of Meissen sauceboats, 4½ins long. £390

1. Meissen ecuelle cover and stand decorated with a mixture of chinoiserie and European subjects. 400gns

3. A fine Meissen ecuelle, cover and stand. 800gns

4. A pair of Meissen figures of Harlequin and Columbine by Kandler. £720

5. Pair of Meissen figures, circa 1840, 1ft 11ins high. £350

6. A pair of Meissen goldfinches. £650

1. Pair of Sevres vases made for the International Exhibition of Fine Arts, London 1871. £420

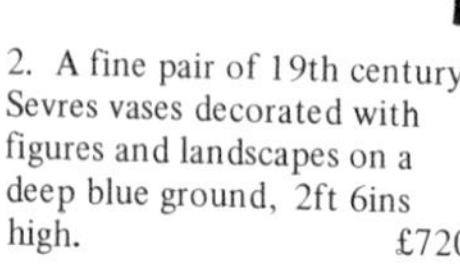

2. A fine pair of 19th century Sevres vases decorated with figures and landscapes on a deep blue ground, 2ft 6ins high. £720

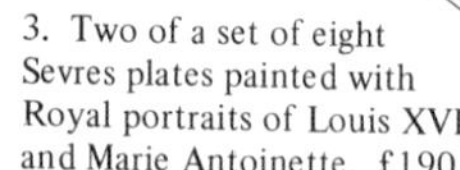

3. Two of a set of eight Sevres plates painted with Royal portraits of Louis XVI and Marie Antoinette. £190

4. A pair of good quality 19th century Sevres vases decorated with a coastland scene. £180

5. A late 19th century Sevres inkstand. £32

1. An extremely fine pair of Sevres 'Rose Pompadour' vases. £7,500

2. An extremely fine pair of ormolu mounted blue Sevres porcelain vases and covers, 25ins high, circa 1860. £795

3. An early 18th century Sevres porcelain plaque. £185

4. A fine Louis XV table with a Sevres porcelain plaque forming the top surrounded by a pierced brass gallery. £10,000

5. Sevres ewer and basin painted by Jean Dubois, 1757. £2,100

6. Early 19th century Sevres tazza mounted on an ormolu base. £145

1. Pair of French faience jardinieres from Nevers. 1,000gns

2. A fine pair of French vases and covers, 11ins high. £350

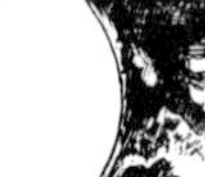

4. An early 19th century Paris porcelain vase of powder blue ground with gold scroll decoration and a polychrome panel romantic scene depicting a young girl with a boy holding a birdcage. £65

3. A Sampson imitation of a Bow figure of Harlequin and Columbine. 75gns

5. 19th century French porcelain figure of a seated gentleman. £18

6. Pair of European porcelain musician figures, 6ins high, both with slight repairs. £34

7. Pair of 19th century blue and white French vases, 13ins high. £35

1. Pair of 19th century Felspar vases with ormolu rams head handles and mounts, and supporting a seven light candelabrum by Millet of Paris, 30ins high. £525

2. Pair of 7inch European porcelain figures of a girl with birdcage and a boy with sheep and doves (slightly damaged scissors mark). £26

3. Pair of Vincenne cabbage leaf tureens with covers and stands. £3,150

4. 19th century Sampson of Paris figure. £35

5. 19th century European figures of a girl and boy, 11ins high. £28

6. Pair of 19th century French oviform vases with royal blue and gilt lids and ormolu mounts, 35¼ins high. £1,125

1. A small 19th century German porcelain figure of a gentleman holding his hat. £8

2. Pair of 19th century German china pin boxes entitled Grandmama and Grandpapa £48

4. 19th century German porcelain rhinocerus 13ins long in naturalistic colours with a cream underbelly. £57

3. An Imperial German Artillery Reservists china Beerstein with coloured scenes of an artillery team mounting a hill, 9½ins high. £17

5. A fine Imperial German ½ litre pottery Beerstein in gilt and colours. £26

6. Pair of Sitzendorf candelabrum, 19½ins high. £140

7. An impressive three litre Imperial German pottery Beerstein. £32

1. A fine Imperial German Reservists ½ litre commemorative pottery Beerstein with a coloured transfer picture. £25

2. German bisque musician figure vase. £10

3. A Cologne ovoid vase. £50

4. German Artillery Reservists decorative china Beerstein, 11ins high. £30

5. 19th century bisque figure group of three boys holding a shell. £12

6. 19th century bisque figure of a boy. £16

7. Pair of fine mint condition Berline vases. £190

8. German pottery Beerstein depicting a coloured scene of advancing infantrymen, the soft metal lid in the form of a picklehaube, 1896. £32

CHINA
DELFT

1. 17th century Dutch Delft tulip vase and cover, 23ins high. £410

2. An unusual small 18th century Delft hand. £16

3. A fine Lambeth Delft wine bottle, 7½ins high. £360

4. A good blue and white Southwark Delft mug. £1,750

5. An early Dutch Delft pottery cow. £210

6. 19th century blue and white Delft style vase, 11ins tall. £10

MENNECY MAGOT

1. An exceptionally fine pair of ormolu mounted Mennecy figures. £9,000

2. A fine Mennecy Magot figure. £800

DRESDEN

1. Mid 19th century Dresden chocolate cup and saucer, complete with lid. £37

2. Dresden figure of Europa and the Bull, 9½ high. £80

3. Early 19th century Dresden candelabrum. £80

4. A pair of 19th century Dresden style four branch china wall sconces. £112

CAPO DI MONTE

1. A rare Royal Vienna style fairing with the Naples Capo Di Monte mark. £140

2. Capo Di Monte figure of Pantaloon from the Italian comedy, modelled by Giuseppe Gricci, 15cm high. £2,940

3. 'The Declaration' by Giuseppe Gricci. £12,000

1. 19th century Royal Dux group of a child playing with a dog. £35

2. A south Italian red figure Amphora 350-325 BC, 16ins high. £220

3. A fine pair of Le Nove figures of a boy and girl sitting on tree stumps. £850

4. An important pair of porcelain greyhounds 12ins long, 7ins high, on flower encrusted bases marked in underglaze blue with the wheel and crown, Hochst 1790. £185

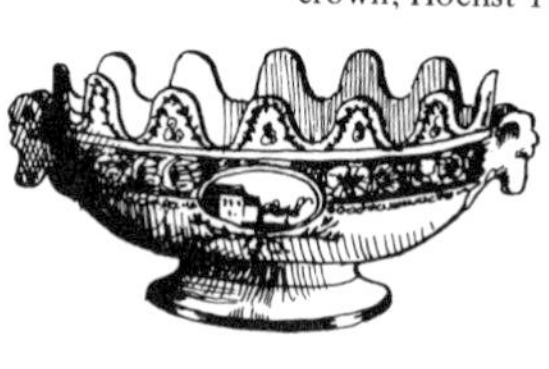

5. A fine Paul I, St. Petersburg verriere. £110

6. A good Nicholas II porcelain urn decorated with figures. £270

7. A pair of mid 19th century French porcelain figures. £25

8. A rare teapot by Vezzi of Venice, circa 1720 (damaged spout). £2,900

1. 19th century Royal Dux figure of a seated girl with a shell. £38

2. A 19th century Paris vase by Francois Boucher. £250

3. A rare Brussels faience tortoise tureen. £1,700

4. Pair of mid 19th century Continental china plates decorated with a hand painted portrait of a Lady and Gentleman, 6ins diameter. £20

5. A Lunds Bristol cup with floral decoration. £45

6. A Russian figure of a dancer, circa 1830. £115

7. A very rare Brussels faience tureen in the form of a duck. £1,250

8. A good Le Nove figure group. £1,000

9. 19th century Continental china chariot pulled by two lions, with a female figure. £10

1. A Crescent Worcester chocolate pot. £100

2. One of a pair of Worcester porcelain dishes. £170

3. A Flight Barr and Barr, Worcester vase of apple green ground with floral paintings on each side. £45

4. Rare set of five Chamberlain Worcester figures of the Rainer brothers and their sister, 6ins high, complete with an original signed lithograph. £1,470

5. Pair of small Dr. Wall apple green vases 5¾ins high. £997

6. A superb first period Worcester tankard 6ins high. 3,000gns

1. A Royal Worcester china ewer shaped vase of the Victorian period, 16ins high. £90

2. First period Worcester porcelain cup and saucer, painted with panels of exotic birds on a scale blue ground. £120

3. A Royal Worcester figure of Psyche. £160

4. Modern Royal Worcester figure of Louisa. £225

5. Pair of Worcester porcelain figures of a gardener and his companion, 6½ins high. £5,000

6. Modern Royal Worcester figure of Rebecca. £225

7. A first period Worcester mug. £75

8. A blue and white Worcester pot pourri bowl. £175

9. First period Worcester teapot. £250

1. A fine Dr. Wall period hot water jug complete with cover. £1,000

2. A crescent Worcester sauceboat 6½ins long. £135

3. 18th century Worcester vase of gilt and blue on a cream ground. £140

4. An exceptionally fine early Worcester group of two birds. £2,800

5. Royal Worcester two handled vase decorated with rural scenes and signed J. Sedgeley, circa 1909. £20

6. A first period Worcester vase decorated with Chinese figures. 500gns

7. A first period Worcester blue and white plate. £35

8. Dr. Wall Worcester blue scale jug. £500

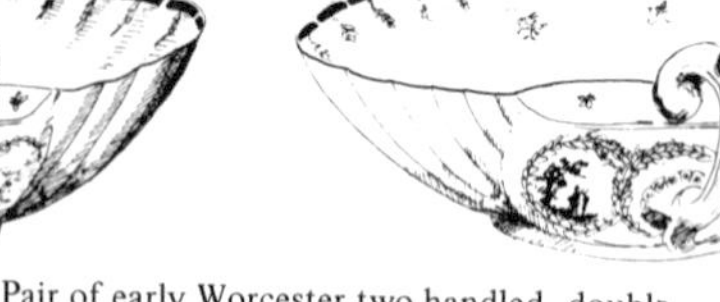

9. Pair of early Worcester two handled, double lipped sauceboats. £2,940

1. One of a pair of Doulton Lambeth silicon vases with white and fawn relief, 9½ins tall. £17

2. A Doulton Burslem blue and floral decorated jug and basin. £5.50

3. Doulton Lambeth urn with raised stag and foliage decoration, 16ins high. £23

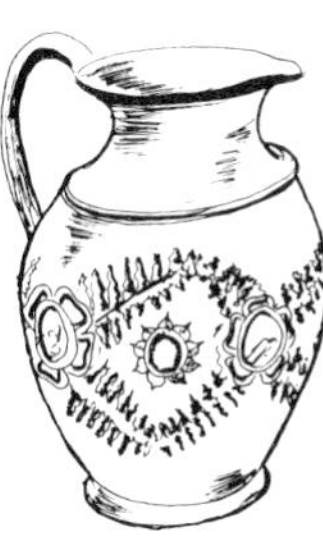

4. A 10ins high Doulton Lambeth jug with raised decoration. £10.50

5. Circular Doulton Lambeth salad bowl having blue and fawn decorations with plated rim and matching plated servers. £42

6. Small pair of Doulton Lambeth vases, dated 1880 and monogrammed by Florence Barlow. £80

7. Royal Doulton bone china figure of 'Antoinette', 6½ins high. £11

8. Pair of Doulton Lambeth vases monogrammed by Florence Barlow and Mark V. Marshall. £110

9. Royal Doulton bone china figure of 'Fragraise', 5½ins high. £10

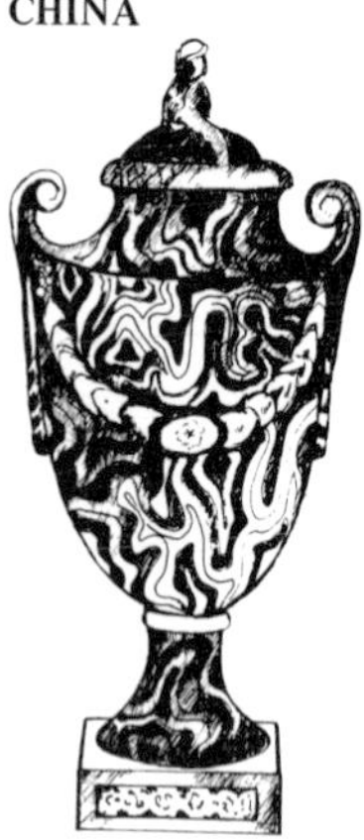

1. Pair of variegated creamware vases and covers by Josiah Wedgwood, circa 1780, 21cm high. £630

2. The Wedgwood 'Pegasus' vase. £640

3. Late 19th century Wedgwood four piece blue and white teaset consisting of teapot, hot water jug, cream and sugar. £75

4. Pair of 18th century Wedgwood green ground vases, 8ins tall. £33

5. Blue and white jasperware plaque of 'The Three Graces' circa 1775, with the mark of Wedgwood and Bentley, 28.6 cm wide. £1,600

1. Pair of Wedgwood Canopic vases. £580

2. 19th century blue and white Wedgwood biscuit barrel with silver mounts. £25

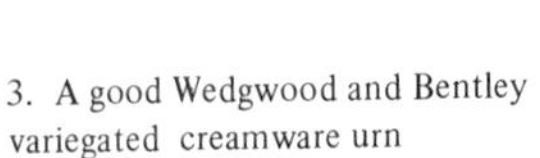

3. A good Wedgwood and Bentley variegated creamware urn shaped vase. £380

4. A Wedgwood copy of 'The Portland Vase'. £20,000

5. An 18th century Wedgwood and Bentley marbled ewer. £250

6. 18th century Wedgwood pot pourri jar. £225

7. Small 18th century Wedgwood three colour vase. £235

8. Pair of late 19th century Wedgwood candlesticks 5 ins tall. £12.50

1. Staffordshire theatrical dancing group, circa 1845. £20

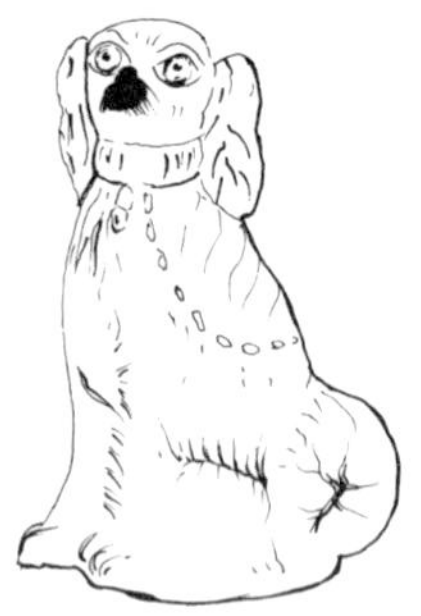

2. One of a pair of Victorian Staffordshire dogs, 10½ins tall. £12

3. An early Staffordshire cow creamer. £15

4. Staffordshire figure of 'The Widow', 11ins high. £40

5. Staffordshire model of 'Stansfield Hall'. £14

6. 19th century, Staffordshire figure of Byron, 7ins tall. £14

7. A small Staffordshire figure of a girl playing a musical instrument, circa 1825. £28

8. Victorian Staffordshire figure of Prince Albert. £24

9. Staffordshire group 'Othello and Iago'. £200

2. Victorian Staffordshire pastil burner. £37.50

3. A fine early 19th century Rockingham retriever. £25

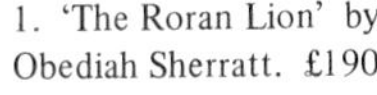

1. 'The Roran Lion' by Obediah Sherratt. £190

4. Staffordshire figure of Queen Victoria. £20

5. Old Staffordshire slip decorated cradle of yellow on a brown ground. £50

6. Fine Staffordshire figure 'The Vicar and Moses', 9½ins high. £300

7. Staffordshire figure of a shepherdess. £10

8. A fine Staffordshire figure 'The Grapplers'. £504

9. Staffordshire figure 'Going to Market'. £22

CHINA
DERBY

1. Modern Royal Crown Derby peacock. £125

2. A 12ins shaped Crown Derby dish 'Near Sydersham', circa 1800-1825. £43

3. Victorian Derby candlestick. £40

PRATTWARE

1. A small Victorian Prattware vase. £40

2. A Prattware teapot cover and stand. £78

3. Rare Prattware Toby, circa 1780, complete with lid, blue and yellow sponge decorated base and handle, translucent blue coat and orange breeches. £175

MINTON

1. 19th century Minton vase embellished with swans. £22

2. An important Minton pot pourri vase, 28ins high. £790

3. Pair of blue Minton vases with pictorial cupid scenes, on ormolu bases, 16ins tall. £295

SPODE

1. Small 19th century Spode dish. £8

2. An 8½ins hexagonal Spode plate with bird and feather decoration, circa 1790-1820. £24

IMARI

1. 19th century shaped Imari dish 9½ins wide. £6

2. Pair of 18th century Arita–Imari high shouldered jars decorated with three petal shaped panels enclosing floral decorations, 30ins high, on carved wooden stands. £2,800

3. Large 19th century Imari vase and cover, 18ins high. £70

BOW

1. An early Bow candlestick depicting a pheasant set among flowering plants. £250

2. A Bow figure of 'Kitty Clive'. £470

3. One of a pair of Bow figures of Kitty Clive as the Fine Lady, and Henry Woodward as the Fine Gentleman in Garricks farce 'Lethe'. £1,300

4. A fine Bow shepherdess. £100

1. Moorcroft pottery vase painted with fruit and foliage on a dark blue ground, circa 1930. £18

2. Pair of Moorcroft pottery mallet shaped vases painted with chrysanthemums, circa 1920. £36

3. Moorcroft pottery bowl decorated with chrysanthemums. £38

RALPH WOOD

1. Ralph Wood Toby jug 11ins high. £130

2. A Ralph Wood St. George and Dragon. £280

3. A fine Ralph Wood Jnr. tree trunk vase with a figure at the base. £200

4. Rare Ralph Wood Toby jug circa 1750, translucent glaze, tortoiseshell coat, blue hair and breeches and a restored hat. £175

5. Late 18th century bust of Minerva. £110

6. Ralph Wood Planter Toby jug. £100

RUSKIN

1. A Ruskin shouldered pottery vase circa 1905. £24

2. Ruskin eggshell pottery bowl, circa 1910. £40

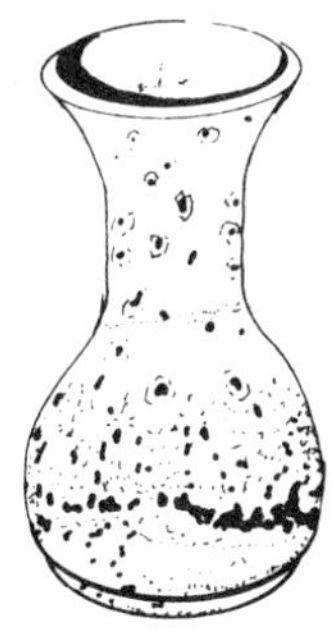

3. Ruskin pottery vase circa 1906. £30

SALTGLAZE

1. Mid 18th century saltglaze teapot. £225

2. A fine saltglaze bear jug. £110

3. Saltglaze plate with the monogram T.H., 9ins diameter. £950

4. Octagonal saltglaze plate. £210

5. A fine saltglaze polychrome punch pot. £1,400

1. Part of a Coalport tea service of thirty-seven pieces with mark no. 946, circa 1825. £225

2. A good quality early 19th century Coalport comport. £20

3. Small pair of 19th century Coalport style vases with flower encrusted decoration. £30

4. Early Coalport spill vase. £30

5. A fine Coalport vase and cover with richly painted floral decoration, 12½ins high, circa 1830. £65

6. 19th century Coalport vase. £34

7. A red and gilt Coalport cup and saucer. £6

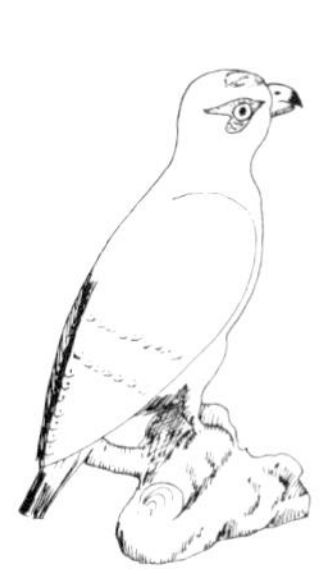

1. Pair of Chelsea bird models with feathers decorated in coloured enamel and the beaks heads and feet similarly treated, 4¾ins high. £2,100

2. A very rare Chelsea red anchor botanical plate of the Hans Sloane type. £2,835

3. A fine pair of Chelsea figures of a lady and gentleman leaning on baskets. £1,000

4. Very rare Chelsea coloured acanthus leaf cream jug, 3½ins high, of the triangle period with crown and trident mark in brilliant underglaze blue. £2,500

5. Chelsea figure of a Chinese man, 7ins high. £8,000

6. Chelsea teapot and cover signed with initials by Jeffryes Hamett O'Neale, 6½ins high, red anchor period (replacement knob and spout). £450

7. Chelsea red anchor sweetmeat dish. £500

1. Florian vase made at Mac Intyres circa 1893. £42

2. A pair of Martinware lovebirds. £280

3. A Wrotham slipware Tyg by George Richardson. £1,417

4. One of a pair of Victorian vases, 14ins high. £6

5. Modern Coalbrookdale urn. £90

6. Linthorpe vase painted with white flowers and foliage. £30

7. One of a pair of Victorian 'Mama and Papa' figures circa 1895. £35

8. A Belleek lattice work basket. £60

9. Early 16th century Madonna and child with original polychrome, 68cm high. £520

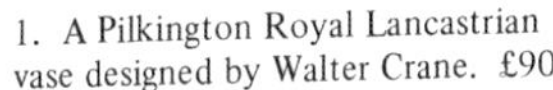

1. A Pilkington Royal Lancastrian vase designed by Walter Crane. £90

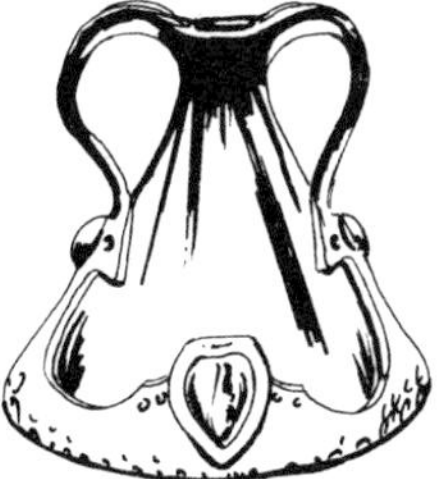

2. Bretby pottery vase with turquoise blue glazed medallions. £16

3. Leeds creamware baluster jug. £315

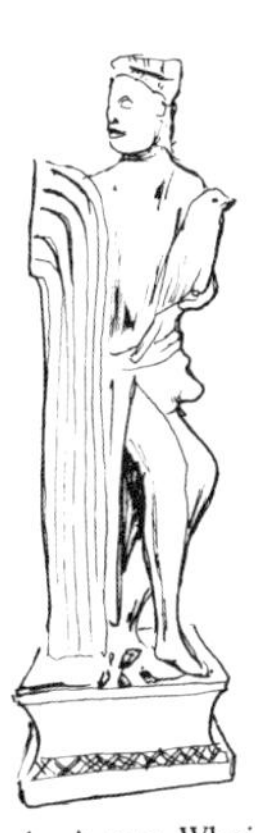

4. A rare Wheilden figure. £115

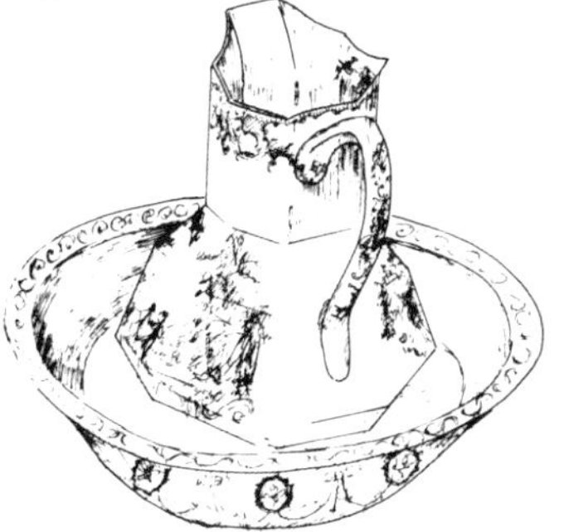

5. Masons blue and white toilet set. £6

6. Wrotham pottery jug by George Richardson. 6½ins high. 1,550 gns

7. One of a pair of Victorian green ground two handled vases with floral decoration. £8

8. 19th century Parian figure of a nude reclining on the back of a lion. £18

9. 19th century vase with a cut out dolphin motif on a salmon pink ground. £72

1. Black polychrome print on a yellow ground of Victoria, 1837. £55

3. Heart shaped pill slab painted with the Arms of Charles II, 9½ins long. £2,800

2. One of a pair of Victorian green ground vases, 16ins tall. £7.50

4. An early 19th century Cadogan teapot made by Rockingham. £32

6. A fine Victorian Sunderland lustre jug. £27.50

5. Polychrome moulded figure of George IV, in a black frame, circa 1821. £95

7. Two of a set of four early wet and dry, blue and white drug jars. £316

8. Pair of Victorian children's china bookends. £7

2. An unusual polychrome moulded impression of the young Victoria. £100

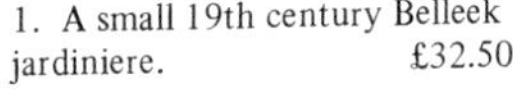

1. A small 19th century Belleek jardiniere. £32.50

3. Victorian moustache cup and saucer. £4

4. Fine Victorian moustache cup with floral decoration. £5

5. A fine 19th century Newhall teapot. £35

6. One of a pair of Minton vases, circa 1845, 10ins tall. £210

7. A Victorian biscuit barrel with a plated lid. £2.50

8. Matched pair of black prints on china in alabaster frames, of Charlotte, and Leopold lamenting her death. £80

1. Victorian fairing ‘ Did you call Sir’. £96

2. Victorian fairing ‘ Death of Nelson’. £120

3. Rare Victorian fairing ‘ The Babes in the Wood’. £210

4. Victorian fairing ‘ The last in bed to put out the light’. £7

5. A rare fairing ‘ No Followers Allowed’. £231

6. Victorian fairing ‘ Every vehicle driven, horse, mule or ass 2d’. £135

7. Victorian fairing ‘ The shoemaker in love’. £231

1. Victorian fairing ' Twelve months after marriage'. £110

2. Victorian fairing ' English Neutrality 1870'. £175

4. Fairing ' Returning at one o'clock in the morning'. £8

5. Staffordshire fairing ' First caresses'. £380

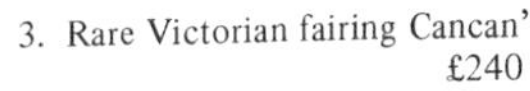

3. Rare Victorian fairing Cancan'. £240

6. Victorian fairing ' Free and Independent Elector'. £175

7. Victorian fairing ' Beware of collision'. £180

1. Walmer Castle, Kent. £30

2. The Chin-Chew River. £18

3. St. Paul's Cathedral. £125

4. The Philadelphia Exhibition 1876. £24

5. Sebastopol. £21

6. The Swallow. £80

7. Shell pot lid. £14

8. Sea Nymph. £60

9. All But Trapped. £55

1. Trafalgar Square. £18

2. The International Exhibition 1851. £45

3. Sir Robert Peel. £310

4. The New Houses of Parliament London. £90

5. Landing the Fare, Pegwell Bay. £20

6. Thames Embankment. £22

7. The Grand International Building of 1851. £30

8. The Shrimpers. £12

9. The Matador. £350

1. 19th century bronze jardiniere and pedestal in the Oriental style with embossed flower and insect decoration, 42½ins high. £47

2. 19th century Minton jardiniere and stand coloured purple with an attractive white wash effect. £58

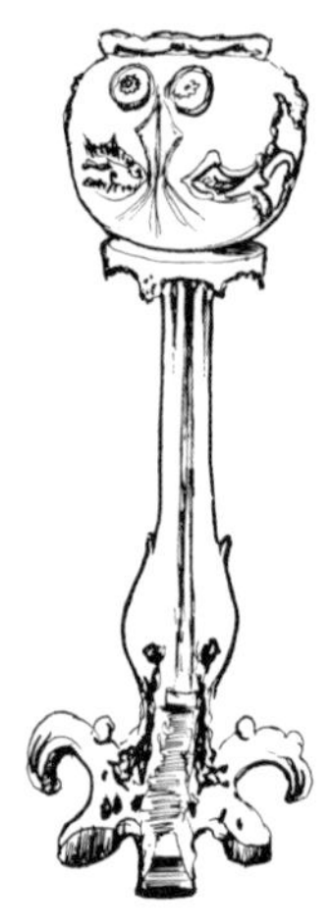

3. One of a pair of French style jardinieres and stands, circa 1870, decorated in brown, yellow and green. £95

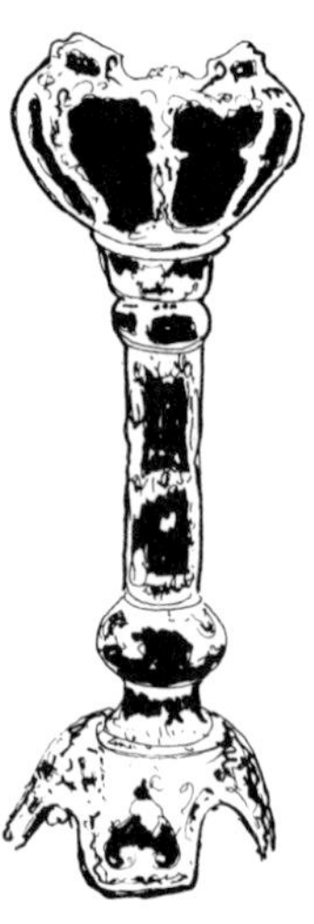

4. Victorian jardiniere and stand, circa 1890. £65

5. An Art Nouveau jardiniere and stand by Bretby featuring imitation jewels and a shipping scene. £65

6. A Bretby earthenware jardiniere with turquoise blue glazed medallions. £48

1. Victorian floral decorated jardiniere and stand. £48

2. Victorian square based jardiniere and stand, circa 1880. £53

3. 19th century gilt and floral decorated earthenware jardiniere and pedestal. £20

4. Victorian hand painted jardiniere stand with an unusual vase shaped pot. £48

5. 19th century Oriental copper jardiniere and stand. £75

6. Mid 19th century simulated green marble jardiniere and stand. £70

1. Carved ivory and wood figure of a woman seated before a mirror, signed Yoshiaki. £150

2. An Oriental rhinoceros horn Libation cup, 6¾ins wide. £210

3. Japanese carved ivory group of a woman carrying baskets and gourds, with a boy at her feet. £80

5. A Louis XVI ormolu mounted ivory vase by Pierre Bouthlore. £3,000

4. A good Persian ivory priming flask, 8½ins overall carved in relief with antelope and tigers heads and birds in panels. £71

6. Early 19th century Netsuke representing 'contentment' sprawled on the back of a huge Fugu fish, Osaka school. £70

7. Webb enamelled ivory cameo vase. £2,100

8. One of a set of six Goanese ivory figures. £245

9. A carved ivory container believed to be of 12th century Coptic design. £1,700

10. 19th century scrimshaw whale's tooth. £20

2. Early 19th century carved ivory jug in the German Renaissance style. £87.50

1. 19th century carved ivory figure of an old man, 8ins tall. £35

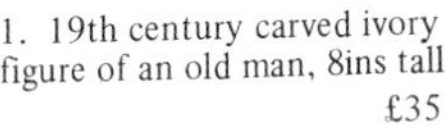

3. A finely carved Japanese ivory group depicting the legendary figures of Kwan Yu and Chohi, signed Tomachika. £45

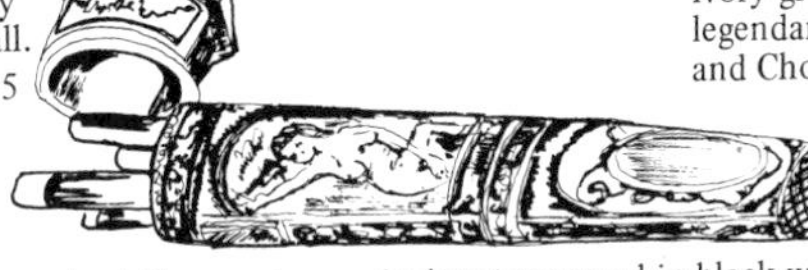

4. A German ivory picnic set engraved in black with Diana and Actaeon, 7ins long, circa 1700. £260

5. Netsuke in the form of a peony flower signed by Masanao of Kyoto, 18th century Japanese. £1,000

6. 18th century ivory Netsuke of a tiger with its cub. £450

7. 19th century carved ivory figure of a woman. £37.50

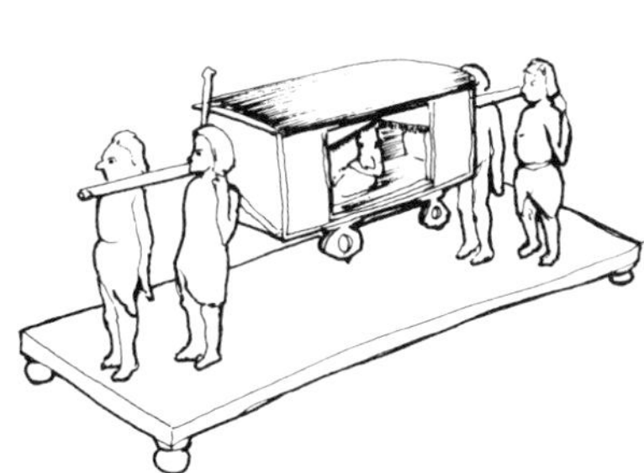

8. Victorian ivory group 4½ins long. £7.50

9. Early 19th century Japanese carved ivory figure of a wildfowler, 7ins high. £60

1. 18th century recumbent Chimera in burnt jade. £265

2. Chinese brush pot carved with 'The Seven Sages of the Bamboo Grove', 1776 in spinach green jade. £3,750

3. 18th century circular white jade bowl 5½ins wide. 700gns

4. Important pair of pale green jade vases with slight brown markings, carved with lotus garlands, 12ins high, with delicate waved rims. 4,800gns

5. Pair of mottled pale green and mauve slender jade vases.

550gns

6. Square mutton fat jade bottle applied with coral, lapis turquoise, malachite and cornelian flowering plants. 65gns

7. 18th century Chinese ivory toned jade carving veined with a black design of a carp among lotus plants, 7ins long. £450

8. A massive mutton jade vase and cover, 20½ins high, the sides carved with a band of archaic ornament and formal foliage. 10,000gns

1. A single horned Chimera from the Ming dynasty, 1368-1644. £450

2. Chien Lung celadon jade Koro and cover, 6½ins tall. 320gns

3. 18th century recumbent Chimera in burnt jade. £265

4. Pair of white jade figures of a bird with lotus sprays in its beak, 9ins high. 620gns

5. Pair of mottled pale green jade vases with domed covers. 350gns

6. An elaborate pale green jade vase and cover, 12ins high. £1,500

7. A mottled yellow brown jade Chimera 7½ins long. 400gns

8. A Wei dynasty jade carving of Avaldkitesvara. £500

1. 18th century wood and ivory group in the manner of Simon Troger. 750 gns

2. An early oak Newel showing a woman beating a devil in the form of a boy and standing on a grotesque acrobat, 90 ins high. £1,050

3. 15th century German painted wood figure. 750 gns

4. An attractive 18th century carved pinewood reclining classical figure, 30 ins x 21 ins. £185

5. A Maori hardwood door lintel. £2,300

6. 18th century German wood and ivory group of a pair of jolly beggars. 750 gns

1. Late 16th century carved walnut figure 88 cm high. £240

2. An early oak Newel dipicting a Jester, 73 ins high. £740

3. 19th century German carved wood bear stickstand 3ft high. £60

4. Painted wooden hawk from an Eygptian tomb of the 26th dynasty. £110

5. 18th century carved wood and silver mounted model of an aged vineyard worker. 1,900 gns

6. New Zealand Maori wooden head with elaborate tattoo marks, 23·5 cm high. £9,000

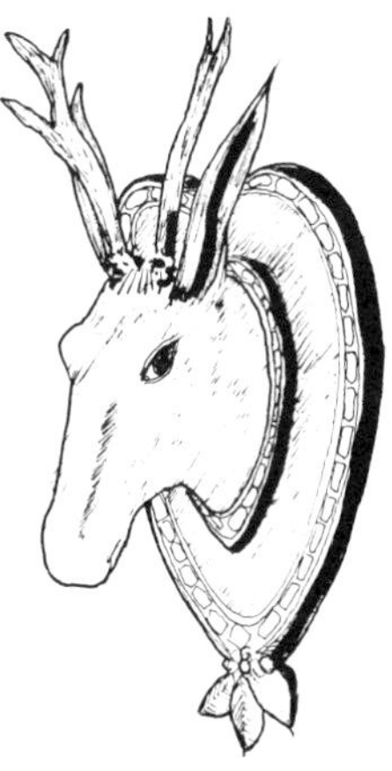

7. One of a pair of 18th century carved wood game trophies with real antlers. 190 gns

1. 16th century Flemish painted wood depiction of St. Barbara. 590gns

2. A large late 18th century carved wood Toby jug. £110

3. Late 15th century carving of St. Barbara. 500gns

4. A South German carved figure of the Archangel Gabriel from an Annunciation group, 66½ins high, late 17th or early 18th century. 1,600gns

5. 19th century Chinese hardwood figure of an old man. £28

6. A finely carved oak Eagle from the 18th century, 21ins high, 23ins wide. £95

7. A carved and painted pine ships Figure Head. £290

1. 16th century Flemish painted and gilded wood carving of St. Mary Magdelene. 240gns

2. 19th century German carved wood tankard surmounted by a fox's head. £10

3. 16th century carved wood heraldic beast. £90

4. Decorative old ship's Figure Head of a King, finely carved in pinewood with the original brown varnish finish, 24ins tall. £225

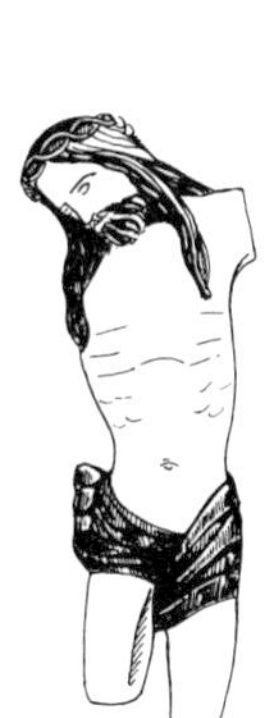

5. 15th century Italian carved wood figure of Christ. 520gns

6. A large 19th century carved wood figure of an elephant with ivory tusks, 18ins high. £32

7. 19th century Chinese root carving of an old man. £25

POWDER FLASKS

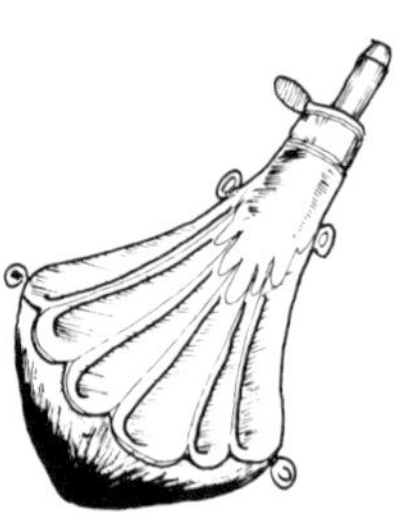

1. Embossed copper gun flask depicting flutes, with patent top. £25

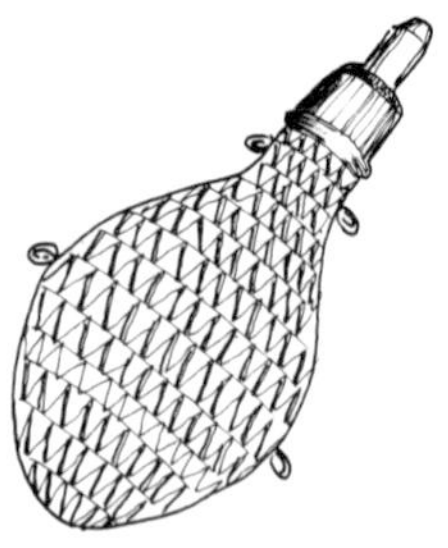

2. Embossed copper gun flask depicting Hob Nail pattern and acanthus. £35

3. Embossed copper gun flask by P. Powell and Son. £16

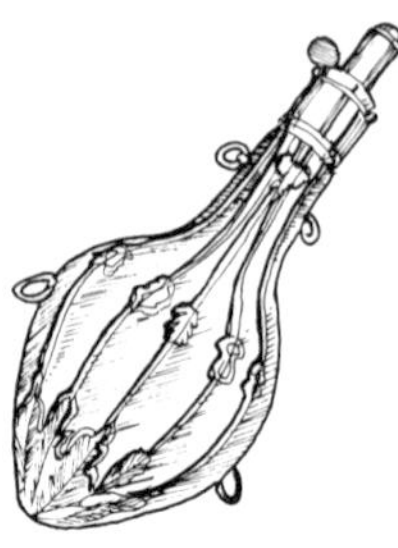

4. Embossed copper gun flask depicting flutes and acanthus. £25

5. A fine early 17th century powder flask of wood inlaid with concentric rings of staghorn, brass wire and circle of dots. £82

6. Embossed copper gun flask depicting dead game birds. £28

7. Slim embossed copper gun flask depicting laurel leaf borders. £16

8. 17th century German flattened horn powder flask. £60

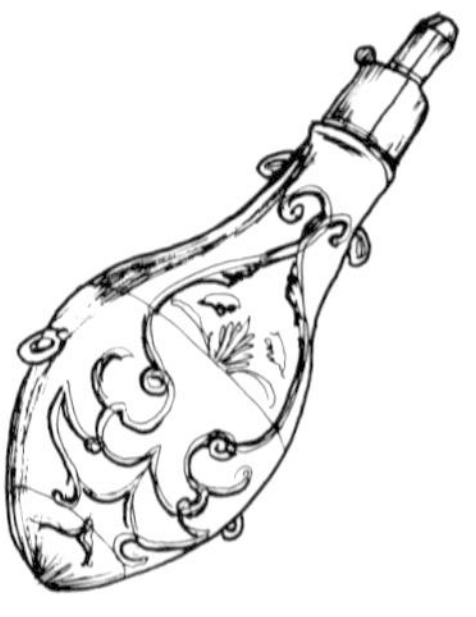

9. Embossed copper gun flask depicting scrolled trellising. £26

1. Embossed copper gun flask depicting dog, oak leaves, stag and fox hounds. £29

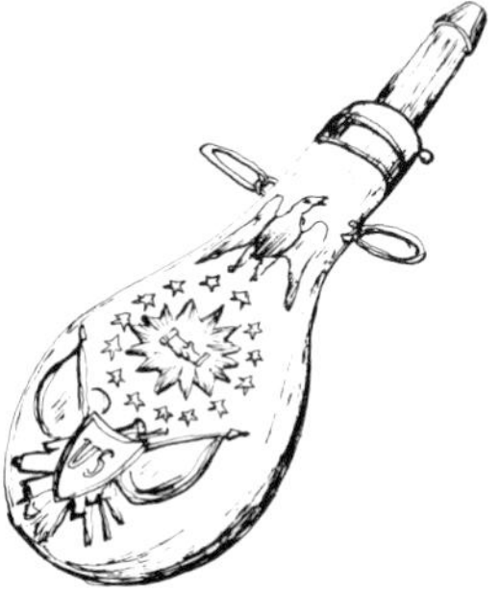

2. A fine and rare copper ' Batty Peace Flask '. £65

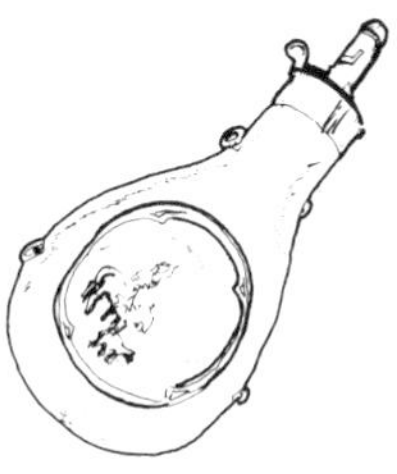

3. Embossed copper gun flask depicting hunter and animals. £27

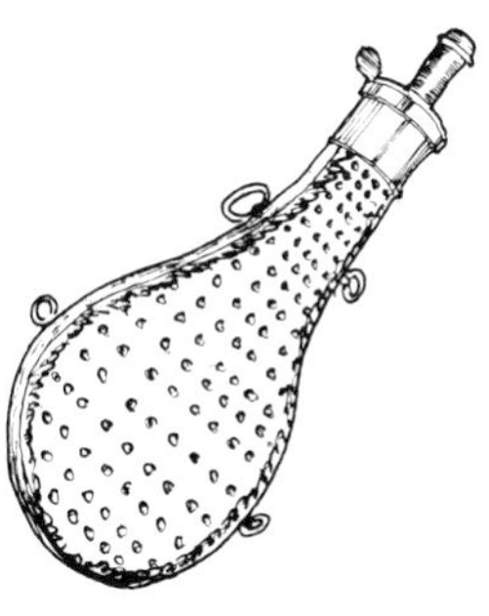

4. Embossed copper flask with stars, dots and acanthus. £30

5. A silver mounted double horn powder flask. £42

6. Embossed copper gun flask depicting flowers and foliage. £27

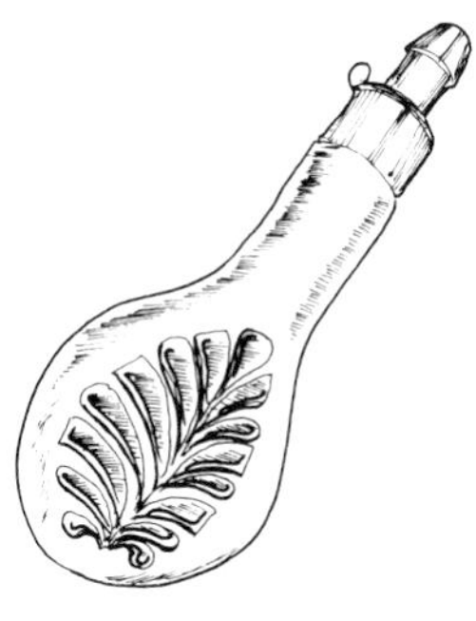

7. Embossed copper gun flask depicting shell ornamentation. £21

8. A 17th century engraved powder horn. £65

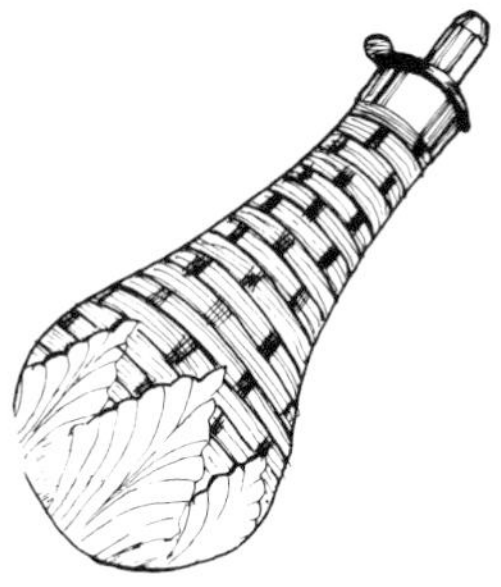

9. Embossed copper gun flask depicting basket weave and acanthus. £30

POWDER FLASKS

1. Embossed copper gun flask depicting a dog and dead game. £21

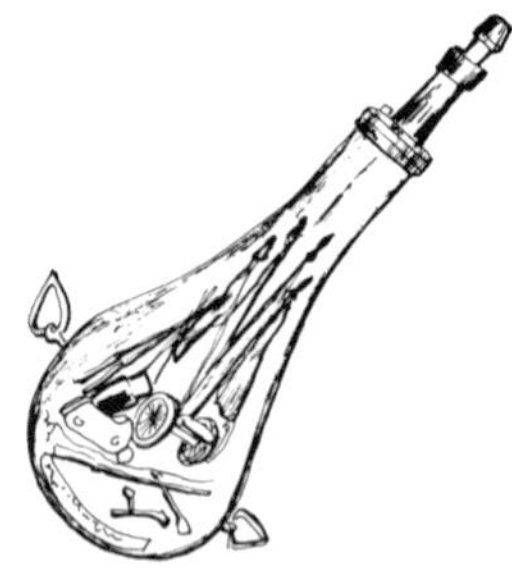

2. A fine and rare Colt patent copper powder flask for the Walker model. £70

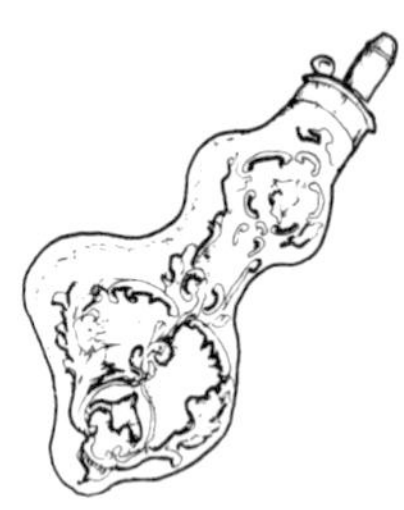

3. Embossed fiddle patterned copper flask depicting game amid foliage. £20

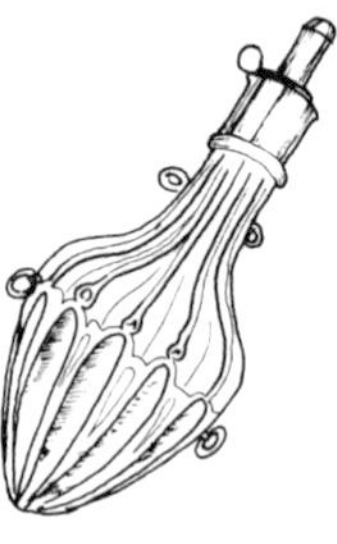

4. Embossed copper gun flask depicting flutes and acanthus. £25

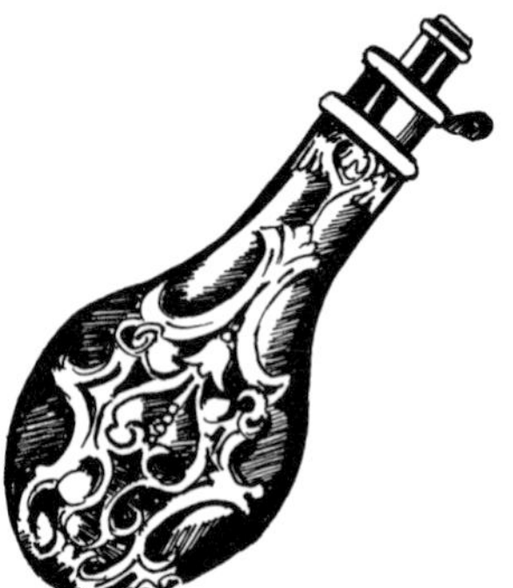

5. A fine embossed copper gun flask. £28

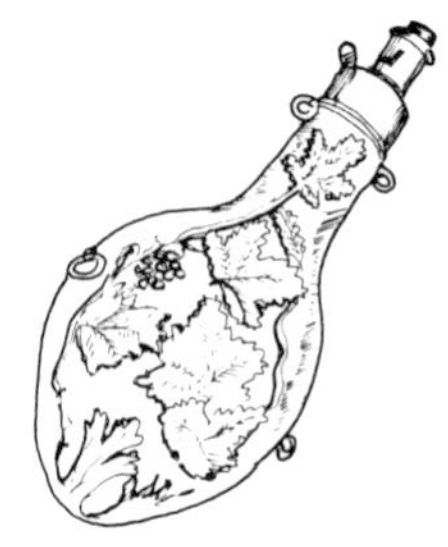

6. Embossed copper gun flask depicting grape vines. £27

7. Embossed copper gun flask depicting flutes. £18

8. An unusual copper bodied two way powder flask. £27

9. Embossed copper gun flask depicting a Greek classical scene. £33

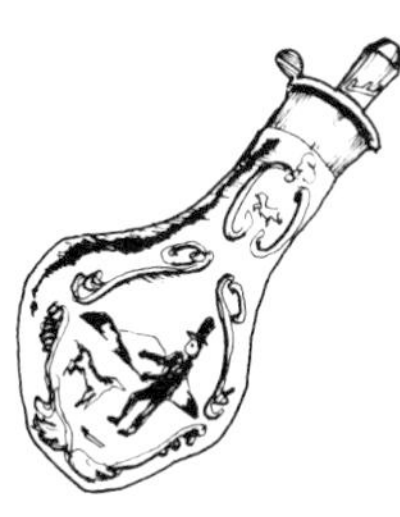

1. Embossed copper gun flask depicting a dog and hunter. £34

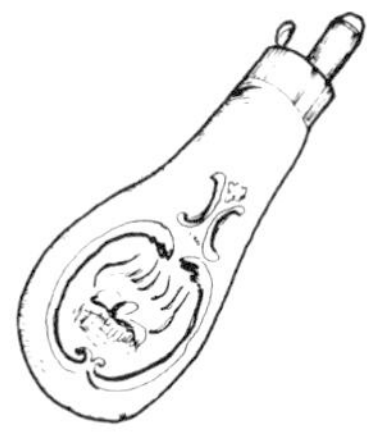

2. Embossed copper gun flask depicting game birds. £28

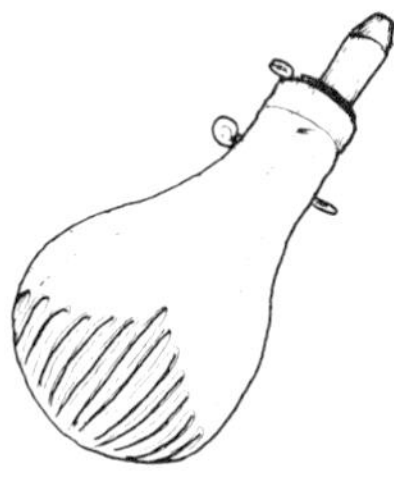

3. Embossed copper gun flask depicting a shell. £17

4. A plain steel powder flask with a tip up charger. £16

5. 17th century style powder flask with a cloth covered wood body encased in fretted iron. £118

6. A rare embossed brass gun flask depicting entwined dolphins. £60

7. A silver plated powder flask by Sykes. £32

8. A good foliate embossed copper gun flask. £22

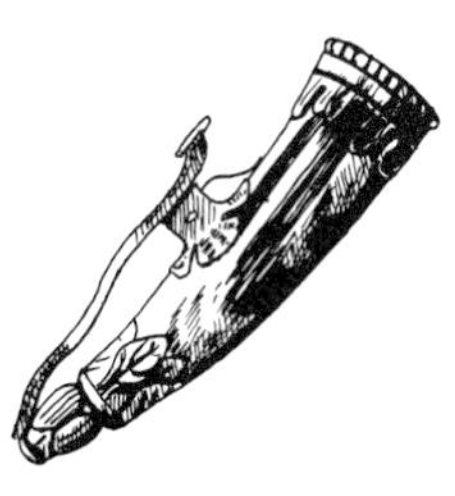

9. A fine horn shaped priming flask with a silver cap. £135

TRANSPORT

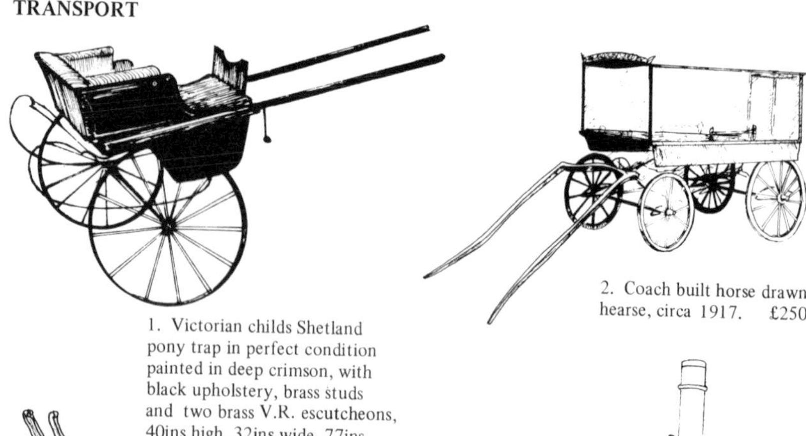

1. Victorian childs Shetland pony trap in perfect condition painted in deep crimson, with black upholstery, brass studs and two brass V.R. escutcheons, 40ins high, 32ins wide, 77ins overall. £165

2. Coach built horse drawn hearse, circa 1917. £250

3. Mid 19th century goat and dog cart for a child, complete with leather harness, 20ins wide, 68ins overall. £145

4. Horse drawn steam driven fire pump by Merryweather of London, late 19th century. £1,020

5. An attractive 19th century handcart with original paint in buff and black with red wood spokes to iron tyred wheels. £120

6. Dolls pram with the original upholstery in black, circa 1860, 24ins high. £28

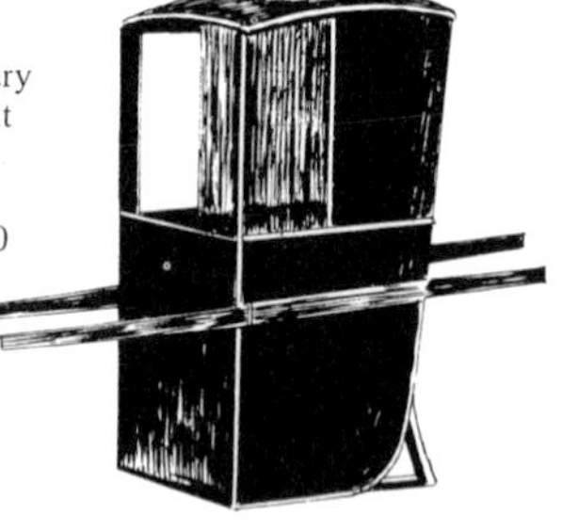

7. 18th century Sedan chair with a yellow silk lining, complete with carrying poles. £295

1. 19th century square shaped Brougham coach. £310

2. A fine mid 19th century knifegrinder's cart in working condition, painted in blue and orange. £80

3. A 19th century barrel top Romany Vardo in good condition. £320

4. 19th century Penny Farthing bicycle in working order. £100

5. Victorian wicker work bath chair with iron wheels and brass fittings. £70

6. An exceptionally fine quality mid 18th century carved and painted Norwegian sledge. £500

7. 19th century Governess cart in original condition. £75

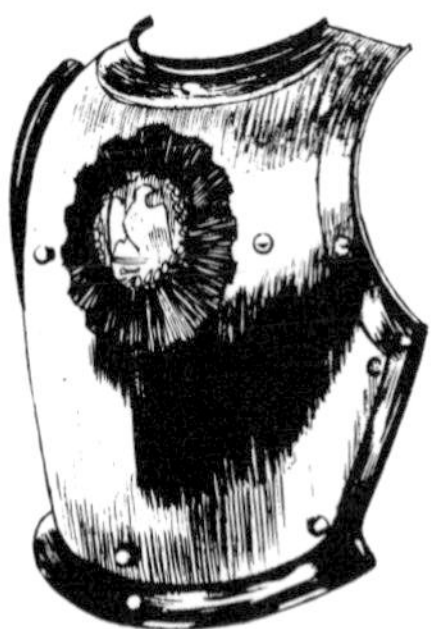

1. A Second Empire French Carabiniers breastplate, having a heavy steel plate brass covered face with an embossed brass eagle against a black sunray. £65

2. A fine complete suite of Pikemans armour, English circa 1600, comprising 'Pot' gorget, breast, backplate and tassels. £390

3. A heavy steel armoured breastplate superimposed with an oval brass imperial eagle. £95

4. A fine late 16th century articulated gorget and shoulder defence. £50

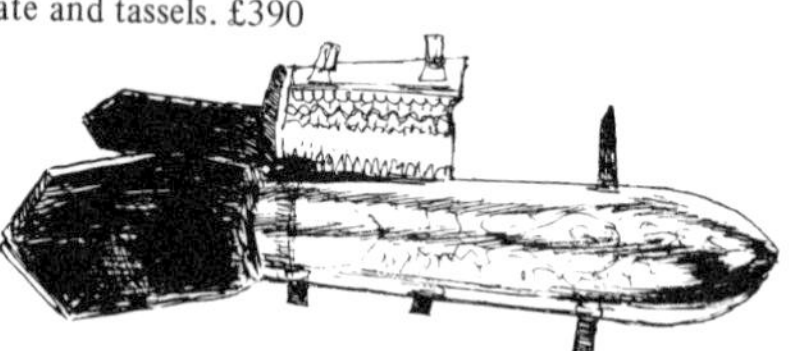

5. A fine Indo-Persian lower arm defence, Bazuland, 21ins long. £25

6. A fine suit of 18th century armour. £600

7. A magnificent antique suit of armour in the Gothic style, manufactured for the 16th Earl of Shrewsbury, circa 1840. £5,000

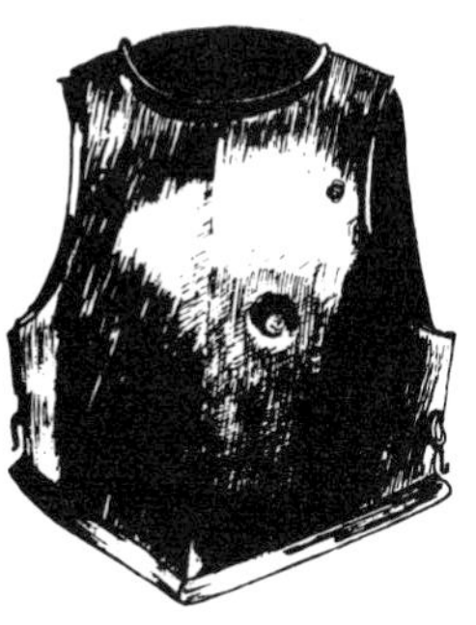

1. A pair of 17th century Cromwellian Troopers breast and back plates, the breastplate of heavy form deeply struck with a musket ball proof. £71

2. A Cromwellian Cuirassiers elbow gauntlet, 18ins long with a riveted two piece upper defence. £38

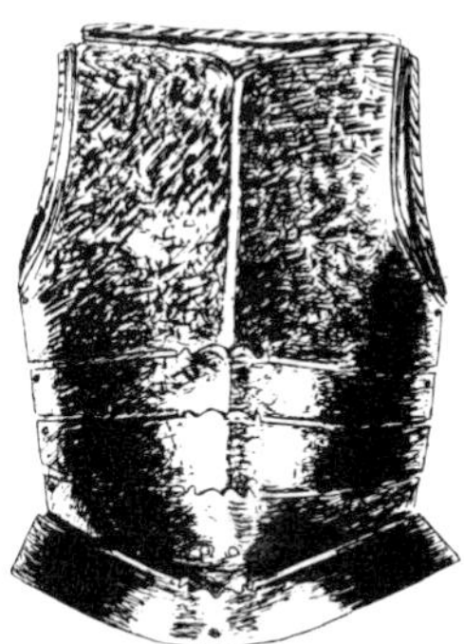

3. A 16th century Venetian laminated breastplate with a roped border. £90

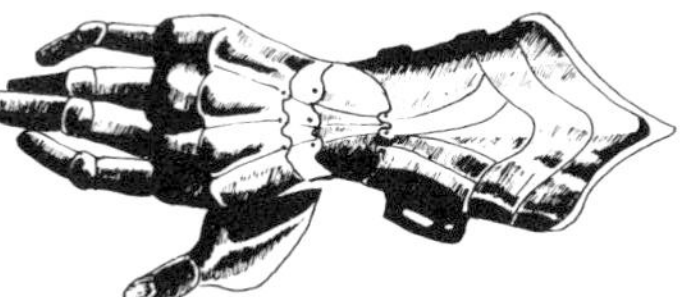

4. A fine late 15th century style fluted Gothic gauntlet possibly by Schmidt of Winkelmayer. £36

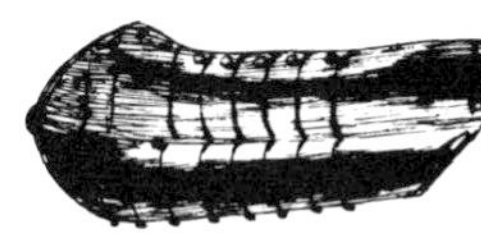

5. A pair of exceptionally well articulated early 17th century upper arm defences, each consisting of nine lames. £45

6. A good Cromwellian suit of Pikemans armour. £250

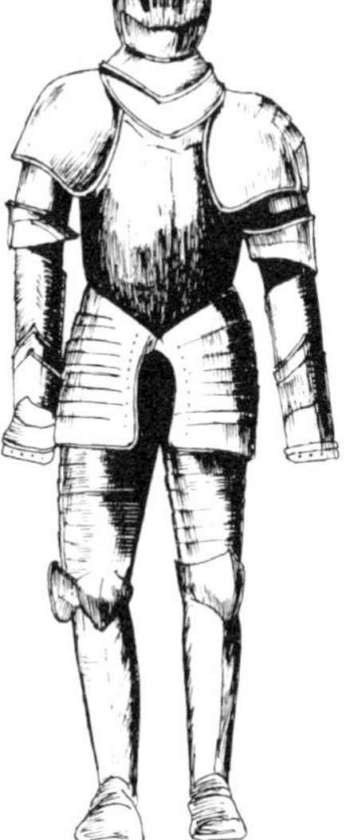

7. A good Victorian suit of armour, fully etched and articulated, 6ft tall, breastplate etched with portrait bust within laurel wreath, lions head within scrolls and mythical dragon. £120

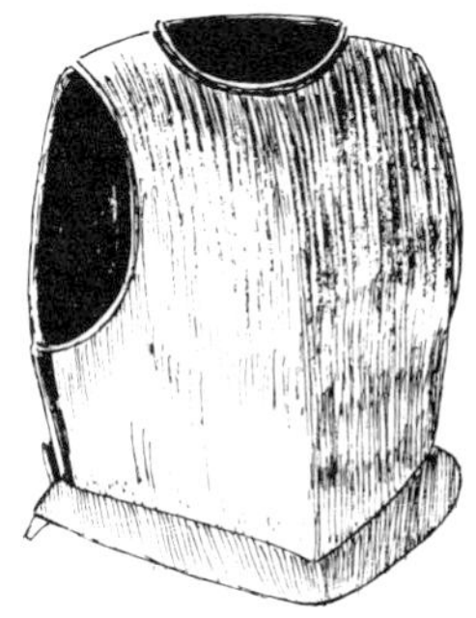

8. A good siege weight pair of Cromwellian breast and back plates. £65

1. A Georgian Officer's scarlet coatee of the Cinque Ports Volunteers. £40

2. A fine Officer's Lancer Tunic of the Lancashire Yeomanry. £35

3. A good scarce Indian fabric body armour Cuirass, with two arm pieces, the quilted jacket bordered with mauve velvet, the red exterior with silver colour woven flowers. £37

4. A good complete uniform for an Officer of the 21st Lancers. £190

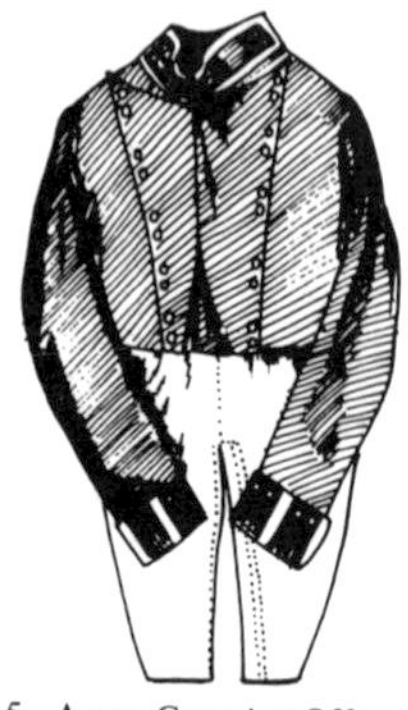

5. A rare Georgian Officer's scarlet coatee of the XVth Regiment, circa 1820, with silver buttons. £90

6. An N.C.O.'s scarlet jacket of the Lothian and Border Horse Imperial Yeomanry. £26

1. A fine Georgian Officer's long tailed scarlet coatee of the South East Hants Local Militia. £85

2. Tunic of a Georgian Inspector of Yeomanry. £65

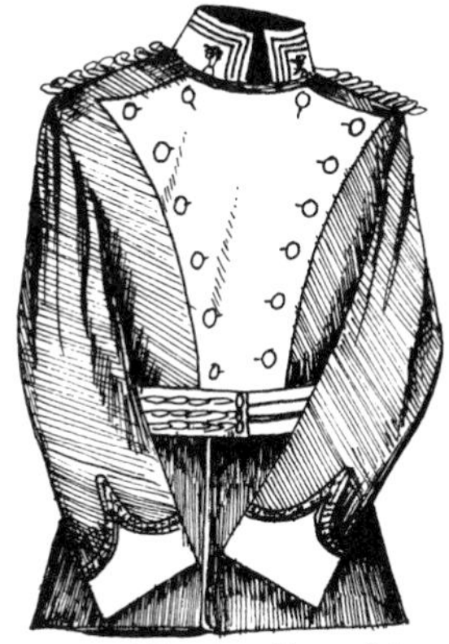

3. An Officer's uniform of the 21st (Empress of India's) Lancers. £40

4. A rare 19th century North American Indian war shirt. £55

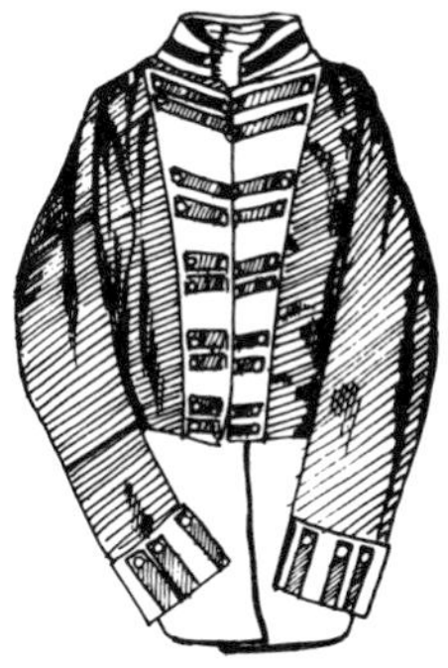

5. A rare Georgian Officer's scarlet coatee of the 37th Regiment, circa 1815, with silver buttons bearing the Regimental Numeral. £130

6. A Georgian Officer's long tailed scarlet coatee of Inspectors of Yeomanry and Volunteers. £80

1. Late 19th century carved oak banjo barometer. £12

2. George I barometer by J.N.D. Halifax of Barnsley, 1694- 1750. £1,900

3. Late 18th century mahogany cased barometer with satinwood inlay and crossbanding. £60

4. George III barometer by Breggazzi of Nottingham in a mahogany case. £110

5. 19th century Admiral Fitzroy barometer in an oak case. £40

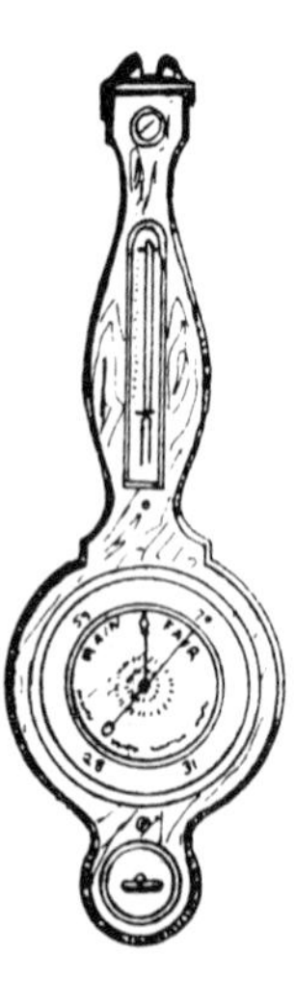

6. Early 19th century mahogany scroll top barometer with boxwood string inlay. £48

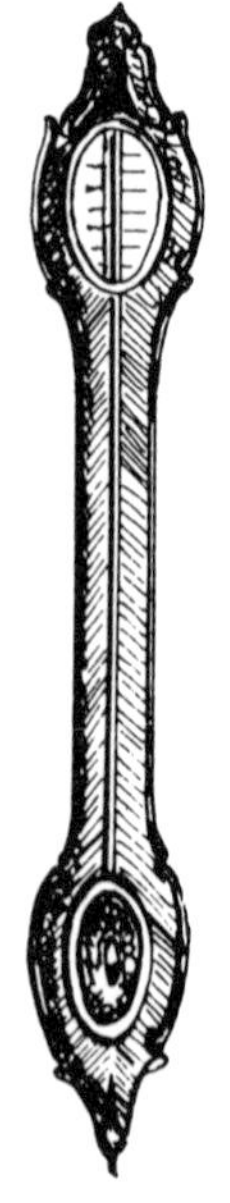

7. A good Georgian mahogany cased barometer. £85

8. Late 19th century banjo shaped aneroid barometer in a carved oak case. £10

3. Victorian barometer in a carved oak case. £16

2. An exceptionally fine quality gilt framed barometer. £220

4. George III barometer with hygrometer, thermometer and clock. £115

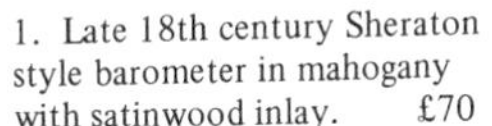

1. Late 18th century Sheraton style barometer in mahogany with satinwood inlay. £70

6. 19th century banjo shaped barometer with an onion top. £110

8. Late 18th century Sheraton style barometer with a centre mirror. £68

5. George III period stick barometer by Couti. £90

7. A good Georgian cistern barometer in a walnut case. £110

TSUBA

1. Shakudo Tsuba carved and inlaid with bamboo trees and foliage, signed. £95

2. A brass Tsuba depicting peacocks beneath cherry trees, signed. £40

3. A good brass Tsuba depicting a tiger in relief being pushed by a boy in high relief, signed. £105

4. A good brass Tsuba of Mokko form depicting many different types of vegetation in relief. £145

5. Brass Tsuba depicting a rat catcher who hides among the cornshieths near his trap. £40

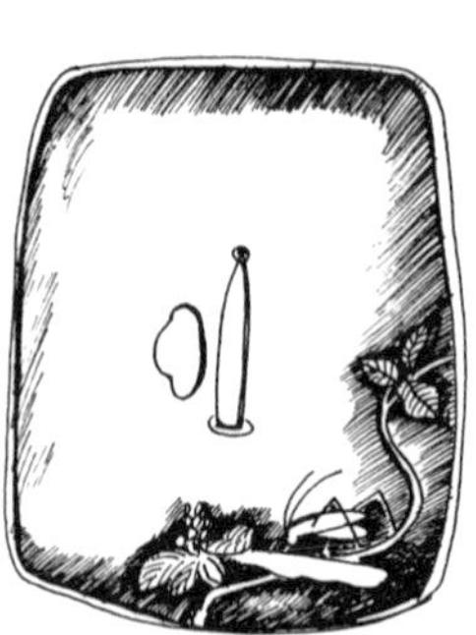

6. A brass Tsuba of square form depicting a locust devouring foliage. £50

7. A good pierced brass Tsuba depicting an eagle perched on Cherry tree boughs. £130

8. A iron Tsuba depicting a warrior who has dismounted and prepared to attack a devil who peers at him from the top of the Tsuba, signed. £65

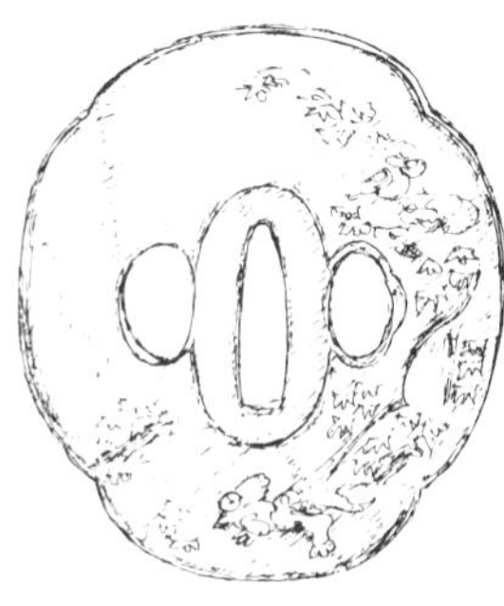

1. A good Shakudo Nannako Tsuba of Mokko form depicting lions gambolling among rocky arborial terrain with a silver waterfall. £75

2. A large 19th century Shakudo Tsuba of round saucer shape with an old man contemplating a doll resting on his finger. £80

3. A Shakudo Tsuba of black colour depicting three large silvered dragonflies in relief, signed. £130

4. A good pierced round Shakudo Tsuba depicting two dapple horses drinking from a stream beneath trees. £70

5. A good iron Tsuba of Mokko form depicting a gold Shakudo dragon chasing a tiger against a background of waves and rocks. £80

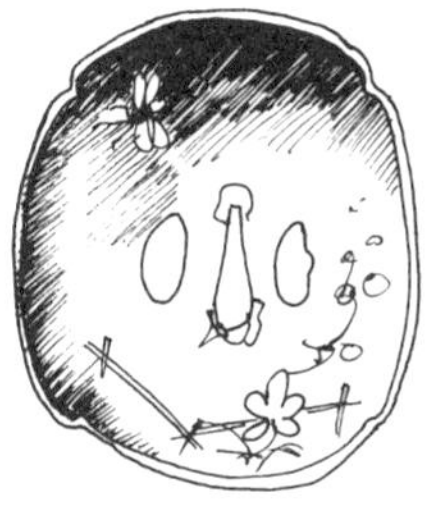

6. An unusual Tsuba of Mokko form depicting dragon flies, chrysanthemums, foliage and a fence. £85

7. An iron Tsuba depicting Lions gambolling about rocky landscape overhung by cherry trees near a waterfall. £55

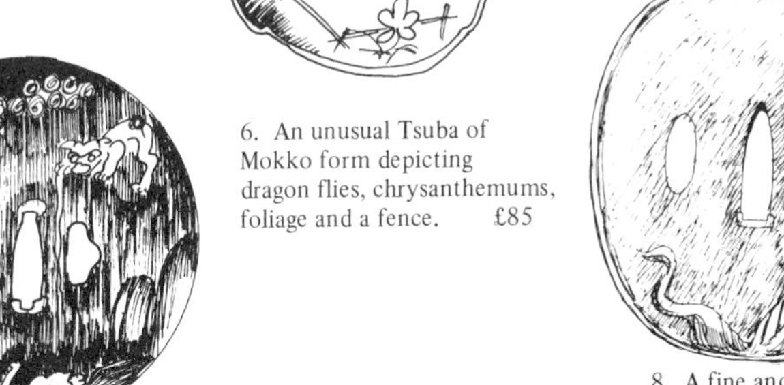

8. A fine and desirable iron Tsuba of squared form depicting an old effeminate Sennin, in high relief of Shakudo, holding a staff. £135

1. Three compartment inro decorated with a pair of silver cranes, signed Koma Kiuhaku. 95gns

2. Japanese four case inro decorated in red, gold and black lacquer, signed Bunryusai. 28gns

3. Three case inro decorated in gold, red grey and other coloured lacquers, signed Katikawa. 120gns

4. Two of an excellent set of twelve inros showing the Japanese signs of the Zodiac. £14,000

5. Five case inro decorated with chrysanthemum blooms and leaves in gold lacquer. 285gns

6. Four case inro decorated with pine trees in various shades of gold with Mount Fuji in the background. £140

7. Four case inro decorated with a Peony flower in mother of pearl. £375

1. A mounted fox head inscribed 'Wexford Hounds 14th Oct 1904'. £5

2. A cased specimen of a cockerel 'Preserved by John Pear, All Saints Green, Norwich'. £10

3. Victorian stuffed bird under a glass dome. £6

4. 19th century mounted leopard's head in good condition. £15

5. A large mounted stag's head. £12

6. A large 19th century mounted lion's head in good order. £35

7. A pair of squirrels under a glass dome. £15

8. A Victorian bird in a glass case. £8

9. A good pair of Victorian stuffed birds under glass domes. £18

STONE

1. A small carved stone garden temple of classical design, the carved frieze supported on columns of the Composite Order, 11ft high, 6ft 8ins diameter. £900

2. A pair of early Georgian style carved stone vases with pedestals en suite. £230

3. A carved stone pedestal with an octagonal plinth surmounted by a bronze armillary sundial, 5ft 10ins high. £280

4. Regency period carved Portland stone garden seat. £265

5. A large 19th century carved stone fountain figure. £140

6. A carved stone bench with dolphin supports, 4ft 11ins wide. £140

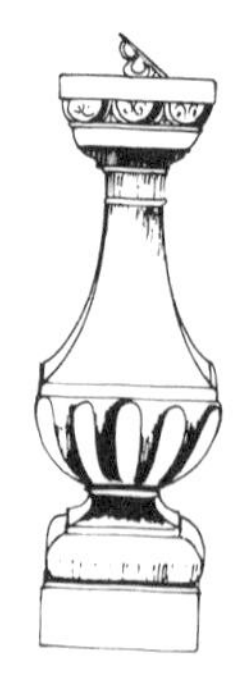

7. Late 18th century carved stone sundial, 4ft high. £230

1. A fine pair of 19th century carved stone lions 2ft 6ins high. £100

2. A carved stone group of two children playing with a goat, with the original pedestal en suite, 3ft 1ins wide, 5ft high. £240

3. A most attractive carved stone three tier fountain with baroque shaped pool around, 7ft diameter, 6ft 3ins high. £650

4. A magnificent large garden fountain in the form of a swan and four playful cherubs. £1,350

5. George III carved stone vase 24ins high. £50

6. A small carved stone fountain of baroque design, 4ft high. £230

7. 19th century carved stone garden table. £100

MARBLE

1. Marble bust of Inigo Jones attributed to J.M. Rysbrack, 20½ins high. 420gns

2. Roman third century marble bust of a Priest of Serapis or Helios, 75.9 cm high. £7,000

3. 19th century marble bust of a Roman Emperor on a-jasper pedestal. £320

4. Cycladic figure of a Goddess in white marble, made in the Greek Islands, 2000 B.C.. 8¼ins high. £575

5. 19th century cream marble bust of a young girl with a white and green variegated marble dress, 16ins high, signed Christopher Vicari. £95

6. A 17th century Italian Istrian marble jardiniere and stand. £155

7. 'The Tinted Venus' by John Gibson 1791-1866 made of marble coloured with waxes, 1.75 metres high. £2,400

8. 19th century marble figure of a child, 3ft 4ins high. £100

9. A fine Victorian marble figure of a child, 2ft 6ins high. £130

1. An early lead garden urn 2ft 5ins high. £90

2. 19th century lead greyhound 2ft 7ins high, on a Portland stone base. £190

3. Late 18th century lead figure 2ft 8ins high. £190

4. A good late 18th century lead figure of a child, 3ft high. £340

5. A good quality lead figure of a youth in costume playing a violin, 4ft 1ins high. £375

6. A lead figure of Mercury, 46ins high. £150

IRON

1. A Victorian wrought iron garden urn. £115

2. 19th century cast iron garden seat. £250

3. Victorian plant stand in iron. £16

PEWTER

1. A fine late 18th century pewter tankard. £15

2. A pewter plate, circa 1730, 15ins diameter. £25

3. A good Queen Anne lidded pewter tankard. £48

4. Pair of 18th century pewter candlesticks, 13ins high. £15.50

5. Victorian pewter teapot. £12

6. 18th century pewter measure. £20

7. 18th century pewter charger 16ins diameter. £40

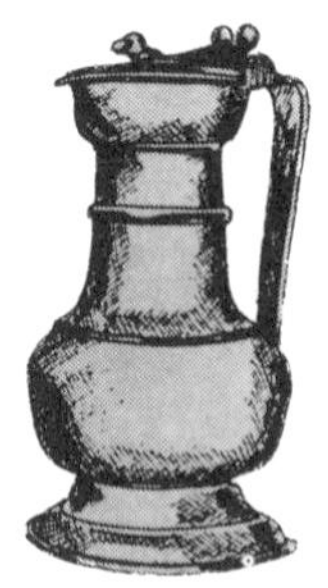

8. 18th century pewter lidded flagon. £48

1. 18th century pewter lipped tankard. £18

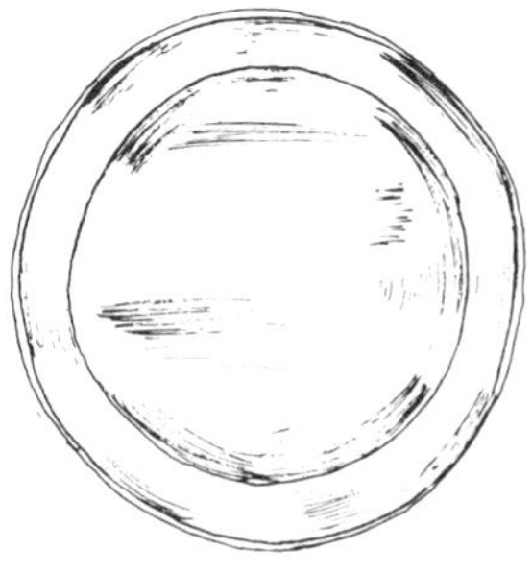

2. 18th century pewter plate, 16ins diameter. £28

3. Art Nouveau pewter sugar bowl. £2.50

4. Victorian pewter coffee pot. £14

5. A large rare pewter Montieth bowl, circa 1700. £460

6. 18th century German pewter lidded tankard. £30

7. 18th century pewter jug. £10

8. 18th century pewter charger with a London mark. £28

9. George II pewter flagon. £32

1. 19th century baluster vase in iridescent mauve green. £13

2. An extremely fine vase by Thomas Webb. £790

3. A fine satin glass bottle, 7½ins high. £60

4. Victorian opal glass vase, 10 ins high. £7

5. An early English covered bowl. £420

6. A Webb glass cameo vase, 9 ins high. £210

7. A fine trial vase by Rene Lalique. £135

8. Chien Lung overlay vase. £135

9. Victorian cranberry glass four branch epergne. £24

10. One of a pair of Mary Gregory cranberry glass vases, each decorated with the figure of a girl in white enamel. £28

11. 19th century opal glass vase. £6

1. A fine rare taperstick, the tapering nozzle set on inverted baluster air twist stem with a terraced foot, height 6½ ins. £370

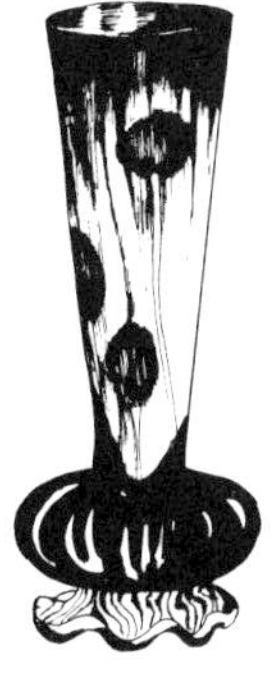

2. A fine and rare marquetry vase by Emile Galle, made in 1900. £2,300

3. A balustroid vase in iridescent blue green 7¾ ins high. £17

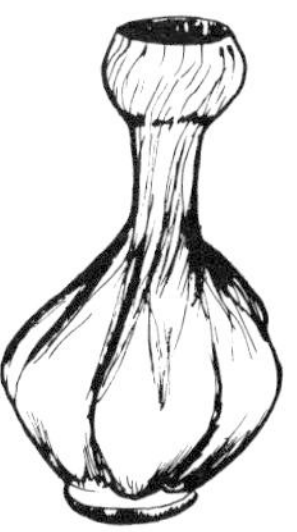

4. Victorian ruby glass vase. £8

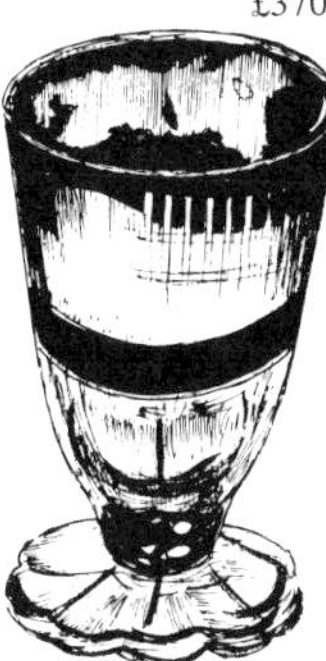

5. 19th century Bohemian glass goblet. £16

6. A cameo and marquetry glass vase by Galle with silver mounts by Cardeilhac. £850

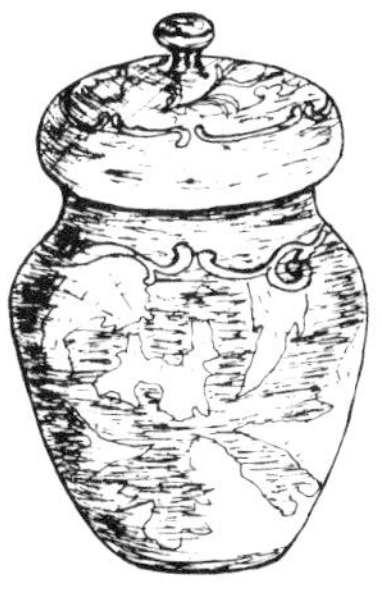

7. Silver mounted cameo and applied glass pot by Galle. £180

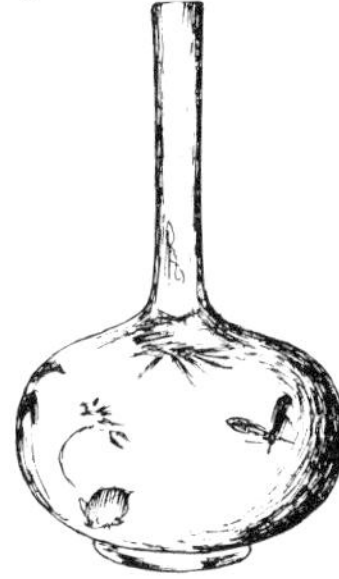

8. A Webb yellow and white satin glass vase. £155

9. Bohemian glass flask. £35

10. Victorian spatter glass epergne. £10

11. A Loetz vase, decorated with green and blue iridescence over pink. £125

GLASS

1. An Oxford tavern bottle dated 1684. £35

2. 18th century decanter engraved 'Burgundy'. £40

3. Early 18th century cut glass decanter. £22

4. A blown and moulded sealed bottle dated 1802. £20

5. A glass decanter by Rene Lalique, 12ins high. £150

6. George III claret jug, circa 1820. £35

7. Adam style cut and engraved lipped and shouldered decanter, circa 1770. £70

8. Late 18th century engraved decanter. £22

9. Victorian hand painted decanter. £9

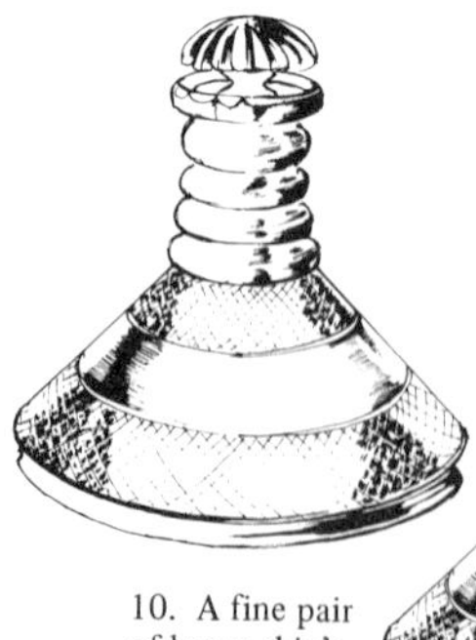

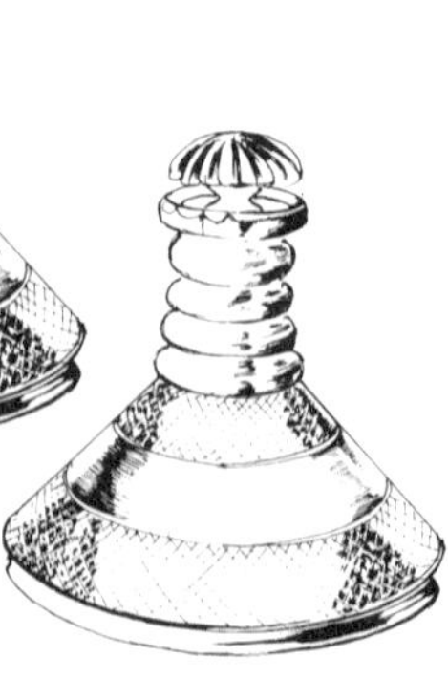

10. A fine pair of heavy ship's decanters, circa 1860. £140

11. Late 17th century English decanter jug complete with stopper. £1,225

1. A blown and moulded sealed bottle dated 1775. £45

2. 18th century decanter engraved 'Port'. £45

3. Victorian 'Mary Gregory' dimpled decanter decorated with a young girl in white glass. £25

4. A Bristol blue glass ketchup bottle. £26

5. Late 18th century engraved decanter. £35

6. One of a pair of 19th century French 'George De Pigeon' opaline and gilt bottles and stoppers, 9½ ins high. £780

7. An early 19th century plain glass decanter. £13

8. 19th century Bristol blue decanter. £18

9. A green Bristol decanter. £22

10. A fine pair of ship's decanters, circa 1850. £135

11. A Bristol amethyst decanter with a silver cork stopper. £30

1. A fine Imperial German glass, half litre beerstein. £28

2. Irish glass yacht cream jug, circa 1800. £34

3. An Imperial German cut glass half litre beerstein with a heavily plated lid surmounted by a Jager shako. £14

4. A fine Victorian cranberry glass water jug, 10 ins high. £10

5. An Art Deco pink tinted, cut glass scent bottle. £15

6. A fine Galle vase, signed. £78

7. A good quality 19th century lutz glass jug. £44

8. A rare Ravenscroft decanter jug of the mid 1680's. £900

9. Victorian pink glass jug with an amber handle. £5

10. Ravenscroft crisselled decanter jug with seven vertical pincered and winged ribs, with a replaced foot. £570

1. A Webb white and blue cameo vase, 6½ins tall. £350

2. Pair of Irish glass boat shaped salts, circa 1800. £34

3. An early English glass ewer engraved with hops and barley, circa 1760. £58

4. An Edwardian silver mounted claret jug. £35

5. One of an unusual pair of bubble glass, flared rim vases painted with 19th century military scenes. £42

6. 19th century cranberry glass jug. £7.50

7. An exceptionally fine Webb cameo glass decanter. £500

8. Victorian cut glass jug with plated mounts. £6

9. Irish glass flat cut cream jug. £26

10. A Mary Gregory cranberry glass jug, 5½ins high. £16

1. A good early English sweetmeat glass. £150

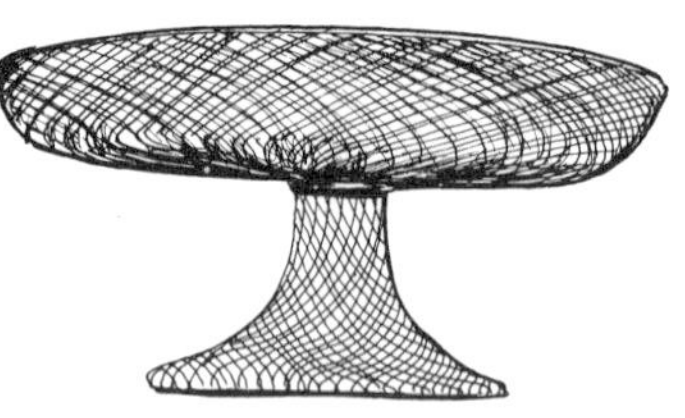

2. 17th century Latticino tazza, 8·8 ins diameter. £170

3. Small, Irish glass pair of salts. £16

4. A fine amber coloured beaker signed Anton Kothgasser (1769-1851). £550

5. Pair of Victorian opal glass vases, 12 ins high. £10

6. A fine English beaker engraved with a church, a mill and a fort flying the Union Jack, circa 1760. £55

7. 19th century cut glass and plated centrepiece. £20

8. A fine quality Victorian tantalus in an oak case with silver mounts. £75

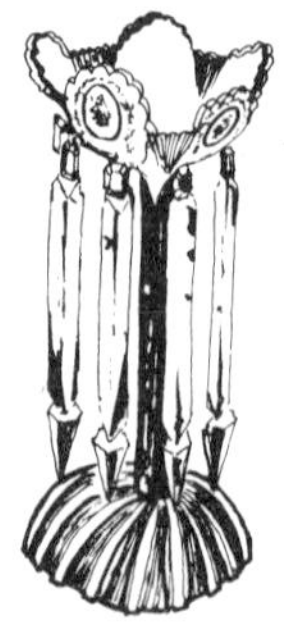

9. One of a pair of 19th century overlay glass lustres, 12 ins high. £35

1. Victorian mauve carnival glass bowl. £3.50

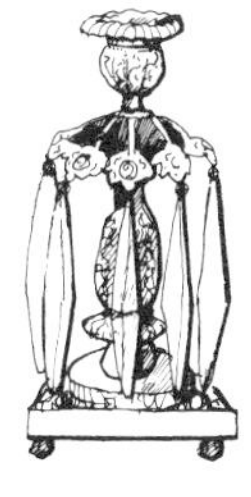

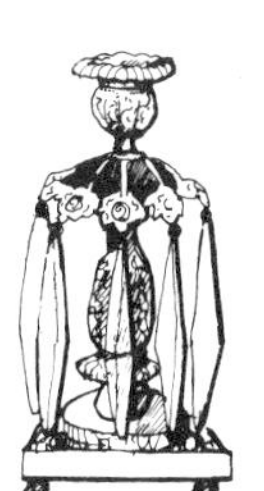

2. Pair of ormolu and crystal lustre sidepieces, circa 1830. £97.50

3. 19th century milk glass crimped bowl. £5

4. Farmer's tumbler with agricultural emblems and the motto 'Speed the Plough', circa 1820. £32

5. 19th century Cranberry glass basket with a plated stand. £14

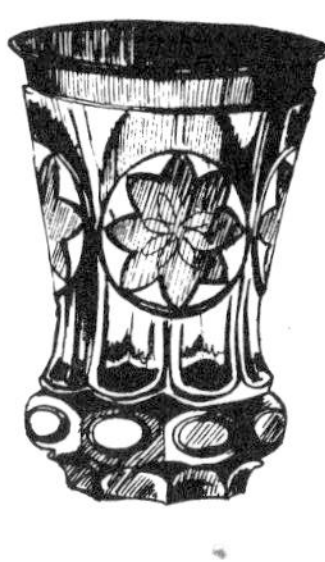

6. Late 18th century Bohemian double overlay beaker. £70

7. 19th century cut glass and plated centrepiece. £20

8. Fine ebony decanter suite believed to be the property of Napoleon III, circa 1850. £355

9. A Webb white and blue cameo vase, 6ins tall. £405

SCENT BOTTLES

1. 19th century blue and white overlay scent bottle. £25

2. Small Victorian silver scent bottle. £15

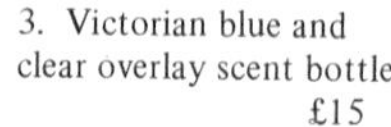

3. Victorian blue and clear overlay scent bottle. £15

4. 19th century ruby glass scent bottle with a silver top. £19

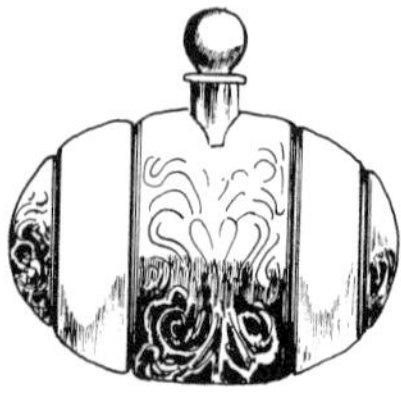

5. Late 19th century engraved silver scent bottle. £15

6. Small Victorian gilt and enamel scent bottle. £20

7. Mid 19th century Bohemian glass scent bottle. £25

8. Fine double ended blue overlay scent bottle with silver tops. £30

9. Victorian vaseline glass scent bottle. £22.50

10. Victorian ruby glass scent bottle. £16

11. A green and clear glass scent bottle with a silver top. £10.50

1. Important Chinese snuff bottle in Canton enamel with a gilt chased metal stopper, blue Ch'ien mark, 2¼ins high. £3,465

2. A white jade bottle with russet markings, carved with a boy and a tiger. 680gns

3. A mutton fat jade bottle carved with figures playing chequers and pulling a pony across a bridge. 60gns

4. A Chinese glass snuff bottle painted on the inside with horses. £150

5. Chinese overlay snuff bottle. £100

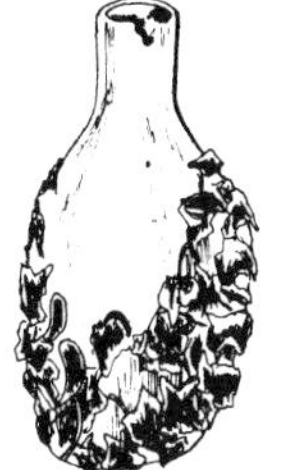

6. Peking glass snuff bottle overlaid with red flowers. £85

7. A 19th century white glass snuff bottle with red overlay. £30

8. 18th century red overlay snuff bottle. £275

MULLS

1. 19th century Scottish snuff mull embellished with a silver thistle. £30

2. An exceptionally fine and desirable Victorian silver mounted and bejewelled Scottish table snuff mull. £80

3. Silver mounted horn snuff mull, Scottish, circa 1840. £22.50

WINE GLASSES

1. An early balustroid wine glass. £38

2. A baluster mead glass with an incurved cup shaped bowl, heavily gadrooned on the lower half, circa 1710. £270

3. A baluster wine glass with a round funnel bowl and a solid base with an acorn knop stem and central elongated air tear, 5¾ ins high, circa 1710. £250

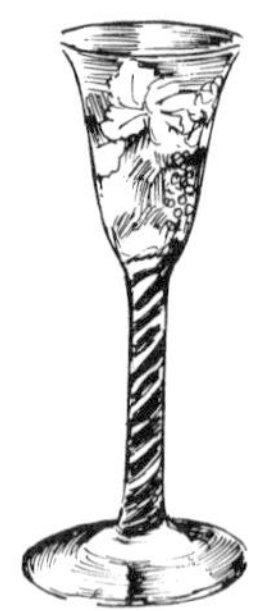

4. An engraved colour twist wine glass with fruiting vine and bird on a white lace twist stem surrounded by two translucent green spirals, 7¼ ins high. £190

5. Colour twist wine glass, the round funnel bowl resting on a stem with opaque white spiral gauze and plain opaque white spiral edged in translucent blue, 5¾ ins high. £90

6. English goblet with a knop in the bowl enclosing a coin dated 1680, 17·2.cm high. £650

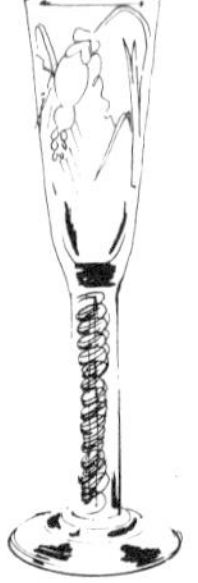

7. A Beilby ale glass decorated with barley hops in white enamel. £210

8. A wine glass with a flared round funnel bowl decorated in coloured enamel with a landscape scene, by William and Mary Beilby, 5¼ ins high, circa 1765. £380

9. One of a pair of early wine glasses with an air twist stem. £40

10. Wine glass with a bell bowl set above a mixed twist stem, circa 1760. £65

11. An early wine glass, the waisted trumpet bowl set in a plain stem of coloured and opaque twists. £270

12. Baluster stem ale glass with triple knop above an inverted baluster, circa 1740. £150

13. Early kit-kat glass with a single tear on the stem. £62

1. An early goblet with raspberry prunts and a silver mount to the foot dated 1924. £95

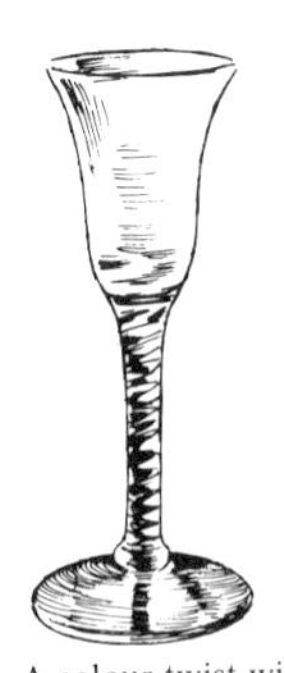

2 A colour twist wine glass with a bell bowl, 6¾ ins high. £175

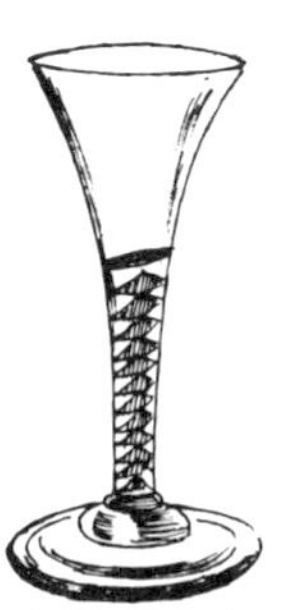

3. 18th century colour twist green and red wine glass. £34

4. Rummer with bucket bowl engraved with a sailing ship under the Sunderland Bridge with the monogram M.J.G., 5½ ins high. £58

5. A rare pan topped colour twist wine glass, the stem containing a central red brick thread surrounded by two opaque white spirals, 5¾ ins high. £375

6. Engraved English wine glass, 5¾ ins high. £37

7. English glass goblet with Jacobite symbolism, 8½ ins high. £400

8. Early English water flute wine glass, 6¼ ins high. £40

9. Early engraved wine glass. £50

10. A large goblet, circa 1700. £100

11. Ratafia glass with a narrow straight sided funnel bowl moulded to two thirds of its height, circa 1745. £100

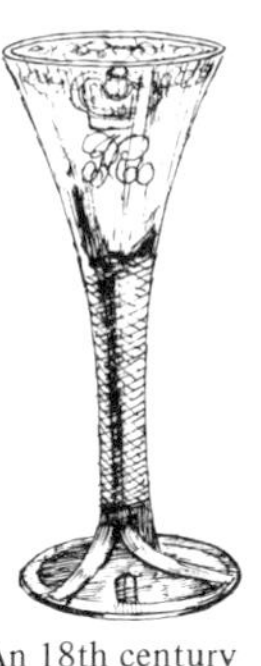

12. An 18th century drawn trumpet bowl Amen glass on a multi-spiral air twist stem with the crowned monogram of the Pretender James III of England and VIII of Scotland and underneath the word Amen,(repaired foot) £880

13. Newcastle glass with a large slightly flared round funnel bowl engraved with a border of scrollwork, 9 ins high, circa 1745. £190

WINE GLASSES

1. An heraldic goblet decorated by Beilby of Newcastle, 8½ ins high. £3,100

2. An excise wine glass with a round funnel bowl engraved with a sprig of fruiting vine, the reverse with a butterfly ,6¼ ins high,circa 1745. £45

3. A composite wine glass with a waisted bowl set over a multiple spiral air twist section terminating in a squat beaded, inverted baluster knop,7ins high,circa 1745. £85

4. A rare 17th century English mead glass on a folded foot, 5 ins high. £280

5 . 18th century mead glass. £48

6 . A superb 17th century baluster stem wine glass. £475

7. An ogee bowl wine glass with colour twist stem, 5¾ ins high,circa 1770. £160

8 . Early English drinking glass. £32

9. A Beilby ogee bowl wine glass 5¼ ins high. £115

10. A massive goblet with a large straight sided bowl, honeycombe moulded to half height with an incised twist stem and high conical foot,9¼ ins high,circa 1760. £140

11. 17th century ale glass with a wrytten bowl. £65

12 . Lead glass goblet with a serpentine stem, circa 1685,11½ ins high. £200

13 . Giant lead glass goblet with prunts on the stem,circa 1690, 12½ ins high. £220

1. Multiple air twist wine glass (chipped base). £10

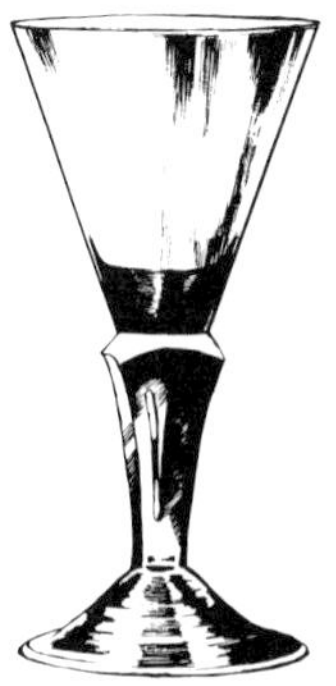

2. A magnificent wine glass with a conical bowl, solid at the base and set on a four sided Silesian stem, circa 1715. £280

3. Cordial glass with a flared bucket bowl wheel engraved with a spray of lily of the valley, 6¾ins high, circa 1760. £65

4. Early 18th century mead glass. £175

5. A double knopped air twist ale glass, circa 1760. £185

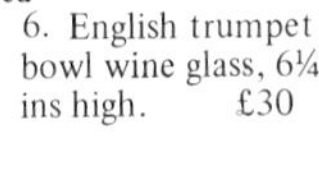

6. English trumpet bowl wine glass, 6¼ ins high. £30

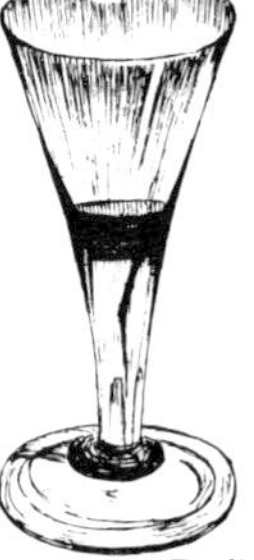

7. Drawn stem English wine glass,7 ins high. £45

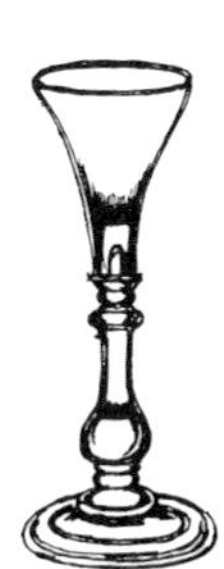

8 . An early English wine glass. £155

9. A rare Williamite glass. £500

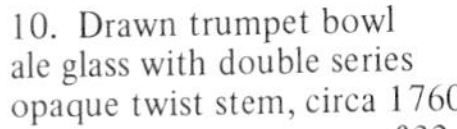

10. Drawn trumpet bowl ale glass with double series opaque twist stem, circa 1760. £32

11. A triple knop solid base baluster wine glass. £125

12. Light baluster stem wine glass with a domed and folded foot. £115

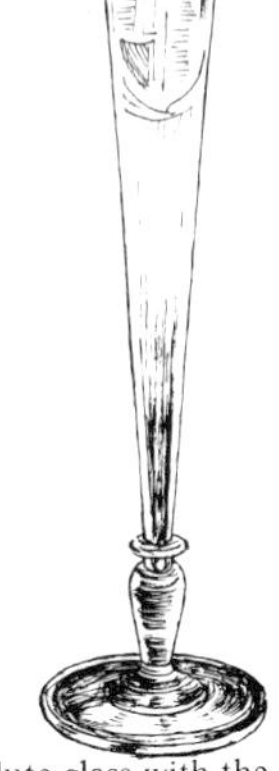

13. Flute glass with the Arms of Charles II and James II engraved in diamond point, made of soda glass and almost certainly Dutch, 15½ ins high. £2,300

1. Old English Tavern sign ' The Sportsman ' painted on a wooden framed metal sheet, 33 ins x 42 ins. £95

2. Polished cast iron American Eagle, circa 1820, 18 ins x 18 ins. £65

3. Old English Tavern sign ' Long John Silver', 49 ins high, 38ins wide. £68

4. A rare Prattware advertising plaque for Cross and Blackwell. £350

5. An attractive old English Fishmonger's hanging shop sign depicting a salmon trout and ' Fresh Fish Daily ' in a wrought iron frame 30ins x 16 ins. £47

6. Armour bright polished Unicorn in cast iron, 24ins wide,16½ ins high, circa 1830. £35

7. An engraved brass Lloyds Insurance Agency sign. £28

8. Unique heavy cast iron sign from the famous London pub ' The Elephant and Castle ' decorated in polychrome with gold leaf highlights. £165

9. Unusual English Tavern sign painted on a framed wood board, 42½ ins x 45 ins. £125

1. Old Tavern sign showing a white and gold unicorn superimposed on the Royal Coat of Arms, on a pale blue background, 40 ins x 34 ins. £48

2. Cast iron Royal Coat of Arms with lion and unicorn supports and the original heraldic colouring, 22 ins x 22 ins. £185

3. Fine old Wine Merchant's hanging shop sign 41 ins x 43½ins, showing a boy with bunches of grapes. £68

4. Old Tavern sign, 'The Sparrow'. £48

5. Tavern sign 'The Butchers Arms' showing an heraldic Coat of Arms with pig supports. £47

6. Old sheet iron Tavern sign from the 'Elephant and Castle', 41 ins high, 36 ins wide, £85

7. Welsh primitive shop sign of a girl in a red dress with blue shoes and sash, 36 ins high, circa 1830. £185

8. Decorative old English Tavern sign entitled 'The Two Brewers', 37½ ins x 43 ins. £65

BOXES AND CADDIES

1. An interesting oak tea caddy made of timbers from H.M.S. Victory. £250

2. Old rum barrel in oak with brass straps, 17½ ins high. £40

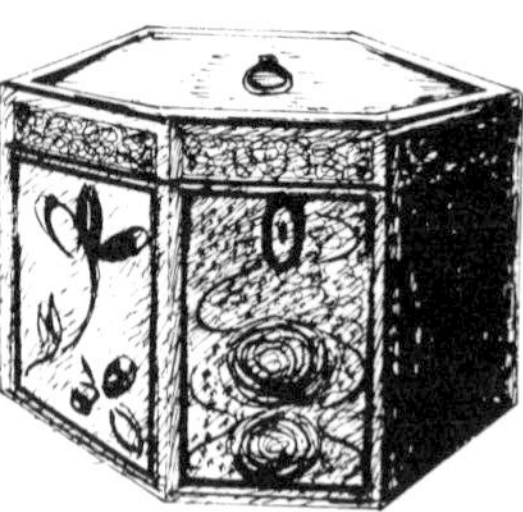

3. 18th century octagonal caddy of curled paper design with leaf sprays. £40

5. 19th century papier mache inkstand with silver mounts, circa 1840. £40

4. A George II mahogany table bureau with tambour top and brass carrying handles. £55

6. Good quality Regency brass inlaid writing box. £24

7. Late 18th century mahogany knife box inlaid with satinwood. £75

8. Brass bound coromandel wood lap desk. £45

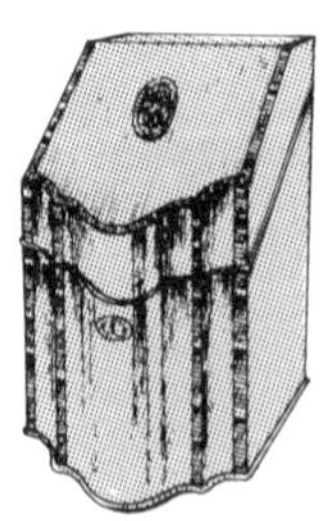

9. Late 18th century Sheraton style mahogany knife box with satinwood crossbanding. £30

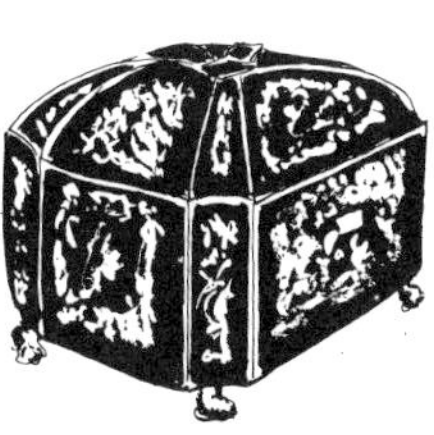

1. 19th century octagonal, black and gilt lacquered two division caddy in the Chinese style. £25

2. Small dog kennel in mahogany 21 ins long, with a detachable chain and brass collar engraved 'Toby'. £95

3. 18th century mahogany caddy with painted oval medallions. £30

4. A handsome country house Royal Mail letterbox in pinewood, simulated to appear as mahogany, with a brass letter opening and Royal Coat of Arms, original black and gilt word 'Letters' and a glass viewing panel at the base, 24½ ins high. £75

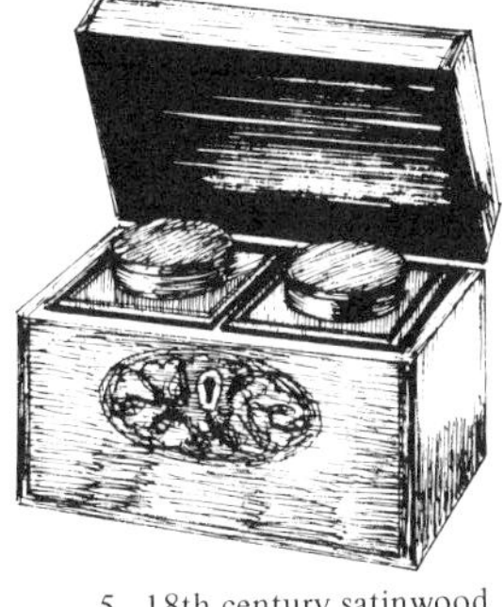

5. 18th century satinwood rectangular casket with inlaid panels designed with shells, containing two rectangular caddies. £120

6. An unusual Victorian papier mache and decorated writing cabinet containing a workbox, writing slide and small drawers. £106

7. Old oak rum barrel with brass straps, 21 ins high. £45

8. An ebony decanter suite contained in a case inlaid with the Imperial Eagle and bees. £355

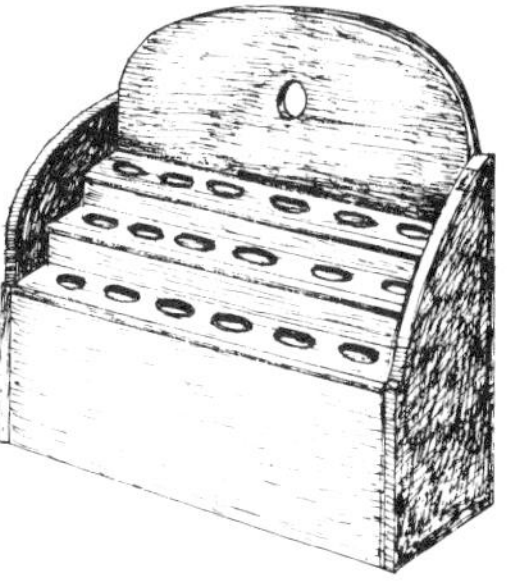

9. Early 19th century wooden spoon rack. £15

BOXES AND CADDIES

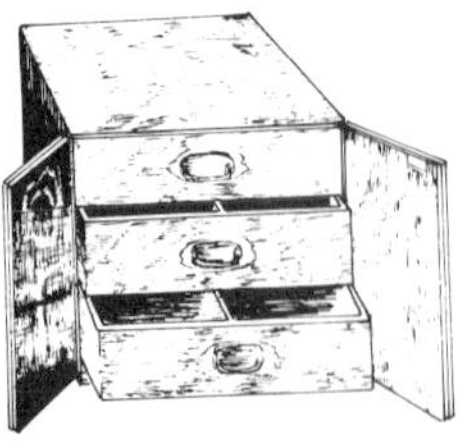

1. Victorian oak and brass bound nest of three drawers. £12.50

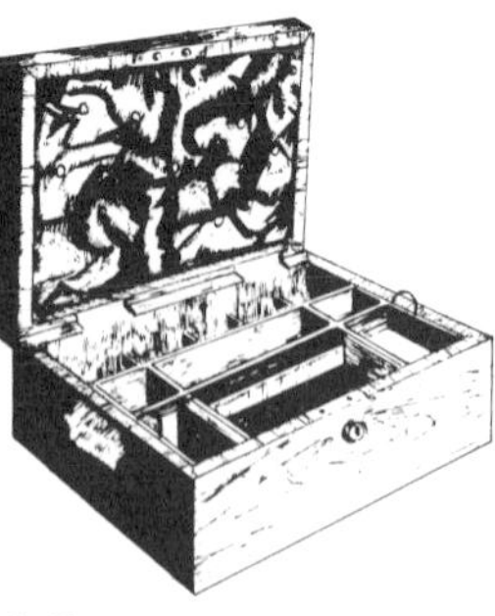

2. Victorian rosewood and brass mounted vanity case. £12.50

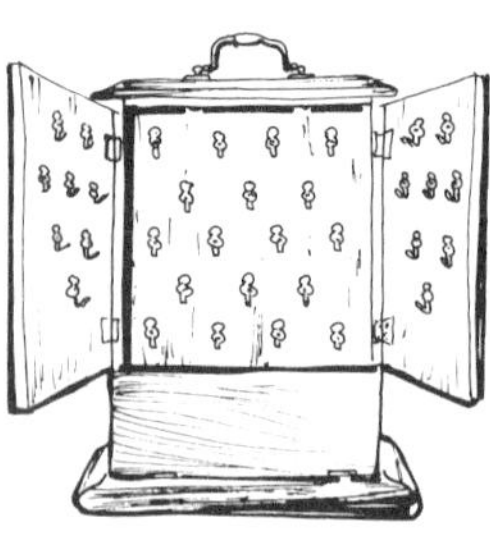

3. Victorian housekeeper's wooden key case for duplicate keys. £11

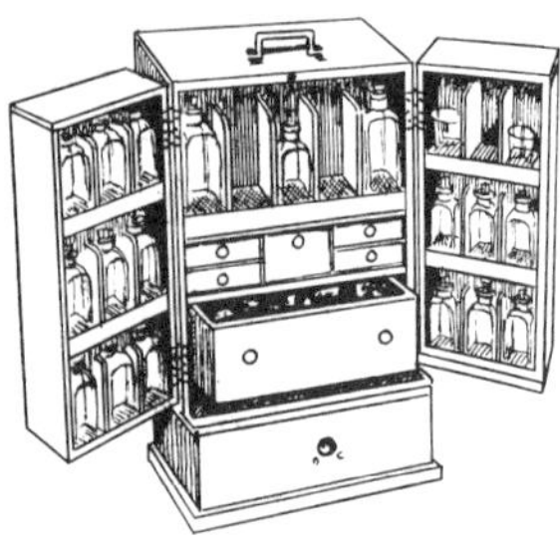

4. Late 18th century mahogany Apothercary's box with the original bottles. £32.50

5. Early 19th century rosewood tea caddy inlaid with brass. £20

6. A mahogany spice box with a fielded panel door and original feet, 12 ins wide, 13 ins high, 6 ins deep. £85

7. Queen Anne tea caddy of veneered walnut on oak with chevron crossbanding on the lid and original handle and escutcheon, circa 1700, 9 ins long. £48

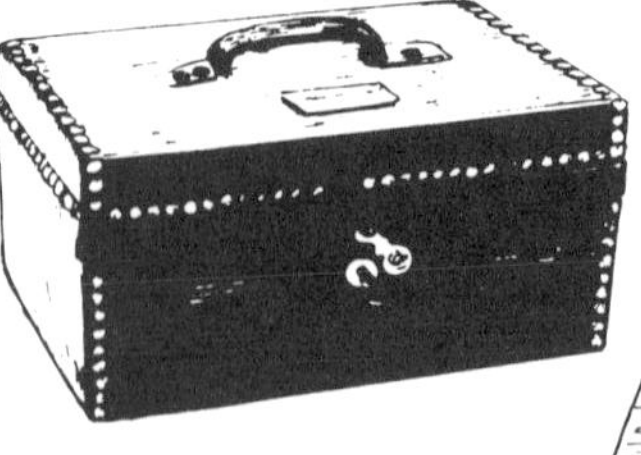

8. An interesting American civil war period Naval Paymaster's strong box, 12 ins x 8 ins x 6 ins. £56

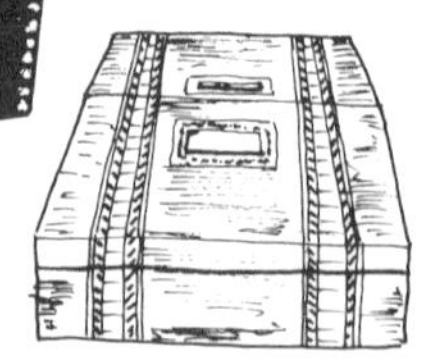

9. Victorian inlaid walnut writing slope. £12

1. Victorian walnut veneered writer'scompanion with a brass carrying handle and fitted drawer. £6

2. An old oak rum barrel, 21 ins long. £35

3. A mahogany Apothecary's cabinet with a secret poison compartment, twenty-six assorted bottles, and brass scales, circa 1790. £55

4. Victorian writing cabinet with brass mounts. £10

5. Early Victorian tortoiseshell tea caddy, £34

6. Fine quality 19th century walnut and brass mounted tea caddy with a glass liner. £30

7. Japanese, 19th century lacquered wood box and cover inscribed, Shiomi Masanari, 17.3cm long. £460

8. A fine 19th century coromandel wood brass bound lap desk. £45

9. A Georgian mahogany cheese coaster. £55

1. Superb bronze of a Turkish horse by Baryea, 11¾ ins high. £3,200

2. 'Apollo and Daphne' after the marble by Giovanni Lorenzo Bernini 1591-1680, 79 cm high. £3,045

3. Bronze pheasant by A.A. Arson, 17 ins high. £300

4. Bronze by Henry Moore entitled 'Warrior with Shield'. £6,000.

5. Fine bronze of a mare and stallion by Monier. £950

6. 'Pluto and Proserpine' a large bronze after Bernini, 30½ ins high. 2,900 gns

7. 'The Sluggard', bronze circa 1890, after Lord Leighton's sculpture at the Royal Academy, 1886, 1 ft 9 ins tall. £190

8. An animalier bronze by Paul Edouard Delabrierre 1802-1912, signed. £775

9. A well made model suit of jousting armour in the style of 1530, 15½ ins high. £50

1. Chinese gilt bronze of the Hau dynasty depicting a bear seated on its haunches, 9-8 cm high. £15,000

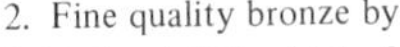

2. Fine quality bronze by L. Madrassi, 29 ins high. £245

3. Good bronze stag by Falkirk, 24 ins high. £165

4. Bronze of George III by Lawrence Gahagan, 11 ins high. 400 gns

5. An original Senegal elephant by Baryea. £560

6. A bronze statuette by Gregoire entitled ' La Charite'. £150

7. A well executed bronze figure of a German mercenary in the style of circa 1600, the base signed Derniere and stamped H. Picard. £80

8. Bronze of an African Horseman being attacked by a lion, by Isidore Bonheur. £370

9. A fine Japanese figure of a warrior wearing his Daisho of swords, he draws his Itatina, 10½ins high. £65

BRONZES

1. 19th century bronze of a draped female figure 23ins high. £78

2. Pair of bronzed brass figures 13ins high, of Charles I and Oliver Cromwell. £70

3. 19th century bronze nude 26ins high. £110

4. Bronze entitled 'L'accolade' by P.J. Mene. £1,000

5. A reproduction of a bronze Senegal elephant by Barbedienne, cast from the original mould. £230

6. Art Nouveau bronze and ivory figure by Colinet £150

7. Pair of early 19th century bronze urns 9ins tall. £46

8. Art Nouveau bronze of a female by Colinet. £95

1. 19th century Italian bronze figure of Cupid, 3ft 1in high. £240

2. An Art Nouveau ivory and bronze figure of a woman throwing a javelin. £290

3. A bronzed brass figure of Napoleon, 7 ins high. £35

4. Bronze figure of a hunter by J. Willis-Good. £290

5. 19th century bronze of two whippets by P.J. Mene. £290

6. One of a pair of late 18th century bronze Chinese vases 17½ins tall. £125

7. A good standing bronze of a Franco-Prussian period German Jaeger Rifleman 12½ins high. £40

8. 19th century French spelter group 'La Fete des Fleurs' by Aug Moreau. £23

1. George II coffee pot by Samuel Courtland, circa 1757. £600

2. Unusual Philadelphia coffee pot by Dubois, circa 1770, 50ozs. £2,650

3. George II part coffee service by William Eley, London 1819, 52 ozs. £290

4. 19th century plated, long handled coffee pot. £8.50

5. Silver coffee pot by Thomas Williamson of Dublin 1739, 39 ozs. £2,700

6. 19th century plated coffee pot. £7.50

7. Coffee pot by Thomas Whipham of London, 1751, 22 ozs. £540

8. Queen Anne tapering cylindrical coffee pot by Anthony Nelme, circa 1711. £850

1. George III oval teapot by Crespin Fuller, 1797, 14ozs 9dwt. £150

2. An important George III teapot by Hester Bateman, London 1785, 13ozs. £260

3. George III oval teapot by Hester Bateman, London 1784, 16ozs. £380

4. Silver teapot by Elizabeth and James Bland, London, 1798. £148

5. Teapot by Christopher Dresser with the London mark for 1880 and marked Ch. Dresser on the body. £750

6. George III embossed silver teapot with foliage handle and scroll feet, 24½ozs. £60

7. Victorian plated teapot. £7

8. Late 19th century silver teapot, 16ozs. £48

1. Four piece tea and coffee set by Elkington & Co., Birmingham, 1855, 86ozs. £580

2. One of three teapots from an Italian teaset by Antonio Cartelazzo, circa 1865. £3,500

3. Early Victorian four piece tea and coffee set. £375

4. Four piece Victorian silver tea and coffee service with the makers mark W.H. London 1843, 76ozs. £400

5. A fine George III silver tea set by Paul Storr.£640

1. Four piece tea and coffee set by Hunt and Roskell, circa 1880, 76ozs. £310

2. Four piece tea and coffee set by Henry Wilkinson and Co, Sheffield 1837, 73ozs. £360

3. Four piece tea and coffee set by Martin Hall and Co, 1871, 76ozs. £400

4. Small silver tea set, London 1937, 26¾ozs. £32

5. Three piece tea service by Paul Storr 1813 and 1818, gross weight 61ozs 15dwt. £700

6. Georgian three piece silver tea set, 1807 and 1828. £285

1. A copper based silver tankard made by Ranglands and Robertson Newcastle, 1780. £330

2. English silver tankard with the makers mark T.S. in a monogram crown, 1683, 19cm high, 30ozs 2dwt. £2,300

3. Silver gilt tankard, makers mark I.B. with a rosette below, 1602, 20.3 cm high, 19ozs 17dwt. £2,300

4. George I tapering cylindrical tankard by Thomas Bamford, circa 1716. £480

5. Late 18th century silver tankard. £470

6. George II lidded quart tankard by Shaw and Priest, London, 1753, 8ins high, 25½ ozs. £600

7. George I Scottish tankard by William Ged, Edinburgh 1715. £1,550

8. One of a pair of late 17th century flagons by 'Master of the Goose in a Dotted Circle' dated 1687 and 1690. £7,800

9. A rare early 18th century silver tankard with a cast handle. 1,000gns

1. Fine quality childs silver christening mug, London 1829. £39

2. George III christening mug by E.Horley, London 1812, with a gilt interior, 2½ins high, 3ozs. £50

3. Victorian christening mug by Elkington and Co, London 1891, engraved with the Royal Garter with "G" in centre and crown above, 4ins high, 8.6ozs. £95

4. Silver mug by W.H. of London, circa 1880.£30

5. Plain Charles II pear shaped mug by Ralph Walley (Chester 1690-2). £2,900

6. Silver mug by William Bateman London 1818. £148

7. An unusual glass and silver mug by John Foligno, 1855. £65

8. George II pint mug by Samuel Woods, London 1755, height 4¾ins, 10ozs. £150

9. An unusual mug by Emes and Barnard, 1815. £49

1. Fine quality silver goblet by John Agnell, circa 1819. £85

2. Pair of heavy quality period gilt egg cups, Dublin. £26

3. One of a pair of Charles II silver beakers, London 1678, 9¾ozs each. £4,200

4. A rare Luftwaffe silver honour goblet, 8¼ins high. £125

5. Silver gilt and enamel beaker, Birmingham 1890, 19ozs. £31

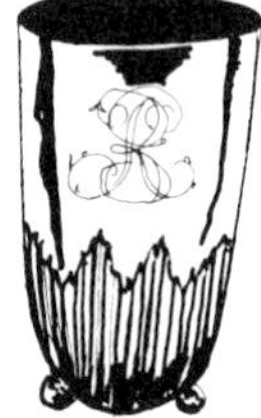

6. An Imperial German silver prize beaker with a fluted base and ball feet. £55

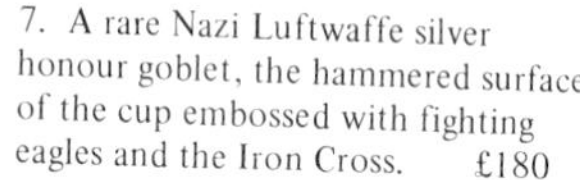

7. A rare Nazi Luftwaffe silver honour goblet, the hammered surface of the cup embossed with fighting eagles and the Iron Cross. £180

8. A fine Imperial German silver presentation shooting goblet, 8ins high. £32

9. Late 16th century Italian enamelled gold and jasper cup. £17,000

10. An inscribed silver racing cup by Barnard, 1873, 12ins high, 31ozs. £68

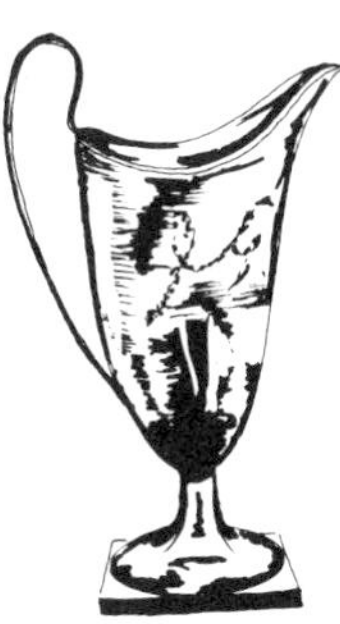

1. An attractive helmet cream jug by William Adley, circa 1790. £55

2. Queen Anne Irish wine jug by Thomas Boulton of Dublin, 1702. £7,000

3. Silver cream jug by William King of London, 1768. £78

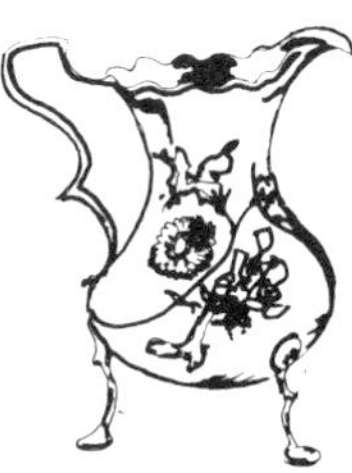

4. Excellent silver cream jug, maker A.N.S., 1767. £97

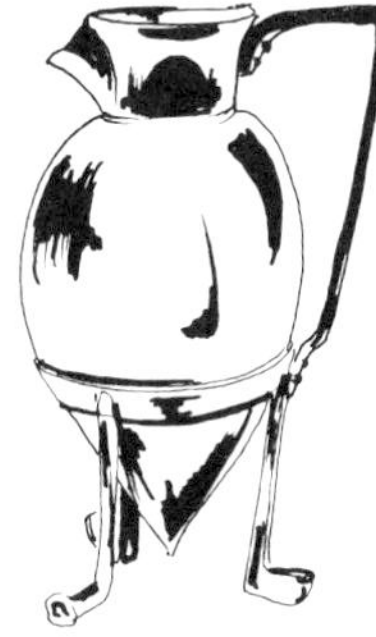

5. Art Nouveau silver plated jug by Christopher Dresser. £100

6. George III cream jug by John Belden, London 1804, 4¼ins high, 5.9ozs. £75

7. William IV covered jug by Paul Storr, 1833. £900

8. A fine Hester Bateman hot water jug, 1783. £900

9. Victorian silver plated hot water jug. £8

1. Small 19th century plated sugar basket. £8

2. Silver sweetmeat dish depicting Windsor Castle, by Nathaniel Mills, 1841. £175

3. George III sugar basket by Thomas Daniel, 1779. £150

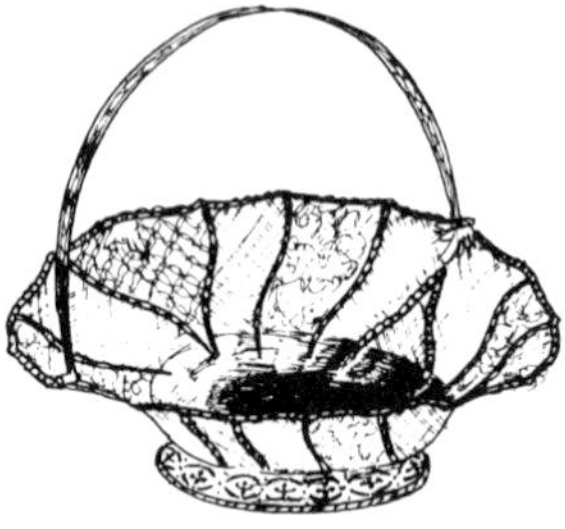

4. A fine mid 18th century basket with a cast silver rim. £220

5. Victorian silver sugar basket with a blue glass liner, London 1846, 5ozs. £48

6. A fine George III Irish sweetmeat basket, Dublin 1794. £175

7. Victorian silver cake basket, circa 1865. £55

8. Late 18th century Adam style boatshaped sugar basket. £150

9. Good quality Victorian cake basket, 32ozs. £85

1. 19th century Sheffield plate egg stand. £28

2. George III silver egg cruet. £105

3. Late Victorian plated egg cruet. £15

4. Victorian silver egg cruet, 24ozs. £90

5. A fine set of three George III casters by Samuel Wood, 1845. £620

6. Victorian plated cruet stand complete with six cut glass bottles. £15

7. 19th century plated egg steamer. £15

8. A fine silver egg cruet in the form of a broody hen by George Fox. £700

9. William IV silver cruet with cut glass bottles. £125

SILVER SAUCEBOATS

1. George II sauceboat by Thomas Farrer, circa 1730. £145

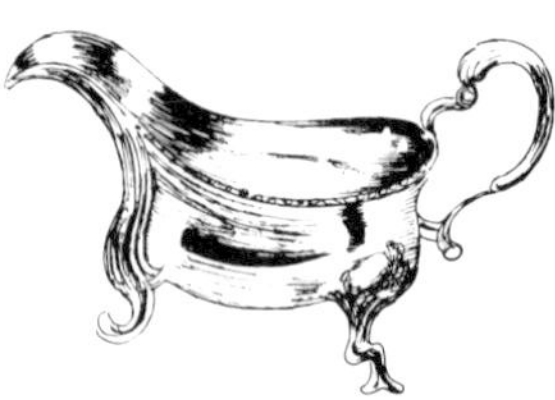

2. George II sauceboat by A.F., London 1767, 7¾ins long, 11.7ozs. £235

3. One of a pair of early 19th century silver sauceboats. £305

4. A good quality late 18th century silver sauceboat. £205

5. George III silver sauceboat. £230

6. One of a pair of George II oval double lipped sauceboats by Thomas Farrer, 1727. £1,800

KETTLES

1. A fine Edwardian silver spirit kettle. £145

2. George III silver tea kettle by Thomas Whipham. £560

3. Part of a five piece tea and coffee set complete with tray by Barnard, 1892/94, 110ozs, the tray 117ozs. £360

BRANDY WARMERS

1. Victorian silver brandy warmer with a turned wood handle. £115

2. Silver brandy warmer with the original case, dated 1937. £95

3. Pleasant George III brandy warmer. £140

4. Victorian plated brandy warmer. £15

5. George II brandy warmer by John Gibbons, 1728.£187

URNS

1. Sheffield plate urn with a gadroon and shell border.£175

2. George III silver tea urn of Neo-Classical form, London, 1789, 23½ins high. £320

3. 19th century plated urn. £20

1. A small Victorian silver bowl,1870, 6½ozs. £28

2. James II montieth bowl by Peter Edwardes of Chester, 1686. £4,200

3. Silver caviar bowl, cover and stand by Robert Garrard 1845. £480

4. George III vase shaped basin by John Crouch, London 1816, 18ozs. £55

5. An early American silver punchbowl by John Coney, circa 1720, 5ins high, 32ozs, £15,500

6. A mid 18th century Censor, the octagonal turned base supporting the globular body and flying scroll handle, the geometrically pierced lid supporting an acorn finial. £26

7. Porringer and cover with the makers mark T.H. or I.H. in monogram, town mark a quartrefoil fleur de lis device, English, circa 1665, 15.9 cm high, 17 ozs 18dwt. £2,100

8. Victorian silver sweet bowl, 7ozs. £30

1. 10½ins rectangular Mappin and Webb entree dish. £7

2. 11ins oval Mappin and Webb Princess plate entree dish. £6

3. A fine silver entree dish by Paul Storr, 66ozs. £400

4. 19th century plated serving dish. £17

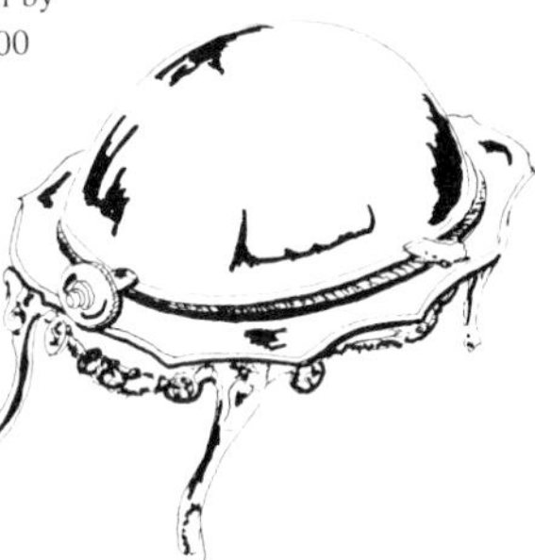

5. 19th century plated bacon dish with a revolving top. £20

6. An early 19th century silver plate oval pie dish in the form of a broody hen. £175

7. One of a pair of George IV soup tureens and covers by Paul Storr, 1824 and 1828, 330ozs. £1,400

8. Good quality early 19th century plated soup tureen supported on claw feet. £44

SILVER WINE COOLERS

1. One of a pair of plated wine coolers by Gainsford and Nicholson. £220

2. Early 19th century ice cooler in Sheffield plate. £39

3. A fine quality George IV silver wine cooler. £375

VASES

1. Victorian silver vase dated 1860, 6ozs. £17.50

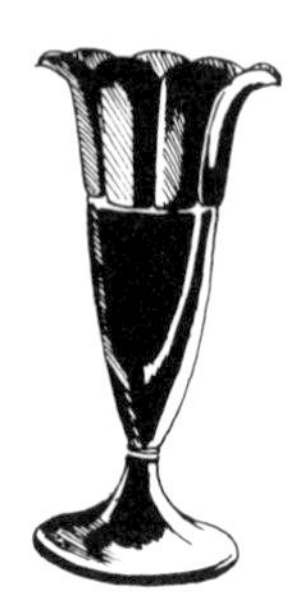

2. Mid Victorian silver vase with a flared rim. £12

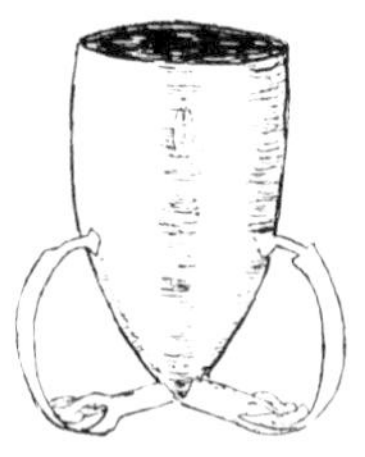

3. Cymric silver vase by Archibald Knox marked Birmingham 1802, 8½ins high. £300

4. Pair of silver gilt ewers with enamelled decorative scenes, Birmingham 1890, 51ozs. £280

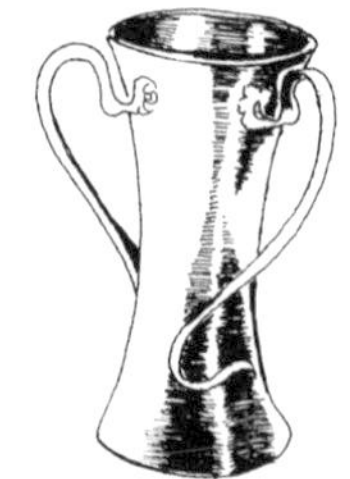

5. A fine Art Nouveau silver vase. £30

COASTERS

1. One of a pair of cast vine coasters, 1810. £375

2. A fine coaster by Peter and Anne Bateman, London 1798. £100

3. Superb early 19th century tall sided silver coaster with London marks. £175

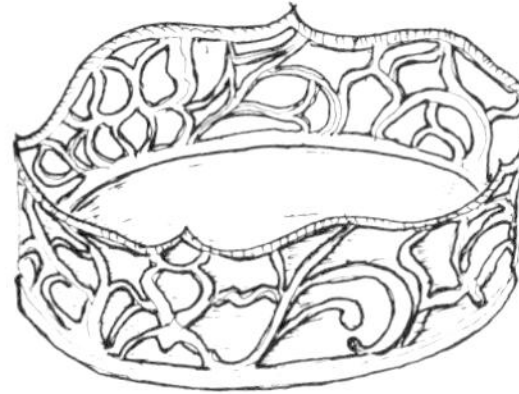

4. Pierced silver coaster, circa 1760. £90

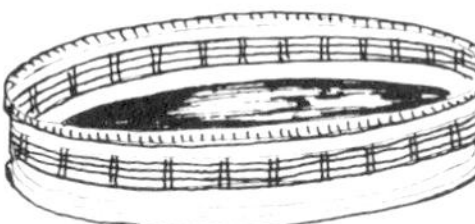

5. Bright cut coaster, circa 1777. £85

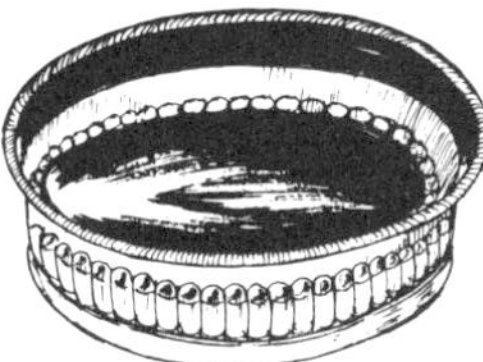

6. One of a pair of coasters by John Roberts, Sheffield 1808. £126

7. Plain round silver coaster, 1815. £40

CASTERS

1. George III muffineer by Thomas Daniel, London 1774, 5ins high, weight 2.6ozs. £110

2. Early 18th century silver pepper caster. £340

3. Early 19th century sugar caster by P & W Bateman. £140

4. Early 19th century egg shaped silver pepper caster. £75

5. Charles II silver sugar caster, 7½ins high, 1683. £1,900

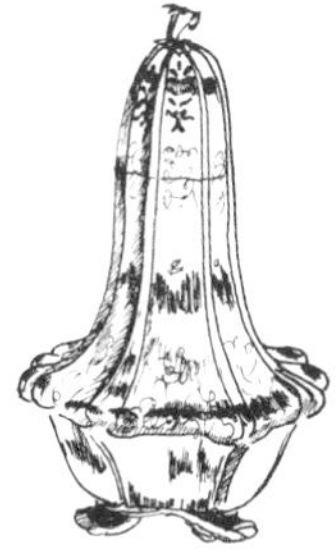

6. A fine Victorian sugar caster in the rococo manner. £105

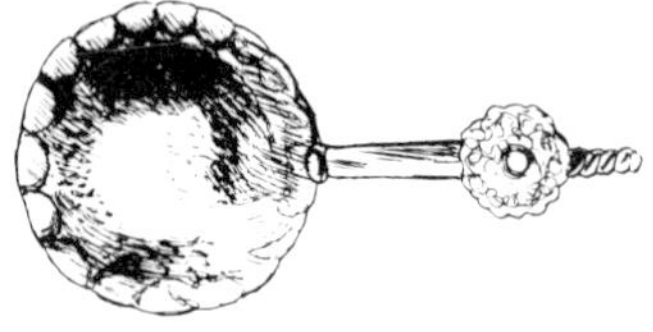

1. 19th century Dutch caddy spoon.£13

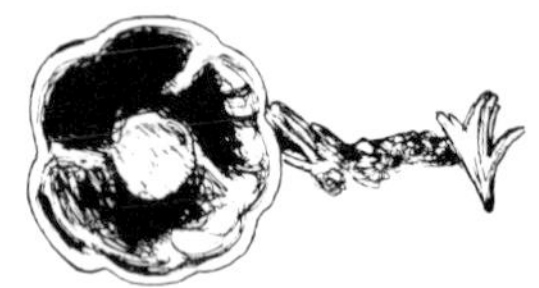

2. An exceptional quality caddy spoon by Francis Higgins. £112

3. Victorian silver gilt caddy spoon, London 1875, by H.L. and H.L., 4½ ins long. £35

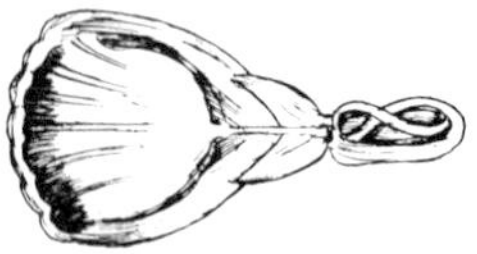

4. An unusual silver tea caddy spoon, Birmingham 1856. £55

5. Silver caddy spoon, London 1852. £30

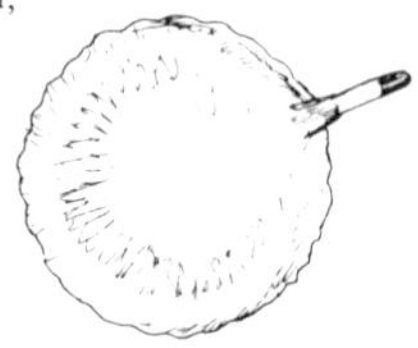

6. Victorian caddy spoon by George Unite, 1860. £25

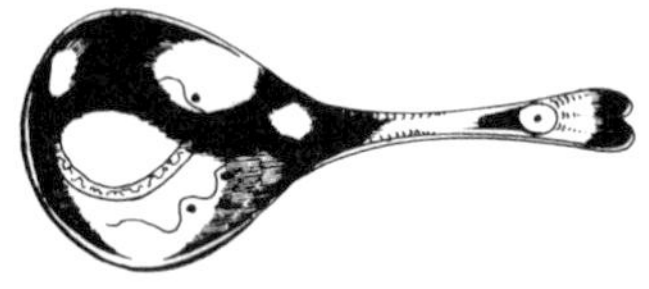

7. Late 18th century bright cut caddy spoon. £22

8. Plain silver caddy spoon, circa 1812. £12

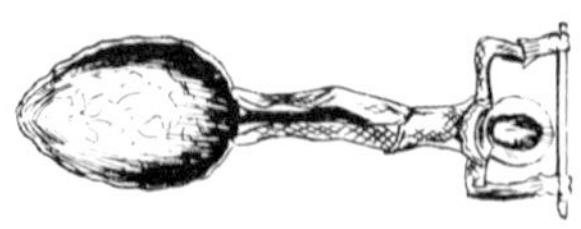

9. Silver gilt harlequin caddy spoon, London 1845. £55

CADDY SPOONS

1. Victorian silver harlequin caddy spoon by S.C., 4½ ins long. £65

2. Silver caddy spoon, London 1823. £15

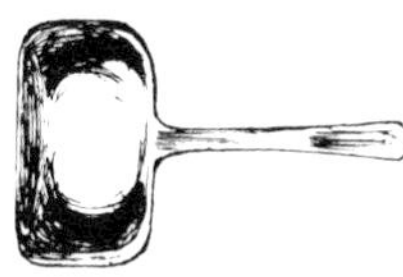

3. Early 19th century caddy spoon by Jas Taylor, circa 1816. £25

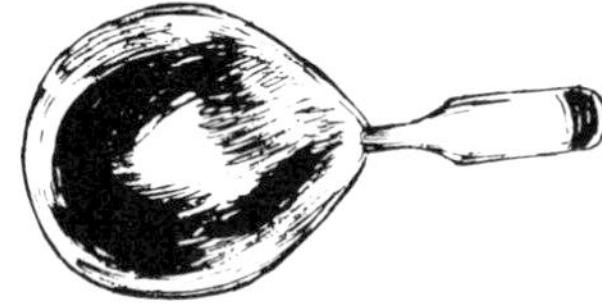

4. Plain silver caddy spoon, London 1823. £15

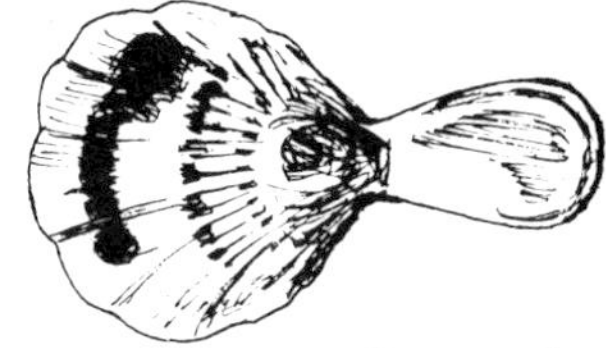

5. Late 18th century caddy spoon, circa 1790. £25

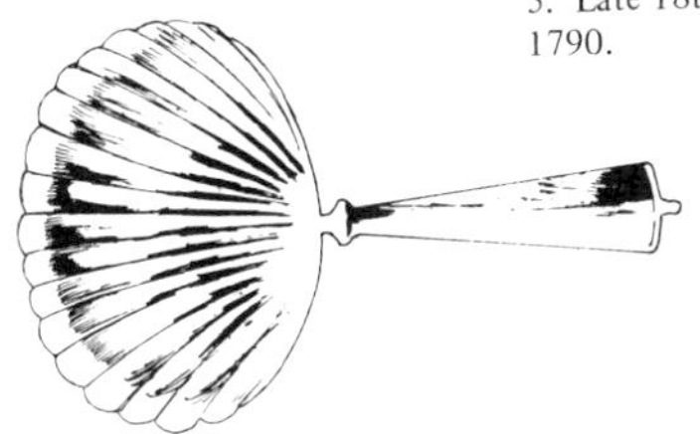

6. Shell shaped caddy spoon, circa 1820. £20

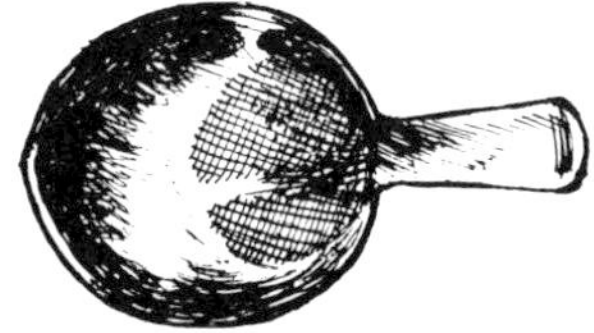

7. A fine basket weave caddy spoon, 1807. £35

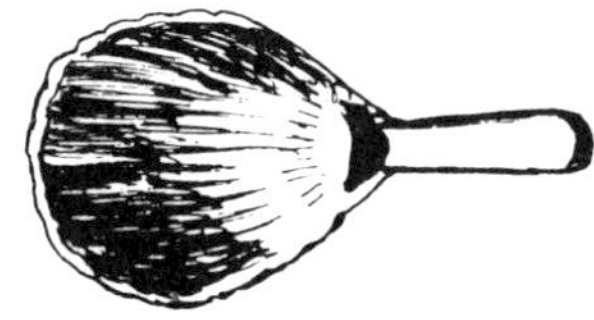

8. Late Victorian silver caddy spoon, 1896. £13

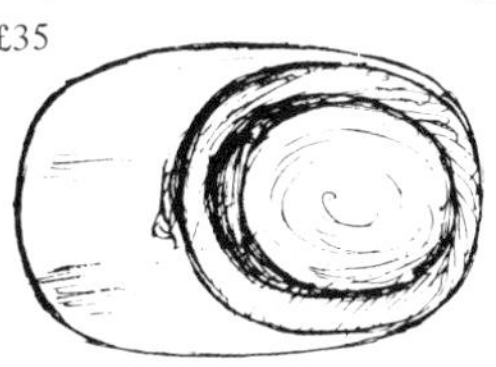

9. Jockey cap caddy spoon, Birmingham, 1810. £48

1. Trefid spoon by John Cory, London 1701.£40

2. Trefid spoon by Sir J. Snow, London 1618. £40

3. A fine example of a Lion Sejant spoon, 1548. £350

4. Georgian cast silver mote spoon. £32

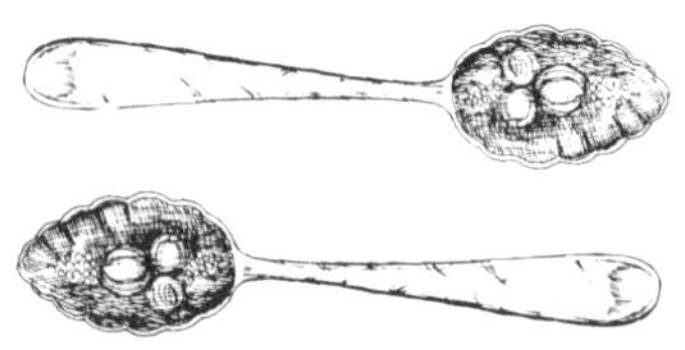

5. Fine pair of Berry spoons by V.S.P., London 1764. £85

6. Early Victorian christening set with mother of pearl handles, circa 1844. £26

7. London trefid spoon with fine marks, 1696. £53

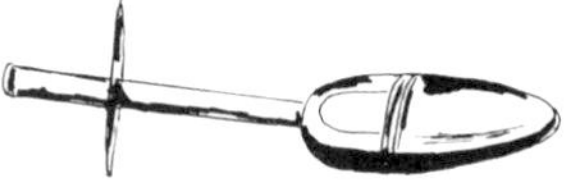

8. Unusual Victorian caster oil spoon, London 1842, maker E.E. £135

9. Victorian carving set with bone handles. £7.50

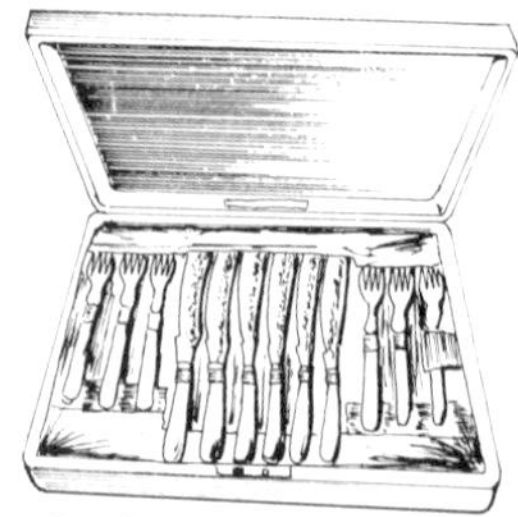

10. Set of twelve 19th century engraved fish knives and forks. £6.50

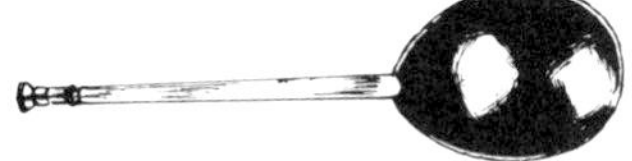

1. Elizabethan seal top spoon, circa 1600. £79

2. George III apple corer, London 1808, 5ins long. £48

3. Early Victorian silver marrow scoop. £19

4. William III silver trefid spoon, 1690. £60

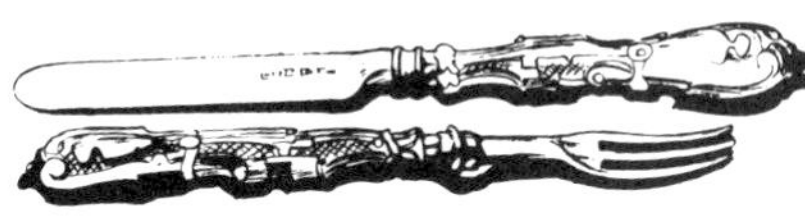

5. Victorian silver christening set dated 1840. £15

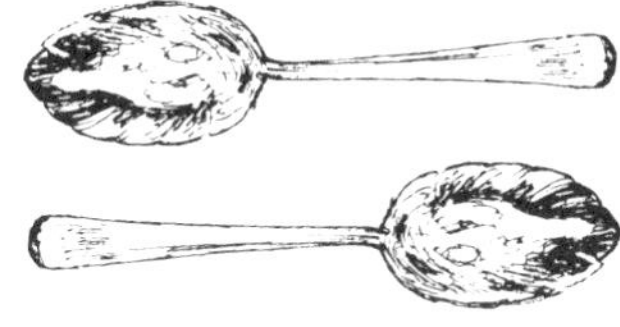

6. Pair of silver embossed fruit spoons. £22

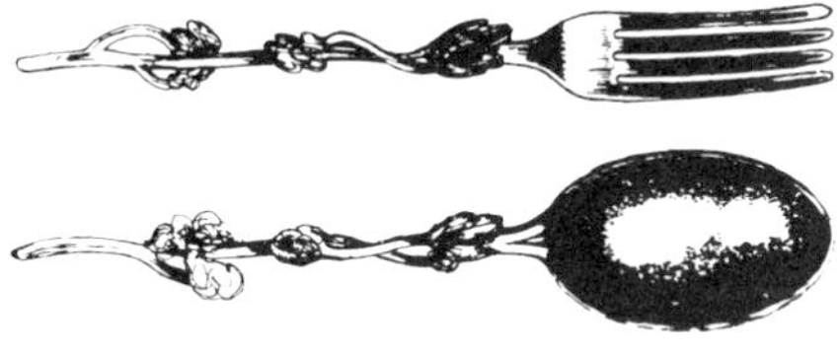

7. A matching silver fork and spoon, 1760. £15

8. Silver gravy spoon by Thos. Dealy, 1806. £18

9. Scroll back marrow scoop by William Turner, 1765. £39

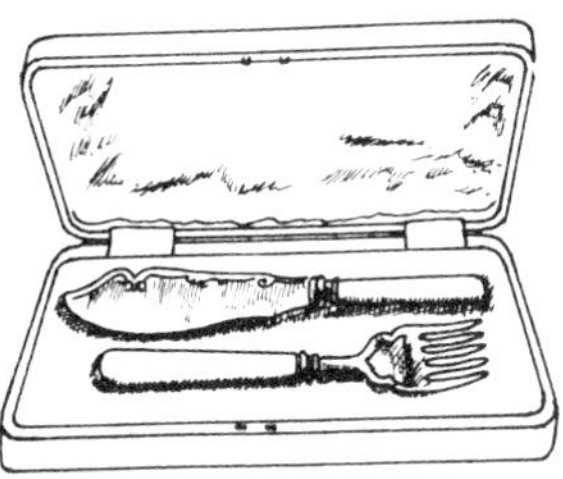

10. Cased set of Victorian silver servers. £18

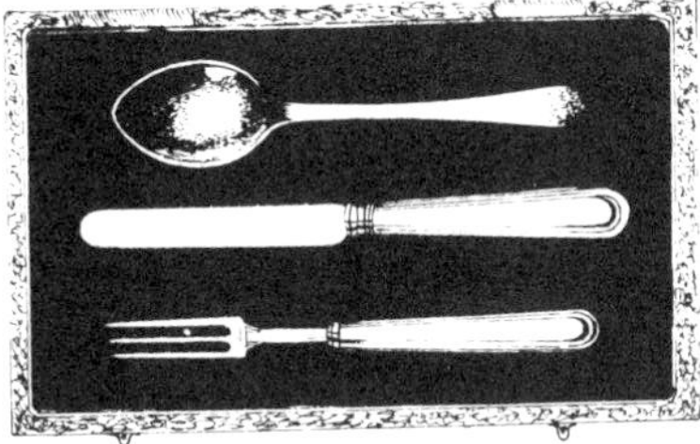

11. George III silver christening set. £20

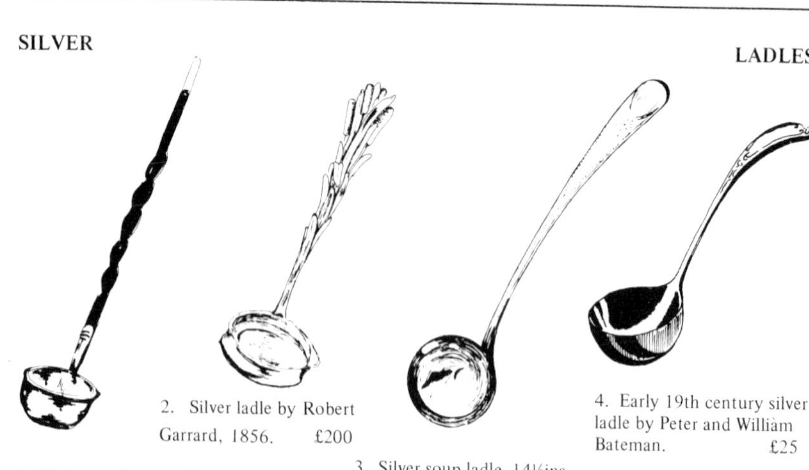

1. Miniature plated toddy ladle, Sheffield 1850.£8.50

2. Silver ladle by Robert Garrard, 1856. £200

3. Silver soup ladle, 14½ins long, 1789. £115

4. Early 19th century silver ladle by Peter and William Bateman. £25

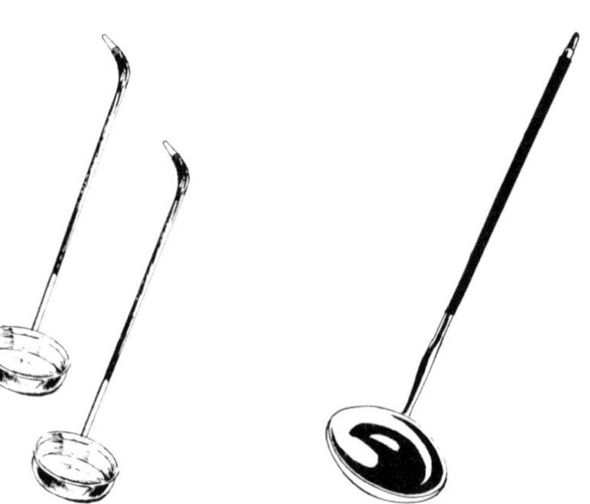

5. Victorian silver sifter spoon by George Unite. £14

6. Pair of toddy ladles circa 1840 by R.K. £65

7. Late 18th century silver punch ladle. £35

8. Pair of Continental silver scissors. £8

9. Fine pair of George III cast silver sugar tongs.£37.50

10. Silver leaf sugar nips, circa 1760. £17

11. Silver sugar tongs, 1785. £25

SALT AND MUSTARD POTS

1. Fine Victorian mustard pot by John Hunt, 1859. £55

2. George IV mustard pot with a blue glass liner, London. £80

3. An excellent mustard pot with a blue glass liner by E.E.J. and W. Barnard, London, 1844, 3ins high, 6ozs. £69

5. Mustard pot by Reily and Storer, London 1837. £46

4. Mustard pot by Barber and North of York, 1838.£56

6. George III silver salt with a gilt interior. £30

7. Heavy quality George III silver salt. £35

9. One of a rare pair of Victorian peppers in the form of helmets with opening visors, Birmingham 1869. £120

8. One of a pair of small attractive silver salts by Hilliard and Thomason, 1870. £39

1. A Victorian oval two handled tray by W& G Sissons, Sheffield 1858, overall width 38ins. £600

2. One of a pair of George I oval salvers by Robert Jones, London 1795, 24½ozs. £325

3. George III circular waiter by Hannan and Mills of London, 1764, with a coat of arms engraved on the plain centre. £95

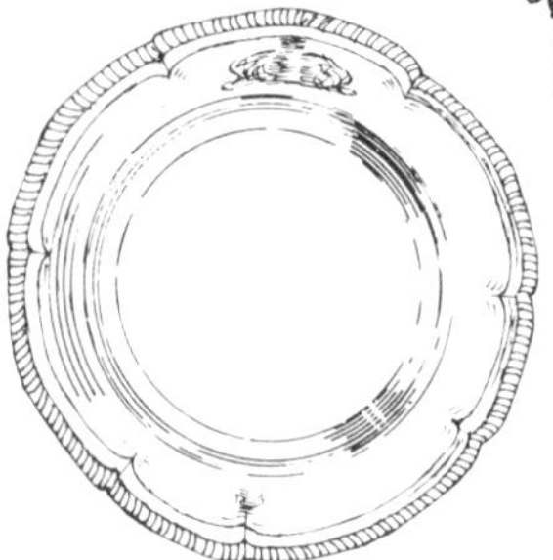

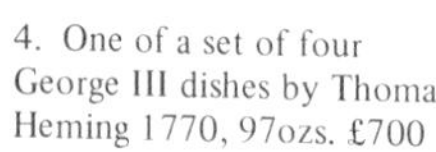

4. One of a set of four George III dishes by Thomas Heming 1770, 97ozs. £700

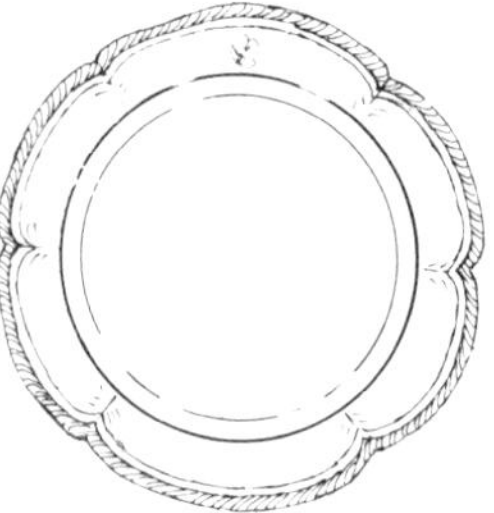

5. One of a set of twelve George II plates by Eliza Godfrey, 1750, 199ozs. £1,650

6. George III tea tray by W. Burwash and R. Sibley, 1807, 86ozs. £350

7. A Japanese pattern tray by Elkington and Co., London, 1879. £155

8. A fine silver gilt charger by Louis Mettayer. £13,000

1. A Nazi silver presentation salver. £55

2. A fine silver meat dish by Wakelin and Garrard, 1801. £195

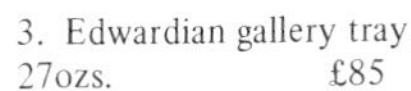

3. Edwardian gallery tray, 27ozs. £85

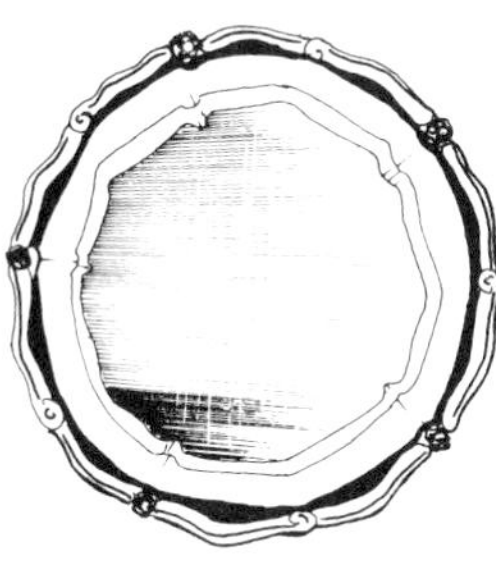

4. A fine silver dish by Robert Garrard, London 1837, 10¼ins diameter, 27ozs. £85

5. George I spoon tray by Edward Vincent, 1717. £325

6. One of a set of twelve dinner plates engraved with the Royal Arms and initials of George III by Thomas Heming, 1780, total weight 209ozs. £2,400

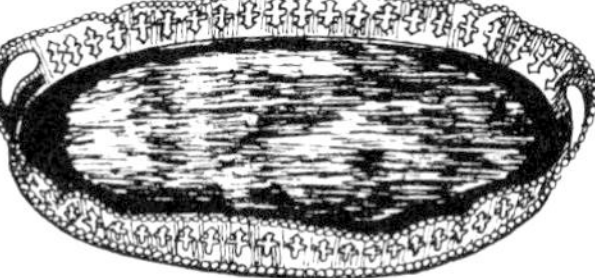

7. Victorian plated gallery tray. £18

8. A T'ang dynasty silver, engraved and gilt dish, 30.5 cm diameter. £40,000

9. 19th century Sheffield plate salver with a shaped border. £12.50

1. George IV travelling inkstand dated 1822. £22.50

2. Rare silver travellers inkwell marked H.D., London. £125

3. George III pocket inkwell, London 1812, by T. Williams, 5¼ins long. £65

4. 19th century silver plated inkwell. £14

5. 19th century silver and horses hoof inkwell. £27

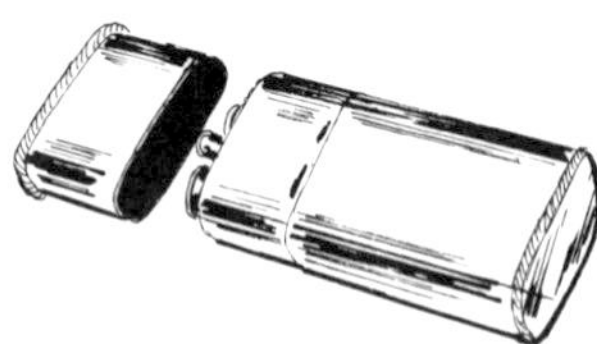

6. George IV travelling writing set, London 1826, maker A.D., 3¼ins long. £55

7. George IV silver inkstand. £140

8. Good quality early 19th century Sheffield plate inkstand. £145

1. Fine quality silver tea caddy by I.P.G., 1762. £275

2. Silver box and cover by Ebenezer Rowe, 1711, London, 8ozs 15dwt, 15cm high. £1,700

3. Silver tea caddy by John Newton 1736, London. £98

4. George III plated tea caddy. £12

5. An exceptionally fine set of George III silver caddies. £470

6. Late Victorian silver tea caddy, 11ozs. £27

7. Fine pair of silver tea caddies and a matchingstand by Messrs. Barnard, London 1878. £310

1. A Lapis Lazuli snuff box by Juste Aurele Meissonier of Paris, 1728. £61,610

2. An English blue glass enamelled snuff box made in the 1760's, 2¼ins wide. 620gns

3. An octagonal tortoiseshell snuff box, set with gold, jewels and enamel, 3ins wide. 1,200gns

4. Victorian silver snuff box dated 1843. £30

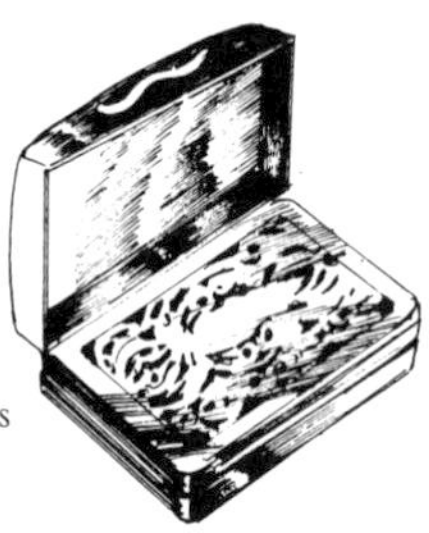

5. Early 19th century vinaigrette. £50

6. Continental silver articulated fish. £35

7. Victorian silver gilt pomander with the original green leather case, London 1862, maker T.J., 2¼ins long. £55

8. Good quality snuff box by N. Mills, 1838. £475

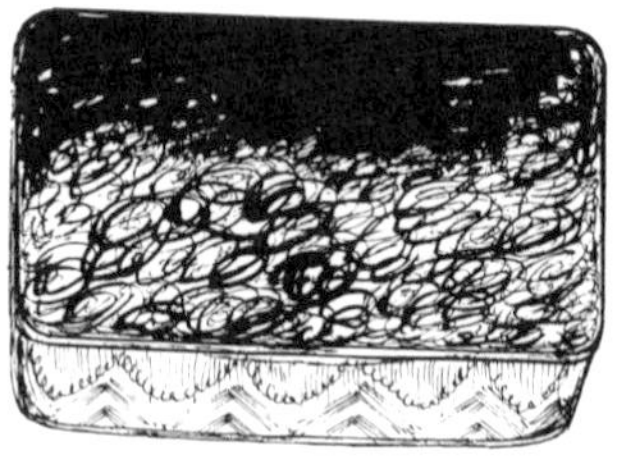

9. Late 19th century silver trinket box circa 1894. £33

1. Victorian silver snuff box, 1828. £55

2. Fine silver snuff box by T.S., Birmingham 1830. £425

3. Silver snuff box by Thomas Shaw, 1828. £43

4. Snuff box by S.P., Birmingham, 1781. £135

5. Small, early snuff box, probably Scottish, circa 1730, 2¼ins long. £50

6. An attractive Continental silver scent flask in the form of a violin. £37.50

7. Swiss gold, enamel and diamond snuff,box, 3¼ins. 1,050gns

8. A nicely shaped Victorian silver snuff box, circa 1855. £130

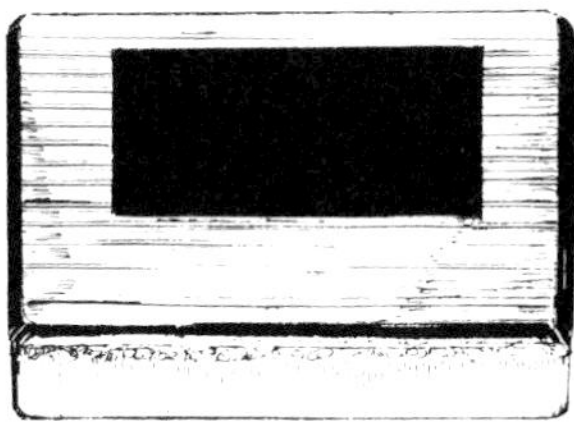

9. Good quality silver snuff box by Thomas Shaw, 1828. £33

1. Pair of George II silver candlesticks by William Gould, 1737, 24½ ozs. £700

2. Pair of early 19th century plated candlesticks. £14

3. Pair of George I silver candlesticks by Thomas Farrer 1723, 29ozs. £1,100

4. One of a set of four George III table candlesticks by J. Parker and E. Wakelin, 1761, 11ins high. £1,200

5. A small pair of Stuart silver candlesticks. £700

6. Pair of table sticks by John Edwards, circa 1749, 43 ozs. £1,200

7. Pair of William IV candlesticks by Benjamin Smith of Birmingham, 52ozs, 1836. £400

CANDLESTICKS

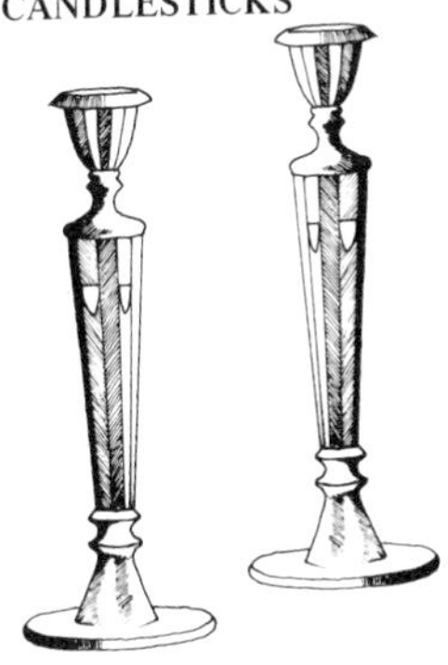

1. A fine pair of early 19th century plated candlesticks. £42

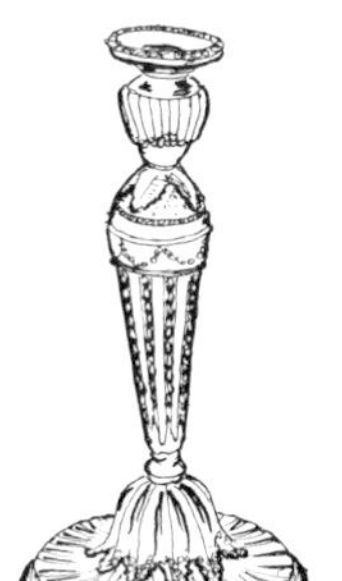

2. Pair of Victorian plated candlesticks 14ins high. £24

3. Pair of Russian silver candlesticks circa 1840. £185

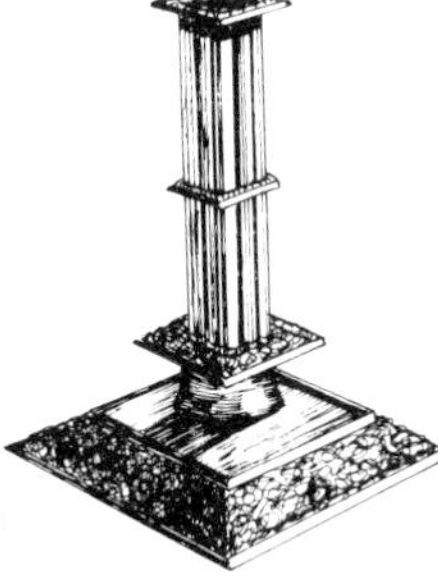

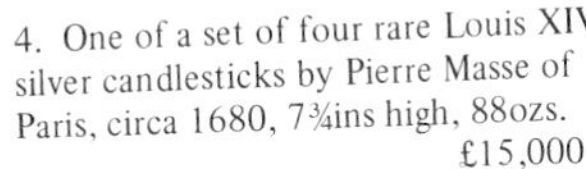

4. One of a set of four rare Louis XIV silver candlesticks by Pierre Masse of Paris, circa 1680, 7¾ins high, 88ozs. £15,000

5. A fine pair of silver candlesticks by John Cafe of London, circa 1748, 39ozs. £825

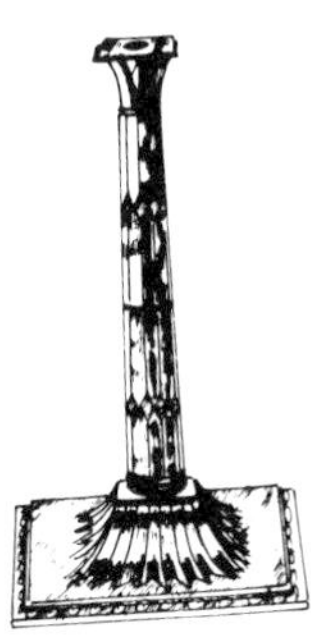

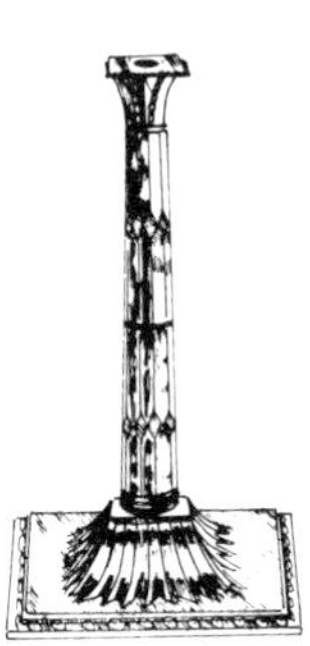

6. A fine pair of George III loaded candlesticks, circa 1785, 13ins high. £205

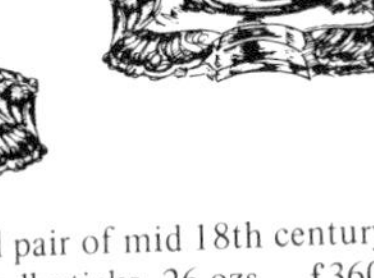

7. Small pair of mid 18th century silver candlesticks, 26 ozs. £360

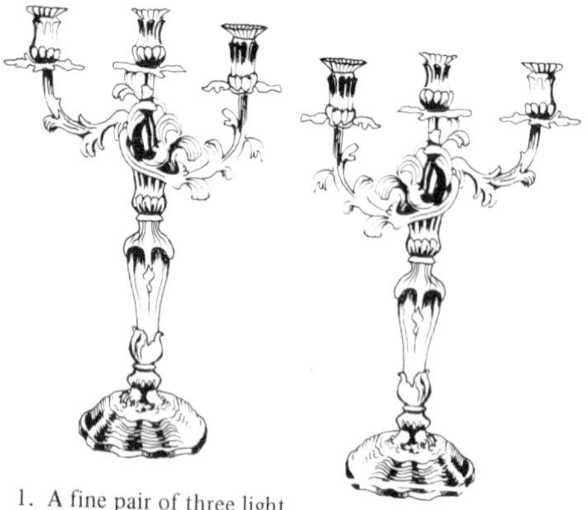

1. A fine pair of three light candelabrum by Friedrich Reinhard Schrodel, 226ozs. £2,300

2. An impressive nine light centrepiece by Paul Storr, 1830. £2,600

3. A four light candelabrum by Emes and Barnard, 1828. £400

4. A pair of Victorian silver gilt, seven light candelabrum . 1,900gns

5. One of an ornate and rare set of single light wall sconces from the reign of James II by T. I., 1687. £26,000

6. One of a pair of Victorian rococo style candelabrum 1864, 260 ozs. £1,200

7. One of a set of four silver sconces by John Jackson of London, circa 1707. £16,275

1. Silver chamberstick and snuffer by Emes and Barnard London, 1822. £245

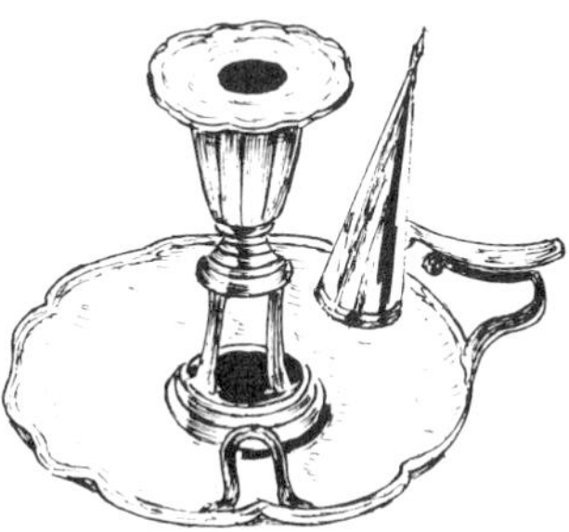

2. Silver chamberstick by Henry Wilkinson of Sheffield, 1839. £135

3. An unusual double chamber candlestick by John Schofield, London 1787, 18¼ozs. £260

4. George III chamberstick by Hannon and Crouch, London 1791, 4½ins high, 10ozs. £150

5. A fine silver chamberstick by T.J. and N. Creswick of Sheffield, 1828. £115

6. A good quality early 19th century silver chamberstick with an elaborate border. £145

7. 19th century plated chamberstick complete with snuffer. £12

8. Silver chamberstick by John Carter, 1770. £225

1. Small silver spirit flask, 1868. £13

2. Silver dish cross by T.B. and A.H., 1780-1781. £275

3. Late Victorian plated hand bell. £5.75

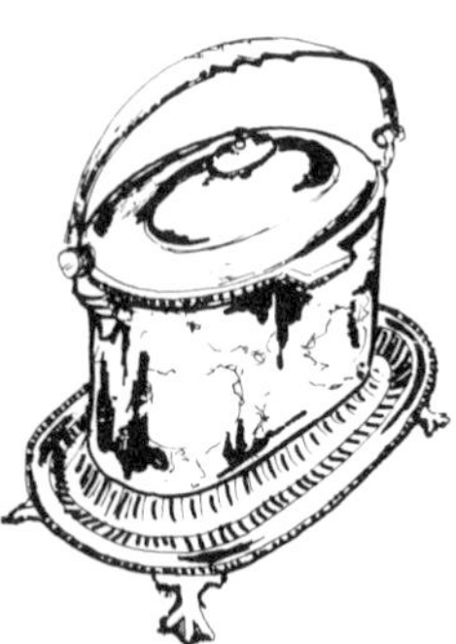

4. 19th century plated biscuit barrel complete with stand. £6.50

5. A fine model of an Augsburg Knight in silver with the head and face in ivory. £640

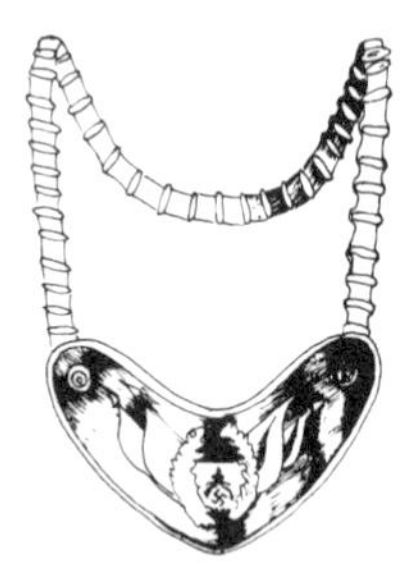

6. A Nazi period Reichskreiger Bund Gorget. £50

7. 19th century silver buckle. £4

8. 18th century silver-mounted stationery holder. £10

9. One of a pair of silver race tickets. £580

1. 19th century Japanese lacquered wood and silver pair of Kashidako in the form of swimming ducklings on a tray, 19.8cm long. £520

2. A small silver embossed ship. £42

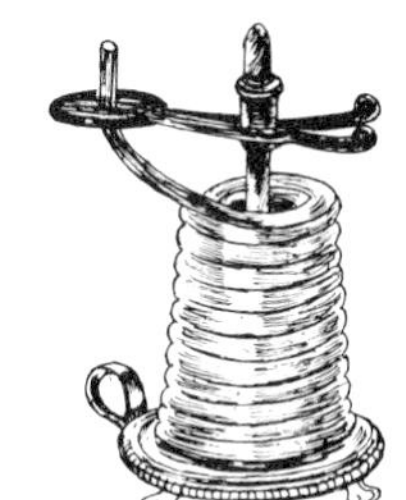

3. Rare silver ' Wax Jack', London circa 1750. £325

4. An impressive five light Victorian plated centrepiece. £95

5. A silver model of an owl with a removable head and glass eyes, made in 1869, with the makers mark E.C.B., 13½ins high. £560

6. A silver posy holder by Nathaniel Mills, 1844. £59.50

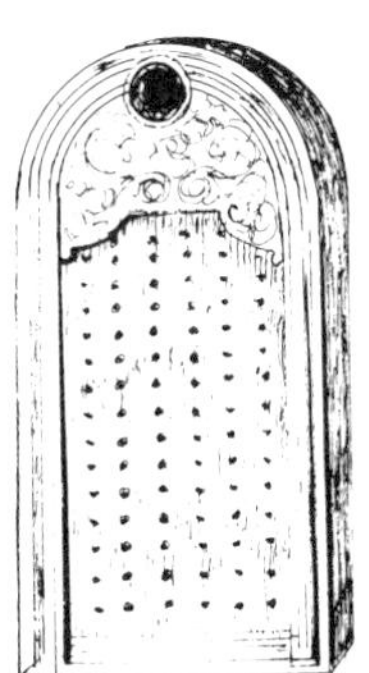

7. 18th century silver tobacco rasp. £95

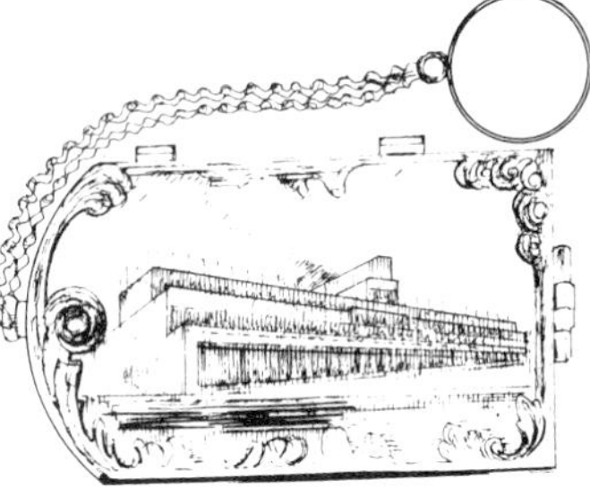

8. A silver covered note pad with ivory leaves by Nathaniel Mills of Birmingham, 1850, engraved with a picture of the Crystal Palace. £45

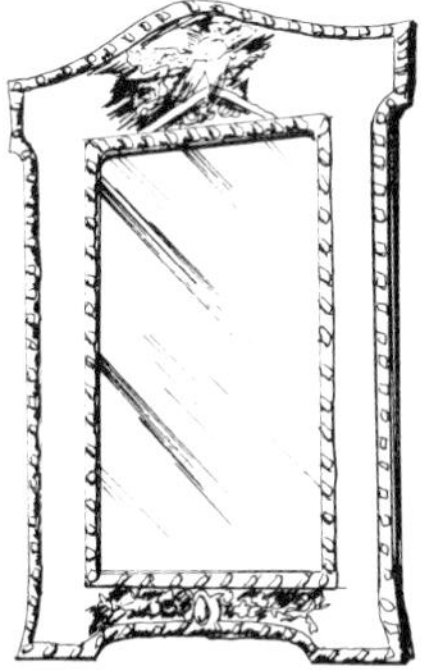

9. Victorian silver frame, 10ins x 7¾ins. £14.50

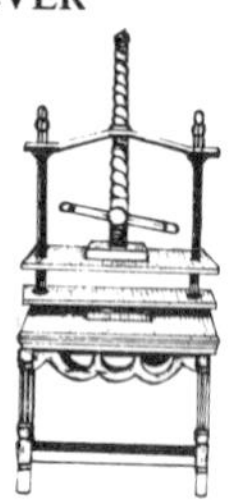

1. Small Victorian silver bookbinder's press, 2ins tall. £30

2. Victorian silver rattle dated 1886. £14

3. Small silver toy of a dancing bear with an attendant. £30

4. The magnificent Sutton cup in silver gilt and rock crystal dated 1573. £36,000

5. A fine pair of early silver wine labels. £40

6. George II table bell by Thomas Whipham, 5½ozs. £560

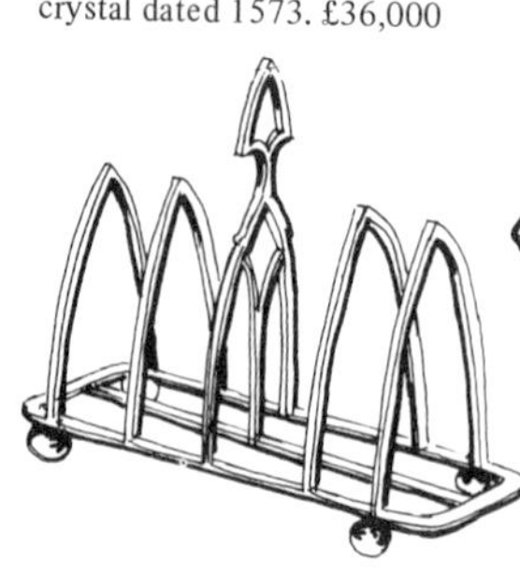

7. 19th century plated toast rack. £7.50

8. 19th century cow cream jug in silver. £45

9. Sherry wine label by Taylor and Perry, 1833. £17.50

10. Large Victorian silver game skewer. £26

1. Fine silver napkin ring dated 1878. £7

2. Small silver coach and horses, 3ins long. £40

3. A U.S. silver ingot approx. 2½ x 1½ x ½ ins, dated Sept. 1870. £225

4. Silver sugar container and cover by Ignace Colombier, Marseilles 1777. £1,730

5. Fine pair of early wine labels. £44

6. Silver gilt two handled cup and cover, circa 1650. £2,500

7. Pair of candelabrum sconces with coronet, London 1795, maker R.S., 8ins high, 50ozs. £220

8. Edwardian silver dressing table service comprising 18 pieces, including a pair of candlesticks. £960

9. Reproduction plated candle snuffer. £6.50

10. French ten light silver surtout de table of the Louis XIV period, 40cm high. £2,310

LAMPS

1. 19th century tin 'bulls eye' lamp. £7.50

2. 19th century ornate silver plated electric table lamp embossed with shells and scrolls, 20 ins high. £32

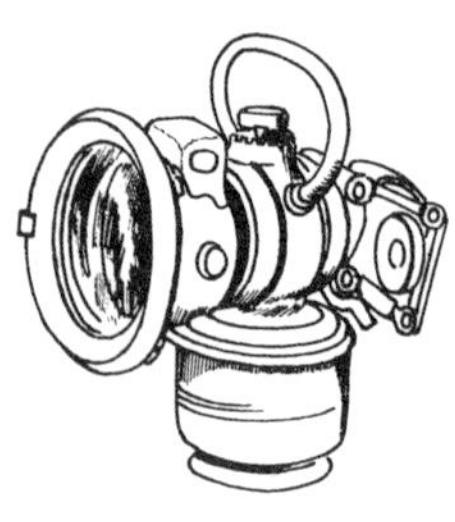

3. Victorian brass carbide lamp. £8

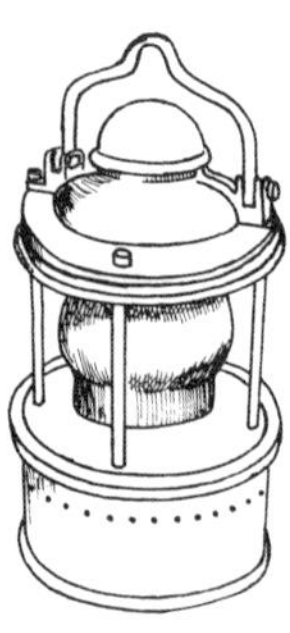

4. Victorian ship's mast lamp in brass. £22.50

5. A good Tiffany 'Wisteria' lamp, 27ins high. £6,500

6. A large ornate brass lamp with crystal glass drops, 24½ ins high. £48

7. 19th century brass argand lamp with white glass shades. £26

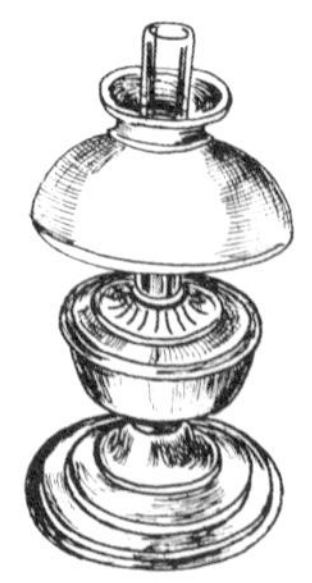

8. 19th century brass oil lamp with a white glass shade. £13

9. Unusual Victorian brass table lamp. £22.50

1. A 19th century brass carriage lamp. £14

2. 19th century Sheffield plate student's lamp. £62

3. A fine Daum overlay lamp with a purple and cloudy glass ground. £200

4. A fine Victorian Doulton china lamp, 20 ins high. £36

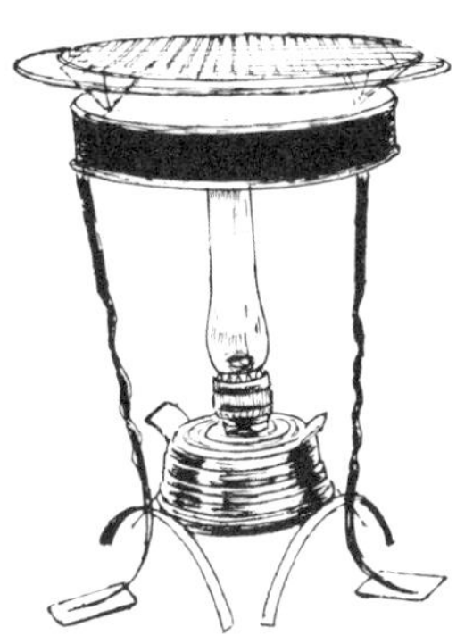

5. Victorian 'Ardent' brass heating lamp on a wrought iron stand with a copper top. £25

6. A very fine quality Muller lamp. £460

7. Victorian brass oil lamp with a green glass shade. £22

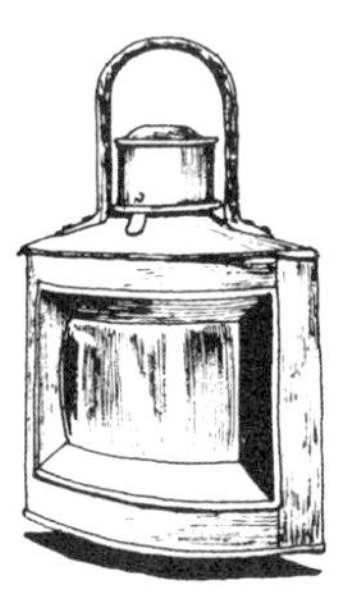

8. 19th century copper ship's lamp. £13

9. Tiffany lamp with a gilt bronze base and coloured glass poppy pattern shade. £820

HANGING LAMPS

1. A fine Victorian copper and steel lantern with the original glass, 3 ft high. £110

2. George III hanging hall lantern, circa 1800, 48 ins overall height. £58

3. Victorian bronze ship's lantern. £60

4. Small 19th century Dutch brass hanging light. £38

5. 19th century cast brass chandelier in the Gothic style, the six solid branches being detachable and dovetail pegged into the centre column, 18ins high. £125

6. French rococo gilt brass nine light chandelier, 35 ins tall, 21 ins wide. £175

7. One of a pair of Louis XV ormolu wall lights, 22 ins high. £175

8. One of a pair of 19th century Delft wall lights, 13 ins high. £32

1. Large Victorian copper street lamp. £25

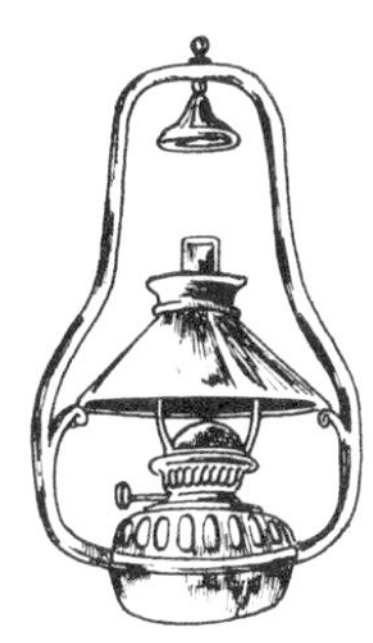

2. 19th century brass hanging lamp with a green glass shade. £25

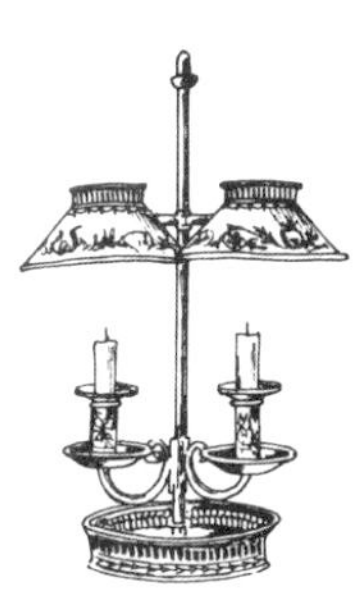

3. An unusual late 18th century Continental hanging lamp. £44

4. Late 18th century six light brass chandelier. £155

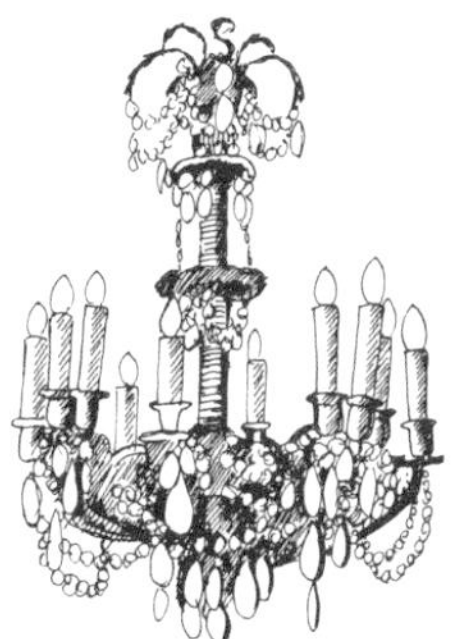

5. Regency twelve light brass chandelier with glass drops. £125

6. A fine early 18th century brass chandelier. £290

7. Regency period chiselled brass six light chandelier. £130

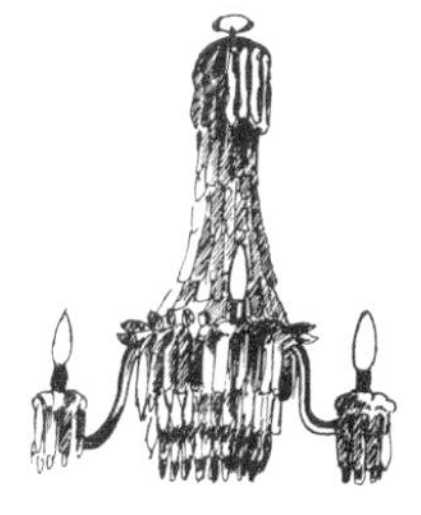

8. A fine large early 19th century chandelier with crystal glass drops. £250

MODEL SHIPS

1. A late 19th century wood and canvas model of a barque. £48

2. Small 19th century silver model of an armed junk. £30

3. Finely made 19th century scale model of a clinker built sailing boat, 27 ins long. £58

4. Boxwood model of a seventy six gun English Ship of the line, 10 ins high, 14 ins long. £490

5. A Napoleonic Prisoner of War bone model of a ship. £600

6. An early 19th century wooden model of a Frigate. £200

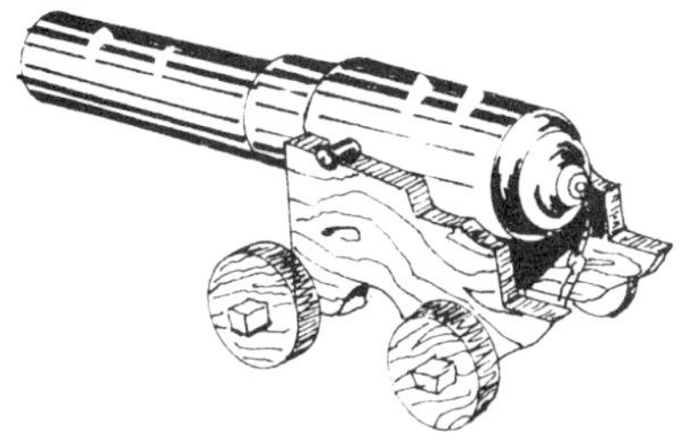

1. Small 19th century bronze model signal cannon. £28

2. One of a pair of French bronze cannon inscribed ' La Prude ' and ' La Juste'. £960

3. A good old model field cannon in the style of the late 17th century, 11 inch barrel. £55

4. A well made bronze starting cannon with a turned barrel, 17 ins long. £34

5. A fine and well made model of a 17th century German field gun with a cast bronze barrel, 16½ ins long. £120

6. A very well made copy of a British 19th century field gun of cast iron, barrel 31 ins. £100

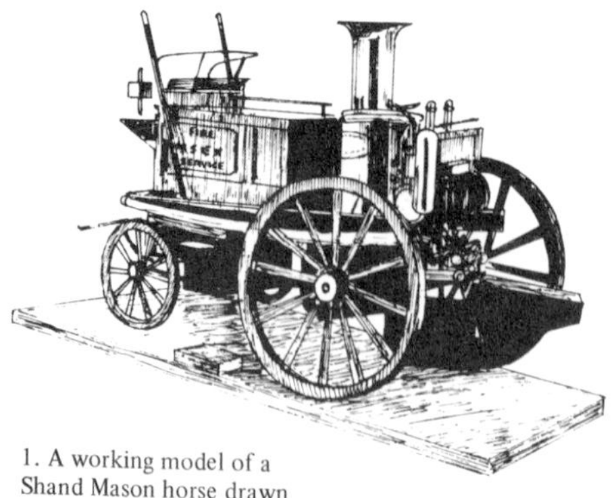

1. A working model of a Shand Mason horse drawn fire engine, circa 1894. £500

2. Scale model of a pony trap with original coach painted woodwork in blue and green with yellow lines, brass and iron fittings, circa 1830, 19ins long. £95

3. A good metal scale model of the Nazi airship Hindenburg, 24ins long, by Marklin. £45

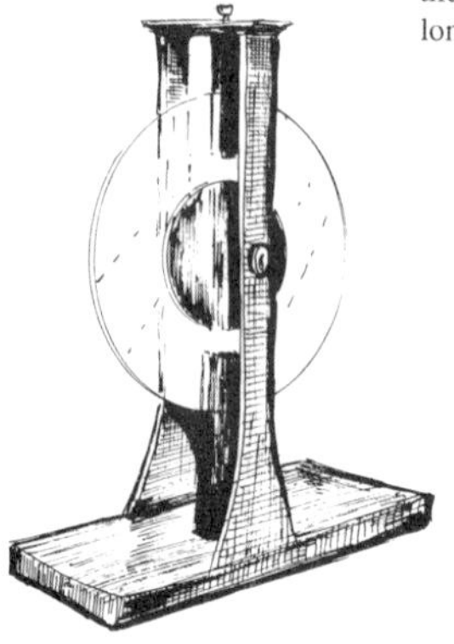

4. A rare early electrostatic friction machine by J. Cuthbertson, 1799. £240

5. A fine and decorative old model of a horizontal steam engine. £40

6. A well made ' O ' guage model of an A3 Pacific 4 - 6 - 2 steam locomotive. £135

1. A well made 3½ in guage 4 - 6 - 2 Pacific class working model loco of 'The Hielan Lassie', 36ins long. £160

2. Scale model of a Waullis and Steevens 'Simplicity Roller', made in the late 20's. £750

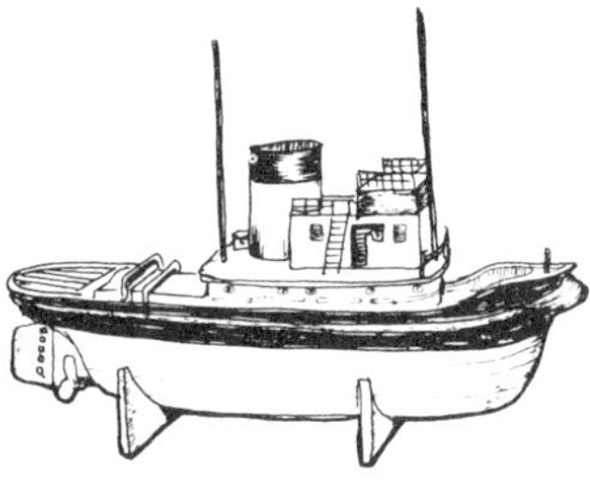

3. A well made steam powered model Thames tug, 58 ins long. £100

4. A Britain's lead model of the pre-1914 Royal Engineers. £35

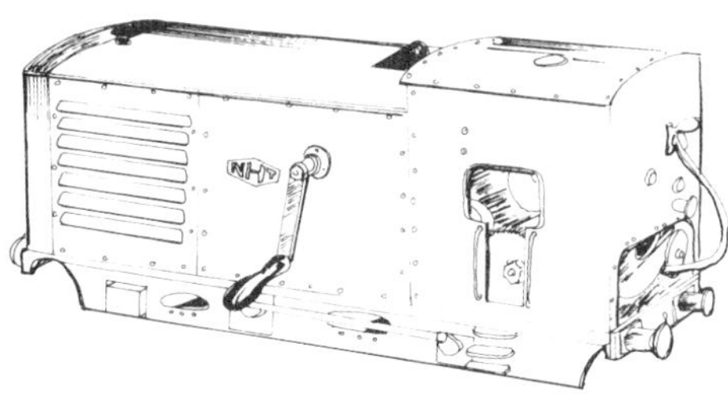

5. A well made working model of a Diesel Shunting Engine, 31½ ins long. £220

6. A Victorian coal fired model steam engine, 13½ ins high. £75

BUCKETS AND HODS

1. 19th century oval polished steel scuttle, 14ins high. £48

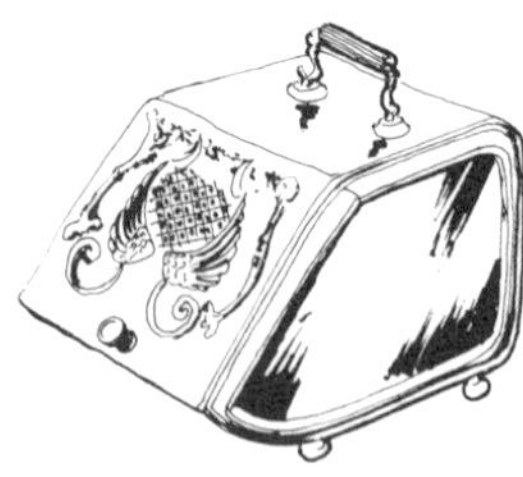

2. Ornate Regency brass coal box with shovel and embossed flap. £25

3. Victorian Fireman's leather bucket decorated with a Coat of Arms. £24

4. A fine George III mahogany bucket with brass fittings, circa 1790. £280

5. Regency brass and copper jardiniere with embossed Coat of Arms, 10ins high. £36

6. A brass handled and banded mahogany plate pail, circa 1755. £145

7. A fine 18th century brass bucket. £80

8. Good quality 19th century mahogany serpentine fronted coal cabinet with an ormolu gallery and mounts, 1ft 4ins wide. £37

9. Early 19th century copper helmet coal scuttle. £22.50

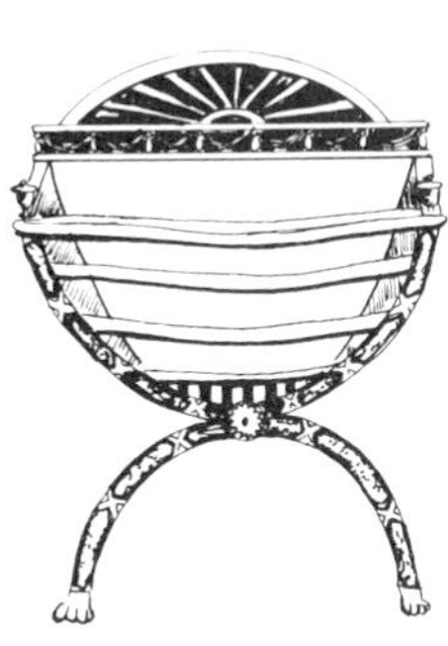

1. A Regency style 'X' frame basket grate. £115

2. An elegant Adam brass dog grate. £195

3. A good Adam brass dog grate. £220

4. A good quality late Regency period statuary marble chimneypiece with original register grate en suite, 4ft high, 5ft 8ins wide. £145

5. Late 18th century French carved walnut fire surround, 40ins high. £145

6. A 19th century Adam style cast iron chimneypiece painted to simulate marble, 4ft 5ins high, 5ft 4ins wide. £135

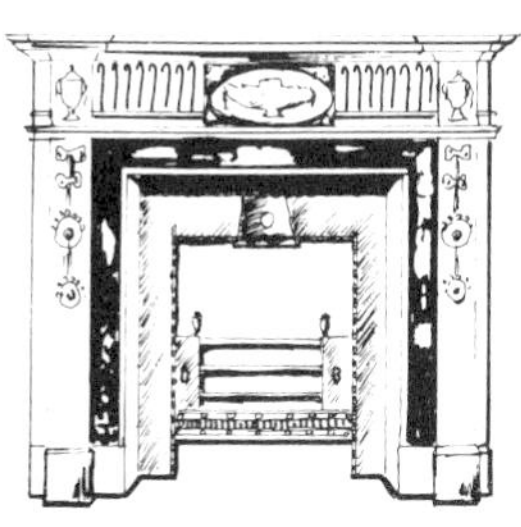

7. An Adam period statuary marble and jasper chimneypiece with original register grate en suite, 4ft 11ins high, 5ft 10ins wide. £850

8. 19th century cast iron fireplace with maroon tiles and brass ornamentation. £79

9. A 19th century carved pine Gothic style chimneypiece, 4ft 3ins high, 5ft 8ins wide. £70

1. Georgian copper coffee pot with fruitwood handle, 8½ins high. £27

2. 19th century brass watering can. £11

3. 19th century copper two handled urn with a brass tap and cover. £19

4. Early 19th century brass revolving magazine rack on shaped legs with paw feet. £51

5. 18th century copper warming pan with a turned fruitwood handle. £20

6. 19th century brass fireguard, 3ft 6ins wide. £7

7. Pair of Victorian brass vases, 10 ins high. £15

8. An old tin and wrought iron well bucket, 18ins high. £25

9. A fine quality copper kettle with a brass spout. £20

1. A fine Victorian brass kettle and stand. £10

2. 19th century copper urn with brass handles and tap. £12

3. Georgian bronze bell with a raised border that reads Arnold Rester Fecit, 1796. £65

4. 19th century copper samovar. £18

5. A small George III steel footman, 13½ins x 10½ins. £12

6. Victorian copper jelly mould. £13

7. An early copper fish kettle and lid with bell metal carrying handles, 20ins wide. £45

8. George III tavern coffee pot in copper, 10ins high. £35

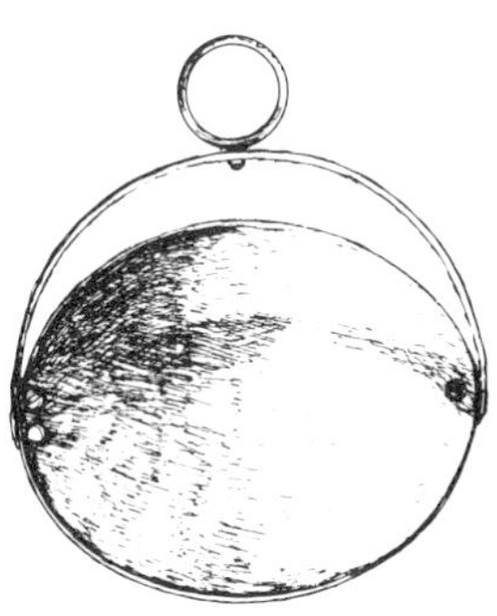

9. An early iron griddle pan with a brass handle. £8

1. A good quality bronze skillet. £26

2. An early Victorian copper pan with a wooden handle. £17

3. Victorian brass preserving pan with a folding iron handle. £5.50

4. An Indian brass lidded jug. £7

5. George III cabriole leg iron footman, 12ins wide, circa 1770. £12

6. Early 19th century copper urn. £50

7. 18th century steel and copper ladle, 24ins long. £10

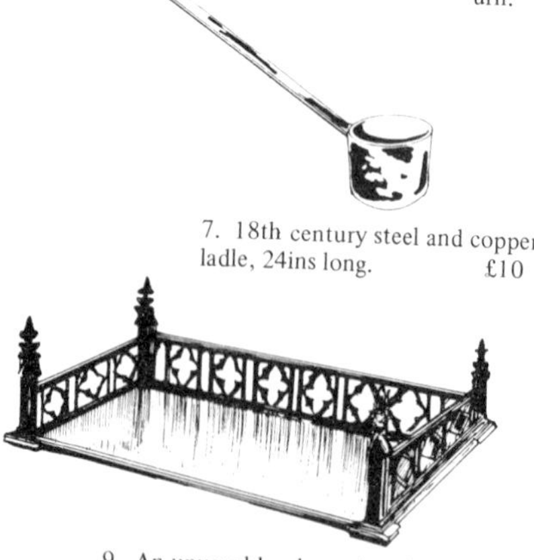

8. Early 19th century brass fire-irons complete with matching stand. £12.50

9. An unusual book carrier of finely figured oak veneer on a mahogany base with a Victorian Gothic bronze gallery. £45

10. Early 19th century shirehorse martingale. £27

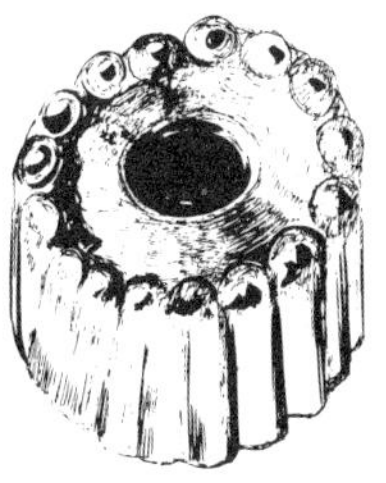

1. Large Victorian copper jelly mould. £15

2. George III copper saucepan complete with lid. £9.50

3. 18th century brass sundial. £7.50

4. Large George III four gallon measure. £30

5. A fine quality 19th century brass birdcage. £11

6. Victorian brass watering can. £3

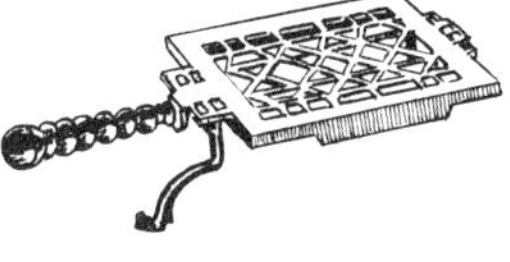

7. Victorian brass trivet with a turned wood handle. £4

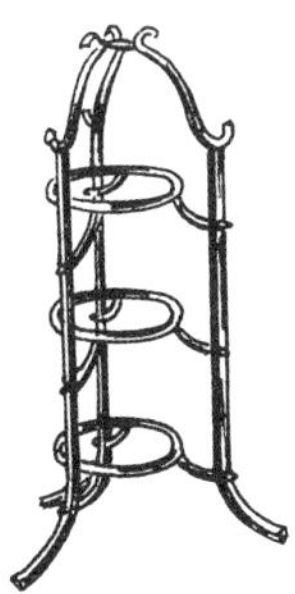

8. 19th century brass three tier cake stand. £10

9. Late 18th century brass tavern footman. £35

10. Victorian brass standard lamp. £40

1. A fine example of a 17th century brass candlestick with a turned and chiselled base, a hand made screw and two ejection holes, 9ins high. £75

2. Small pair of brass candlesticks, circa 1800. £120

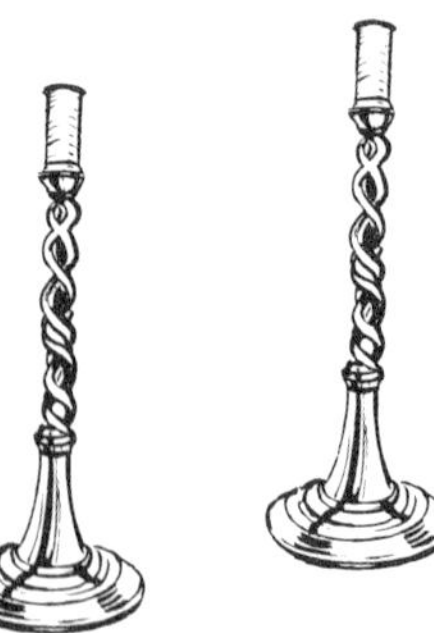

3. Pair of Victorian brass twist candlesticks, 12ins high. £8.50

4. Fine pair of ormolu and bronze candelabrum, circa 1815. £18

5. Pair of the finest 18th century French brass candlesticks with chiselled decoration, 9¾ins high. £65

6. Pair of French Empire bronze and ormolu candelabrum, 23ins high. £265

7. Pair of late 18th century marble and ormolu candelabrum, 15ins high. £105

1. Pair of Georgian brass candlesticks, 10ins high. £13

2. Pair of brass candlesticks, circa 1800. £12

3. Pair of tall 19th century brass candlesticks on claw feet. £10

4. One of a pair of Victorian brass candelabrum, 16ins tall. £45

5. Square based William and Mary bell metal candlestick on four small stump feet, hand made screw, 5ins high. £38

6. One of a pair of 17ins green marble and ormolu four branch candelabrum, circa 1890. £17.50

7. Pair of elegant ormolu wall lights with urn knobs and leaf scroll double branches, 13½ins high. £45

8. 19th century Oriental brass candelabra with glass jewel decoration, 18ins high. £35

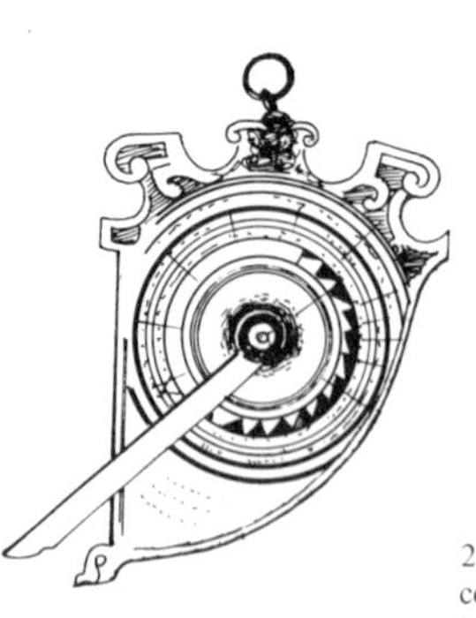

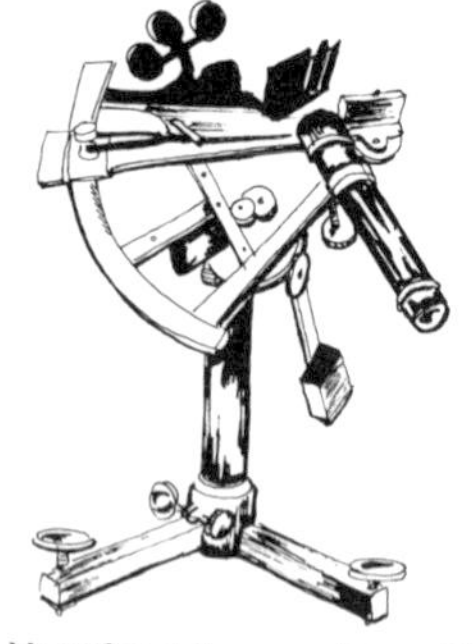

2. Magnificent lacquered brass 19th century pillar sextant by Cary of London. £450

1. 16th century Italian gilt metal quadrant. £1,050

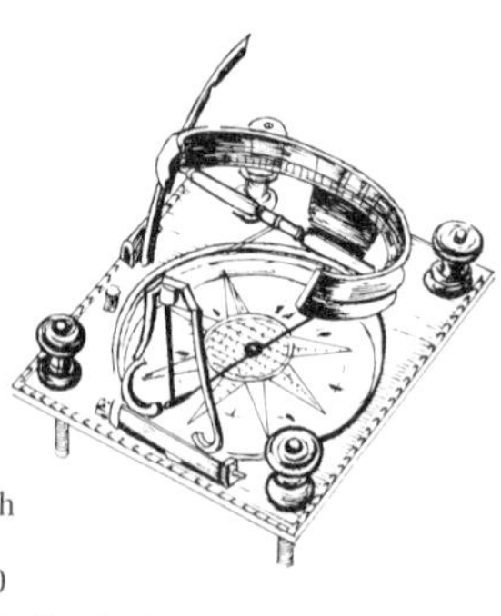

3. Russian brass equatorial dial circa 1780. £380

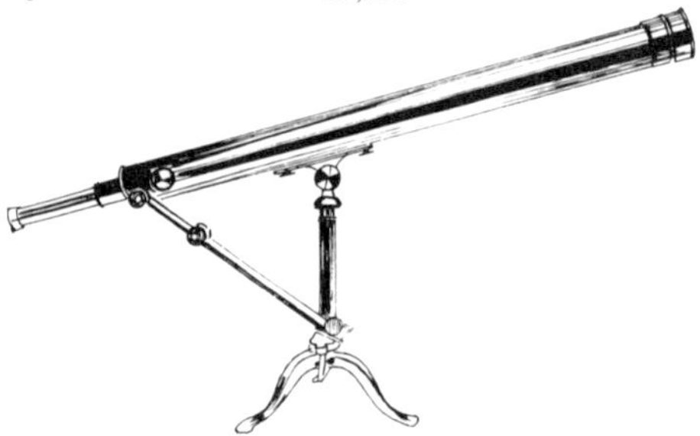

4. A fine late Victorian astronomical and terrestrial telescope, 39ins long by J. Casartelli of Manchester. £95

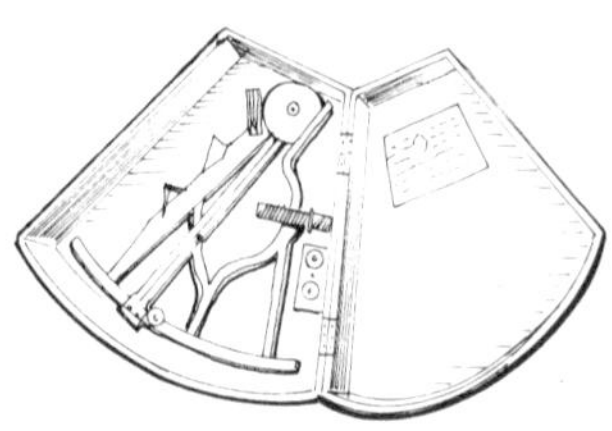

5. Mahogany cased brass sextant by Harrison of Hull with a platinum scale. £48

6. A fine early equinoctrial dial. £200

7. A 'New Planetarium' by Benjamin Martin of London, circa 1770. £2,800

8. An unusual early brass ring dial. £540

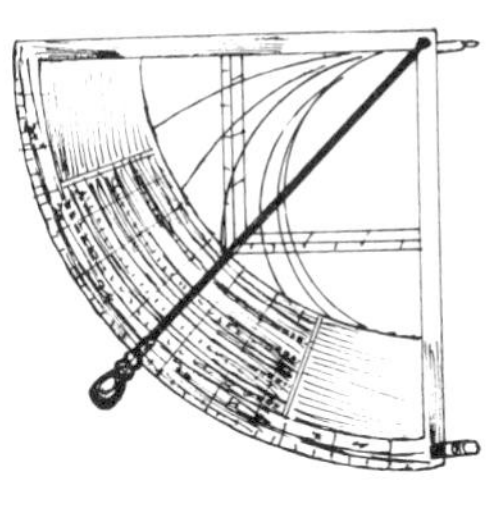

2. 16th century Italian gilt metal quadrant. £950

3. An ivory tablet dial in the form of a book by Paul Reinman, circa 1610. £680

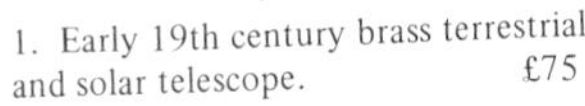

1. Early 19th century brass terrestrial and solar telescope. £75

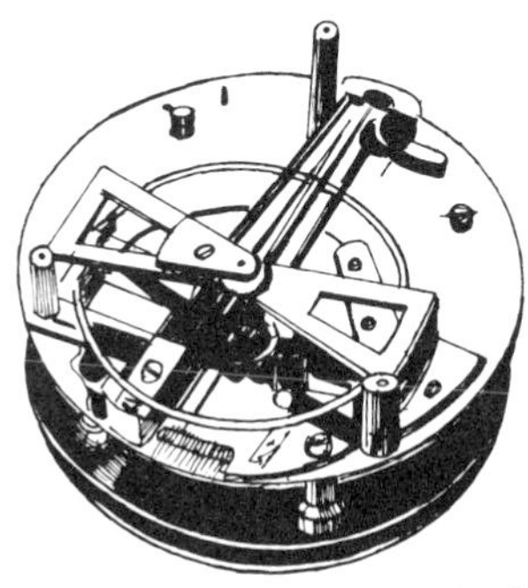

4. A fine marine chronometer, circa 1770. £2,730

5. A gilt tablet dial by Tobias Volchmer, circa 1612. £700

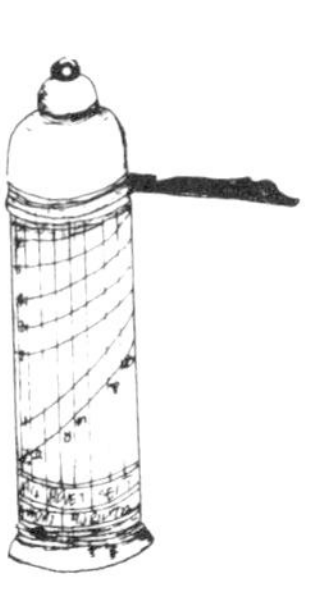

6. 17th century ivory pillar dial. £820

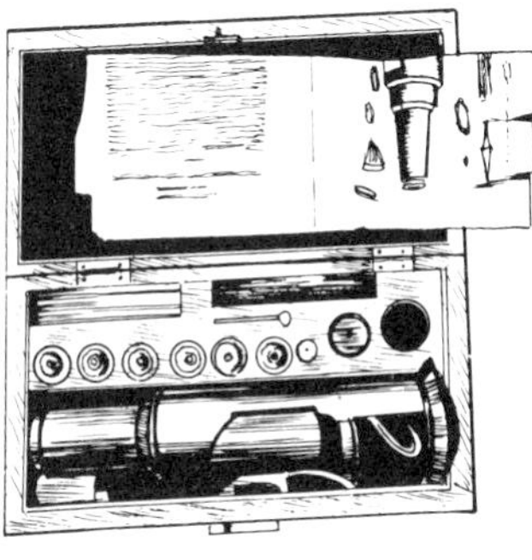

7. A monocular microscope, circa 1820 by D. Davis, of the original lacquered brass, 10ins high, in a mahogany case with ebony stringing, complete with all accessories. £65

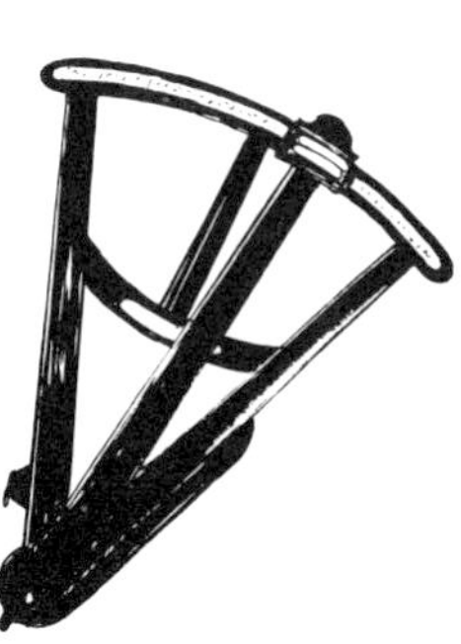

8. Mid 18th century sextant. £45

INSTRUMENTS

1. Captain's bronze boat tiller arm engraved 'Grecian 1812 Baltimore'. £48

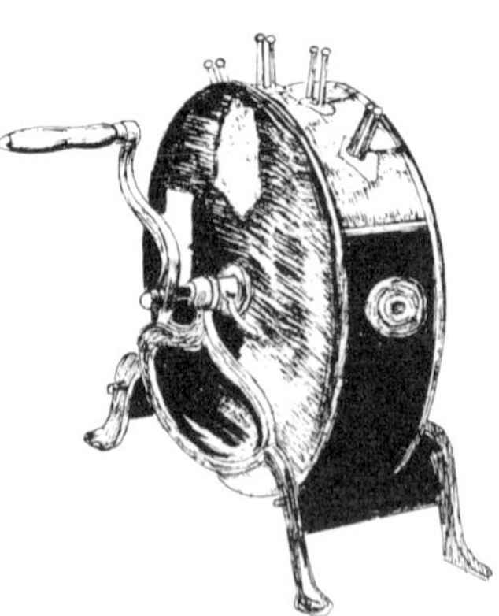

2. Late Victorian knife cleaner. £14

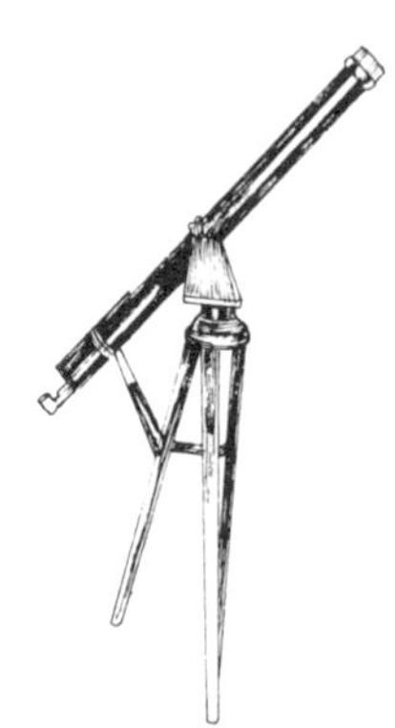

3. Superb bronzed brass 4ins telescope on a mahogany tripod by Thomas Cooke of York. £450

4. Mid Victorian coffee grinder. £10

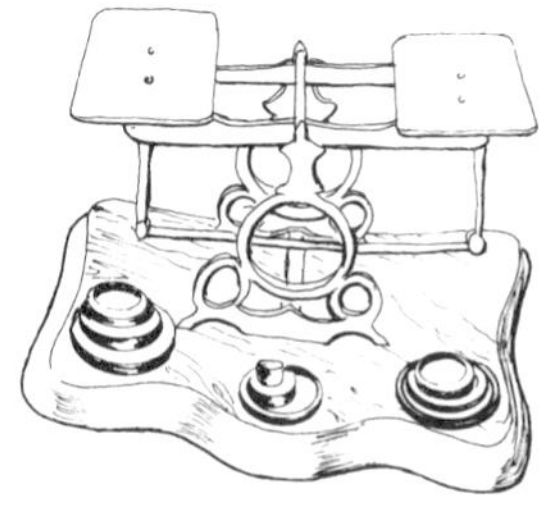

5. Victorian brass letter scales. £10

6. Decorative brass rimmed teak Clipper ship's wheel, 41ins overall. £58

7. A Victorian chromatic stereoscope on an adjustable stand. £22.50

8. Collapsable George III Apothecary scales with brass pans, and seven graded weights, on a mahogany base, 19ins wide, 25ins high, 9½ins deep. £37

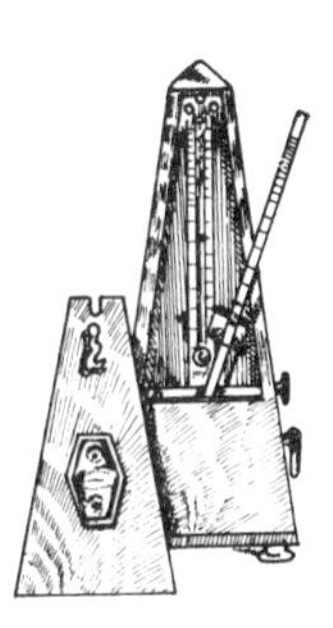

1. Victorian metronome in an oak case. £4

2. Georgian mahogany and brass wig stand. £9.50

3. Victorian chromatic stereoscope. £7.50

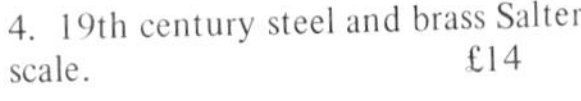

4. 19th century steel and brass Salter scale. £14

5. Victorian kitchen scales with brass pans and cast iron stand. £16.50

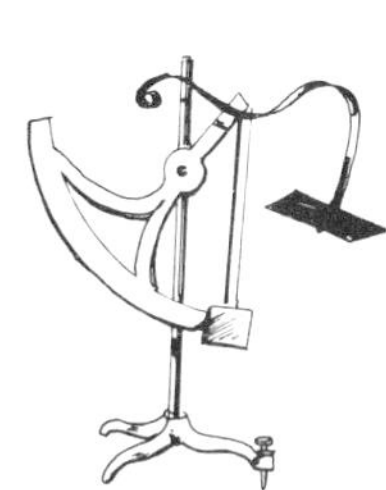

6. Unusual brass and steel gold scales by E. Levrig and Co. of London, 16ins high, circa 1850. £38

7. 19th century mahogany and brass 'Waywiser' by Nigretti and Zamba. £150

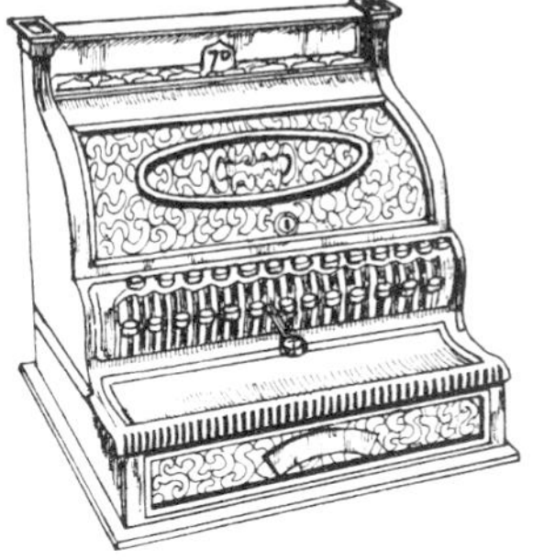

8. Edwardian brass cash till. £40

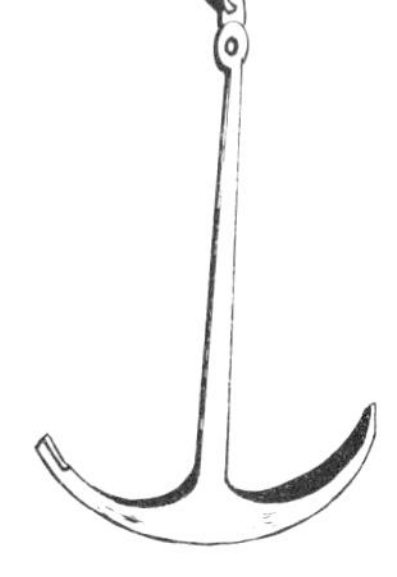

9. Heavy 19th century bronze, anchor, 3ft 2ins long. £70

INSTRUMENTS

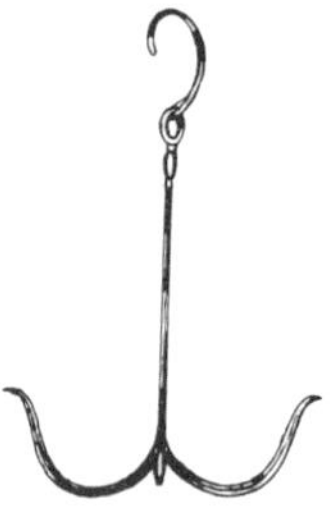

1. Queen Anne period steel game hook. £9

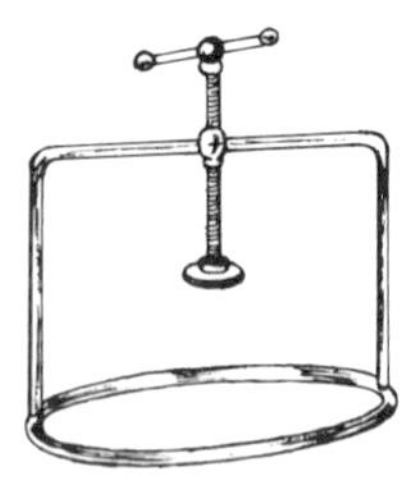

2. Mid 19th century polished steel press. £28

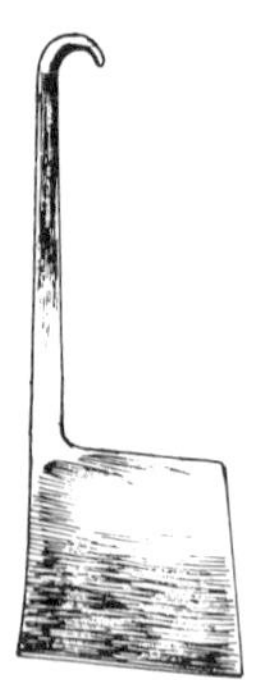

3. Exceptionally large old butcher's cleaver, 26ins high. £18

4. 17th century brass and iron trivot toaster, 25ins long. £17

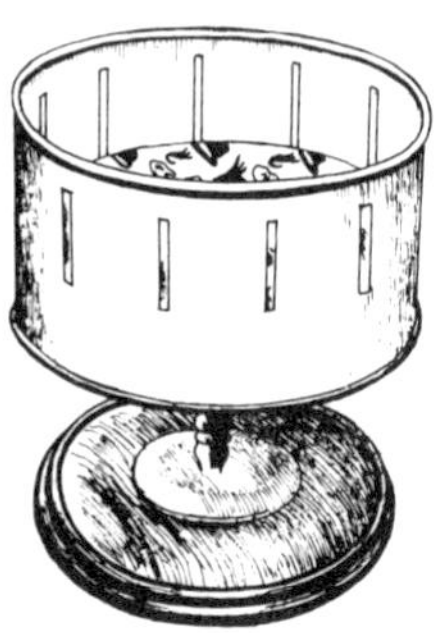

5. A good quality Victorian zeotrope. £24

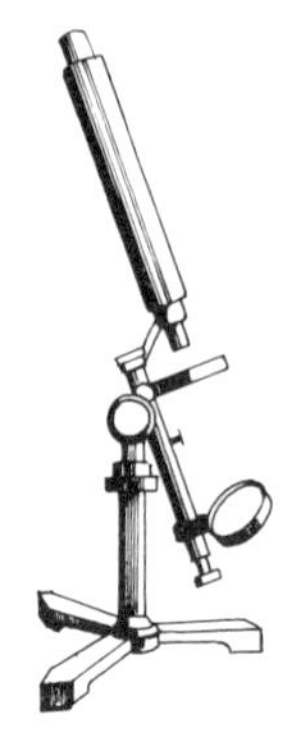

6. A large Victorian brass microscope by J. Cross. £90

7. 19th century brass heliograph on an extending base. £90

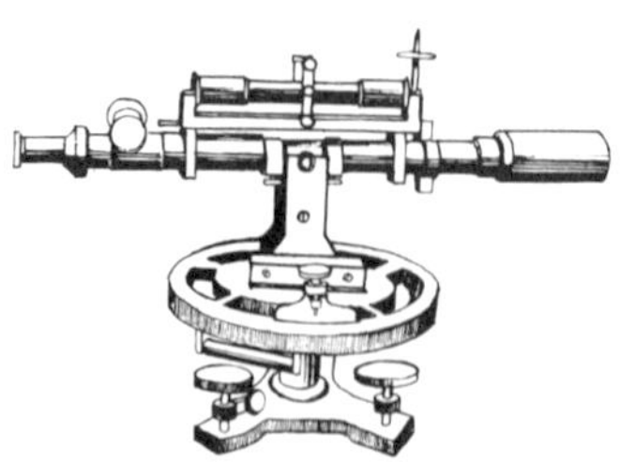

8. Mid 19th century brass theodolite. £125

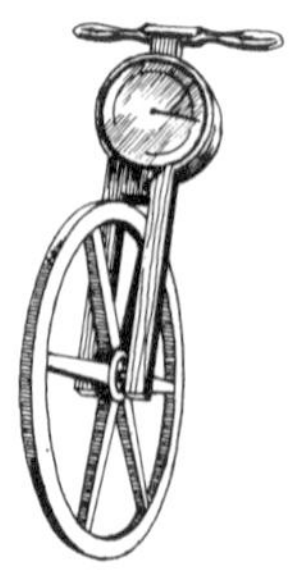

9. 19th century mahogany and brass hoddmeter. £105

1. An early sycamore and walnut, steel toasting fork. £14

2. Decorative 18th century copper and wrought iron weather vane, the whole surmounted by an imposing silhouette wolf of polished steel, overall height 65ins. £150

3. Queen Anne rush-light holder, 36ins high. £65

4. Pair of Victorian brass bankers scales. £38

5. A fine early 19th century ships chronometer in a mahogany case with brass fittings. £340

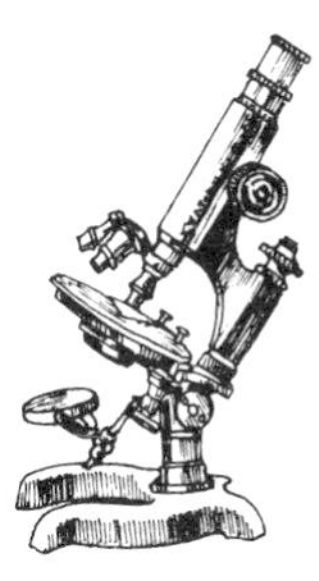

6. A good quality Victorian brass microscope complete with fitted case. £40

7. George II brass and steel scales on a mahogany base. £55

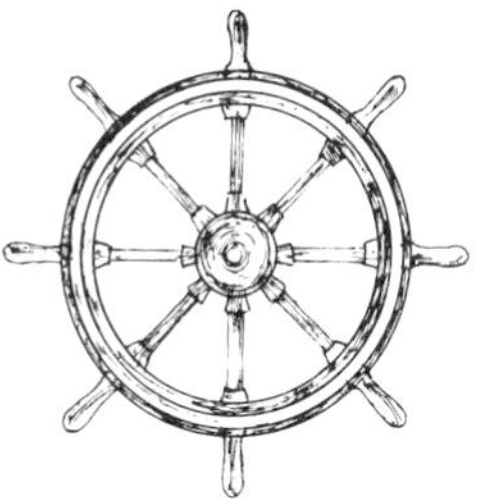

8. Teak wood and brass, ship's wheel from the yacht "S.S. Tita".

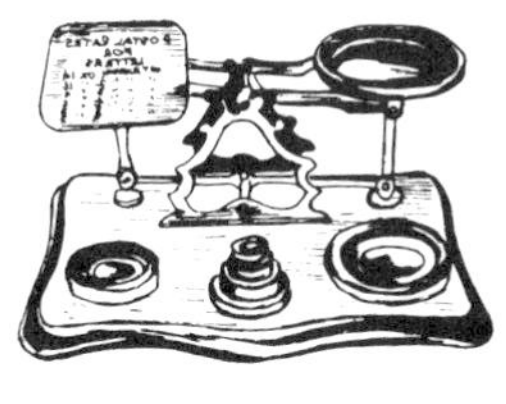

9. Victorian brass letter scales on a mahogany base. £6.50

GRANDFATHER CLOCKS

1. A fine mahogany longcase clock by George Negus of Huntingdon, circa 1795, 6 ft 5 ins high. £450

2. A fine longcase clock in a walnut case signed Windmills of London. £785

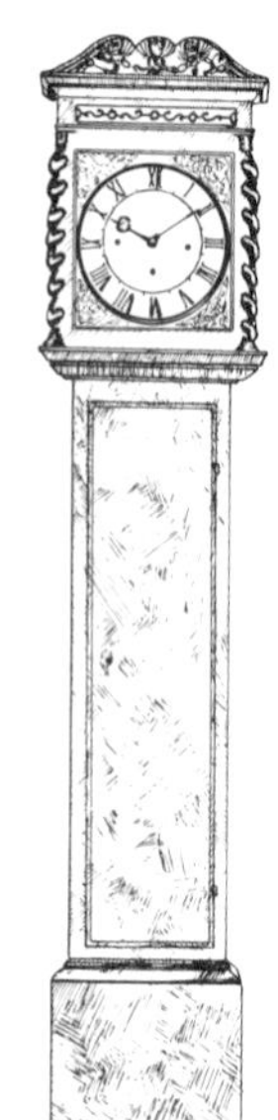

3. An exceptionally fine longcase clock by Joseph Knibb in a walnut case. £16,800

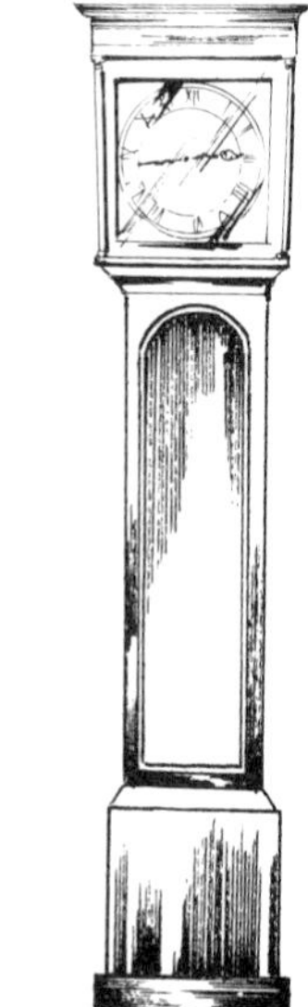

4. George III oak longcase clock with mahogany crossbanding by Dickerson of Egremont, circa 1790. £135

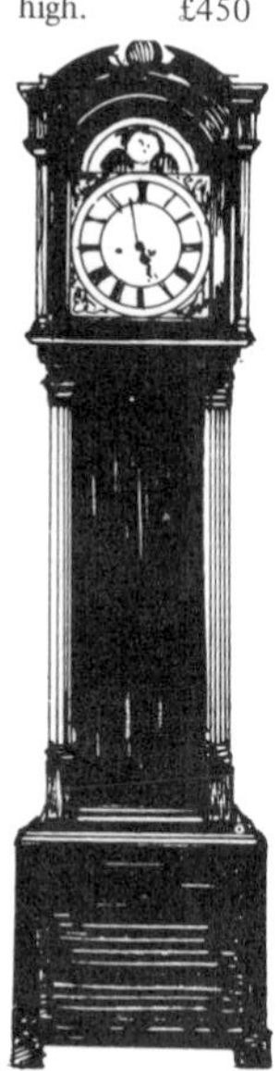

5. Mid 18th century mahogany longcase clock by John Owen of Llanwrst. £180

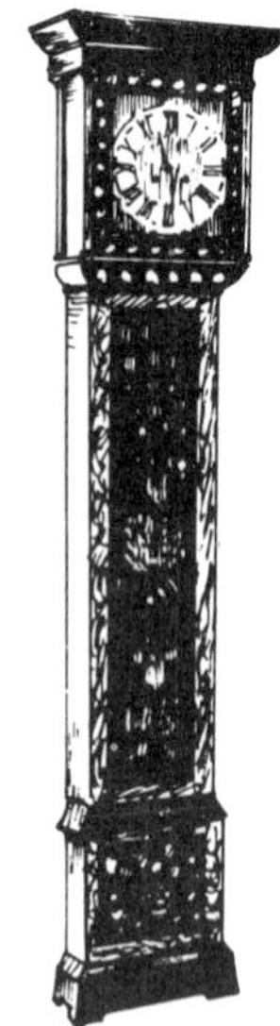

6. A fine floral marquetry longcase clock with an 11 ins square brass dial and eight day movement, by Thomas Trout of London, circa 1700. £875

7. Mid 18th century Comtoise or Morbier longcase clock made for the Italian market with three train alarum movement sounding hours and quarters on three bells. £330

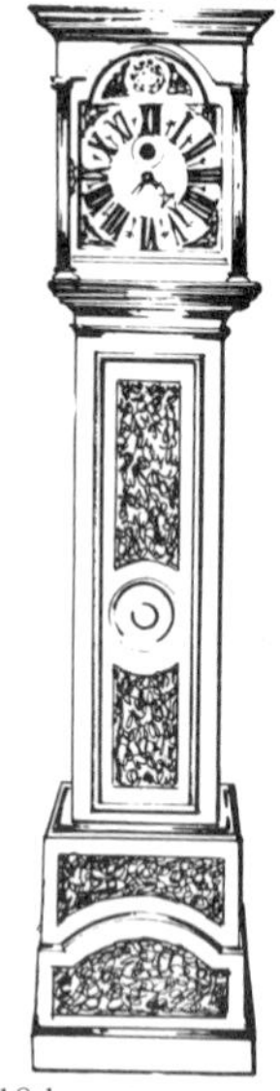

8. 18th century longcase clock by Samuel Steven's of London in a fine marquetry case. £860

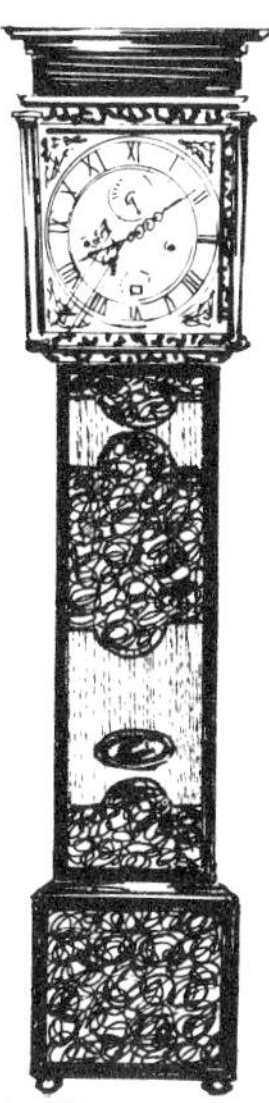

1. Fine marquetry clock by Thomas Johnson of Ratcliffe Cross, 11 ins square face, circa 1705. £1,650

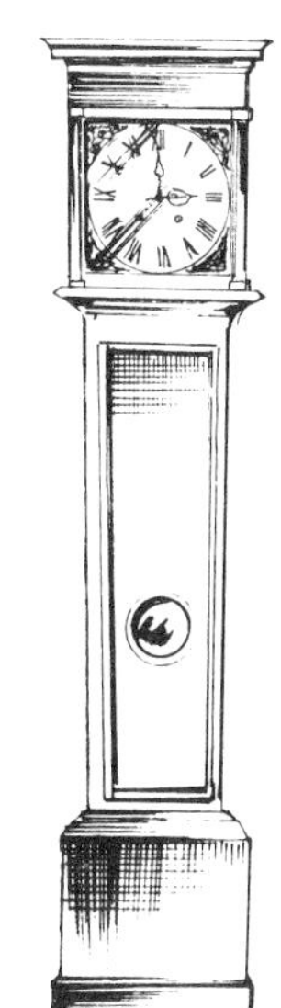

2. A fine walnut longcase clock by Jno. Speakman of London, circa 1710-1715. £925

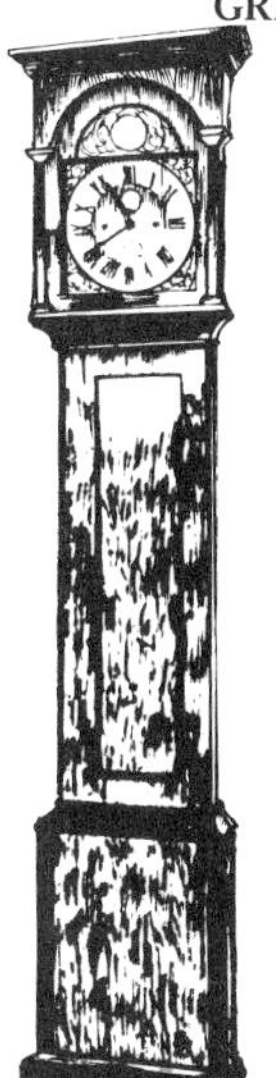

3. Grandfather clock by Richard Wallis of Truro, circa 1730, in yew wood case, 7 ft 5 ins high. £495

4. An extremely fine walnut and panelled marquetry longcase clock by Sam Stevens of London with an 11 ins square brass dial and eight day movement, circa 1685. £1,450

5. 18th century mahogany cased grandfather clock with a brass dial and dead beat escapement. £180

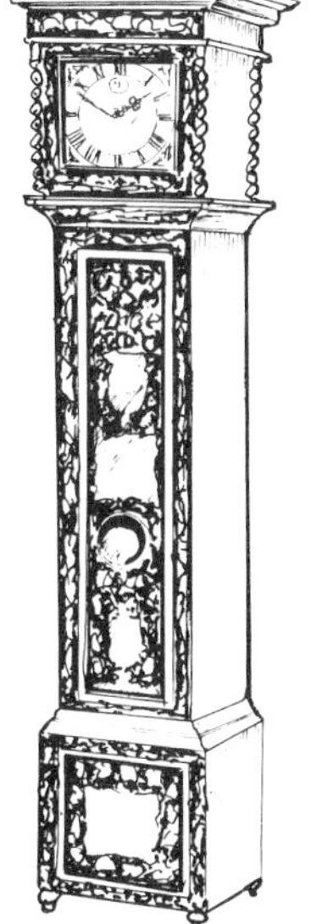

6. A good Queen Anne walnut and marquetry longcase clock with an eight day movement, signed on the chapter ring John Cotsworth, London, 7 ft high, circa 1710. £975

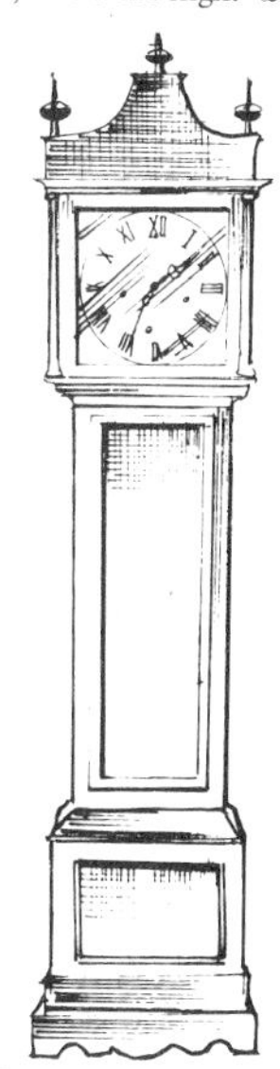

7. A fine mahogany longcase clock chiming on seven bells, silvered dial by Ainsworth Thwaites of London, 7ft, circa 1790. £550

8. Good quality Scottish longcase clock, circa 1830. £195

GRANDFATHER CLOCKS

1. A mid 18th century longcase clock by Giles Bennett of Malmesbury. £85

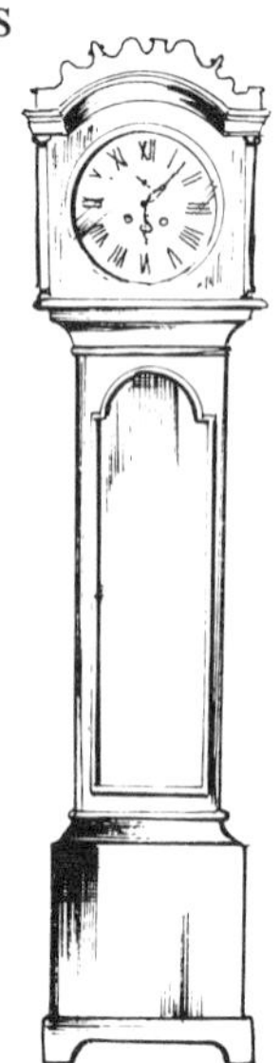

2. Late 18th century longcase clock by Waldre of Arundel, with a white enamel face and oak case. £60

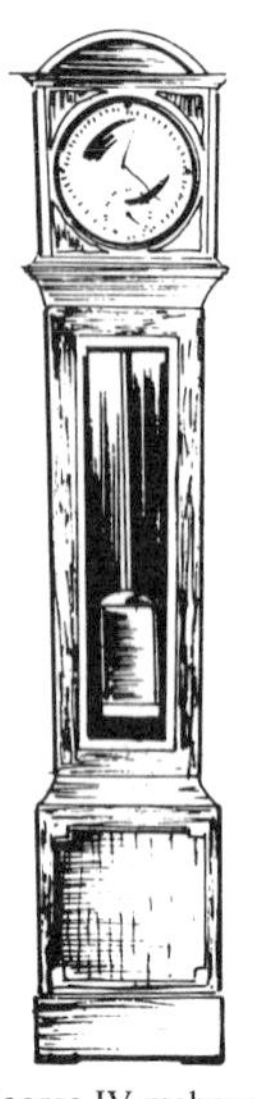

3. George IV mahogany regulator by Ogston of London. £680

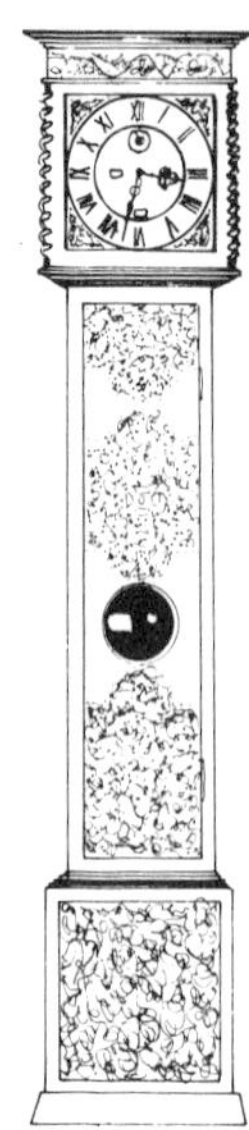

4. A fine walnut and panelled scroll marquetry longcase clock by Chris Gould of London, circa 1690. £1,250

5. Oak cased eight day painted face grandfather clock by Kemp of Oxford. £70

6. An extremely elegant longcase clock by Ellicott of London circa 1750, in its original burr walnut case, 7 ft 5 ins high. £1, 120

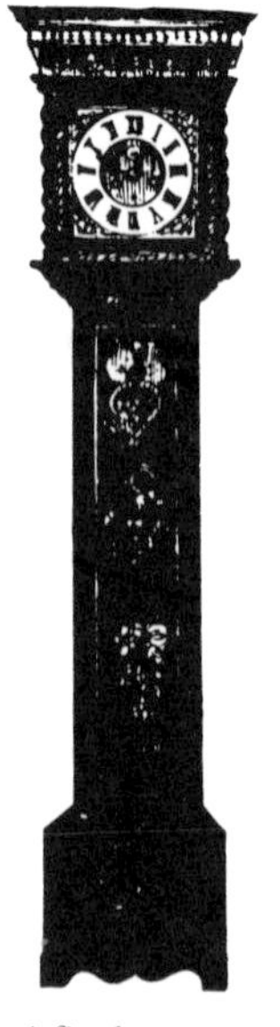

7. A fine longcase clock by W.M.Bale of Bister with a brass and silver dial and an inlaid marquetry walnut case, 7ft 4ins high. £675

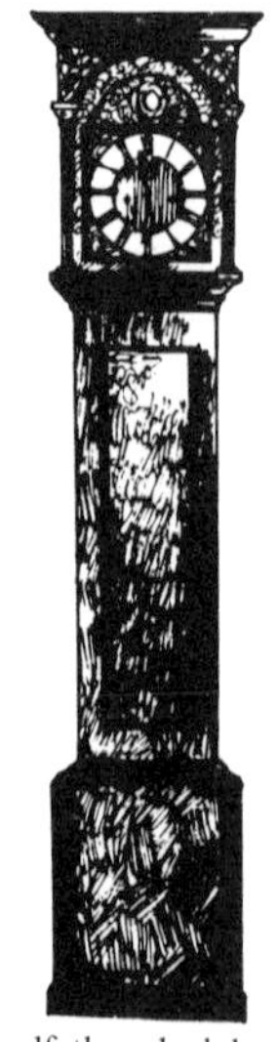

8. Grandfather clock by Richard Wallis of Truro in a yew wood case, 7 ft 5 ins high, circa 1730. £495

1. Late 18th century oak cased eight day grandfather clock. £65

2. Edwardian mahogany grandfather clock with Westminster and Whittington chimes, 7 ft 3 ins high. £595

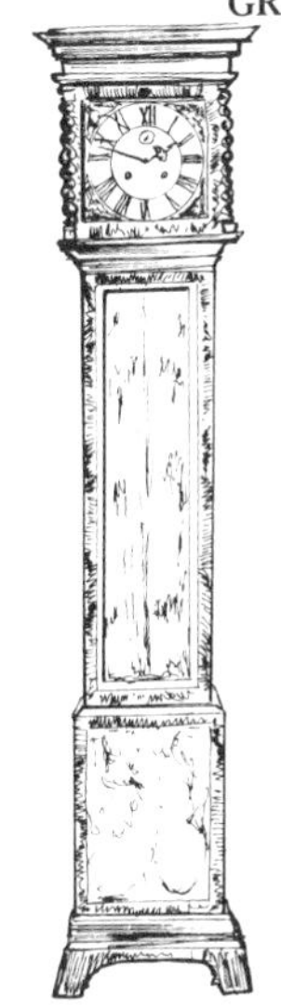

3. A walnut cased clock by ' Thomas Tompion ' 6 ft 11 ins high. £1,155

4. A fine walnut and marquetry clock by Joseph Windmills, Londini Fecit, with an eight day movement circa 1695, 6 ft 9 ins high. £1,475

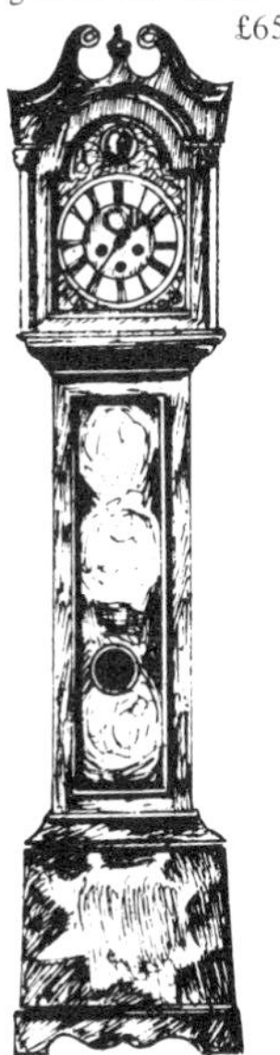

5. A rare pollard oak and oyster walnut longcase clock by Thomas Ogden of Halifax, circa 1750. £925

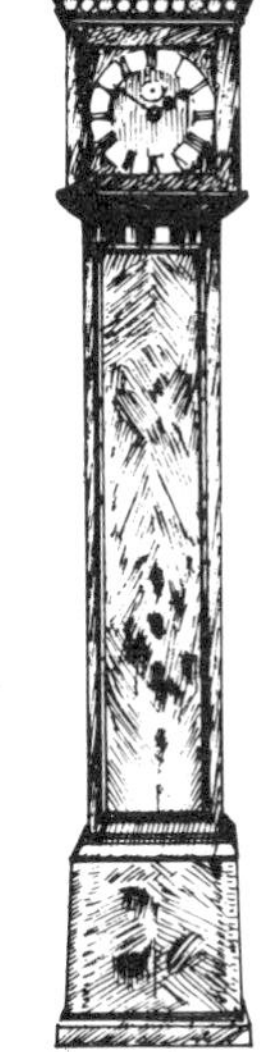

6. A fine 17th century longcase clock, the movement with latched plates, bolt and shutter maintaining power, by Francis Coulton of London, 6 ft 6 ins high, circa 1690. £1,150

7. An 18th century longcase clock in a mahogany case with a brass dial and striking lunar movement inscribed Hartley, Norwich. £740

8. Late 17th century longcase clock in a walnut and floral marquetry case. £1,000

GRANDFATHER CLOCKS

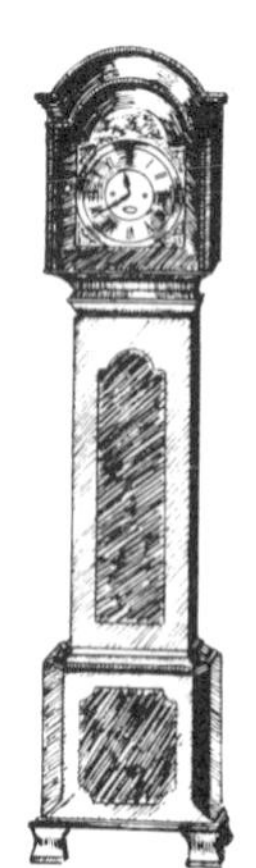

2. A mahogany grandfather clock, the painted panel bearing a plate with the name of Oba Gardner. £400

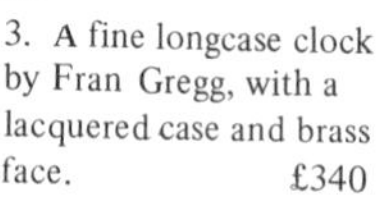

3. A fine longcase clock by Fran Gregg, with a lacquered case and brass face. £340

4. Rare walnut and mahogany miniature longcase clock with an eight day weight driven movement by Peter Brown of Manchester, 3ft 6ins high, circa 1850. £395

1. George III oak longcase clock by Charles Cooper, 6ft 6ins tall, circa 1780. £125

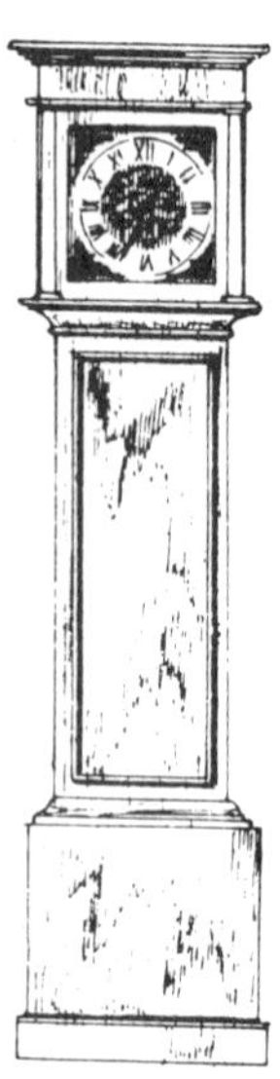

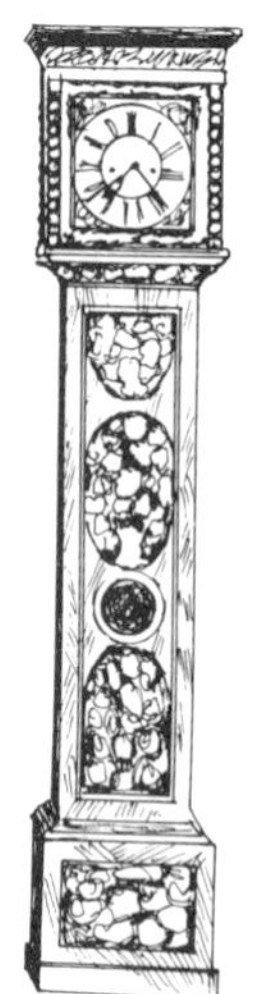

6. A good small walnut and marquetry longcase clock by William Wright of London, 6ft 7½ins high, circa 1695. £1,875

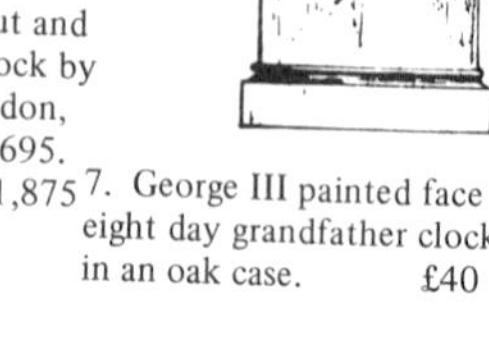

5. Late 18th century brass faced eight day grandfather clock in an oak case. £48

7. George III painted face eight day grandfather clock in an oak case. £40

8. Good quality late 17th century Dutch marquetry longcase clock. £1,250

1. Rare 18th century miniature longcase clock by Obadia Gardner of London with a weight driven movement, circa 1760, 4ft 6ins high. £975

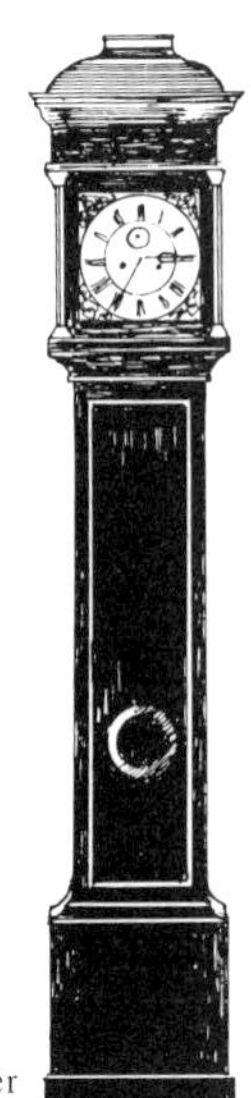

2. An attractive small size ebonised longcase clock with a caddy top, brass face and eight day movement by John Wise of London, circa 1695. £475

3. 18th century mahogany grandmother clock with a brass face and eight day movement, 4ft 4ins high. £280

4. Good quality late 17th century brass faced grandfather clock with an ebonised case. £360

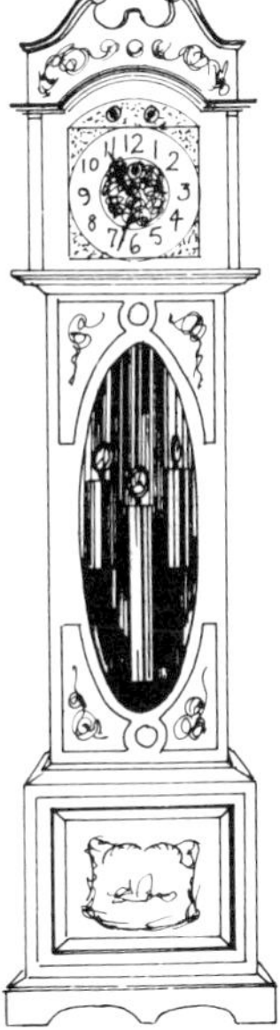

5. A fine Edwardian inlaid mahogany longcase clock. £600

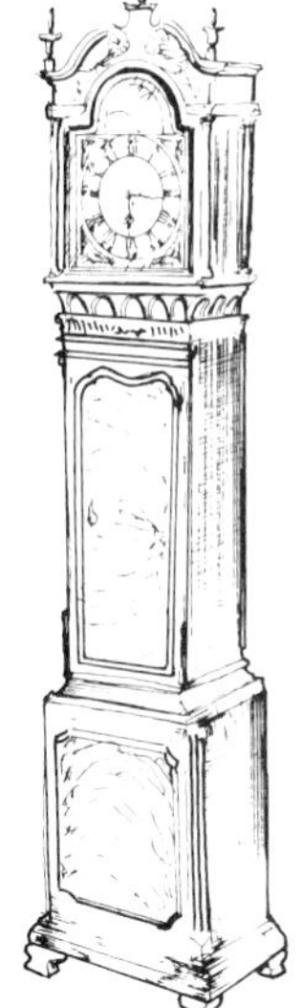

6. A fine quality late 18th century mahogany cased grandfather clock on ogee feet. £285

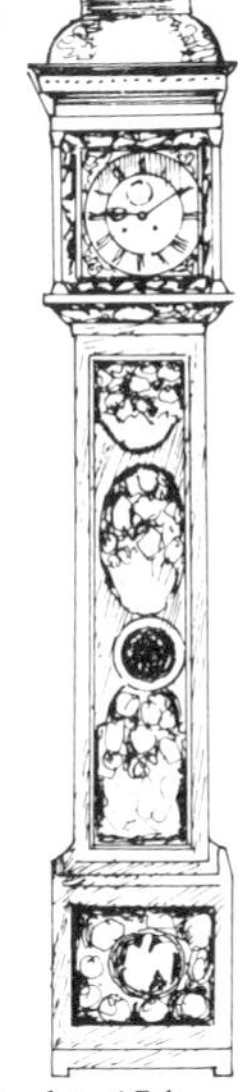

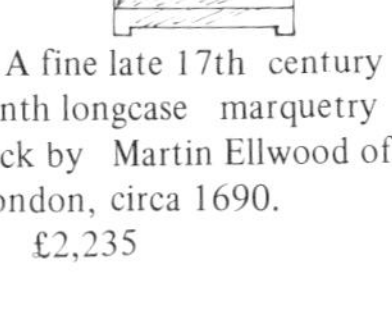

7. A fine late 17th century month longcase marquetry clock by Martin Ellwood of London, circa 1690. £2,235

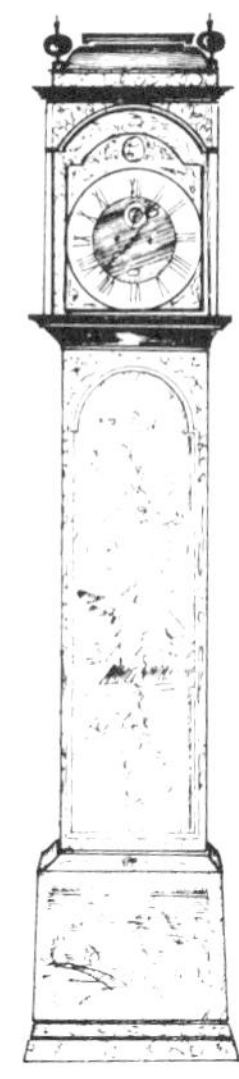

8. Late 18th century red lacquered clock by Charles Mauson of London. £800

BRACKET CLOCKS

1. A fine mahogany cased bracket clock by Edward Tutet Jnr. of London. £390

2. Victorian striking bracket clock in a carved walnut case with a silvered dial. £10

3. A good 19th century eight day English ebonised striking bracket clock with a brass face. £190

4. A fine ebonised basket top bracket clock by John Elsworth of London with a verge escapement, tulip engraved back plate and pull repeat on three bells, circa 1690. £1,850

5. A fine bracket clock by Daniel Quare. £1,500

6. Early 18th century bracket clock in an ebony veneered case, by Thomas Cliff of Hull. £325

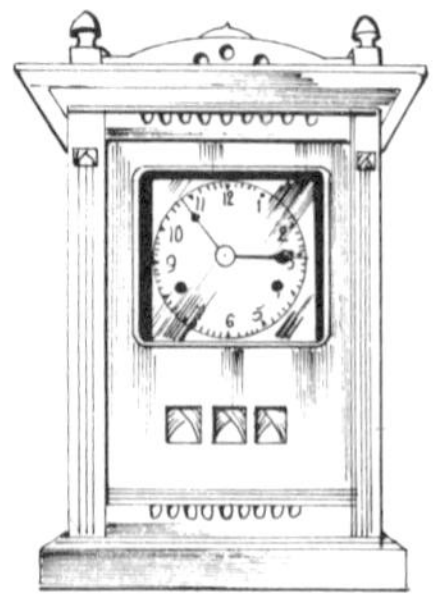

7. Victorian oak cased striking bracket clock. £8

8. An 18th century two train bracket clock with anchor escapement, engraved back plate and hour repeat. £265

9. A good quality early 19th century mahogany cased bracket clock. £230

1. Rare Queen Anne bracket clock, the original bracket, by Peter King of London with verge escapement and engraved back plate, circa 1710. £1,675

2. An extremely fine Victorian ebonised bracket clock with a three train musical movement, 30 ins high. £300

3. A yew wood bracket clock by Isaac Nickols of Wells, Somerset, 20 ins high. £130

4. Bracket clock by Joseph Martineau Senior of London. £210

5. Late Regency mahogany deep broken arch bracket clock by James McCabe, 17 ins high. £230

6. Mid 18th century ebonised bracket clock with a verge escapement, striker and engraved back plate. £335

7. An extremely fine early 18th century bracket clock by Sam Humphreys of London. £410

8. Mahogany bracket clock by Abraham Perinot of Paddington with a double stepped base, circa 1760. £390

9. Bracket clock by Daniel Quare with a repeating alarm, in fine original condition. £6,000

1. George III bracket clock by Edmund Pistor of London. £410

2. Bracket clock by James Cowan of Edinburgh in an ebonised case. £575

3. Early 19th century bracket clock in an ebonised case with brass string inlay. £85

4. Verge escapement bracket clock by Alderslade of Islington, strikes the hour, in a mahogany case, 16 ins high, circa 1790. £535

5. A fine mahogany cased bracket clock by Abraham Louis Breguet of Paris, circa 1815. £175

6. 18th century bracket clock by Peter Nichols of Newport, with a verge repeater movement. £330

7. A fine George III bracket clock in a mahogany case by Allen and Clements. £435

8. 19th century chiming bracket clock in an oak case. £55

9. A good George I three train quarter chime bracket clock in a mahogany case. £500

1. A ¼ pull repeat bracket clock by Robert Rouch of Bristol in an ebonised case, 20 ins high, with moon phases calendarium, converted to anchor, circa 1760. £585

2. A large early 19th century three train ebonised bracket clock with fine ormolu mounts. £310

3. An exceptionally fine quality George III bracket clock by Stephen Rimbault of London. £1,300

4. Early 19th century bracket clock in an ebonised case with ormolu mounts. £200

5. A three train chiming bracket clock by William Sutton of London. £1,300

6. Edwardian bracket clock in a mahogany case with an eight day French movement. £30

7. Bracket clock by William Tomlinson in a figured walnut case. £445

8. Bracket clock by I.C. Fennens of London in an ebonised case, circa 1850. £135

9. Late 18th century mahogany cased bracket clock by William Shilling of Milton with an engraved backplate. £385

CARRIAGE CLOCKS

1. French carriage clock with five porcelain panels, by T. Detardin, circa 1875. £775

2. Small 19th century French brass carriage clock in a serpentine shaped case. £115

3. A fine French travelling clock 8ins high, the case with pierced friezes and columns and the dial with enamel chapter ring and alarm enclosed by a matt pierced design of scroll leafage. £380

4. Fine Georgian carriage clock by James McCabe of London. £997

5. An extremely fine English cased carriage clock with an engraved dial mask, striking and repeating movement and very rare bottom winding handles, circa 1850. £290

6. Early 19th century French grande sonniere carriage clock by Leroy et Fils of Paris. £920

7. 19th century French brass carriage clock with a cloisonne enamel centre panel surrounded by pierced and chased floral scrolls. £210

8. A fine quality 19th century French carriage clock by Leroy et Fils of Paris. £525

9. English gilt brass carriage clock with repeat and alarm, circa 1880. £185

1. 19th century gilt soft metal carriage clock with repeat and alarm. £200

2. Small Victorian brass carriage clock with an eight day movement. £45

3. An attractive oval carriage clock with blue Roman numerals, strike and repeating movement, circa 1870. £280

4. An unusual Victorian brass carriage clock with a pale green enamel dial, ½ hour strike and alarm. £125

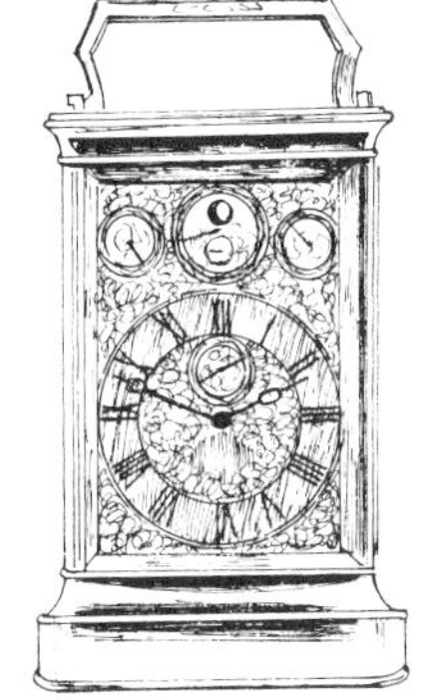

5. An exceptionally fine carriage clock by Frederick Dent. £13,650

6. Victorian brass carriage clock with full repeating sonniere movement on two gongs. £215

7. Victorian brass carriage clock timepiece, circa 1850. £65

8. Miniature ¼ repeat carriage clock with a blue enamel face, complete with travelling case. £240

9. Fine oval repeat alarm carriage clock in a gilded engraved case. £320

WALL CLOCKS

1. American wall clock by Jerome and Co., New Haven, Connecticut. £10

2. A good quality Regency period rosewood, octagonal wall clock inlaid with brass. £47

3. 19th century eight day red boulle wall clock with ormolu decoration. £90

4. 18th century Continental wall clock in a walnut case. £85

5. Late 19th century American regulator wall clock in a mahogany case. £12

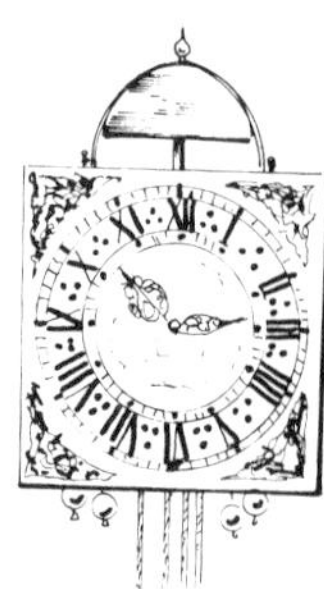

6. Rare brass wall clock by Peter Guy of Liverpool, circa 1700. £275

7. Continental wall clock with an enamel dial and pressed brass decoration. £125

8. Early 19th century ' Big Ben ' picture clock. £35

9. Regency period Parliament clock in a mounted rosewood case with brass inlay. £45

1. Early 19th century drop dial wall clock with full hour strike and two train movement. £68

2. 19th century mahogany cased fusee movement wall clock with a quarter strike. £85

3. Late 18th century mahogany wall clock with a 16 inch dial and fusee movement. £38

4. Mid 18th century brass faced wall clock with a thirty hour movement. £115

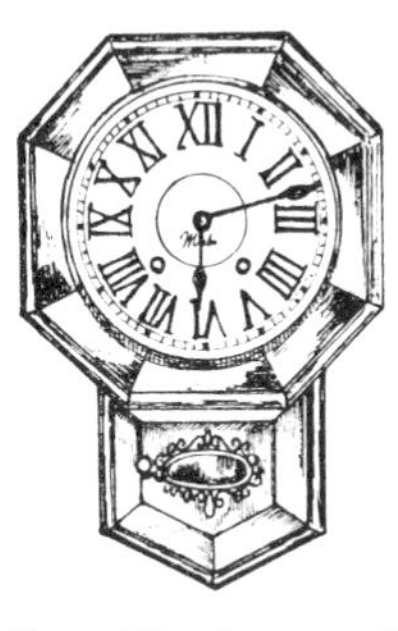

5. George III mahogany wall clock with an eight day movement and enamel dial. £20

6. A rare organ clock with an Austrian case and clockwork, circa 1760, and an English organ circa 1735. £1,475

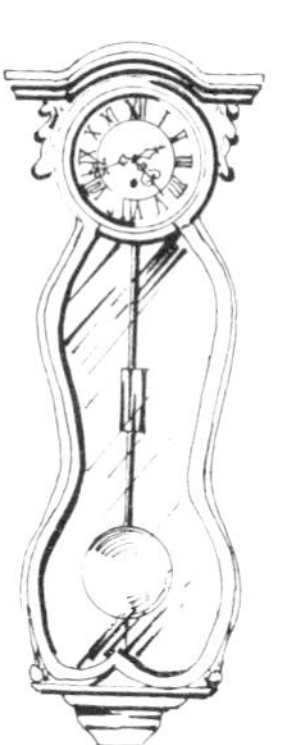

7. Viennese mahogany regulator timepiece, circa 1860. £75

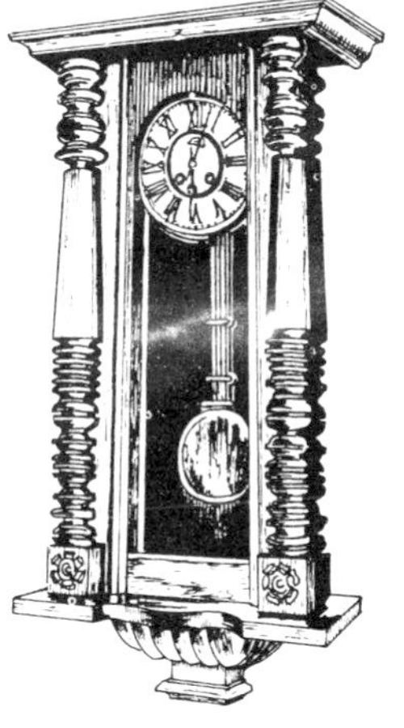

8. Victorian mahogany wall clock with a fine brass pendulum. £20

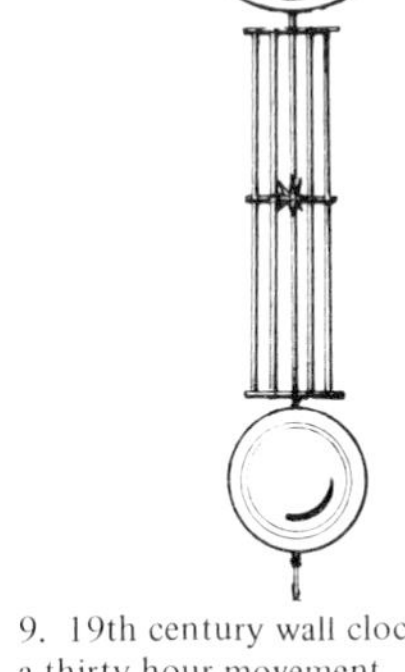

9. 19th century wall clock with a thirty hour movement. £16

MANTEL CLOCKS

1. Mid 19th century ormolu mantel clock. £45

2. 19th century ormolu mantel clock with a white porcelain face. £55

3. A good quality early 19th century French ormolu clock, circa 1810. £1,000

4. Regency period two train clock in an inlaid mahogany case. £108

5. Louis XVI ormolu and black marble mantel clock with striking movement, signed Schmit a Paris. £630

6. Blue Sevres porcelain and ormolu French clock, circa 1850, 20ins high, 16ins wide, 6ins deep. £395

7. 19th century French mantel clock in a mahogany case with ormolu decoration, 18ins high. £55

8. Late 19th century French marble and spelter striking mantel clock. £15

9. 19th century French boulle clock, tortoiseshell case with brass inlay and ormolu mounts, 16ins high. £195

1. Blue Sevres porcelain and ormolu mounted clock, circa 1860, 13ins high, 11ins wide, 6ins deep. £295

2. Mid 19th century white marble and ormolu clock decorated with floral swags, urns and beading, 13ins high. £150

3. Bronze and ormolu Regency Fountain clock, circa 1810. £325

4. 19th century oak cased striking clock decorated with carved dolphins. £12

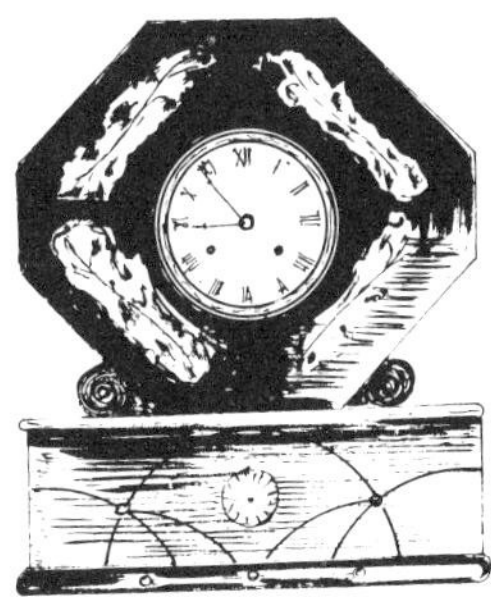

5. Regency eight day mantel clock with a mahogany and brass inlaid case. £33

6. Louis XVI ormolu and marble mantel clock. £125

7. Good quality red boulle mantel clock, circa 1830. £350

8. Fine 19th century French ormolu eight day striking clock by Muirhead of Paris, 20ins high. £175

9. An original fine gilded French striking clock, circa 1820. £155

MANTEL CLOCKS

1. An early 19th century musical clock by Warren of London with seventeen bells and with seven various tunes, in a brass inlaid case. £270

2. 19th century French ormolu and marble mantel clock. £150

3. An unusual 'Black Forest' fusee movement cuckoo clock. £165

4. Heavy black marble and brass mounted clock by ' Ansonia Clock Co. ' USA. £6.50

5. 19th century silver grande sonnerie Tourbillon clock by Vicole Nielson. £5,460

6. An early 19th century French lacquered mantel clock with ormolu mounts, 13½ins high. £135

7. 19th century replica of a highly decorated 18th century clock for the Middle East market coromandel wood with ormolu mounts. £485

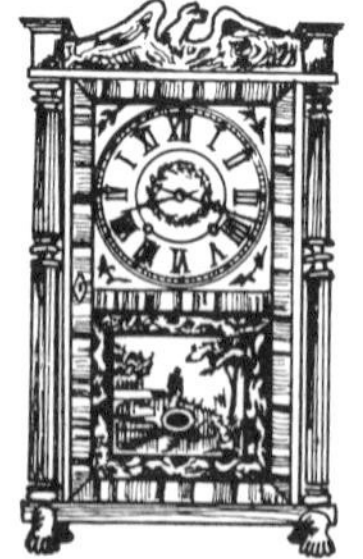

8. A fine 19th century American clock in a rosewood veneered case. £24

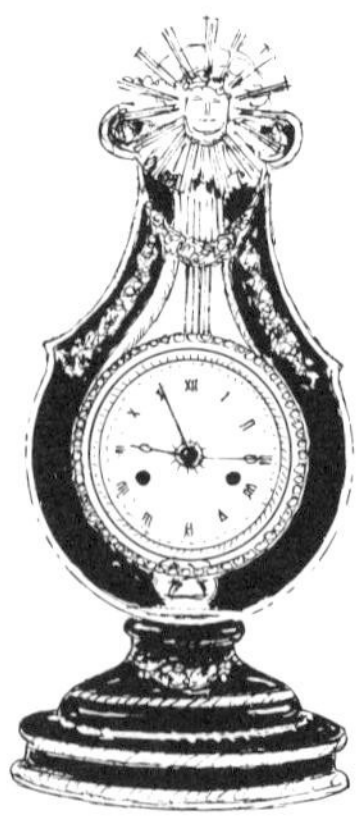

9. A Napoleon I ormolu mounted 'bleu de roi' Sevres porcelain lyre clock by Collas of Paris. £1,400

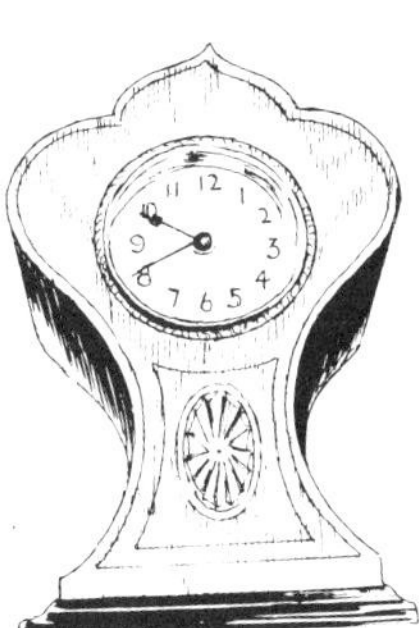

1. 19th century Victorian oak cased balloon shape clock. £9

2. Louis XVI ormolu and porcelain mantel clock with striking movement by Charles Dutertre. £1,575

3. Victorian brass 'picture frame' desk clock with an eight day movement. £78

4. Large Victorian oak cased striking mantel clock. £26

5. Art Deco soft metal mantel clock in the form of a female figure. £17.50

6. An unusual Edwardian inlaid rosewood and marquetry miniature striking longcase clock, 2ft 3ins high. £66

7. An unusual 19th century mahogany cased clock. £125

8. Early 19th century mantel clock by Leroy De Fils. £275

9. Japanese pillar clock timepiece, circa 1800. £280

MANTEL CLOCKS

1. Regency period eight day clock in a rosewood case. £72

2. French ormolu clock by Adolphe Japy made for the French Great Exhibition in 1855. £300

3. 19th century French ebony mantel clock with ormolu mounts. £55

4. Late 19th century German mantel clock in an oak case. £18

5. Hand painted blue porcelain and ormolu clock by Aubert and Klaftenburger of Geneva, circa 1850. £210

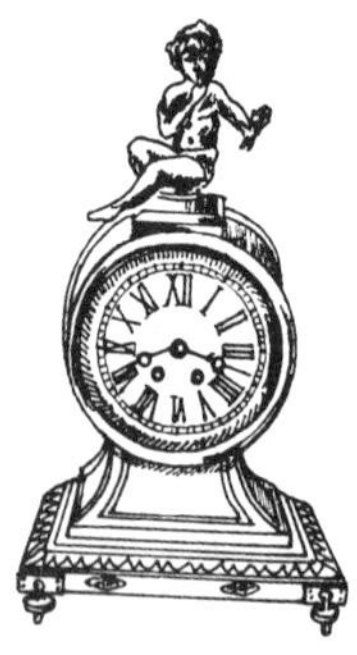

6. 19th century brass mantel clock surmounted by a cherub. £45

7. Large 19th century Dresden striking clock encrusted with flowers, 2ft 1ins tall £155

8. Large Victorian brass mantel clock with an eight day movement. £75

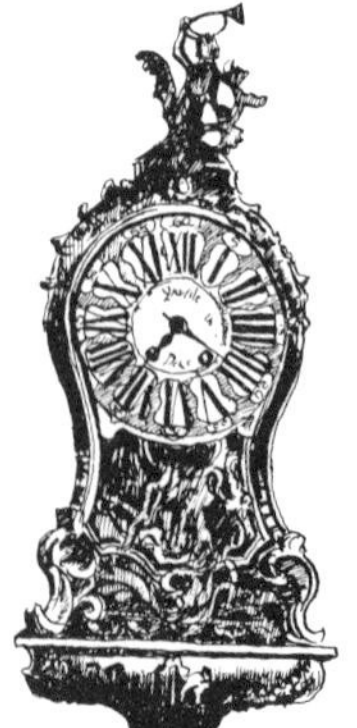

9. A fine quality Louis XV Cartel clock in tortoiseshell and brass. £375

1. Victorian black marble mantel clock. £4.50

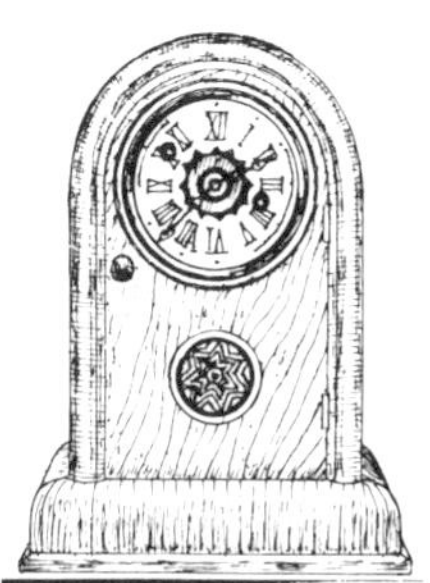

2. 19th century walnut cased mantel clock with an American movement. £9

3. 19th century French striking mantel clock with pink ground Sevres panels. £135

4. An interesting 19th century French maritime clock. £155

5. Late 18th century French brass mantel clock. £140

6. Victorian alabaster mantel clock with an eight day French striking movement and large brass pendulum. £60

7. Victorian lancet clock in a mahogany case with boxwood string inlay. £20

8. Large 19th century French brass mantel clock. £80

9. A fine early 19th century French boulle clock. £200

SKELETON CLOCKS

1. A fine 19th century skeleton clock in good order. £135

2. Brass skeleton clock by R. Morrison of Inverness, 15 ins high. £290

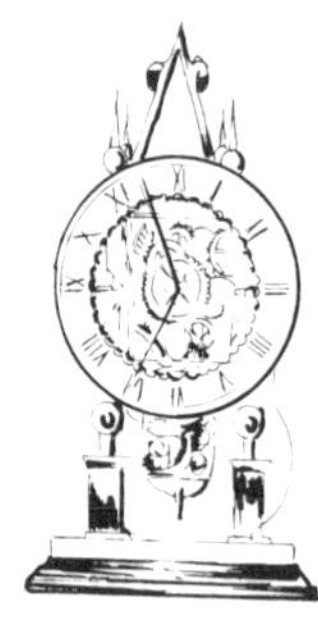

3. A two train skeleton clock by Moore of Worthing. £275

4. Early 19th century French architectural clock, under a glass dome. £125

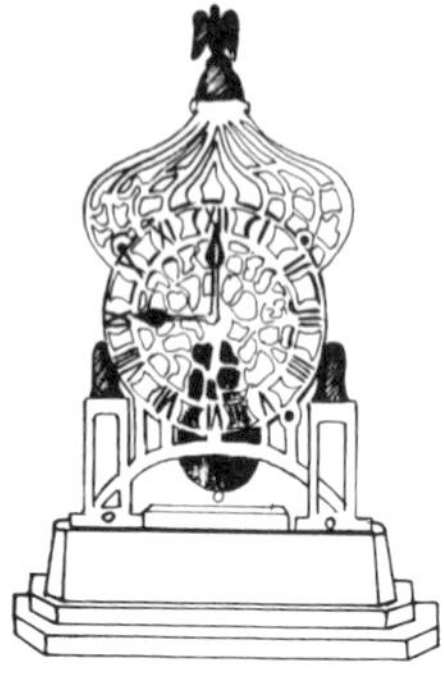

5. Regency brass 'Brighton Pavilion' two train skeleton clock. £235

6. Victorian brass skeleton clock with a half second dead beat escapement. £125

7. 19th century Gothic design skeleton clock complete with a glass dome, circa 1855. £185

8. Victorian brass skeleton clock with a glass dome. £65

9. A fine 19th century brass skeleton clock with a strike. £90

1. Lantern clock by William Selwood with the original balance escapement, circa 1620. £1,600

2. A miniature lantern timepiece alarm by John Knibb, Oxon, with original verge escapement, 8 ins high circa 1675. £750

3. A good original wing lantern clock, circa 1670. £750

4. Wing lantern clock by Thomas Wheeler, circa 1680. £685

5. Lantern clock by Richard Smith of Harlistone with an anchor escapement. £210

6. Victorian brass reproduction lantern clock with an eight day French movement. £35

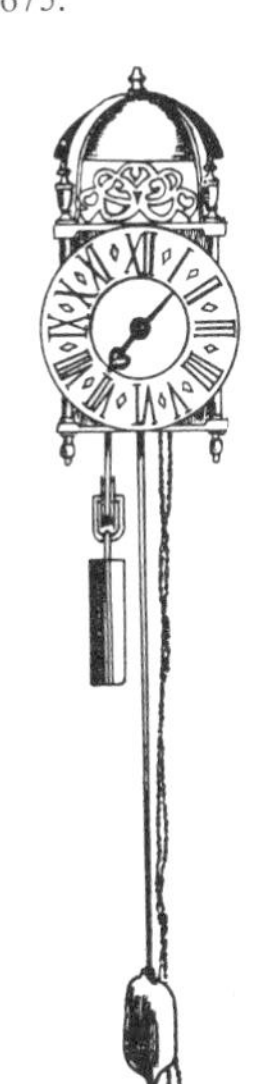

7. Early 18th century brass lantern clock. £205

8. Transitional lantern clock by Thomas Parker. £225

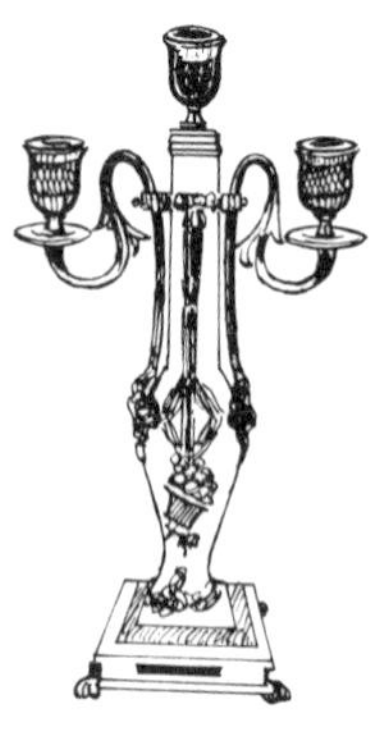

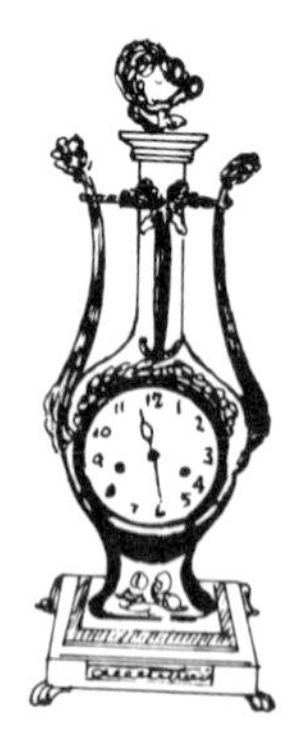

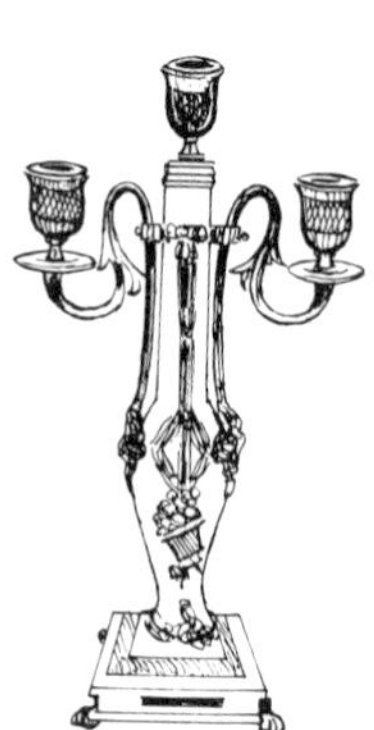

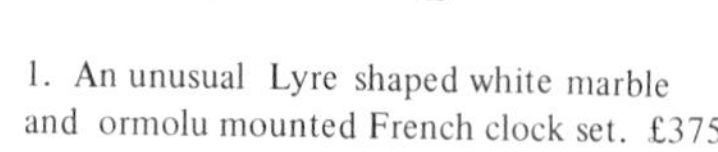

1. An unusual Lyre shaped white marble and ormolu mounted French clock set. £375

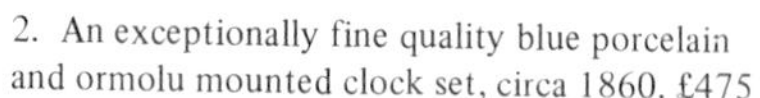

2. An exceptionally fine quality blue porcelain and ormolu mounted clock set, circa 1860. £475

3. A three piece green onyx marble and porcelain clock set with ormolu mounts, circa 1860. £350

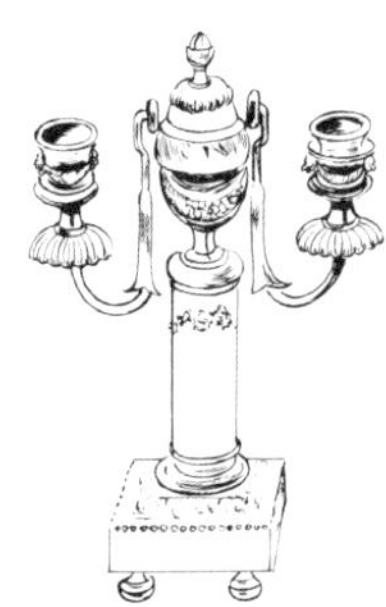

1. White marble and ormolu mounted French clock set with candelabra cassolet sidepieces, circa 1860. £295

2. Early 19th century ormolu Dolphin mounted clock set on a green marble base. £425

3. A fine quality French ormolu garniture, the candelabrum 34ins high. £500

1. A good 18th century Sevres garniture de cheminee decorated with male and female figures in ormolu. £280

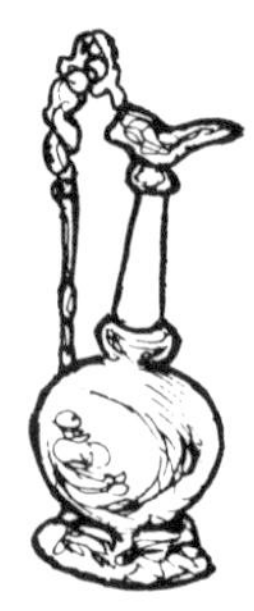

2. Three piece ormolu mounted blue Sevres hand painted porcelain clock set by Vincente. £495

3. A 19th century French clock set in ormolu with decorative porcelain plaques. £100

1. Early 19th centuryEmpire style white marble and ormolu clock set. £180

2. A French Sevres and ormolu Lyre clock with matching candelabrum, circa 1840. £595

3. 19th century vase shaped clock set in bleu de roi mounted with ormolu. £245

INDEX

INDEX

NAME INDEX

INDEX

THE END.
FINEM RESPICE.